ANTS

COLUMBIA BIOLOGICAL SERIES

NUMBER 9

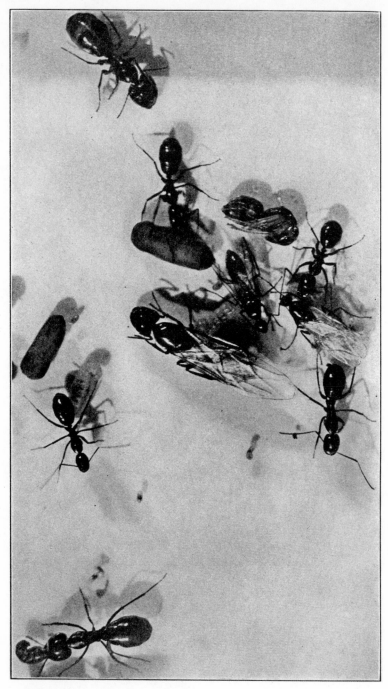

Female, males, major and minor workers and brood of *Camponotus americanus*, × 2.
(Photograph by Mr. J. G. Hubbard and Dr. O. S. Strong.)

ANTS

THEIR STRUCTURE, DEVELOPMENT AND BEHAVIOR

BY William Morton Wheeler, PH.D., SC.D.

PROFESSOR OF ECONOMIC ENTOMOLOGY, HARVARD UNIVERSITY
DEAN OF THE BUSSEY INSTITUTION; HONORARY FELLOW AND
RESEARCH ASSOCIATE, AMERICAN MUSEUM OF NATURAL HISTORY

COLUMBIA UNIVERSITY PRESS
NEW YORK

TO MY WIFE

DORA BAY EMERSON

" The Subject indeed is small, but not inglorious. The Ant, as
the Prince of Wisdom is pleased to inform us, is exceeding wise.
In this Light it may, without Vanity, boast of its being related to
you, and therefore by right of Kindred merits your Protection."

—WILLIAM GOULD, " *An Account of English Ants,*" 1747.

PUBLISHED IN GREAT BRITAIN, INDIA, AND PAKISTAN
BY THE OXFORD UNIVERSITY PRESS
LONDON, BOMBAY, AND KARACHI

Manufactured in the United States of America

PREFACE

This volume had its inception in a series of eight lectures delivered at Columbia University during the spring of 1905, and represents, in a much condensed form, the results of a decade of uninterrupted study of the Formicidæ, and of the works that have been written on these insects.

If an excuse were required for its publication, one might be found in the fact that for many years no comprehensive treatise on the ants has appeared in the English language. This may be regarded as a reproach to English and American zoölogists, since during all this time almost the only active contributors to myrmecology were to be found on the European continent. It must be admitted, however, that the methods of publication adopted by continental writers have not been such as to attract the attention of English-speaking students, since their works have not only been issued in a variety of languages—French, German, Swedish, Italian, Russian, etc.—but also in a great number of often very obscure, local or inaccessible journals and proceedings of learned societies. Moreover, most of the continental observers within recent years have been too busy with special lines of investigation to publish compendia on myrmecology. It thus happens that although ants are our most abundant and most conspicuously active insects, they have not, till very recently, received any serious attention from American systematists, and the descriptions of most of our species must still be sought in a lot of more or less fragmentary foreign contributions.

My work began in an endeavor to increase our systematic knowledge of the North American ants, but I was fascinated by the activities of these insects and soon saw the advantage of studying their taxonomy and ethology conjointly. This method, which was, indeed, unavoidable, has greatly retarded the appearance of the present work, for it was impossible to write about the behavior of many of our most interesting forms till their taxonomic status had been definitely settled. On the other hand, I could find no satisfaction in devoting all my energies to collecting and labelling specimens without stopping to observe the many surprising ethological facts that were at the same time thrusting themselves upon my attention. My observations have now covered so much of our fauna that I shall soon be able to publish a systematic monograph, which will, I hope, enable the student to form a rapid acquaintance with our ants, without recourse to the scattered and often very meager descriptions that have hitherto served as the taxonomy of the North American species.

I frankly admit that in writing the following pages I have endeavored to appeal to several classes of readers—to the general reader, who is always more or less interested in ants; to the zoölogist, who cannot afford to ignore their polymorphism or their symbiotic and parasitic relationships; to the entomologist, who should study the ants if only for the purpose of modifying his views on the limits of genera and species, and to the comparative psychologist, who is sure to find in them the most intricate instincts and the closest approach to intelligence among invertebrate animals. Of course, the desire to interest so many must result in a work containing much that will be dull or incomprehensible to any one class of readers; thus the technical terms and descriptions, which are full of significance to the entomologist, are merely so much dead verbiage to the general reader, and the laboratory zoölogist, who shrinks at the mention of psychological matters, will care little about ant behavior beyond its physiological implications.

With the exception of the appendices and the first chapter, which serves as an introduction, my account of the ants falls naturally into two parts: a first, which is largely morphological, and comprises Chapters II to X; and a second, devoted to ethological considerations and embracing the remaining chapters. To some it may seem that too much space has been devoted to the relations of ants to other organisms and to other ants (Chapters XVI–XXVII), but I justify my procedure on the ground that this subject is the one in which I have been most interested, the one in which most advancement has been made within recent years, and the one that has been fraught with the greatest differences of interpretation.

The series of appendices has been added largely as an aid to the beginner in the study of myrmecology. The tables for the identification of our North American ants are very incomplete, but could not have been extended to embrace the species, subspecies and varieties, and the different castes, as well as the genera, without unduly increasing the size of the book. I hope to make good this defect in the monograph to which I have alluded. In the meantime, I shall be glad to identify ants for anyone who is interested in their study, especially if the specimens are collected in America north of Mexico. The identification of such material serves a double purpose: that of increasing our knowledge of the geographical distribution of our species, and of spreading throughout the country collections of correctly identified specimens. The dearth of such collections, both of ants and of all other groups of insects, excepting, perhaps, the Coleoptera and Lepidoptera, has not ceased to be a great drawback to the study of entomology in America.

The bibliography (Appendix E), which has been carried down to the close of the year 1908, is unfortunately very voluminous and includes many titles of unimportant works. Like all such compilations, it is necessarily incomplete, and undoubtedly contains positive errors. A serious attempt has been made, however, to reduce these to a minimum, and I shall be glad to receive any additions or corrections.

For portions of the text and many of the figures I have drawn rather freely on my previously published papers. A few entire chapters, in fact, such as those on polymorphism, have been reproduced with only slight verbal alterations. Others, like Chapters XVIII and XX, are abridgments of longer accounts of the fungus-growing and honey ants recently published in the Bulletin of the American Museum of Natural History.

I am under lasting obligations to Professor H. C. Bumpus for the interest he has shown in the progress of my work, and the aid which I received in its prosecution while I was Curator of Invertebrate Zoölogy in the American Museum of Natural History. To Mr. Roy W. Miner, Assistant Curator of Invertebrate Zoölogy in that institution, I am deeply indebted for much assistance in making out the table of contents, and especially in arranging and verifying the bibliography. Many of the illustrations have been made by Miss Ruth B. Howe. My friend, Professor Oliver S. Strong, of Columbia University, has most generously permitted me to use a number of the remarkable photographs which he and Mr. J. G. Hubbard took of living colonies of various ants in the possession of Miss Adele M. Fielde. Three of my former pupils, Messrs. A. L. Melander, C. T. Brues and C. G. Hartman, have also contributed several interesting figures, and Mr. Brues has aided me in reading the proof.

BUSSEY INSTITUTION,
   FOREST HILLS, BOSTON, MASS.,
      October 30, 1909

PREFACE TO THE SECOND IMPRESSION

The demand for this volume, which has been out of print for some time, has induced the publishers to issue a reprint. A treatment commensurate with our present knowledge would undoubtedly require the addition of several new chapters and many new illustrations. Such a revision would swell the work probably to two volumes of the size of the present one, would much increase the cost and would take several years to complete. The result would be, I fear, to bewilder the general reader while still not meeting the requirements of the investigator. The work is therefore presented again in its present form in the belief that it may continue to serve a useful purpose for general orientation in a very interesting field of entomological knowledge.

W. M. WHEELER

BUSSEY INSTITUTION,
FOREST HILLS, BOSTON, MASS.,
November 23, 1925

TABLE OF CONTENTS

CHAPTER I

ANTS AS DOMINANT INSECTS

CHAPTER II

THE EXTERNAL STRUCTURE OF ANTS

CHAPTER III

THE INTERNAL STRUCTURE OF ANTS

CHAPTER IV

THE INTERNAL STRUCTURE OF ANTS (CONCLUDED)

CHAPTER V

THE DEVELOPMENT OF ANTS

CHAPTER VI

POLYMORPHISM

CHAPTER VII

POLYMORPHISM (CONCLUDED)

CHAPTER VIII

THE HISTORY OF MYRMECOLOGY AND THE CLASSIFICATION OF ANTS

CHAPTER IX

The Distribution of Ants

CHAPTER X

Fossil Ants

CHAPTER XI

The Habits of Ants in General

1. Care of the Young. 2. Care of One Another. 3. Care of
the Nest. 4. Methods of Defence and Attack. 5. Means
of Preventing Mixture of Alien Colonies.

1. Terrestrial Mating. 2. The Nuptial Flight. 3. The Founding of the New Colony. 4. Social Parasitism. 5. The Number of Individuals in a Colony.

CHAPTER XII

Ant-Nests

1. Small Crater Nests. 2. Large Crater Nests. 3. Mound, or
Dome and Masonry Nests. 4. Nests under Stones, Boards,
etc.

CHAPTER XIII

Ant-Nests (concluded)

1. In Preformed Cavities. 2. In Woody Plant-tissues (*a*)
Carpenter Ants; (*b*) Gall Ants.

CHAPTER XIV

THE PONERINE ANTS

CHAPTER XV

THE DRIVER AND LEGIONARY ANTS

CHAPTER XVI

THE HARVESTING ANTS

1. *Solenopsis geminata,* the " fire ant." 2. The Genus *Pheidole.* 3. The Genus *Messor.* 4. *Ischnomyrmex cockerelli* and *albisetosus.* 4. The Genus *Pogonomyrmex.* (*a*) Characterization, Range, and Classification. (*b*) *Pogonomyrmex imbericulus,* etc. (*c*) The Florida Harvester, etc. (*d*) The Texan Harvester and the " Ant-rice " Theory. (*e*) The Marriage Flight of the Texan Harvester. (*f*) The Founding of Colonies by *P. molefaciens.* (*g*) The Occident Harvester. (*h*) The Stinging Habits of *Pogonomyrmex.*

CHAPTER XVII

THE RELATIONS OF ANTS TO VASCULAR PLANTS

1. Dwelling-places for Ants. (*a*) Cavities in Stems. (*b*) Tubers, Bulbs, Pseudobulbs, Rootstocks, etc. (*c*) Ascidiæ or Bursæ of Leaves and Petioles. (*d*) Spaces between or under Leaves. (*e*) Thorns. (*f*) Seed-pods. (*g*) Galls. 2. Food-supplies for Ants. (*a*) Floral Nectaries. (*b*) Extrafloral Nectaries. (*c*) Food-bodies. (*d*) Bead-glands ("Perldrüsen"). (*e*) Pith and Other Vegetable Tissues.

1. The Arboreal Genera. 2. The Habits and Structural Adaptations of *Azteca* and *Pseudomyrma,* and their Relations to the Problem. 3. The Relations of *Azteca muelleri* to *Cecropia adenopus.* 4. The Relations of Ants to *Myrmecodia, Hydnophytum* and *Myrmephytum.* 5. The Relations

CHAPTER XX

Honey Ants

CHAPTER XXI

Persecuted and Tolerated Guests

CHAPTER XXII

True Guests, Ecto- and Entoparasites

CHAPTER XXIII

The Compound Nests

CHAPTER XXVI

THE AMAZONS, OR OBLIGATORY SLAVE-MAKERS

CHAPTER XXVII

THE DEGENERATE SLAVE-MAKERS AND PERMANENT SOCIAL PARASITES

CHAPTER XXVIII

THE SENSATIONS OF ANTS

CHAPTER XXIX

The Instinctive Behavior of Ants

CHAPTER XXX

The Plastic Behavior of Ants

APPENDICES

CHAPTER I

ANTS AS DOMINANT INSECTS

"In turba insectorum vastissima prae ceteris Familiis omnium Ordinum eminent *Formicæ* numero maximo individuorum, viribus tenacissimis, strenuitate et industria infatigabili atque vitae genere sociali et cultura (ut ita dicam) instinctus naturalis longe præcellente; quibus multisque adhuc aliis virtutibus hæc animalcula, ad speciem externam, staturam coloresque exilia et vilia, attentionem Scrutatorum summorum temporum labentium sane meruerunt sibique allexerunt."—Nylander, "Adnotationes in Monographiam Formicarum Borealium Europæ," 1846.

"Il n'est pas contestable que le succès soit le criterium le plus général de la supériorité, les deux termes étant, jusqu'à un certain point, synonymes l'un de l'autre. Par succès il faut entendre, quand il s'agit de l'être vivant, une aptitude à se développer dans les milieux les plus divers, à travers la plus grande variété possible d'obstacles, de manière à couvrir la plus vaste étendue possible de terre. Une espèce qui revendique pour domaine la terre entière est veritablement une espèce dominatrice et par conséquent supérieure. Telle est l'espèce humaine, qui représentera le point culminant de l'évolution des Vertébrés. Mais tels sont aussi, dans la série des Articulés, les Insectes et en particulier certains Hyménoptères. On a dit que les Fourmis étaient maitresses du sous-sol de la terre, comme l'homme est maitre du sol."—H. Bergson, "L'Évolution Créatrice," 1908.

It is a matter of common observation that the higher animals— those, namely, that in structure and behavior are most like ourselves— are also the ones which arouse our keenest interest, for besides the interest prompted by purely æsthetic or gastronomic motives, or by that atavic love of the chase, so universal among healthy men, there is a more intellectual interest which zoölogists and laymen alike experience when they contemplate in the nearest of their animal kindred the vague but unmistakable prototypes of the human body and its activities. The only lower animals that from immemorial time have retained a like interest for man, are certain insects—the social bees and wasps, the termites and the ants. And among these what appeals so forcibly to the imagination is not the structure or activities of the individuals as such, but the extraordinary instincts which compel them to live permanently in intimate consociations. In this case also our interest is aroused by an undeniable resemblance to our own condition. Reflection shows that this resemblance cannot be superficial, but must depend on a high degree of adaptability and plasticity common to man and the social insects, for in order to live in permanent commonwealths, an organism must be not only remarkably adaptive to changes in its external environment, but must also have an intense feeling of coöperation, forbearance and affection towards the other members of its community. In other words, to live in societies, like those of man and the social insects, implies a shifting of proclivities from the egocentric to the sociocentric plane through a remarkable increase in the amplitude and precision of the individual's responses to all the normal environmental stimuli.

Of the four groups of social insects above mentioned, adaptive plasticity attains its richest and boldest expression in the ants. The extraordinary character of these creatures will appear in its proper light if we undertake to compare them on the one hand with the remaining social insects, and on the other hand with man, the paragon of social animals. It is certain that the ants occupy a unique position among all insects on account of their dominance as a group, and this dominance is shown first, in their high degree of variability as exhibited in the great number of their species, subspecies and varieties; second, in their numerical ascendancy in individuals; third, in their wide geographical distribution; fourth, in their remarkable longevity; fifth, in their abandonment of certain over-specialized modes of life from which the other social insects seem not to have been able to emancipate themselves, and sixth, in their manifold relationships with plants and other animals—man included.

Ants are to be found everywhere, from the arctic regions to the tropics, from timberline on the loftiest mountains to the shifting sands of the dunes and seashores, and from the dampest forests to the driest deserts. Not only do they outnumber in individuals all other terrestrial animals, but their colonies even in very circumscribed localities often defy enumeration. Their colonies are, moreover, remarkably stable, somtimes outlasting a generation of men. Such stability, is, of course, due to the longevity of the individual ants, since worker ants are known to live from four to seven and queens from thirteen to fifteen years. In all these respects the other social insects are decidedly inferior. Not only are the colonies of the wasps and bumblebees of rather rare occurrence, but they are merely annual growths. The honeybees, too, are very short-lived, the workers living only a few weeks or months, the queens but a few years. The termites, though perhaps longer-lived than the bees and wasps, are practically confined to very definite localities in the tropics. Only a few of the species have been able to extend their range into temperate regions.

Not only do the ants far outnumber in species all other social insects, but they have either never acquired, or have completely abandoned, certain habits which must seriously handicap the termites, social wasps and bees in their struggle for existence. The ants neither restrict their diet, like the termites, to comparatively innutritious substances such as cellulose, nor like the bees to a very few substances like the honey and pollen of the evanescent flowers, nor do they build elaborate combs of expensive materials, such as wax. Even paper as a building material has been very generally outgrown and abandoned by the ants. Waxen and paper cells are not easily altered or repaired, and insects that are wedded to this kind of architecture, not only have to expend much time and energy in collecting and working up their building materials, but they are unable to move themselves or their brood to other localities when the nest is disturbed, when the moisture or temperature become unfavorable or the food supply fails. The custom of depending on a single fertilized queen as the only reproductive center or organ of the colony has also been outgrown by many ants. At least the more dominant and successful species have learned to cherish a number of these fertile individuals in the colony. Finally, the manifold and plastic relationships of ants to plants and other animals are in marked contrast with the circumscribed and highly specialized ethological relationships of the social bees and wasps. The termites undoubtedly resemble the ants most closely in plasticity, but the careful studies of Grassi and Sandias, Sjöstedt, Froggatt, Silvestri, Heath and others, have shown that these insects, too, are highly specialized, or one-sided in their development. This is best seen in their extreme sensitiveness to light, for this practically confines them to a subterranean existence and excludes them from many of the influences afforded by a more varied and illuminated environment.

There can be little doubt that the ants have become dominant through their exquisitely terrestrial habits, a fact which Espinas (1877) was, I believe, one of the first to notice. He says: "Ants owe their superiority to their terrestrial life. This assertion may seem paradoxical, but consider the exceptional advantages afforded by a terrestrial medium to the development of their intellectual faculties, compared with an aërial medium! In the air there are the long flights without obstacles, the vertiginous journeys far from real bodies, the instability, the wandering about, the endless forgetfulness of things and oneself. On the earth, on the contrary, there is not a movement that is not a contact and does not yield precise information, not a journey that fails to leave some reminiscence; and as these journeys are determinate, it is inevitable that a portion of the ground incessantly traversed should be registered, together with its resources and its dangers, in the animal's imagination. Thus there results a closer and much more direct communication with the external world. To employ matter, moreover, is

easier for a terrestrial than an aërial animal.   When it is necessary to
build, the latter must, like the bee, either secrete the substance of its
nest or seek it at a distance, as does the bee when she collects propolis,
or the wasp when she gathers material for her paper.   The terrestrial
animal has its building materials close at hand, and its architecture may
be as varied as these materials.   Ants, therefore, probably owe their
social and industrial superiority to their habitat."

The dominance of ants is clearly indicated by the small number of
their enemies.   They are preyed upon by comparatively few mammals,
birds, reptiles, parasitic insects and other ants.[1]   And however much
their philoprogenitive instincts may be exploited by their various guests
and mess-mates, the adult ants enjoy, in temperate regions at least, a
singular immunity.   A further indication of dominance is seen in the
peculiar and widely distributed defensive modifications of the integument of those animals which are most frequently exposed to the attack
of ant colonies.   The scales of reptiles, the feathers of birds and the
hairs of mammals and caterpillars suggest themselves as such defensive
adaptations.   At any rate it would be difficult to conceive of structures
better suited to the protection of arboreal and terrestrial animals against
these ubiquitous insects.

Some very striking resemblances between human and ant societies
are implied in the fact already mentioned, that animal communities, in
order to deserve the name of societies, must have certain fundamental
traits in common.   Indeed, the resemblances between men and ants are
so very conspicuous that they were noted even by aboriginal thinkers.
Folk-lore and primitive poetry and philosophy show the ants as an
abiding source of similes expressing the fervid activity and coöperation
of men.   Although these similes have become trite from repetition,
the scientific student can hardly free himself from the many anthropomorphisms which they suggest.   He is forced to admit that the social
and psychical ascendancy of the ants among invertebrates and of the
mammals among vertebrates, constitutes a very striking example of
convergent development.   And the paleontologist may be inclined to
admit that this convergence has a deeper significance, that it may have
been due, in fact, since ants and mammals seem to make their appearance simultaneously in Mesozoic times, to some peculiar transitory
conditions that favored the birth of forms destined to dominance
through extraordinary psychical endowment.   What these conditions
were we have but the slenderest hope of ever knowing.   Perhaps they
may be conceived as having favored psychical mutations, which are

---

[1] As Forel says: "The ants' most dangerous enemies are other ants, just as
man's most dangerous enemies are other men."

more remarkable, but also more obscure than the physical mutations now engrossing the attention of biologists.

Be this as it may, there is certainly a striking parallelism between the development of human and ant societies. Some anthropologists, like Topinard,[2] distinguish in the development of human societies six different types or stages, designated as the hunting, pastoral, agricultural, commercial, industrial and intellectual. The ants show stages corresponding to the first three of these, as Lubbock has remarked (1894): "Whether there are differences in advancement within the limits of the same species or not, there are certainly considerable differences between the different species, and one may almost fancy that we can trace stages corresponding to the principal steps in the history of human development. I do not now refer to slave-making ants, which represent an abnormal, or perhaps only a temporary state of things, for slavery seems to tend in ants as in men to the degradation of those by whom it is adopted, and it is not impossible that the slave-making species will eventually find themselves unable to compete with those which are more self-dependent, and have reached a higher plane of civilization. But putting these slave-making ants on one side, we find in the different species of ants different conditions of life, curiously answering to the earlier stages of human progress. For instance, some species, such as *Formica fusca,* live principally on the produce of the chase; for though they feed partially on the honey-dew of aphids, they have not domesticated these insects. These ants probably retain the habits once common to all ants. They resemble the lower races of men, who subsist mainly by hunting. Like them they frequent woods and wilds, live in comparatively small communities, as the instincts of collective action are but little developed among them. They hunt singly, and their battles are single combats, like those of Homeric heroes. Such species as *Lasius flavus* represent a distinctly higher type of social life; they show more skill in architecture, may literally be said to have domesticated certain species of aphids, and may be compared to the pastoral stage of human progress—to the races which live on the products of their flocks and herds. Their communities are more numerous; they act much more in concert; their battles are not mere single combats, but they know how to act in combination. I am disposed to hazard the conjecture that they will gradually exterminate the mere hunting species, just as savages disappear before more advanced races. Lastly, the agricultural nations may be compared with the harvesting ants."

[2] "Science and Faith, or Man as an Animal, and Man as a Member of Society." Translated by T. J. McCormack. Chicago, Open Court Publishing Co., 1899, p. 192 *et seq.*

Although Lubbock has not been altogether fortunate in the selection of species to illustrate his views, I believe we may adopt his conclusion that among ants "there seem to be three principal types, offering a curious analogy to the three great phases—the hunting, pastoral and agricultural stages—in the history of human development." It is obvious that a further development towards the three remaining stages in human progress—the commercial, industrial and intellectual—is not even foreshadowed in the ants. Nor would this be possible, or indeed conceivable, without conceptual thought and an appreciation of values to which the ants have never attained.

Granting the resemblances above mentioned between ant and human societies, there are nevertheless three far-reaching differences between insect and human organization and development to be constantly borne in mind:

1. Ant societies are societies of females. The males really take no part in the colonial activities, and, in most species, are present in the nest only for the brief period requisite to insure the impregnation of the young queens. The males take no part in building, provisioning or guarding the nest or in feeding the workers or the brood. They are in every sense the *sexus sequior*. Hence the ants resemble certain mythical human societies like the Amazons, but unlike these, all their activities center in the multiplication and care of the coming generations.

2. In human society, apart from the functions depending on sexual dimorphism, and barring individual differences and deficiencies which can be partially or wholly suppressed, equalized or augmented by an elaborate system of education, all individuals have the same natural endowment. Each normal individual retains its various physiological and psychological needs and powers intact, not necessarily sacrificing any of them for the good of the community. In ants, however, the female individuals, of which the society properly consists, are not all alike but often very different, both in their structure (polymorphism) and in their activities (physiological division of labor). Each member is *visibly* predestined to certain social activities to the exclusion of others, not as in man through the education of some endowment common to all the members of the society, but through the exigencies of structure, fixed at the time of hatching, *i. e.,* the moment the individual enters on its life as an active member of the community.

3. Owing to this preëstablished structure and the specialized functions which it implies, ants are able to live in a condition of anarchistic socialism, each individual instinctively fulfilling the demands of social life without "guide, overseer or ruler," as Solomon correctly observed,

but not without the imitation and suggestion involved in an appreciation of the activities of its fellows.

An ant society, therefore, may be regarded as little more than an expanded family, the members of which coöperate for the purpose of still further expanding the family and detaching portions of itself to found other families of the same kind. There is thus a striking analogy, which has not escaped the philosophical biologist, between the ant colony and the cell colony which constitutes the body of a Metazoan animal; and many of the laws that control the cellular origin, development, growth, reproduction and decay of the individual Metazoon, are seen to hold good also of the ant society regarded as an individual of a higher order. As in the case of the individual animal, no further purpose of the colony can be detected than that of maintaining itself in the face of a constantly changing environment till it is able to reproduce other colonies of a like constitution. The queen mother of the ant colony displays the generalized potentialities of all the individuals, just as the Metazoan egg contains *in potentia* all the other cells of the body. And, continuing the analogy, we may say that since the different castes of the ant colony are morphologically specialized for the performance of different functions, they are truly comparable with the differentiated tissues of the Metazoan body.

Two further matters call for consideration in connection with the dominant rôle of ants, namely, their importance in the economy of nature and their value as objects of biological study. The consideration of their economic importance resolves itself into an appreciation of their beneficial, noxious or indifferent qualities as competitors with man in his struggles to control the forces of nature. As objects of biological study their importance evidently depends on the extent to which a study of their activities may assist us in analyzing and solving the ever-present problems of life and mind.

The activities of ants may interfere with those of man in three different directions—first, through their feeding habits; second, through their habit of appropriating certain portions of the earth as nesting sites, and third, through their aggressive, *i. e.*, stinging and biting, habits. The first of these activities is far and away the most important. In respect to all of them, however, ants of different species have very different economic importance, some being highly beneficial, others as highly injurious to man, while a great number, owing to the small size and scarcity of their colonies, may be regarded, from an economic standpoint, as indifferent or negligible organisms. On this account, some myrmecologists regard ants in general as more noxious than beneficial, whereas others maintain the opposite view. I believe that

a consideration of all the facts forces us to admit, with Forel, that as
a group ants are eminently beneficial and that for this reason many
species deserve our protection.   Some of our species, however, are certainly noxious, and these offer strong resistance to all measures for
their extermination,[3] owing to the tenacity with which they cling to
their nesting sites, their enormous fertility and the restriction of the
reproductive functions to one or a few queens that are able to resist
destruction by living in the inaccessible penetralia of their nests.

The greatest usefulness of ants, which lies in their power to hasten
the decomposition of organic substances, is easily overlooked or belit-
tled, like all the great forces which act very gradually but incessantly.
Of the millions of insects annually born into the world, many are
undoubtedly consumed by insectivorous vertebrates, but a vast number
survive till they have provided for the next generation and then fall
exhausted to the earth.   These, together with many that have just left
their pupal envelopes, or for other reasons are unable to escape, are
the natural food of most ants.   A vast number of wingless and larval
insects, spiders, etc., thus fall a prey to these omnipresent and vigilant
free-booters.   Let anyone who doubts these statements fix his attention
for an hour on some populous formicary during a warm summer day
and he will be astonished at the number of dead and disabled insects
carried in by the foraging workers.   Forel observed that a large colony
of ants brought in 28 dead insects per minute and estimated that they
would bring in 100,000 daily during the hours of their greatest activity.
While this is certainly a high estimate and based on more than 28 per
minute, one half or one third of the number, which is well within the
bounds of probability, is certainly enormous.   In the tropics this daily
consumption of insects must be vastly greater than in temperate regions,
and while the ants do not, of course, distinguish between the beneficial
and harmful insects that they kill, they probably dispose of more of
the latter.   Eminent economic entomologists like Taschenberg and
Ratzeburg, who have studied the ants in the German forest preserves,
are of the opinion that they are highly beneficial.   A German law,
passed in 1880, punishes with a fine of 100 marks or a month's impris-
onment any person who collects the cocoons of the fallow ant, *Formica
rufa,* or wantonly disturbs its nests in the forest preserves.

The driver ants (Dorylii) in the tropics of the Old World and the
allied legionary ants (Ecitonii) in the corresponding regions of America,
do not confine themselves to collecting dead or disabled insects.   They
move in long files over or immediately beneath the surface of the

[3] In Appendix D I have given a brief outline of the most approved methods
of destroying noxious ants.

ground and capture myriads of living insects and their larvæ. So efficient are they in exterminating all kinds of vermin, including rats and mice, that they are welcomed into the houses, even if their owners are obliged to vacate for the time being. In some countries, the ants are regarded as useful allies in destroying the insect pests of plantations. According to Magowan, quoted by McCook (1882): " In many parts of the province of Canton, where, says a Chinese writer, cereals cannot be profitably cultivated, the land is devoted to the cultivation of orange-trees, which being subject to devastation from worms, require to be protected in a peculiar manner, that is, by importing ants from the neighboring hills for the destruction of the dreaded parasite. The orangeries themselves supply ants which prey upon the enemy of the orange, but not in sufficient numbers; and resort is had to hill people, who, throughout the summer and winter, find the nests suspended from branches of bamboo and various trees. There are two varieties of ants, red and yellow, whose nests resemble cotton bags. The orange-ant feeders are provided with pig or goat bladders, which are baited inside with lard. The orifices they apply to the entrance of the nests, when the ants enter the bag and become a marketable commodity at the orangeries. Orange-trees are colonized by depositing the ants on their upper branches, and to enable them to pass from tree to tree, all the trees of an orchard are connected by a bamboo rod."

Many years ago McCook suggested that foreign ants might be advantageously introduced into our country for similar purposes. This suggestion was apparently followed by the Department of Agriculture when it recently introduced a Guatemalan ant, the " kelep " (*Ectatomma tuberculatum*) into Texas for the purpose of destroying the very injurious cotton-boll weevil. This experiment resulted in failure owing, as I have shown (1904*a*, 1904*b*), to the selection of an inappropriate species. Notwithstanding this failure, McCook's suggestion still merits careful consideration on the part of economic entomologists.

The activities of ants in excavating their nests have a very useful aspect. Most of the species, especially in temperate latitudes, nest in the ground, and many of them in so doing are obliged to comminute and bring to the surface, often from a depth of several feet, considerable quantities of subsoil. This is spread over the surface either by the elements or by the ants themselves and exposed to the sun and atmosphere. The burrows, moreover, quickly conduct air and moisture into the deeper recesses of the soil. Thus the ants act on the soil like the earthworms, and this action is by no means inconsiderable, although as yet no one has studied it in detail. The common garden ant (*Lasius niger*), whose little craters are often extremely abundant over great stretches of country in the northern hemisphere, and the large species of *Atta* in tropical America, may be cited as conspicuous examples of the ants that are constantly engaged in renewing the soil.

There are a number of more trivial but interesting ways in which ants prove themselves useful to man. Young naturalists have often employed them for skeletonizing small vertebrates and cleaning birds' eggs by placing these objects near or in their nests. In Europe the cocoons of the fallow ant have long been carefully collected for bird-food. Many years ago the formic acid expressed and distilled from the workers of the same species held a prominent place in the pharmacopœia. In the Western States and in Mexico garments are sometimes freed from vermin by placing them on the large hills of *Formica* and *Pogonomyrmex*. Mr. Hatcher found the occident ant of the plains (*Pogonomyrmex occidentalis*) very useful to the collector in bringing to the surface the teeth of small fossil mammals. A few species, like the honey-ants of the Southwest (*Myrmecocystus melliger*) are used by the Indians for food and medicinal purposes. The huge heads of the soldiers of the South American leaf-cutting ants (*Atta cephalotes*) have been employed by the native surgeons in closing wounds. After the two edges of the wound have been brought together and have been grasped by the mandibles, the ant's head is severed from its body and left as a ligature.

Leaving out of consideration many of our ants as economically indifferent, there nevertheless remains a considerable number of species decidedly injurious to man and to the products of his toil. Most prominent among these are the house-ants, almost without exception small species that conceal their teeming formicaries in the woodwork and masonry of ships and dwellings and forage on the saccharine and oleaginous substances in kitchens, pantries and storerooms. These species are nearly all of tropical origin, and some of them, like Pharaoh's ant (*Monomorium pharaonis*), have been carried by commerce to all the inhabited regions of the globe. Other species, like *Monomorium destructor, Pheidole megacephala, Tetramorium guineense, T. simillimum, Prenolepis longicornis, Iridomyrmex humilis* and *Plagiolepis longipes,* though abundant about dwellings in the tropics, are unable to survive in temperate regions except in hot-houses. Only two of our native species, the tiny thief-ant (*Solenopsis molesta*) and the carpenter ant (*Camponotus pennsylvanicus*), have become house ants since the settlement of North America. In its native haunts the latter species nests in decayed wood. It preserves this habit as a house ant and often does considerable damage to beams and rafters.

Other species of ants are well-known garden pests. In the United States *Lasius americanus, Prenolepis imparis* and *Formica subsericea* sometimes disfigure the lawns and flower-beds with their excavations and untidy castings, while in tropical America the larger leaf-cutting ants of the genus *Atta* are a serious menace to horticulture. These latter ants defoliate garden shrubs and fruit trees in an incredibly short time. But the greatest harm is undoubtedly done both in tropical and temperate regions by a host of species that have a pronounced fondness for pasturing and guarding plant-lice (*Aphides*), mealy bugs (Coccidæ) and tree-hoppers (Membracidæ) on roots, stems or foliage. All these insects suck the juices of plants and their protection must therefore be regarded as pernicious. The honey-dew which they excrete is eagerly sought by all our species of *Camponotus, Formica, Lasius, Prenolepis, Cremastogaster, Myrmica* and *Dolichoderus,* but only the most abundant species of these genera are to be regarded as positively harmful. Such a species is the commonest of all our ants, *Lasius niger,* which is known to hoard the eggs of the corn-root louse (*Aphis maidiradicis*) in its nests over winter and to distribute the just-hatched young in the spring along the roots of the maize. The noxious character of some aphidicolous species is, however, slightly mitigated by the fact that in the absence of ants the plant lice discharge their sweet excretions on the leaves where, especially during protracted dry weather, it forms a varnish that interferes with the respiration of the plant and affords a favorable substratum for the growth of destructive leaf-fungi.

Ants are often feared on account of their stinging and biting habits, but these, at least in the United States, have been greatly exaggerated. In reality only a few of our species like the fire-ant (*Solenopsis geminata*) and the larger harvesting ants (*Pogonomyrmex barbatus* and *P. occidentalis*) are sufficiently abundant in the neighborhood of human dwellings to be at all formidable. The fire-ant, which occurs only in the tropics and in our Southern States, is very fond of nesting in door-yards and along paths and roads. It is extremely pugnacious, and, as its name indicates, can sting severely. The sting of the larger harvesting ants is even more formidable, but these species, confined to the great plains and the deserts of the Southwest, do not thrive in the neighborhood of human settlements. In general it may be said that ants do not go out of their way to sting and bite, but resort to these offensive measures only when their nests are violently disturbed.

In concluding this chapter attention may be called to the great value of ants as objects of study. No other group of animals presents such a maze of fascinating problems to the biologist, psychologist and sociologist. It will suffice to mention the unrivalled material which they present for the study of variation and geographical distribution, both from the taxonomic and experimental standpoints, the extraordinary phenomena of polymorphism, parthenogenesis and sex-determination; the wonderful cases of parasitism and symbiosis, and last, but not least, the great importance of these insects in the problems of instinct and intelligence. The researches of Janet and others have shown what a wonderful field of anatomical study they present, and the embryonic and post-embryonic development have scarcely been studied. Add to all this the great facility with which they may be obtained in all localities and, owing to their remarkable adaptability, the ease with which they can be kept for long periods in artificial nests, and it becomes a matter of surprise that they have attracted so few students. To what extent this neglect on the part of entomologists and other biologists may be due to the absence in ants of a powerful appeal to the æsthetic sense, so readily aroused by birds, beetles and butterflies, would be an interesting matter for discussion. If this is, indeed, responsible for the very general neglect of the ants, their lack of æsthetic qualities may perhaps be regarded as a further advantage, since it must tend to discourage those who approach the subject merely as collectors of pretty things, while it does not necessarily repel the more serious and philosophical student.

CHAPTER II

THE EXTERNAL STRUCTURE OF ANTS

Διὸ δεῖ μὴ δυσχεραίνειν παιδικῶς τὴν περὶ τῶν ἀτιμοτέρων ζῴων ἐπίσκεψιν. Ἐν πᾶσι γὰρ τοῖς φυσικοῖς ἔνεστί τι θαυμαστόν· καὶ καθάπερ Ἡράκλειτος λέγεται πρὸς τοὺς ξένους εἰπεῖν τοὺς βουλομένους αὐτῷ ἐντυχεῖν, οἳ ἐπειδὴ προσιόντες εἶδον αὐτὸν θερόμενον πρὸς τῷ ἱπνῷ, ἔστησαν· ἐκέλευσε γὰρ αὐτοὺς εἰσιέναι θαρροῦντας· εἶναι γὰρ καὶ ἐνταῦθα θεούς· οὕτω καὶ πρὸς τὴν ζήτησιν περὶ ἑκάστου τῶν ζῴων προσιέναι δεῖ μὴ δυσωπούμενον, ὡς ἐν ἅπασιν ὄντος φυσικοῦ καὶ καλοῦ.

"Wherefore we ought not childishly to neglect the study even of the most despised animals, for in all natural objects there lies something marvellous. And as it is related of Heraclitus that certain strangers who came to visit him, when they found him warming himself at the kitchen fire, stopped short—he bade them enter without fear, for there also were the gods: so we ought to enter without false shame on the examination of all living beings, for in all of them resides something of nature and beauty."—Aristotle, "De Partibus Animalium," I, 5.

The ants form a natural family (Formicidæ), or, according to some authorities, a superfamily (Formicina or Formicoidea), comprising five subfamilies (Ponerinæ, Dorylinæ, Myrmicinæ, Dolichoderinæ and Camponotinæ), embracing about 5,000 described species, subspecies and varieties, and are placed at the head of the order Hymenoptera, a vast assemblage of insects including also the bees, wasps, ichneumon flies, velvet-ants, saw-flies and many smaller groups. From all the other members of the order the ants may be readily distinguished by a series of characters, perhaps the most striking of which is the differentiation of the abdomen into two strongly marked regions, a slender one- or two-jointed, highly mobile pedicel, and a larger, more compact terminal portion, the gaster. Another distinguishing character is furnished by the antennæ which are elbowed and have the first joint greatly elongated in the female. The species are all social, and with the exception of a few parasitic forms, are always at least trimorphic, i. e., the female is not only sharply differentiated from the male, but itself appears under two very distinct phases, a fertile, queen, or female phase proper, and a usually sterile worker phase. The former is nearly always winged like the male, but loses the wings after fecundation, the latter, except in rare abnormalities, never bears these organs. In a few species the females, and in many the workers may again show differentiation into two sub-phases (Fig. 1). Owing to this remarkable morphological instability or tendency of the female to assume different aspects, the Formicidæ have also been called Heterogyna. All of the species have retained in their development the four salient stages known as the egg, larval, pupal and imaginal instars, which are peculiar to all holometabolic insects. These stages and their relations to the polymorphism of ants will be considered in subsequent chapters. In this and the two following chapters I shall endeavor to give a rapid survey

FIG. 1. *Camponotus americanus.* (Photograph by J. G. Hubbard and O. S. Strong.) Virgin queens and major and minor workers, natural size.

of the external and internal anatomy, as these have become known to us through the careful researches of a number of investigators, notably Adlerz, Berlese, Dewitz, Emery, Forel, Janet, Lubbock, Meinert and Nassonow.

The Segmentation of the Body.—There can be little doubt that the ants are phylogenetically related, through the lower families of Hymenoptera with the oldest and most primitive of all the existing insects, the Blattoidea, or cock-roaches. But while the Blattoid body, as seen, for example, in the common cock-roaches, is generalized, that of the ants in its sharp demarcation of the head, thorax and abdomen is highly specialized. These accentuated subdivisions enable anyone to recognize an ant at a glance. In this respect the ants are the most typical of insects, and may be the ones to which the terms ἔντομον and *insectum* were originally applied. While these and many other characters make it seem a far call from the ant to its remote Blattoid ancestors, it must be borne in mind that the individual ant still passes in its embryonic development through a stage in which the body consists of twenty like, or homonomous segments. Six of these belong morphologically to the head, three to the thorax and the remaining eleven to the abdomen. The first and third segments bear no appendages, the second bears the antennæ, the three thoracic segments bear the three pairs of legs, and the second and third of these segments in the males and females develop, at a much later stage, the two pairs of wings. The first abdominal, which has long been known as the mediary segment, becomes fused with the hind portion of the third thoracic segment during pupal development, as Janet and Emery have demonstrated, and becomes the epinotum of the latter author. The pedicel consists of the second abdominal segment, or of this and the third segment, while the remaining seven or eight form the gaster.

The Integument.—The chitinous investment, or integument varies greatly in thickness in the different species of ants, being very hard and brittle in many of the more primitive groups (Ponerinæ, Myrmicinæ, *Dolichoderus, Polyrhachis*) and thinner and more pliable in the more recently developed forms (most Dolichoderinæ and Camponotinæ). The microscopic character of the integument is of considerable importance to the taxonomist, especially in the more delicate discrimination of geographical subspecies and varieties and may be considered under the captions of sculpture, pilosity, pubescence and color. These all present a bewildering variety of modifications. In some ants the surface of the body is very glabrous and shining, in others opaque, punctate, foveolate, rugulose, rugose, tuberculate, striate or reticulate, and these sculptural characters may be combined in the most diverse patterns. The term pilosity applies to the longer, reclinate, erect or suberect hairs, the term pubescence to the minute, appressed tomentum, which may cover the whole or portions of the body and appendages. Both the hairs and pubescence vary greatly in length and density or abundance, and the former may be tapering and pointed, straight, flexuous, or hooked, obtuse or clavate, or dilated and flattened to form scales.

No doubt all of these differentiations in sculpture, pilosity and pubescence are correlated with the delicate tactile sense of the ants. Certainly one who has examined many species of ants will have no difficulty in understanding why these blind or nearly blind insects seem to display such keen delight in palpating with their antennæ and burnishing with their tongues the exquisitely chased or chiselled armor of their fellows. In some ants the hairs may be specialized for particular functions on certain portions of the body. I find this to be the case, for example, in several genera of desert ants (Fig. 2), which have the hairs on the lower surface of the head greatly elongated and directed forward (*Pogonomyrmex, Ocymyrmex, Cratomyrmex, Messor, Goniomma, Oxyopomyrmex, Holcomyrmex*), or arranged in a tuft on the lower lip (*Myrmecocystus, Melophorus*). These hairs, which I have called gular and mental ammochætæ (1907), are employed by the ants in removing the dust and sand from the strigils or combs on the fore-legs (*vide infra*, p. 24). In deserts these insects easily become covered with the dry soil or sand and have to remove it from their bodies and limbs by means of the strigils. These organs are then thrust along the ammochætæ in much the same way as we clean a comb by means of threads. The clypeus and mandibles of many ants are also fringed with unusually long hairs (clypeal and mandibular ammochætæ) which are employed in re-

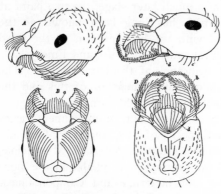

FIG. 2. Ammochætæ of desert ants. (Original.) *A,* Head of *Messor pergandei* in profile; *B,* ventral aspect of same; *C,* head of *Myrmecocystus bicolor* in profile; *D,* ventral aspect of same; *a,* clypeal; *b,* mandibular; *c,* gular; *d,* mental ammochætæ.

moving the dust, etc., from the surfaces of the fore-legs.

The colors of ants are, as a rule, testaceous, yellow, brown, red, or black, but a few genera (*Rhytidoponera, Calomyrmex, Macromischa, Iridomyrmex*) and a few North American species of *Pheidole* (*metallescens* and *splendidula*) have metallic colors. The non-metallic tints are often highly variable, even within the limits of single species. Color patterns are rarely developed and are usually found only on the upper surface of the gaster, a region which often differs in color from the head and thorax. The appendages, as in other insects, are apt to be paler than the trunk. The coloration of the hairs and pubescence, like that of the surface, may be extremely variable in the same species. To the integument belong also a number of glands, but these will be described in connection with the glands of the internal organs.

The Head.—After this very general review of the segmentation and integument we may take up the different parts of the body in somewhat greater detail. The head varies enormously in shape. It may be circular, elliptical, rectangular or triangular, and all its parts may show an extraordinary diversity of adaptive characters (Fig. 3). It consists of the cranium proper, which is very much constricted behind at its articulation with the thorax, the eyes, the clypeus, or epistoma, a plate of very variable outline and immovably articulated with and set into the anterior portion of the cranium, the antennæ, and the mouth-parts,

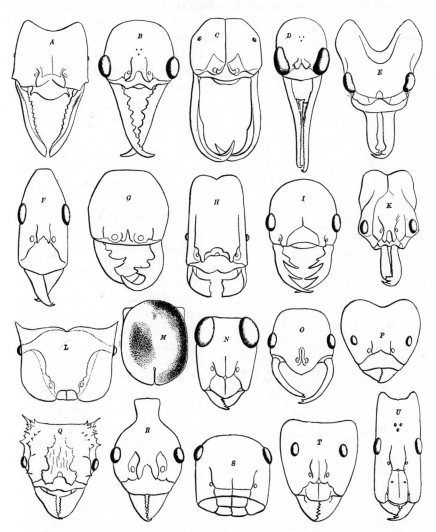

FIG. 3. Heads of various ants. (Original.) *A, Mystrium rogeri,* worker; *B, Myrmecia gulosa,* worker; *C, Eciton hamatum,* soldier; *D, Harpegnathus cruentatus,* female; *E, Daceton armigerum,* worker; *F, Leptomyrmex erythrocephalus,* worker; *G, Cheliomyrmex nortoni,* soldier; *H, Pheidole lamia,* soldier; *I, Thaumatomyrmex mutilatus,* worker; *K, Odontomachus hæmatodes,* worker; *L. Cryptocerus clypeatus,* soldier; *M, Cryptocerus varians,* soldier; *N, Opisthopsis respiciens,* worker; *O, Leptogenys maxillosus,* worker; *P, Azteca sericea,* soldier; *Q, Acromyrmex octospinosus,* worker; *R, Dolichoderus attelaboides,* worker; *S, Colobopsis impressa,* soldier; *T, Camponotus cognatus,* soldier; *U, Camponotus mirabilis,* female.

comprising an unpaired upper lip, or labrum, the mandibles, maxillæ
and labium, or lower lip.   In the last the originally separate and paired
embryonic appendages are fused in the median line so that they form
a continuous floor for the mouth or buccal cavity.   In the cranium the
following regions may be distinguished: the front, a region bounded
anteriorly by the posterior edge of the clypeus and laterally by a pair
of ridges, the frontal carinæ or
laminæ, just mesial to the insertions of the antennæ.   A small,
usually triangular, median region,
the frontal area, can be easily
seen in the middle line just back
of the clypeus, and often there is
an impressed line, the frontal
groove, extending back from this
area over the middle of the front.
The frontal region passes without definite boundary into the
vertex and temples, the former
extending posteriorly, the latter
lying above and behind the eyes.
The short region between the
vertex and the narrow opening,
or foramen through which the
alimentary tract and nervous
system pass into the thorax, may
be called the occiput.   The
cheeks, or genæ, comprise the
portions of the cranium anterior
to the eyes and lateral to the
frontal carinæ.   The ventral portion of the head, bounded in
front by the labium, on the sides
by the cheeks and extending to
the occipital foramen, is the
throat, or gula.   It is well-developed in the ants and is usually
divided into two equal halves by
a longitudinal suture.

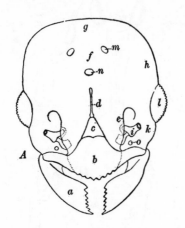

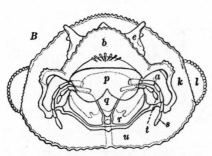

Fig. 4.   External structure of head
in *Myrmica rubra* worker. (Janet.) *A,*
Dorsal aspect of head; *B,* anterior
aspect; *a,* mandible; *b,* clypeus; *c,*
frontal area; *d,* frontal groove; *e,*
frontal carina; *f,* vertex; *g,* occiput;
h, temple; *i,* base of antennal scape;
k, cheek; *l,* eye; *m,* lateral ocellus; *n,*
median ocellus; *o,* tentorial pit; *p,*
labrum; *q,* labium; *r,* maxilla; *s,* maxillary palp; *t,* labial palp; *u,* gula.

The mandibles, being the parts with which the ant comes into most
effective relations with its environment, present, like the beaks of birds
and the teeth of mammals, a bewildering variety of structure (Fig. 3).

They are used for excavating soil or wood, cutting up the food, fighting, carrying the prey, their young or one another, and in some species, even in leaping by closing them rapidly against hard bodies. Ants are remarkable in being able to open and close their mandibles independently of the maxillæ and labium. These organs, which lie underneath the small and vestigial labrum and close the mouth completely except when the insect is feeding, have a complicated and interesting structure. The maxillæ (Fig. 5, *B, D*) are paired and each consists of the following pieces, or sclerites: the hinge (cardo), the stem (stipes), the maxillary

palp, which may be from 1–6-jointed, an inner blade (lacinia) and an outer blade, the galea. The galea bears a row of gustatory papillæ and a row of bristles which are used in cleaning the legs and antennæ. The lacinia is membraneous and toothless and shows that the ant feeds on liquid substances only. This is also proved by the structure of the labium (Fig. 5, *C*), which consists of the following sclerites: the hind chin (submentum), the chin (mentum) and the tongue (glossa), all unpaired, and the labial palpi, consisting of from one to four joints, the paraglossæ and hypopharynx, which are paired. The tongue, with which the ant rasps

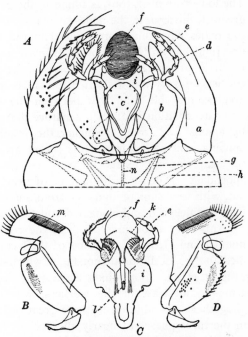

Fig. 5. Mouthparts of *Myrmica rubra*. (Janet.) *A,* Seen from the lower, or ventral side, *in situ; B* and *D,* maxillæ; *C,* labium, seen from the upper, or dorsal side, detached; *a,* mandible; *b,* maxilla; *c,* mentum; *d,* maxillary palp; *e,* labial palp; *f,* glossa, or tongue; *g,* adductor muscle of mandible; *h,* abductor muscle of mandible; *i,* labium; *k,* gustatory organs; *l,* duct of salivary glands; *m,* maxillary comb; *n,* gular apodeme.

off or laps up its liquid or semi-liquid food, and cleans itself and its fellows, is a protrusible, elliptical pad, covered with fine transverse ridges. At its base lies the opening of the salivary duct. The paraglossæ are small sclerites beset with rows of bristles. The hypopharynx, which is less developed than in some of the other

Hymenoptera, such as the wasps, covers the mentum and paraglossæ. Its upper portion is somewhat lobed and bears two rows of backwardly directed bristles, which form a V and seem to be used for holding the food fast in the mouth. The upper lip, or labrum, forms the roof of the mouth. It is poorly developed and ·consists of a bilobed plate hidden beneath the anterior border of the clypeus (Fig. 4, *Bp*).

The antennæ are far and away the most important sense organs of the ant. They are inserted in sockets on each side of the frontal carinæ, and consist of a series of joints of variable number and length. The lowest number, four, is found in the genus *Epitritus* (Fig. 75); the greatest, thirteen, in the males of many of our common ants. Usually the males have one more joint than the females and workers. The first joint, known as the scape, is always considerably elongated, except in the males of some species. The remainder of the antenna, the funiculus, consists of very much shorter joints, the articulations between which are less movable than that between the scape and funiculus. This latter articulation is of such a nature that the funiculus can be folded up against the scape producing the peculiar Formicid elbow in the antenna, and both this and the socket articulation at the insertion of the scape permit extraordinary freedom in the movements of the appendage. The funiculus may be of nearly uniform diameter throughout, with very similar joints, or from one to four of the terminal joints may be thickened and elongated and thus constitute a club.

Ants have two kinds of eyes: the compound, lateral eyes, two in number and placed on the sides of the head (Fig. 4, *l*), and the simple, median eyes, ocelli, or stemmata, of which there are three on the vertex (Fig. 4, *m, n*). Both kinds are best developed in the males, less in the females and least in the workers, which often lack the stemmata altogether. In addition to these great differences, which are constant in the three phases of nearly all species, there are considerable differences in the development of the eyes in the different genera. A more detailed account of these organs and the antennal sense organs is given in Chapter IV.

The Thorax.—Owing to the fusion of the first abdominal segment of the embryo and larva with the hindermost portion of the thorax during pupation, the thorax of the adult ant may be said to consist of four segments, a pro-, meso- and meta-thoracic and a mediary segment, or epinotum. In our description we may follow Emery (1900*d*) who has carefully studied the external morphology and reviewed the nomenclature of these four segments in the male, female and worker. The primitive condition of the thoracic region may be readily traced through the ergatoid females and workers of these forms to the much reduced and specialized condition in the workers of more highly developed ants like the Camponotinæ.

Emery starts with a primitive form like the male *Streblognathus æthiopicus* (Fig. 6). In this in-sect the various elements or sclerites of which the thorax is composed are clearly delimited by sutures. The prothorax is very small and consists dorsally and laterally almost entirely of the un-paired pronotum, with a slender ventral element, the prosternum, to which the coxa of the fore-leg is articulated. Owing to the de-velopment of the wings, the meso- and metathorax are much larger. The former is especially well-de-veloped, in correlation with the larger size of the fore wings, and comprises dorsally a large un-paired, convex plate, the mesono-tum; ventrally on each side, and articulated below with the coxa of the middle leg, is the meso-sternum, which also forms much of the pleural wall of the thorax. The space on each side between the mesonotum and the mesosternum is occupied by a pair of elements, one of which, the mesepisternum, is ventral; the other, the mesepi-meron, dorsal. The fore-wing is articulated just above the mesepimeron and below a small sclerite, which is behind the mesonotum and may be called the mesoparapteron, or præscutellum. The insertion of the fore-wing is covered by a small chitinous scale, the tegula. Viewed from above the large mesonotum in some male ants presents a Y-shaped groove, known as the Mayrian furrow (Fig. 7, *sM*). Each side of the mesonotum is marked off for some distance from the median portion of the segment by a distinct suture, which may be called the parapsidal suture. The area thus cut off on each side is the parapsis. The sides and the ventral portions of the metathoracic segment are similar to those of the mesothorax, but smaller. It is possible to dis-tinguish a metasternum, to which the coxa of the hind-leg is articulated, a metepisternum and a metepimeron. Dorsally, however, the metano-

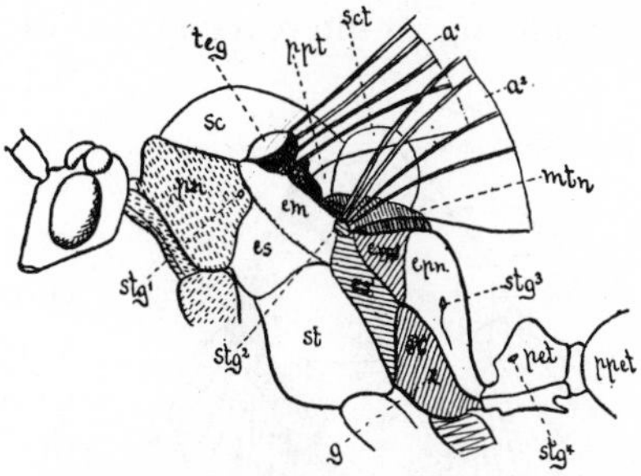

FIG. 6. Thorax of a male Ponerine ant, *Streblognathus æthiopicus* in profile. (Emery.) *a'* and *a²*, Anterior and pos-terior wings; *em* and *em'*, meso- and metathoracic epimera; *es* and *es'*, epis-ternites of the same segments; *epn*, epi-notum; *g*, metasternal gland; *mtn*, meta-notum; *pet*, petiole; *ppet*, postpetiole; *pn*, pronotum; *ppt*, parapteron; *sc*, scu-tum of mesonotum; *sct*, scutellum; *st* and *st'*, meso- and metathoracic ster-nites; *stg'*, *stg²*, *stg³* and *stg⁴*, stigmata of meso- and metathorax, epinotum and petiole. The parts of the prothorax are shaded with broken lines, those of the mesothorax, epinotum and petiole are unshaded, those of the metathorax are shaded with unbroken lines; the wing articulations are dotted.

tum, which, of course, is serially homologous with the mesonotum, is
very narrow antero-posteriorly and separated from the mesonotum by
a large, unpaired, semi-circular element, the scutellum. Between the
scutellum and metanotum, a small piece, the metaparapteron, or post-
scutellum, is intercalated on each side. The hind-wing is inserted
between this metaparapteron and the
metepimeron. The epinotum, which, as
we have seen, is morphologically the
first abdominal segment, is large and
convex and in many ants furnished with
a pair of stout spines or teeth. It is
closely applied to the metathorax from
the posterior edge of the mesonotum
above to the ventral edge of the metathorax below.

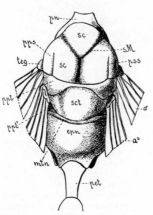

Fig. 7. Dorsal aspect of
thorax of male Ponerine ant,
Paraponera clavata. (Emery.)
a′ and *a²*, Anterior and posterior
wings; *pn*, pronotum; *sc*, scutum
of mesonotum; *sM*, Mayrian
furrow; *pss*, parapsidal furrow;
pps, parapsis; *teg*, tegula; *ppt*
and *ppt′*, paraptera of meso- and
metathorax; *sct*, scutellum; *mtn*,
metanotum; *epn*, epinotum; *pet*,
petiole. ·

The thorax has on each side three
openings, or stigmata, to the respiratory
tubes, or tracheæ. The first, belonging
morphologically to the mesothorax, lies
beneath a small flap-like expansion of
the pronotum where it abuts on the
mesepimeron. The second or metathoracic stigmata lies beneath the insertion of the hind-wing and near the posterior end of the mesepimeron. The
third stigma, belonging to the first abdominal segment, is distinctly seen on
the side of the epinotum.

In the female ant (Fig. 8, *A*) the thorax is constructed on the same
plan as that of the male, but is more robust and lacks the Mayrian
furrow, which is also absent in the males of many genera. The males
and females of most species, however, exhibit a greater simplification,
of the pleural region of the thorax, owing to the fusion of the epimera
and episterna with each other and often also with the sterna in the
meso- and metathorax, and a very intimate fusion of the epinotum with
the latter segment.

Turning to the workers, which are wingless, there is noticeable a
great reduction in the size of the meso- and metathorax *plus* the epinotum, so that the three divisions of the thorax are more nearly of
uniform size (Fig. 8, *C*, Fig. 9, *a*). In certain species, and especially
in the ergatoid females (Fig. 8, *B*) and soldiers of a few genera, the
various dorsal elements, such as the paraptera, scutellum and meta-

notum may still be recognized as very small sclerites, but in the workers
of the highest and most specialized ants of the genera *Formica* and
Camponotus the thorax appears to consist of three similar segments,

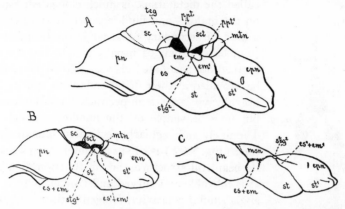

FIG. 8. Thorax of female, ergatoid and worker Ponerine ants in profile. (Emery.)
A, *Myrmecia pyriformis*, deälated female; *B*, *M. spadicea*, ergatoid female; *C*, *M. pyriformis*, worker; *msn*, mesonotum; the remaining letters the same as in Figs. 6 and 7.

owing to the disappearance of the scutellum, paraptera and metanotum
as separate sclerites and to the fusion of the various elements in the
pleural region of each segment.

The legs of the ant show much less variation in structure than the

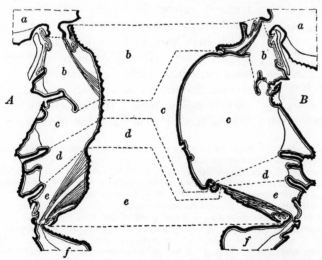

FIG. 9. Median sagittal sections to show difference of development of thoracic
segments in the worker and female *Myrmica rubra*. (Janet.) *A*, Worker; *B*, female;
a, posterior portion of head; *b*, prothorax; *c*, mesothorax; *d*, metathorax; *e*, epinotum (first abdominal segment); *f*, petiole (second abdominal segment).

thorax and are, therefore, of less taxonomic value. Each of these appendages consists of the same fixed number of joints, the coxa, trochanter, femur, tibia, and five tarsal joints. The first tarsal joint, often

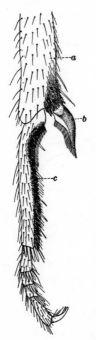

called the metatarsus, is much elongated, especially on the middle- and hind-legs, where it functions as a kind of secondary tibia, while the terminal tarsal joint bears a pair of usually simple, but sometimes toothed, or pectinated claws. All of the tibiæ may be provided at their distal ends with spurs. These are always large and pectinated on the fore-legs, but may be simple on the middle and hind pairs. The finely and regularly pectinated spur of the fore tibia (Fig. 10, b) is of special interest on account of its beautiful structure and its function as a strigil. It is movable and curved and its concavity is opposite a similar concavity, fringed with bristles, on the base of the metatarsus. The ant draws its antennæ and posterior legs between the two opposed, pectinated surfaces and thus wipes off any adhering foreign matter.

The wings have not been used to as great an extent in descriptive works on ants as in those on other families of Hymenoptera, owing to their frequent absence in female specimens and to the permanently apterous condition of the workers, which have hitherto formed the basis of our systematic study. The venation of the fore wings, however, often exhibits important generic or even specific characters and its study, especially in fossil ants, is indispensable. It is sometimes highly variable in detail, even in males and females reared from

Fig. 10. Strigil of Texas harvester (*Pogonomyrmex molefaciens*. (Original.) *a*, Distal end of fore tibia; *b*, movable, pectinated spur; *c*, first tarsal (metatarsal) joint.

Fig. 11. Anterior wings of ants. (Original.) *A, Ichnomyrmex cockerelli*, female; *B, Camponotus sansabeanus*, female; *C, Eciton schmitti*, male; *D, Strumigenys pergandei*, female; *E, Lasius claviger*, female; *F, Dolichoderus mariæ*, female; *G, Solenopsis molesta*, female; *H, Forelius maccooki*, female; *I, Myrmica scabrinodis*, female; *K, Pachycondyla harpax*, male; *L, Pogonomyrmex molefaciens*, female; *M, Tetramorium cespitum*, female; *N, Aphænogaster fulva*, female; *O, Trachymyrmex septentrionalis*, female. The following are the veins of the wing: *a*, costal; *b*, subcostal; *c*, externomedian; *d*, anal; *s*, apterostigma; *c*, and *g*, cubital; *h*, discoidal and subdiscoidal; *f*, marginal, or radius; *z*, transverso-median; *n*, basal; *m*, recurrent; *o*, first section of radius in *A, B, C, E* and *O*, transverse cubitus in *F, I* and *N*. The following are the cells: *u*, first discoidal; *v*, costal; *i*, median; *x*, submedian; *y*, second discoidal; *w*, first cubital; *w'*, second cubital. (These terms are used in myrmecography. Some authors, like Handlirsch, regard what is here called the "subcostal" as the radius + median, and the "subdiscoidal" as a branch of the median.)

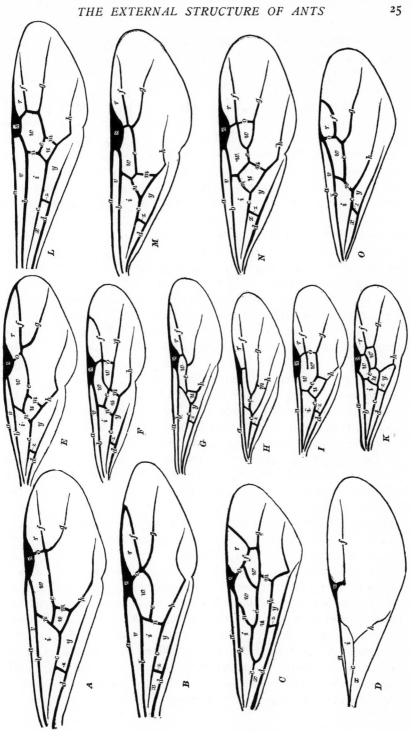

the same mother.   Several of the different types of venation which have
been recognized are represented in the accompanying illustrations (Fig.
11), to which the reader is referred for the names and disposition of
the various veins and cells.

The Abdomen.—This region in ants is very highly specialized in all
three sexual phases.   In some of the most primitive tribes, like the
Amblyoponii and Cerapachysii, there is no sharp separation of the segments into a pedicel and gaster; the basal, though somewhat narrower and more accentuated, preserving essentially the same structure
as the more distal segments.   In most ants, however, there is a well-
defined pedicel which may consist of either one or two segments, very
movably articulated with each other and with the thorax and gaster.
In the subfamilies Dolichoderinæ and Camponotinæ the pedicel always
consists of but a single segment, the petiole, which is morphologically
the second abdominal segment.   The same condition prevails in most
Ponerinæ, except that there is a constriction behind the following or
third segment, foreshadowing the development of a postpetiole.   This
segment is clearly separated off in all Myrmicinæ, so that in the ants
of this subfamily the pedicel consists of two highly specialized, nodiform segments, and the first gastric is the fourth instead of the third
abdominal segment, as in the Camponotinæ, Dolichoderinæ and Ponerinæ.   In the Dorylinæ the genera *Eciton* and *Ænictus* have a distinct
petiole and postpetiole in the worker, but only a single segment, the
petiole, in the male and female.   In *Dorylus* and *Cheliomyrmex* the
base of the abdomen of the worker is more primitive and more like that
of certain Ponerine ants (*Amblyopone* and *Cerapachys*).

The base of the abdomen is the seat of an interesting sound-
producing, or stidulatory, organ.   Landois, in a book called "Thier-
stimmen," published in 1874, was the first to find this organ in a
Ponerine ant ("*Ponera quadridentata,*" probably *Ectatomma quad-
ridens*).   He believed that he had seen a similar structure in the Camponotine *Lasius fuliginosus,* and a few years later Lubbock (1877)
figured what he took to be a stridulatory organ in *L. flavus.*   Sharp
(1893) and Janet (1893*b*, 1894*b*) have since carefully investigated these
organs in several different ants.   The former succeeded in finding them
only in the Ponerinæ and Myrmicinæ (excepting the Cryptocerii) and
believed them to be absent in the Dorylinæ, Dolichoderinæ and Camponotinæ.   The organ (Fig. 12) is best described as a file made of
extremely fine, transverse and parallel ridges on a small area in the
mid-dorsal, chitinous integument at the very base of the first gastric
segment, where it is covered by the overlapping portion of the preceding segment.   The edge of this segment (Fig. 12, *Bp*) is sharp and

turned slightly downward or inward so that it may scrape back and
forth over the file (*str*) when the two segments are moved on
each other and thereby produce a sound of very high pitch. The
file is, in all probability, merely a local specialization of the fine,
polygonal elevations or asperities which cover the adjacent portions
of the segment and are so characteristic of the chitinous investment of many parts of the body. Each of these minute elevations is
evidently secreted by one of the hypodermal chitinogenous cells.
Sharp found great diversity in the structure of the stridulatory organ
both among the different species and in the castes of the same species.

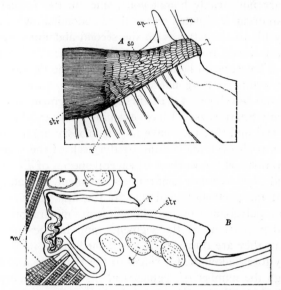

FIG. 12. Stridulatory organ of *Myrmica levinodis*. (Janet.) *A*, Surface view of
right half of the organ; *str*, stridulatory surface; *l*, lateral, reticulate surface; *so*,
sense-organs; *m*, tendon of muscle; *ap*, lateral apophysis; *r*, radiating rugæ at base
of first gastric segment. *B*, Median sagittal section of organ; *str*, stridulatory surface
at extreme anterior border of first gastric segment; *p*, edge of postpetiole which
scratches the stridulatory file *str*.

An interesting modification was found in an Australian Myrmicine ant
of the genus *Sima,* which has the file divided into two parts, one consisting of coarse, the other of fine, ridges, and Sharp remarks that " a
stridulatory performance by this insect might produce very extraordinary effects." Janet, in his studies of *Myrmica rubra,* calls attention
to the fact that there are accumulations of chitinous asperities at various
widely separated regions of the ant's body, especially on articulations
which might, by their movements, produce sounds. But the true
stridulatory organs he finds to be situated where they were seen by

Landois and Sharp, *i. e.,* at the base of the first gastric segment, and also on the corresponding part of the postpetiole. These two segments certainly admit of the greatest amplitude and freedom of movement and are, therefore, the most favorable spots for the development of organs like those under discussion. In *Myrmica rubra* there are more than 50 ridges to the postpetiolar file, but in the organ at the base of the gaster there are more than 130 and these are much finer. The ridges, however, are twice as broad in the anterior as they are in the posterior portion of the gastric file. It appears, therefore, that the most highly developed stridulatory surfaces of the Myrmicinæ and Ponerinæ are not strictly homologous, since in the former subfamily the principal organ is situated on the third abdominal, whereas the only stridulatory file of the latter is on the second abdominal segment. In both cases, however, the main organ is at the base of the first gastric segment. What seem to be incipient stages in the development of the organ from ordinary polygonal asperities of the chitinous integument, are seen in the Dorylinæ. Of the first gastric segment in one genus of this subfamily Sharp says: " I have examined workers of several species of *Eciton,* and find that they have no stridulatory organ, the sculpture being uniform all over the dorsum of the neck of the segment." My own observations on the workers of several species of *Eciton, Ænictus, Dorylus* and *Cheliomyrmex* confirm this statement. In all these genera the neck of the postpetiole and that of the first gastric segment are covered with polygonal asperities, but these are much more conspicuous than on other portions of the segments, and in one species (*Eciton opacithorax*) they are transversely lengthened in the mid-dorsal region so that they foreshadow the file ridges of the Ponerinæ and Myrmicinæ.

Although the number of segments in the gaster is morphologically eight, when the pedicel consists of a single segment, and seven when it consists of two, only four segments are externally visible in the worker and female and five in the male. The remaining segments are very small and telescoped into the larger ones in front of them. Tracheal stigmata are present on the eight basal abdominal segments, *i. e.,* on the epinotum, pedicel and the five or six basal gastric segments.

The terminal segments in the female and worker may bear a sting, which is of considerable interest, because it can be traced back to its primitive homologue, the ovipositor. In many Orthoptera, like the katydids and crickets, this organ consists of three pairs of appendages, which, as I have shown (1893), are the modified embryonic legs of the eighth, ninth and tenth abdominal segments. Owing to a very early embryonic fusion of their corresponding segments the pair belonging to the tenth segment moves up and comes to lie between the ninth pair, so that the ninth segment appears to bear two pairs of appendages. In the Hymenoptera the ovipositor is still retained with its Orthopteroid function in certain families like the ichneumons and gall-flies, which oviposit in the tissues of insects and plants. In the bees, wasps and ants, however, the organ has lost this primitive function and has become an organ of defence. Its embryological origin in these forms, however, is the same as in the Orthoptera. Dissections of the sting of the pupal and adult ant show that the pairs of appendages become closely applied to one another so that they appear as a single organ. The appendages of the tenth segment actually fuse to form a single, pointed, grooved piece, the gorgeret (Stachelrinne) which encloses the pair of appendages belonging to the eighth segment. These are very slender and pointed and are known as the stylets, or prickles (Stechborsten). The appendages of the ninth segment become somewhat lamelliform and, without fusing with each other, enclose the gorgeret as the sting-sheath (Stachelschiede). In stinging, the pointed gorgeret is thrust into the skin and then the stylets are alternately pushed deeper into the wound beyond the tip of the gorgeret which they do not surpass when the sting is at rest. The duct of the gland that supplies the poison, which produces the burning sensation, enters the base of the gorgeret. The stylets are smooth and not barbed on their sides as they are in the bee; hence the ant is able to withdraw its sting from the wound. While the sting is very large and well-developed in the Ponerinæ, Dorylinæ and most Myrmicinæ, it is vestigial or absent in the other subfamilies.

At the tip of the male gaster there are three pairs of rather complicated appendages forming the genital armature. They are developed on the ninth abdominal segment, *i. e.*, the segment which in the female gives rise to the sting sheath. The sternal plate of this segment, which in the male lies in front of the appendages, is known as the annular lamina (Fig. 19, *la*). The three pairs of appendages enclose one another, so that we may distinguish an outermost, a median and an innermost pair. The outermost pair has been called the stipites (*st*). The median pair is sometimes more or less completely divided into two pairs, known as the volsellæ (*v*) and laciniæ respectively; and the whole group of appendages comprising the stipites, volsellæ and laciniæ are known as the external paramera (Verhöff and Emery). The innermost pair alone is known as the internal paramera. They are closely applied to each other in the median sagittal plane of the body and function as a penis (*p*). During copulation the stipites, which are large, robust and often covered with hairs, function as claspers. The volsellæ and laciniæ, which are smaller and less heavily chitinized and furnished with numerous tactile sense organs, in all probability also have a clasping function. The inner paramera are very delicate. In some ants they have serrated edges which probably serve to hold them in place in the vagina of the female. In addition to the genital valves there is a pair of small, hairy appendages, the penicilli, attached to the tergite, or dorsal plate of the tenth abdominal segment. There can be little doubt that these represent the cerci of Blattoid and other primitive insects and must therefore belong to the anal or eleventh abdominal segment. The presence or absence of the penicilli and the conformation, permanent retraction or protrusion of the different paramera are used in classification as valuable diagnostic characters. Although we may be tempted to homologize the three pairs of male genital appendages with the three pairs of appendages which go to form the sting in the female, it is very doubtful whether more than one of these pairs, the stipites, develop from rudiments of the embryonic walking limbs. If this is true, the stipites correspond with the pair of appendages of the ninth segment in the female, which give rise to the sting sheath, and the volsellæ, laciniæ and penis are merely differentiations of the median portion of the ninth sternite.

CHAPTER III

THE INTERNAL STRUCTURE OF ANTS

"In his tam parvis, atque tam nullis, quæ ratio, quanta vis, quæ inextricabilis perfectio!"—Pliny, "Historia Animalium," XI, 2.

The Alimentary Tract.—This extends the entire length of the body from the mouth to the anus as a tube with but a slight tendency to convolution in the gaster. The walls of this tube are curiously modified in different portions of its length, so that we can recognize a number of regions known as the infrabuccal chamber, buccal tube, pharynx, œsophagus, crop, proventriculus, stomach, small intestine and rectum. The shape and extent of these regions are indicated in the accompanying diagram taken from Janet (Fig. 13). Owing to the volume of the brain and cephalic glands, to the narrowness of the thorax and pedicel in the worker, and the great development of the wing muscles and glands in

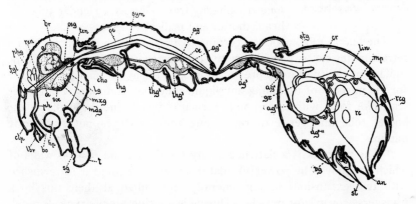

Fig. 13. Sagittal section of worker *Myrmica rubra*. (Janet.) *t*, Tongue; *lbr*, labrum; *clp*, clypeus; *sg*, opening of salivary gland; *bo*, mouth opening; *hp*, infrabuccal chamber; *ph*, pharynx; *phg*, pharyngeal glands; *oe*, œsophagus; *cr*, crop; *gz*, gizzard; *st*, stomach; *lin*, large intestine; *mp*, Malpighian vessels; *rc*, rectum; *rcg*, rectal gland; *an*, anus; *fgl*, frontal ganglion; *rec*, recurrent nerve; *br*, brain; *mdg*, mandibular ganglion; *mxg*, maxillary ganglion; *lg*, labial ganglion; *soe*, subœsophageal ganglion; *cho*, prothoracic chordotonal organ; *thg'*, *thg²*, *thg³*, pro-meso- and metathoracic ganglia; *ag'-ag²*, *ag*, 8-11, first to eleventh abdominal ganglia; *sym*, sympathetic connective, running along œsophagus to prestomachal ganglion (*stg*); *st*, sting; *vg*, vagina; *ten*, tentorium in section.

the thorax of the male and female, the alimentary canal is cramped for space and hence very tenuous, except in the gaster, where its most important parts are situated. The mouth opening, which, as we have seen, is bounded above by the labrum and clypeus, on the sides by the maxillæ, and below by the protrusible tongue, leads into a short, compressed buccal tube, dilated ventrally to form a spheroidal sac, the infrabuccal cavity or chamber (*hp*). This chamber is of great importance to the ant as a receptacle both for the fine particles of solid and semi-solid food rasped off or licked up by the tongue, and for the foreign matter scraped from the surfaces of the body by this organ and the strigils. Any juices that may be contained in the substance are sucked

back through the pharynx into the crop and the useless solid residuum is eventually thrown out as a little body which preserves the form of the chamber in which it was moulded. Such bodies, called by Janet "corpuscles de nettoyage," are often seen scattered about the floors of artificial nests after the ants have been fed on starchy substances or after their bodies have been dusted with plaster of paris (Fig. 14). The short buccal cavity is continued back into the muscular pharynx which narrows still further to form the long œsophagus traversing as a slender tube the head, thorax and pedicel (Fig. 13, *oe*).

FIG. 14.   Pellets or castings from the infrabuccal chamber of *Formica rufa*, enlarged. (Janet.)

The buccal tube, which, according to Janet, " has a protractor and a retractor muscle, is provided with soft lips that can be applied to the surface of the substances previously rasped off by means of the tongue for the purpose of obtaining any liquid they may contain. Transverse scale-like folds with their points turned outward line the walls of the buccal tube and serve to retain any solid particles not sufficiently minute."

" The pharynx is a flattened cavity the dorsal and ventral walls of which are moved by powerful dilator muscles. Behind it is furnished with two expansions arising laterally and united at their tips by a transverse constrictor muscle. During aspiration the pharynx, through the action of its dilators and a kind of posterior sphincter, opens in front and closes behind. In swallowing there is first produced a steel-yard-like movement of the dorsal wall, whereupon the pharynx is opened behind, while the buccal tube is closed in front. Then, owing to the action of the transverse constrictor, the dorsal approaches the ventral wall from before backward. The two walls thus come in contact with each other and the liquid which was contained in the pharynx is pushed into the œsophagus." Immediately behind the pharynx two groups of finger-shaped post-pharyngeal glands open by a pair of orifices into the alimentary tract (Fig. 13, *phg*).

The thin chitinous lining of the œsophagus is covered with delicate hairs which point backwards. At the base of the gaster the œsophagus begins to dilate to form the ingluvies, or crop (Fig. 15, *cr*), a thin-walled, pyriform bag, whose walls, like those of the œsophagus, consist of a layer of longitudinal and one of transverse or ring-shaped muscle fibers and a delicate chitinous lining. In the œsophagus the chitinous lining is beset with fine hairs pointing backwards. There are no glands in the crop and the chitinous walls completely resist the absorption of food, so that this organ serves merely as a reservoir for the liquid that has been imbibed or lapped up directly or sucked out of the more solid

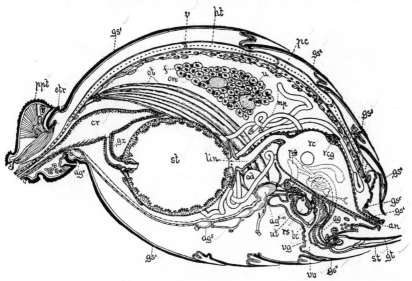

FIG. 15. Gaster of female *Myrmica rubra* in sagittal section. (Janet.) *ppt*, Postpetiole; *str*, stridulatory organ; *gs'-gs⁶*, first to sixth gastric segments; *ht*, heart; *v*, cardiac valve; *pc*, pericardial cells; *u*, urate cell; *f*, adipocyte; *on*, œnocyte; *ot*, ovarian tubules; *od*, oviduct; *ut*, uterus; *rs*, receptaculum seminis; *bc*, bursa copulatrix; *vg*, vagina; *vv*, vulva; *st*, stylets of sting; *gt*, gorgeret; *pg*, poison gland; *ag*, accessory gland. Remaining letters as in Fig. 13.

substances moulded in the infrabuccal chamber. Forel aptly calls the crop " the social stomach," because the food it contains is at least in great part fed by regurgitation to the other ants of the colony or to the brood. The crop is remarkably distensible, especially in certain Camponotinæ, like the honey-ants, so that its replete or deplete condition determines the volume, and in a measure also the shape of the gaster in the worker.

The crop is succeeded by a remarkable structure, the proventriculus, or pumping stomach, which has been carefully studied by Forel (1878*b*) and Emery (1888*c*), who have found it to vary greatly and to afford valuable characters for the delimitation of genera and even of subfamilies. The proventriculus of our common carpenter ants (*Camponotus*) may be described as a paradigm (Fig. 16, *A*). It is a narrowed or constricted portion of the alimentary tract and consists of several successive sections. The most anterior of these is the calyx (*c*). As the name implies, this is a cup-shaped section with chitinous walls differentiated into eight bands, four greatly thickened, and very convex towards the lumen, alternating with four thinner chitinous bands which are more or less concave towards the lumen. The thickened bands have been called the sepals. At the posterior narrow end of the calyx

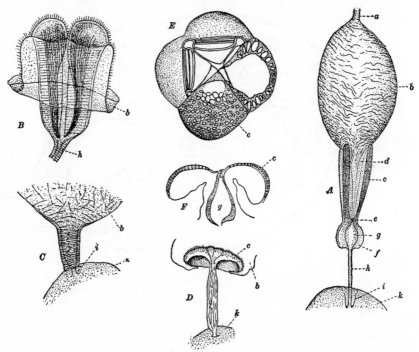

FIG. 16. The gizzard, or proventriculus, of various ants. (Emery.) *A, Campo-notus ligniperdus; B, Liometopum microcephalum; C, Atta sexdens; D, Cryptocerus atratus; E, Technomyrmex strenuus,* seen from the anterior end; *F,* sagittal section of same; *a,* œsophagus; *b,* crop; *c,* sepal; *d,* membrane between sepals; *e,* valve; *f,* bulb of calyx (pumping stomach proper); *g,* cavity of bulb; *h,* cylindrical portion; *i,* knob-shaped valve; *k,* stomach, or ventriculus.

these can be applied so closely to one another as to shut off the lumen and thus assume the function of a valve at this point. Posterior to this valve, the walls of the organ again dilate suddenly to form a globose section, the bulb (*f*), which repeats the structure of the calyx with some modification. This is the pumping stomach proper. It is succeeded by a slender, thin-walled tube, the cylindrical section (*h*), opening behind into the much more voluminous stomach on the summit of a knob, which is also valvular in structure (*i*). At this point the chitinous lining of the alimentary tract stops abruptly. The walls of the proventriculus, especially of its bulb, are furnished with powerful transverse and feebler longitudinal muscles.

The function of the proventriculus as a pump has been explained by Emery. It is clear from the shape of the chitinous folds in the bulb and the arrangement of the musculature that the contraction of the latter must bring the folds close together and occlude the lumen, whereas the relaxation of the muscles permits the chitinous folds to flatten out through their own elasticity and thus enlarge the cavity and suck the liquid back out of the crop. Hence the organ functions like a rubber bulb with a tube and an appropriately constructed valve at each end. When the bulb is squeezed its liquid contents are forced into one tube, and when it is permitted to expand, it draws the liquid out of the other tube. The proventriculus has an important function, not only in passing the liquid food back from the crop to the true stomach, but also in filling the crop in the first place.

The proventriculus of *Camponotus* may be regarded as representing a structure from which we can pass on the one hand through greater simplification to the Myrmicine and Ponerine proventriculus, and on the other through greater complication to that of the other Camponotinæ (*Plagiolepis, Prenolepis,* etc.) and Dolichoderinæ. This complication consists, in great part, in a shortening of the calyx and a spreading and recurving of its lips till they form a bell-shaped structure more or less completely enclosing the remainder of the proventriculus. Extreme forms of this kind are seen in *Iridomyrmex* and *Technomyrmex* (Fig. 16, *E, F*). In these ants it is possible to see how the proventriculus may play an important rôle in regurgitation as well as in ingurgitation, for the contraction of the walls of the crop, especially of the ring-muscles at the posterior end, and the pressure of its liquid contents must tend to close the openings between the sepals, thus preventing the liquid from moving backward and determining its flow in the opposite direction. As the musculature of the crop is poorly developed, some authors, like Janet, regard the pharynx as the organ which by its peristaltic contractions probably initiates regurgitation and may even be of great importance in filling the crop during ingurgitation.

All of the above-described regions of the alimentary tract arise in the embryo as a tubular infolding of the outside skin, or ectoderm, the so-called stomodæum. This is indicated in the adult by the almost complete absence of glands and the presence of a chitinous lining which is continuous at the mouth with the chitinous investment of the body and appendages. The true or individual stomach (ventriculus) which succeeds the proventriculus, represents a sudden departure in structure and function (Figs. 13 and 15, *st*). It is a small, elliptical sac, hardly capable of dilatation, with very glandular walls devoid of a chitinous lining. This region alone arises from the inner germ-layer of the embryo, in which it is called the mesenteron. Its structure shows very clearly that it is adapted to digesting and absorbing the liquid food that may be permitted to pass the valve at the posterior end of the proventriculus. Though of relatively large size in the embryo and larva, the stomach in the adult ant forms but a small portion of the alimentary tract. The portion lying between the stomach and anus, and comprising the small intestine (Fig. 15, *lin*), Malpighian vessels (*mp*) and the rectum (*rc*), arises in the embryo like the stomodæum from a tubular infolding of the ectoderm, the proctodæum, and, like the stomodæum, has a chitinous lining, which in this case is continuous with the integument at the anus and ends abruptly at the junction with the posterior end of the stomach.

The small intestine is a narrow tube usually more or less wrinkled by the action of its transverse musculature. Its histological structure is similar to that of the cylindrical section of the proventriculus. Near its insertion into the stomach, where it forms a valve, it receives the Malpighian, or urinary, vessels, which are merely so many long, tubular evaginations of its walls. These vessels seem to vary considerably in number in different ants. Thus, according to Adlerz (1886) there are 6 in *Leptothorax, Formicoxenus* and *Harpagoxenus,* 8 in *Anergates,* 8–10 in *Lasius,* 12 in *Tapinoma,* 14 in *Polyergus* and 20 in *Formica* and *Camponotus.* According to Meinert (1860) the number may vary in the different castes of the same species. Thus the female of *Lasius flavus* is said to have 7–14, the male 6–16 and the worker 7–8. According to Janet there are 6 in all three phases of *Myrmica rubra.*

The rectum consists of an ampulliform enlargement which narrows posteriorly to its termination in the anus. Its thin walls are furnished with a single dorsal and a pair of lateral lentiform glands. The fæces and the urinary excretions from the Malpighian vessels accumulate in the rectal ampulla and are expelled by a contraction of the thin muscle-layer in its walls. The anus (Fig. 15, *an*) is provided with a sphincter muscle and is situated on a papilla, which, in a state of repose, is concealed within the small, telescoped terminal segments of the gaster. In the Camponotinæ the anal orifice is fringed with a regular row of delicate hairs, or cilia.

The Glandular System.—Glands are well-developed in ants, and, owing to their importance in the ethological relations of these insects, deserve particular notice. They have been studied by Meckel (1846), Leydig (1859), Meinert (1860), Forel (1874, 1878), Lubbock (1882), Nassonow (1889) and Janet (1894, 1898). The following groups may be distinguished:

1. Integumentary glands, arising in the embryo, larva or pupa as invaginations of the ectodermal cell-layer (hypodermis), and including the antennary, mandibular, maxillary, labial and metasternal glands, those of the sixth abdominal (third or fourth gastric) segment, and of the fore metatarsus. Here, too, may be included the unicellular glands connected with the olfactory and tactile organs, to be considered in the next chapter. All the integumentary glands are present in the male as well as in the worker and female ant.

2. Reproductive glands, including the penial glands of the male, and in the worker and female the homologous glands of the sting-sheath, belonging to the ninth abdominal (sixth or seventh gastric) segment; the poison, accessory and repugnatorial, or anal glands of the worker and female, and the glands of the seminal vesicle of the male.

3. Glands of the alimentary canal. These comprise the post-pharyngeal, ventricular and rectal glands and the Malpighian vessels.

4. Glands of the circulatory system, including the œnocytes, pericardial cells and adipocytes, or fat body. These, unlike the three other categories of glands, are ductless.

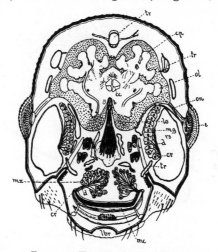

Fig. 17. Frontal section of head of *Myrmica levinodis* worker. (Janet.) *cc,* Central body of brain; *cp,* pedunculate bodies; *ol,* optic lobe; *on,* optic nerve; *e,* eye; *lo,* olfactory lobe with glomeruli; *mg,* mandibular gland; *rs,* reservoir; *cr,* cribellum; *d,* ducts from gland cells; *tr,* tracheæ; *mx,* maxillary gland; *lbr,* labrum; *mc,* buccal cavity.

The glands of the alimentary tract have been briefly described, and those of the circulatory and reproductive systems will be taken up later, so that here only the integumentary glands will be considered. The antennary glands consist of a few isolated cells with slender ducts opening on a small area in a depression at the base of each antenna. The mandibular glands (Fig. 17, *mg*) are well-de-

veloped and comprise a large cluster of cells in each side of the head
just in front of the optic ganglia. Their ducts, grouped in bundles,
but not uniting, open separately on a cribellum, or sieve-like plate on
the thin wall of a larger cavity, which narrows anteriorly and opens
as a small slit at the base and near the upper surface of the
mandible. The maxillary glands (*m.x*) consist of two groups of cells
near the median sagittal plane of the head, above the buccal tube and
near the infrabuccal pocket. Their separate ducts open on each side
on a cribellum in the lateral wall of the buccal tube. The labial,
usually called the salivary glands, are paired, like the preceding, but
are situated in the thorax. Their duct, however, is unpaired and opens
on the labium. These glands are derived from the spinning glands, or
sericteries of the larva. In *Formica rufa,* according to Meinert, each
of the lateral ducts, before uniting with its fellow to form the unpaired
terminal duct, becomes inflated and functions as a receptaculum for
the glandular secretion.

The metasternal glands (Fig. 18), which were first seen by Meinert
and Lubbock, have been carefully investigated by Janet. He regards them as belonging to the epinotum and calls them "glands de l'anneau médiaire," but Emery asserts positively that they belong to the metasternal or ventral pieces of the third thoracic instead of to the epinotal, or first abdominal segment. In *Myrmica rubra,* according to Janet, "the fine ducts of the numerous gland cells unite in a large bundle

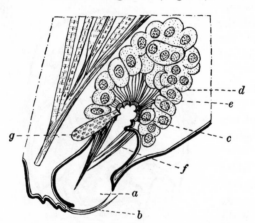

FIG. 18. Section of metasternal gland of *Lasius flavus.* (Janet.) *a,* Orifice of episternal chamber; *b,* hairs guarding orifice; *c,* cribellum; *d,* glandcells; *e,* ducts of same; *f,* trichodes projecting into episternal chamber; *g,* ganglion.

and open separately on a depressed cribellum, situated on the ceiling of a
large chamber formed by an invagination of the chitinous exoskeleton.
From near the surface perforated by the orifices of the secretory ducts,
seven or eight little chitinous folds arise and extend laterally along the
walls of the chamber. These folds, which form small projecting ridges,
soon unite in two groups which border a small gutter on a slight
eminence. Towards the ventral region all traces of the ridges dis-

appear, but the gutter, reduced to a simple depression of the wall, is continued very distinctly to the slit which forms the opening of the chamber. This latter is always filled with air." In *Lasius flavus* "the chamber is widely open to the exterior and the grooves of its walls are absent and replaced by hairs." In one of his preparations Janet found that "these hairs are inserted inside the chamber around the cribellum and converge in such a way as to appear like a pointed, hollow brush, *i. e.,* one reduced to the hairs that form its external surface. This pencil recalls the trichodes of myrmecophilous beetles (see Chapter XXII). In *Formica rufa* the chamber is much reduced and opens more widely to the exterior than in *Lasius flavus*. The cribellum is beset with hairs which form a brush long enough to project outside the chamber. The glands of the sixth abdominal segment consist of two small clusters of cells whose ducts open on the dorsal interseg-mental membrane just in front of the rigid chitinous border of the seventh segment. The metatarsal gland is situated in the fore-leg at the base of the tarsal comb of the strigil.

The Reproductive Organs.—In the female, or queen ant, the repro-ductive organs comprise the two ovaries, each of which consists of a number of tubes, or ovarioles, in which the elliptical eggs are formed in a single series, very small at the distal or anterior and gradually increasing in size towards the proximal or posterior end of the tube. Each egg is surrounded by a follicular epithelium, which secretes from its inner surface the thin, transparent chorion enveloping the ripe egg, and is accompanied by a cluster of nurse cells. The ovarioles, which are bound together in a fascicle by richly ramifying tracheæ, are attached at their tapering anterior ends to the pericardium in the antero-dorsal region of the gaster (Fig. 15, *ot*). The number of ovarioles in each ovary varies considerably in the queens of different ants. Miss Bickford (1895) gives the following numbers for several European species: *Formica rufa* 45, *F. rufibarbis* 18–20, *Lasius niger* 30–40, *L. flavus* 24, *L. brunneus* 9–11, *Camponotus* 39–40, *Myrmica ruginodis* 8, *M. levinodis* 12, *M. scabrinodis* 8–9, *M. sulcinodis* 9–11, *Anergates atratulus* 12, *Plagiolepis pygmæa* 4–5; and Miss Holliday (1903) finds the following numbers in several American ants: *Pachycondyla harpax* 5–7, *Odontomachus clarus* 5, *Eciton schmitti* about 250, *Leptothorax emersoni* 2, *Cremasto-gaster minutissima* 2, *Colobopsis etiolata* 6–7, *Camponotus decipiens* 12, *C. festinatus* 15–18, *C. sansabeanus* 6–17, *Pogonomyrmex mole-faciens* 25–30. The ovarioles of each ovary unite at their posterior ends to form a short oviduct, and the two oviducts in turn unite to form the uterus, which bears on its dorsal surface a small subspherical pocket, the seminal receptacle, which is filled with sperm by the male during the nuptial flight. The sperm is kept alive in the receptacle for years, apparently by a nutritive fluid secreted into the cavity of the organ near its orifice by a pair of appendicular glands. The eggs are fertilized as they pass through the uterus by sperm which is permitted to escape in small quantities from the orifice of the receptacle. The uterus opens behind into the short vagina, which bears on its dorsal surface a rather thin-walled sac, the copulatory pouch (Fig. 15, *bc*). The vagina (*vg*) opens to the exterior by means of a transverse slit (*vv*) just in front of the sting or its vestige on the sternal articular membrane of the seventh abdominal (fourth gastric) segment.

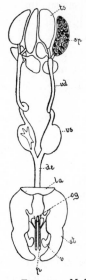

FIG. 19. Male reproductive organs of *Myrmica rubra*. (Janet.) *ts*, testis; *sp*, spermatozoa; *vd*, deferent duct; *vs*, seminal vesicle; *de*, ejaculatory duct; *la*, annular lamina; *og*, genital orifice; *st*, stipes; *v*, volsella; *p*, penis.

In the worker the ovaries are also present, but, as a rule, with a greatly reduced and often highly variable number of ovarioles. Adlerz (1887) gives the following numbers for each ovary in the workers which he examined: *Formica sanguinea* 3–6, *Camponotus herculeanus* 1–5, *Polyergus rufescens* 3, *Lasius flavus* 1, *Tapinoma erraticum* 1, *Harpagoxenus sublevis* 3–6, and Miss Bickford gives the following data: *F. pratensis* 2–6, *F. rufa* 4–10, *L. fuliginosus* 1–2, *Myrmica levinodis, ruginodis, scabrinodis, Aphænogaster subterranea* and *Cremastogaster scutellaris* 1. The numbers observed by Miss Holliday are: *Leptogenys elongata* 2–3, *Pachycondyla harpax* 2–9, *Odontomachus clarus* 2–8, *Leptothorax emersoni* 2–4, *Colobopsis etiolata* 1, *Camponotus decipiens* 1–4, *C. festinatus* 1–11, *C. sansabeanus* 1, *Pogonomyrmex molefaciens* 1–7. Lespez (1863), Adlerz and Miss Bickford failed to find any tubules in the worker *Tetramorium cespitum*, and Miss Holliday had no better success with the worker of *Eciton schmitti*. It is very doubtful, however, that the ovaries have completely disappeared in the workers of any of the Formicidæ. A well-developed seminal receptacle was found in the workers of quite a number of species by Miss Holliday, but copulation of workers with males has not been observed.

In the male ant each testis (Fig. 19, *ts*) consists of a number of compact lobules (according to Adlerz 17 in *Camponotus ligniperdus*, 21 in *Formica sanguinea*, 3 in *Leptothorax acervorum* and *Anergates atratulus;* according to Janet 4 in *Myrmica*), occupying a position in the gaster like that of the ovaries in the female. The lobules, which are crowded with cysts containing mature sperm, or testicular cells in various stages of spermatogenesis (*sp*), unite in each testis to form a

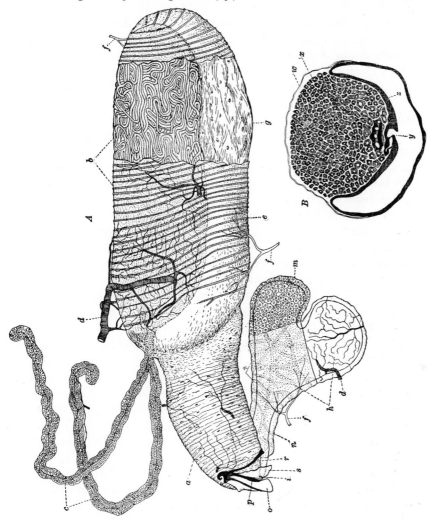

Fig. 20. Poison apparatus of *Formica*. *A*, Lateral and slightly dorsal aspect of apparatus in *Formica rufibarbis*. (Forel.) *a*, Duct of poison vesicle, or reservoir; *b*, cushion formed by the long convoluted portion of the duct from the two free glandular tubes (*c*); *d*, tracheæ; *e*, ring-muscles of vesicle wall; *f*, nerves; *g*, intima of vesicle; *h*, accessory gland; *i*, its orifice; *m*, gland-cells of its walls; *n*, muscles; *o*, sting-sheath; *p*, vestigial sting-groove; *r*, somewhat dislocated, vestigial right sting-stylet; *s*, piece of the cloacal membrane which has been almost entirely removed. *B*, Transverse section through poison apparatus of *Formica rufa*. (Beyer.) *w*, Dorsal wall of vesicle; *x*, sections of convoluted duct forming the cushion-shaped mass; *y*, opening of duct into the vesicle, the lining of which is represented by the more heavily shaded layer (*z*).

long deferent duct (*vd*). Each duct is enlarged near its posterior end
to form a thick-walled seminal vesicle (*vs*). The two deferent ducts
unite to form a slender ejaculatory duct (*de*) which opens on the ninth
abdominal (sixth gastric) segment at the base of the paired penis (*p*).

The poison apparatus belongs morphologically to the sting, and is,
therefore, absent in all male ants. It appears under two different forms,
which Forel (1878) distinguishes as the pulvinate and the bourreleted.
The former is confined to the ants of the subfamily Camponotinæ
(*Formica, Lasius, Camponotus,* etc.), a group in which the parts of
the sting have all but completely disappeared, the latter occurs in all the
other subfamilies, which have the sting either highly developed or very
small. In *Formica* the poison apparatus consists of a large, elongated,
thin-walled but muscular sac or vesicle and a glandular portion (Fig. 20).
The former opens by means of a rather large orifice between the scarcely
recognizable sclerites of the highly vestigial sting. To the inside of
the dorsal wall of this vesicle is applied an elongate, elliptical, flattened
cushion made up of a delicate, much convoluted and somewhat branched
glandular tubule, which is fully 20 cm. in length when uncoiled. One
end of this tubule opens into the vesicle at the middle of the ventral
surface of the cushion, the other leaves the posterior end of the vesicle
in the mid-dorsal line and bifurcates to form a pair of glandular tubules
which terminate blindly and lie freely in the body cavity. The walls of
these tubules consist of polygonal cells, each of which has a minute
duct starting within its cytoplasm and opening into the axial duct, or
lumen of the tubules.

The second, or bourreleted type of poison apparatus is of a much
simpler structure. It, too, consists of a vesicular and a glandular portion, with the former opening into the groove of the sting. The vesicle
is smaller, however, and more pyriform or globular, and its duct to the
exterior is more slender than in the pulvinate type. The glands are a
pair of tubules which unite and enter, and in *Myrmica* (Fig. 21, *B*)
and many other genera, form an unpaired and somewhat convoluted
tubule within the vesicular cavity. This tubule is enlarged or button-
shaped at the free end where its opening is situated. In *Bothriomyr-*
mex (Fig. 21, *A*) Forel found the unpaired tubule reduced to a small
sub-globular structure with the opening on its summit. As the bourreleted gland is usually associated with a well-developed sting, except
in the Dolichoderinæ, and, moreover, closely resembles the poison
gland of the wasp and bee, it must be regarded as the more primitive
of the two types. The pulvinate gland secretes a more copious amount
of liquid, which is stored in the vesicle whence it can be either ejected
by some ants (*Formica rufa* and its allies) in a fine spray to a distance

of 20–50 cm., or injected into wounds inflicted with the mandibles. Beyer (1890), who has made a comparative study of the development of the poison apparatus in the honey-bee, wasp, *Myrmica* and *Formica*, finds that it is smallest in the forms with the largest sting (bee) and largest in forms with only a functionless vestige of this organ. The enlargement and extraordinary convolution of the gland in the Camponotinæ is therefore correlated with a degeneration of the sting as an organ of defence and the development of a novel method of using the poison in conflicts with hostile ants and other animals.

Apart from a recent paper by Melander and Brues (1906), little has been published on the chemical constitution of the poison of ants in general. These authors find appreciable traces of formic acid, as a

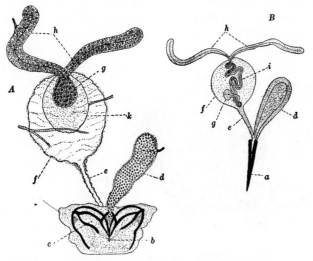

FIG. 21. Poison apparatus of a Dolichoderine and a Myrmicine ant. (Forel.) *A, Bothriomyrmex meridionalis; B, Myrmica levinodis. a,* Sting; *b,* sting-groove; *c,* sting-sheath; *d,* accessory gland; *e,* duct of poison vesicle; *f,* poison vesicle; *g,* bourrelet-like termination of poison glands; *h,* poison glands; *i,* unpaired, convoluted portion of poison gland; *k,* film of secretion(?) surrounding bourrelet.

rule, only in the Camponotinæ, that is, in the forms with the pulvinate glands. In this group, as would be expected, the species of *Formica* head the list with more than twice as much acid relatively to their size as the species of *Camponotus*. In the Doryline ants (various species of *Eciton*) the secretion has a very strong and nauseating, fecal odor like that of the lace-wings (*Chrysopa*). Melander and Brues believe this to be due to leucine, and they state that "these ants are totally blind, and migratory in their habits, so that they must depend almost entirely upon a sense of smell to follow one another about. Thus it can easily be seen how such a strong odor might be developed through the action of natural selection, from the small trace of leucine that is usually present in insect feces." As I have found a secretion precisely like that of *Eciton* in certain carnivorous *Pheidole* (*Ph. ecitonodora* and *antillensis*), I infer that its chemical constitution may, perhaps, depend on the diet of the insects.

In all ants, both in those with the pulvinate and those with the bourreleted glands, there is present a so-called accessory, or Dufour's gland (Fig. 20, *h*, Fig. 21, *d*), which opens into the duct of the poison vesicle very near its termination. This gland is ventral to the poison apparatus and though of variable form (pyriform, cylindrical or bilobed) is rather uniform in structure throughout the family Formicidæ. It is a small, elongated sac, with rather thin walls composed of polygonal gland cells enveloped by delicate muscles and tracheæ. Several authors have regarded its rather thick, yellowish secretion as a lubricant for the parts of the sting, but Janet has shown that no such lubricant is

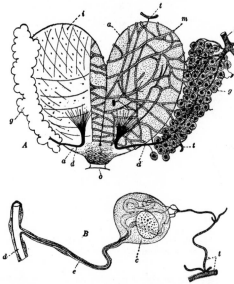

necessary. Moreover, the gland is often best developed in virtually stingless ants like the Camponotinæ. Others have surmised that the secretion is added as a necessary ingredient to the poison. Janet finds that it is alkaline and conjectures that its chief use is to neutralize any of the highly acid poison which may happen to adhere to the ant's own body or remain on the parts of the sting or on the anal circlet after the gland has been discharged. He also finds that all the other integumentary glands, except those of the poison apparatus, have an alkaline reaction, and believes that this is important in pre-

FIG. 22. Repugnatorial glands and vesicles of worker *Bothriomyrmex meridionalis.* (Forel.) *A,* Whole structure seen from above; *a*, vesicles; *o*, common orifice of same; *g*, clusters of unicellular glands; *d*, duct; *i*, intima; *m*, muscles in wall of vesicle. *B*, Single gland cell (*c*) containing the convoluted termination of the ductlet (*e*) in its cytoplasm; *d*, main duct; *t*, trachea.

venting the nest chambers from becoming acid, for the secretions of the poison glands, if allowed to accumulate in a closed cavity, soon become fatal to the ants. This is easily demonstrated when Campo-notinæ are confined in a vial and irritated till they discharge their secretions. But as there seems to be little or no acid in the poison of any species except those belonging to this subfamily, Janet's con-jecture, at least so far as the accessory gland is concerned, is far from being applicable to all ants.

The repugnatorial, or anal glands (Figs. 22 and 23), were dis-covered by Forel. They are present only in the female and worker Dolichoderinæ and coexist with well-developed poison glands of the bourreleted type. They consist of grape-like clusters of large, spher-ical gland-cells, the fine intracytoplasmic ducts of which unite to form a pair of much larger ducts that open into the posterior portions of two large, thin-walled sacs, dorsal to the poison gland and closely applied to each other in the medium sagittal plane of the ant's body. These sacs have muscular walls and serve as reservoirs for the gland-ular secretion. They have a common opening just dorsal to the anus.

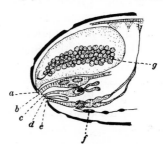

FIG. 23. Sagittal section through tip of gaster of worker *Bothriomyrmex meri-dionalis.* (Forel.) *a,* Orifice of repugnatorial vesicles; *b,* anus; *c,* orifice of poison vesicle; *d,* orifice of acces-sory gland; *e,* vaginal orifice; *f,* terminal ganglion of ven-tral cord; *g,* repugnatorial gland of right side.

Their secretion is quite unlike that of the poison glands described above, being more sticky and having in nearly all Dolichoderinæ a very characteristic odor, which Forel calls the " Tapinoma odor " because it is very noticeable in the common species of this genus in Europe and North America (*T. errati-cum* and *sessile*). Others aptly describe the odor as that of " rotten cocoanuts." Melander and Brues have studied the secretion in *Iridomyrmex analis* (*Fore-lius fœtidus*) and find that " when dis-tilled with steam the odor passes over and remains dissolved in the aqueous distillate. Thus freed it retains the very evident odor of rancid cocoanuts. By saponification with potassium hydroxide solution it loses all odor, but on adding dilute sulphuric acid to excess an odor closely re-sembling that of *fresh* cocoanuts is developed. From this it is quite evident that the odorous principle is an ether of some sort." During conflicts with other ants the Dolichoderinæ smear the secretion of their repugnatorial glands on the bodies of their enemies, and from the behavior of the latter it is evident that the liquid is fatal, or, at any rate, very irritating, and that it constitutes a most efficient protection

even for the most diminutive and soft-bodied species of *Iridomyrmex,*
Tapinoma, Azteca, etc.

The Circulatory System.—Janet (1902) has studied this system in
Myrmica. It comprises, as in other insects, the heart, aorta, hæmo-
lymph, or blood plasma, amœbocytes, or blood-corpuscles, and several
ductless glands of very simple structure. The heart (Fig. 15, *ht,* Fig.
24, *c*) is a tube lying in the mid-dorsal region of the gaster and presenting five dilatations corresponding with the first to fifth gastric
(fourth to eighth abdominal) segments, and each of these metameric
regions is pierced by a pair of osteoles provided with valves. The wall
of the tube is only a single cell-layer in thickness and the cells of its
two halves are in pairs, indicating that they arise from the pairs of
embryonic cells which I have called cardioblasts (1893). There is·
no layer of muscles enveloping the tube, but very contractile muscle
fibrillæ are differentiated in the cytoplasm of the cells themselves. The
tube is held in place by numerous suspensory filaments and five pairs
of so-called aliform muscles, belonging to the first to fifth gastric segments. These muscles are fan-shaped, with their broad ends meeting
and uniting in the middle line below the cardiac tube and their pointed
ends inserted on the supero-lateral walls of the gaster. Anteriorly the
heart is continued through the slender abdominal pedicel and into the
thorax as the aorta, a slender non-contractile tube which opens into
the head cavity.

The blood, as in other insects, is a colorless liquid filling the body
cavity or spaces between all the internal organs and containing very
small, colorless, amœboid and nucleated corpuscles. Circulation is
effected by the systole and diastole of the heart, the pulsations of which
proceed in a wave from its posterior to its anterior end. These movements are described as follows by Janet, with the aid of the accompanying diagram (Fig. 24, *B*) : " During systole the aliform muscles (*am*),
the suspensory filaments (*sf*) and the heart (*c*) occupy the positions
represented by the unbroken lines. In contracting, the aliform muscles
shorten, and owing to this shortening, they recede in the middle region
from the dorsal integument and take the position represented by the
dotted lines. This movement draws down the suspensory filaments
attached to the muscles and changes the direction of those attached to
the dorsal integument. As these filaments can be but slightly elongated,
the changes of position here described are produced, so to speak, entirely
at the expense of the elasticity of the cardiac wall, which dilates considerably. With this dilatation the valvules move away from the points to
which they were applied and the blood streams through the osteoles and
fills the heart. The blood, propelled by the contracting heart, pours

into the head, bathes all the organs and then leaves it through the neck to traverse the whole thoracic cavity in an antero-posterior direction. After having passed through the much constricted peduncle of the petiole and postpetiole, it enters the gaster and flows through two passages, separated by a diaphragm that divides the body cavity into a ventral, or neural, and a dorsal, or visceral, sinus. One current descends through the dorsal, another through the ventral sinus, following the latter to the tip of the gaster. The dorsal sinus, which is very large and supplies the heart with the blood it propels into the head, is thus

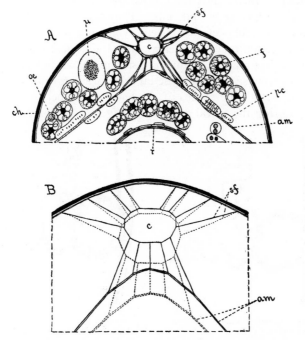

FIG. 24. Transverse section through heart of *Myrmica rubra*. (Janet.) *A*, Through region of rectum; *c*, heart; *sf*, suspensory filaments; *am*, aliform muscle; *pc*, pericardial cells; *f*, fat-cells; *u*, urate-cell; *oe*, œnocyte; *ch*, dorsal integument; *r*, dorsal wall of rectum. *B*, Diagram to illustrate position of heart, suspensory filaments and aliform muscle during systole (continuous lines) and diastole (dotted lines).

supplied simultaneously by the posterior portion of the postpetiole and the posterior portion of the ventral sinus of the gaster."

Connected with the circulatory system are some four different kinds of cells, which are suspended either singly or in clusters in the blood current. These are the pericardial cells (Fig. 24, *pc*), the œnocytes (*oe*), the adipocytes (*f*), forming the fat body, or corpus adiposum and the urate cells (*u*). The pericardial cells are of small size and are attached to the suspensory filaments and aliform muscles. In the living insect these cells have an acid reaction. They probably function as ductless glands, taking certain substances from the blood, transforming them and returning them to the circulation in such a form that they can be absorbed and excreted by the Malpighian vessels (Cuénot). Some authors are of the opinion that these pericardial cells also give rise to the amœbocytes, that they constitute, in other words, a hæmato-poëtic organ. The œnocytes are glandular cells which arise in segmental clusters from the ectoderm of the embryo just behind the tracheal invaginations. In the ants these cells are very small and in the adult scattered about among the fat cells. They are very conspicuous in the young larva and still occupy their embryonic position, but in aged ants, according to Janet, they disappear. Like the pericardial cells they are probably ductless glands, producing some unknown but physiologically important internal secretion. The fat cells form large masses or packets, often filling out all the spaces of the body cavity between the viscera, especially during the larval and pupal stages. As the name indicates,

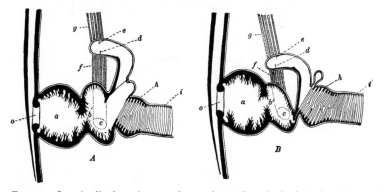

FIG. 25. Longitudinal sections to show valve and method of closing the tracheæ in *Myrmica rubra*. (Janet.) *A*, Last abdominal trachea open; *B*, closed; *o*, stigmatic orifice; *a*, anterior stigmatic chamber; *b*, occluding chamber; *c*, fixed insertion of occluding muscle; *d*, mobile insertion of same; *e*, mobile insertion of opening muscle; *f*, occluding muscle; *g*, opening muscle; *h*, stiffened portion of trachea; *i*, stigmatic or main tracheal trunk.

these cells have their cytoplasm filled with fat globules, which are often so numerous that the nucleus is reduced to a stellate or irregular body. Unlike the œnocytes, the fat cells are of mesodermal origin. The urate cells are found singly or in clusters among the fat cells. They are large and opaque, owing to a mass of urate crystals stored in their cytoplasm. They are most easily seen in larvæ and pupæ and may be regarded as a very primitive form of kidney adapted for storing instead of excreting the products of tissue metabolism.

The Respiratory System.—The tracheæ of ants are not unlike those of many other insects, as shown by Janet's studies (1902) of *Myrmica* and other genera. In all ant-larvæ there are ten pairs of stigmata or tracheal orifices occurring on the meso- and metathoracic and first to eighth abdominal segments. These stigmata also persist in the adult ant as small, round openings. According to Janet the meta-thoracic pair is closed in the Myrmicinæ (*Myrmica*), but remains open in the Camponotinæ (*Formica*) and Dolichoderinæ (*Tapinoma*). Each stigmatic orifice leads into a short stigmatic trunk which is furnished with a very interesting valve by means of which it can be closed (Fig. 25). The stigmatic trunks of the thorax and gaster bifurcate in an anterior and posterior direction and the two branches fuse on each side of the body to form a continuous longitudinal trunk. This is very large in the gaster, but much more tenuous in the thorax, where a second pair of more dorsal longitudinal trunks is formed, which, in the queens and males, supplies the wing muscles with air. The gastric trunks dilate and contract with the so-called respiratory movements of the external skeleton and in this manner the air is pumped into and out of the finest ramifications of the tracheæ. The gastric trunks are united by ventral, transverse, anastomosing tracheæ and also give off segmental dorsal branches which break up into finer and finer ramifications to supply the various viscera.

The Muscular System.—For an account of this system in ants the reader must be referred to the articles of Janet, Nassonow, Berlese and Lubbock, as the subject is one of too great complexity and detail to be treated within the limits of this work. Still there is an ontogenetic change in the muscular system of the adult queen ants, which cannot be passed over, as it is of no little ethological importance. I have often observed that aged, deälated queens will float when placed in water or alcohol, and that when the thorax of immersed specimens is pierced with a needle, large bubbles of air escape, showing that the wing muscles must have atrophied. Janet (1906, 1907*a*, 1907*b*) has studied the histological changes, which lead up to this peculiar condition in *Lasius niger,* and finds that the muscles, which in the virgin queen fill up most of the thoracic cavity and are well-developed and beautifully striated till the marriage flight occurs, are completely broken down within a few weeks after deälation (Fig. 26). He maintains that this sarcolysis is not due to phagocytes devouring the muscles piece-meal, but that the blood corpuscles (amœbocytes) which creep in among the fibrillæ take up spontaneously the dissolving muscle substances and convert these within the cytoplasm into fat globules and albuminoid granules. Thus the amœbocytes become adipocytes and replace the muscle fibrillæ (Fig.

26, *B*). Somewhat later the amœbocytes discharge the fat globules and albuminoid granules from their cytoplasm into the blood plasma, which from being a limpid liquid assumes a more granular appearance as it becomes charged with more and more of the metabolized products of sarcolysis. Eventually nothing remains of the muscles but their sheaths, and the thoracic tracheæ become greatly enlarged, which accounts for the floating of the insect in liquid and the emission of air bubbles when the thorax is pricked under water (Fig. 26, *D*). The fatty and albuminoid substances derived from the histolyzed wing-muscles are carried in the blood to the abdomen, where they are taken up by the

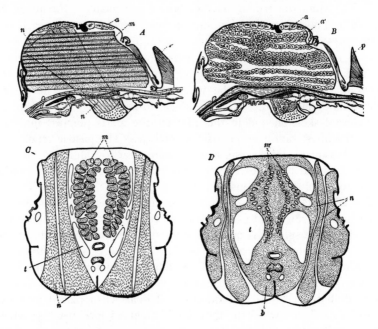

Fig. 26. Wing muscles of *Lasius niger* queen, to show their degeneration after nuptial flight. (Janet.) *A*, Sagittal section of thorax and petiole of queen immediately after nuptial flight; *B*, ten months later; *C*, transverse section through mesothorax on day of nuptial flight; *D*, same five weeks later; *m*, longitudinal vibratory muscles; *n*, transverse vibratory muscles; *b*, blood coagulated and charged with the products of muscle dissolution; *t*, tracheæ.

ovaries and, no doubt, contribute greatly to the growth of the eggs. The queen ant thus resembles the salmon, in which, according to Miescher, there is at the time of sexual maturity a conversion of part of the trunk musculature into substances that are appropriated by the reproductive cells and further their growth and maturation.

CHAPTER IV

THE INTERNAL STRUCTURE OF ANTS (CONCLUDED)

"It is certain that there may be extraordinary activity with an extremely small absolute mass of nervous matter; thus the wonderfully diversified instincts, mental powers, and affections of ants are notorious, yet their cerebral ganglia are not so large as the quarter of a small pin's head. Under this point of view, the brain of an ant is one of the most.marvellous atoms of matter in the world, perhaps more so than the brain of man."—Charles Darwin, "The Descent of Man."

The Nervous System.—The structure of the central nervous system is best considered in connection with the primitive segmentation as this is revealed in the embryonic ant. As stated in a previous chapter, the body of the ant, like that of all other true insects (Pterygogenea), consists of a series of twenty metameres, or segments. The first and last of these are peculiar in certain respects and have been called the acron and telson respectively. In the embryo the ectoderm of the mid-ventral portion of each segment (except the telson) thickens and gives rise to a pair of ganglia that soon split off from a thin surface layer of cells which then become the ventral integument. The ganglia of each segment are closely approximated and connected with each other by a pair of commissures, while the ganglia of successive segments are united by pairs of connectives which therefore run longitudinally. Later these connectives lengthen, and as the body grows more rapidly than the ganglia, we find the latter forming a chain extending through the ventral region of the head, thorax and abdomen. Not only do many of the ganglia thus become rather widely separated from one another, but there is also a tendency for some of them to fuse together and make larger masses. Thus the ganglia of the first (acron), second (antennary) and third (intercalary) segments, known respectively as the proto-, deuto- and tritocerebrum of Viallanes, fuse to form the brain, or supraœsophageal ganglion. As the latter term indicates, this mass is dorsal to the œsophagus, and therefore preoral. This is true, however, only of the protocerebrum of the embryo, the two other pairs of ganglia being postoral at first, but moving forward and becoming preoral before the hatching of the larva. The ganglia of the mandibular, maxillary and labial segments also unite to form a single mass, the subœsophageal ganglion, which, as its name implies, lies behind the gullet. This ganglion is united to the brain by means of a pair of circumœsophageal connectives. The pro- and mesothoracic ganglia

remain distinct and lie in their respective segments even in the adult
ant. The first (mediary) and second abdominal ganglia, however, are
drawn up into the metathorax and fused with the metathoracic ganglion,
and the ganglion of the third abdominal segment comes to lie in the
petiole (second abdominal segment) (Fig. 13, ag^3). The fourth, fifth,
sixth and seventh abdominal ganglia retain their independence, but the
latter two are close together and are immediately succeeded by the fused
eighth to tenth, which constitute a single ellipsoidal mass, terminating
the chain and in the adult ant lying some distance in front of the posterior end of the gaster (Fig. 13, ag^{8-11}). The central nervous system of
the adult ant therefore presents only eleven ganglionic masses, formed
by condensation of the primitive nineteen. For convenience in description, this system may be divided into the brain and ventral cord, and
these, with their ganglia and peripheral nerves, may be briefly considered before we take up the sympathetic nervous system and the sense
organs.

The Brain.—I agree with those authors, who, following Rabl-
Rückard (1875), restrict the term " brain " to the supraœsophageal ganglion, although it must be admitted that in ants and other Hymenoptera
the circumœsophageal connectives are so short and robust that the
supra- and subœsophageal ganglia seem to form but a single mass perforated by the gullet. Leydig called this whole mass the brain; Janet
suggests for it the term " encephalon." The three primitive pairs of
ganglia, constituting the proto-, deuto- and tritocerebrum, though intimately fused, can still be recognized in the adult brain, at least by their
innervations, but the three apparent segments indicated by the outline
of the organ do not correspond to the primitive segments. The protocerebrum is the largest single pair of ganglia in the central nervous
systems and differs markedly from all the others in form and complexity of structure. It is broadest in the middle where it is continued
on each side into the optic nerves (Figs. 28–30, on) to the compound
eyes. The portion between the optic nerves may be called the mid-
protocerebrum. It is flanked on each side by an optic ganglion (og)
of complicated structure and projects anteriorly as a pair of rounded
frontal lobes (pb). From the notch between these, nerves are given off
to the three stemmata, or ocelli (oc), when these organs are present.
As the median stemma has two nerves, it must have been a paired structure originally. The deutocerebrum is represented by a pair of rounded
protuberances known as the olfactory lobes (ol), which are morphologically behind, though apparently somewhat in front of the other brain
segments. According to Janet, each antenna is supplied with six nerves
which arise close together from each olfactory lobe (Fig. 27). These

are: first, the infero-internal sensory nerve (*nani*), second, the supero-external sensory (*nans*), third, the chordotonal (to *acho*), fourth, the nerve to the anterior (adductor) muscles of the scape, fifth, the nerve to the posterior (abductor) muscles of the scape (*nsc*), and sixth, a nerve which supplies the little muscles in the funicular joints (*nf*). The tritocerebrum is so much reduced that it is represented only by a pair of small bodies, concealed under the olfactory lobes and connected with each other by a slender commissure, which, however, passes under the œsophagus, thus indicating the originally postoral position of this portion of the brain. Each tritocerebral lobe gives off a nerve which soon subdivides into two branches, one (Fig. 27, *cnf*) going to the

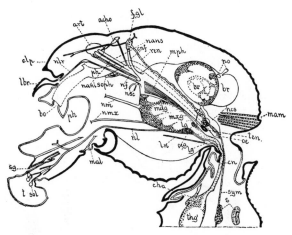

Fig. 27. Sagittal section of head of worker *Myrmica rubra*. (Janet.) *acho*, Antennary chordotonal organ; *cnf*, connective of frontal ganglion; *art*, antennary articulation; *nans*, superior antennary nerve; *nani*, inferior antennary nerve; *nf*, funicular nerve; *nsc*, nerve to scape; *nlr*, labral nerve; *soph*, sense-organs of pharynx; *mph*, inferior dilator muscle of pharynx; *no*, nerves to ocelli; *hcs*, hypocerebral ganglion; *mam*, adductor muscle of mandible; *lg*, labial sympathetic ganglion; *ln*, labial sympathetic nerve; *nl*, labial nerve; *sol*, labial sense-organs; *nmx*, maxillary nerve; *nm*, mandibular nerve; *s*, portions of salivary gland; *cn*, connective between sub-œsophageal and prothoracic ganglion; *mal*, adductor muscle of labium. Remaining letters as in Fig. 13.

frontal ganglion (to be described below in connection with the sympathetic nervous system) the other again subdividing to innervate the labrum and the wall of the pharynx (*nlr*).

The minute structure of the brain, with its ganglion cells and fibers, the former comprising the deeply-staining, the latter the more achromatic portions, or "Punktsubstanz" of authors, is too intricate to be considered in the present work. For these details the reader must be referred to the papers of Dujardin (1850), Leydig (1864), Rabl-

Rückard (1875), Brandt (1876), Dietl (1876), Flögel (1878) and Kenyon (1896). I cannot, however, omit consideration of two regions of the ant brain, namely, the frontal and olfactory lobes, which have frequently been compared with the cerebrum and olfactory lobes of vertebrates. The frontal lobes contain two pairs of extraordinary structures, the pedunculate, or mushroom bodies (Figs. 28–30, *pb*), each consisting of a cup-shaped mass of nerve-fibers, the calyx, with a stem formed of a stout bundle of similar fibers which run back into the mid-protocerebrum. The calyces are embedded in a dense accumulation of minute, deeply-staining ganglion cells, which form the bulk of the frontal lobes and evidently give rise to the fibers of the calyces and their stems. Each olfactory lobe consists of a central fibrous portion containing peripherally a large number of round bodies of still denser fibrous structure and a cortical portion made up of larger ganglion cells. The round bodies have been called glomeruli from their resemblance to the well-known structures in the olfactory lobes of vertebrates. Since the antennæ of ants are mainly organs of smell, the occurrence in the deutocerebrum of structures so much like those in the olfactory organs of vertebrates is not without interest.

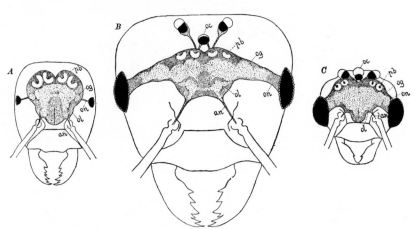

Fig. 28. Heads of worker (*A*), female (*B*), and male (*C*), *Lasius brevicornis*, drawn under same magnification, with brain, eyes and ocelli viewed as transparent objects. (Original.) *oc*, Median ocellus; *pb*, pedunculate bodies; *og*, optic ganglion; *on*, optic nerve; *ol*, olfactory lobe; *an*, antennary nerve.

It has been customary since the time of Dujardin to compare the pedunculate bodies with the cerebrum of vertebrates and to regard them as an organ of intelligence. Dujardin based his opinion on the fact that these bodies are largest and most elaborately developed in the social Hymenoptera. Leydig and Rabl-Rückard expressed a similar opinion.

Forel (1874) first observed that these bodies are largest in worker ants, smaller in the queens and vestigial in the males, and as the worker was supposed to be the most, and the male the least, intelligent, this was regarded as additional evidence in favor of Dujardin's opinion. The condition described by Forel for the ants was affirmed by Brandt (1876) for the social Hymenoptera in general. More recently Kenyon (1896), after an elaborate study of the bee's brain, has reached a similar conclusion. He says: "All that I am able at present to offer is the evidence from the minute structure and the relationships of the fibers of these bodies. This seems to be of no inconsiderable weight in support of the general idea started by Dujardin. For in connection with what was made known by Flögel and those before him and has since been confirmed and extended by other writers, one is able to see that the cells of the bodies in question are much more specialized in structure and isolated from the general mass of nerve fibers in those insects where it is generally admitted complexity of action or intelligence is greatest." He also cites experiments of Binet (1894) which tend to show that in insects "when connections between the dorso- and ventro-cerebron are destroyed, the phenomena afterwards observed are similar to those seen in a pigeon or mammal when its cerebral hemispheres are removed."

In support of Dujardin's hypothesis, Forel has published a series

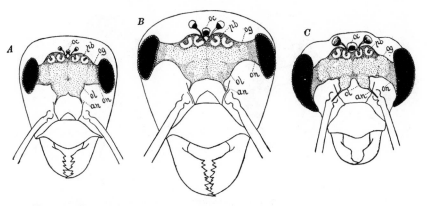

FIG. 29. Heads of worker (*A*), female (*B*), and male (*C*), *Formica fusca,* drawn under the same magnification, with brain, eyes and ocelli viewed as transparent objects. (Original.) Letters as in Fig. 28.

of figures of the brain of the worker, female and male of the European *Lasius fuliginosus,* drawn to the same scale (1904). I here introduce a similar series of the American *L. brevicornis* (Fig. 28). Comparison of these figures shows that the pedunculate bodies do, indeed, vary quite independently of other portions of the brain and in the manner noticed by Forel. In a similar series of *Formica glacialis* (Fig. 29), however, there are no such striking differences in the three phases. The pedunculate bodies (*pb*) are as highly developed in the female as they are in the worker, and they can hardly be said to be vestigial in the male. In *Pheidole instabilis* (Fig. 30), too, the female and soldier have well-developed pedunculate bodies, though these seem to be insignificant in the male. While, therefore, the male brain in all these species, apart from the huge development of its optic ganglia and stemmatal nerves, is manifestly deficient, I doubt whether we are justified in regarding the brain of the female as being inferior to that of the worker. It is true that the worker brain is relatively larger, notwithstanding the smaller eyes and stemmata, or the complete absence of the latter, but I would interpret this greater volume as an embryonic char-

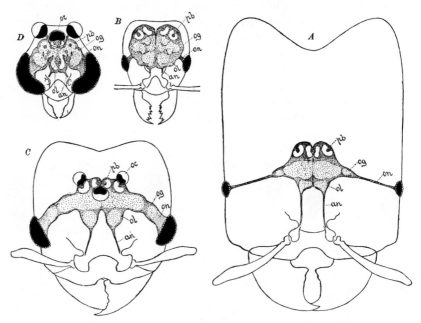

FIG. 30. Heads of soldier (*A*), worker (*B*), female (*C*), and male (*D*) of *Pheidole instabilis*, drawn under the same magnification, with brain, eyes and ocelli viewed as transparent objects. (Original.) Letters as in Figs. 28 and 29.

acter. The worker is, in a sense, an arrested, neotenic or more immature form of the female, and it is well known that the volume of the brain and of the central nervous system in general is much greater in proportion to that of the body in embryonic and juvenile than in adult animals. Forel was probably influenced in his interpretation by the view, so long accepted, but now abandoned by myrmecologists, that the queen ant is a degenerate creature like the queen bee. In future chapters of this work I shall have occasion to show the untenability of this supposition in the light of recent observations.[1]

The foregoing considerations do not, of course, invalidate Dujardin's hypothesis. It is also true that the conditions throughout the insect class point to a direct correlation between the development of the pedunculate bodies and the instinctive activities, but a study of these structures in other Arthropods is not so unequivocal. Turner, in a contribution from my laboratory (*Zool. Bull.*, II, 1899, pp. 155–160), showed that the pedunculate bodies not only occur in Crustacea (*Cambarus*) and the king crab (*Limulus*), but also in annelids (*Nereis, Lepidonotus, Polynoë*), and that they reach their greatest development in the king crab. In this animal they are a much-branched mass, which forms the bulk of the brain, and as Turner says, "simulates in structure the vertebrate cerebellum." On Dujardin's hypothesis we should therefore expect the king crab to be the most intelligent of arthropods. But although no one will deny that this animal has had ages in which to acquire a high psychical endowment, it shows no signs of having profited by its opportunities. It would seem, therefore, that the pedunculate bodies must be subjected to a more critical morphological and physiological study before they can be accepted as the insectean analogue of the human fore-brain.

The Ventral Nerve-Cord.—Although the subœsophageal ganglion, like the brain, consists of three fused ganglia, these have become less modified and are clearly discernible in sagittal sections (Fig. 27). The rule that each ganglion of the central nervous system innervates only the segment in which it originated in the embryo also holds good of the subœsophageal ganglion. We find that it sends off three pairs of nerves, containing both motor and sensory fibers. The first pair (*nm*), which is stouter than the two others, innervates the sense organs and muscles of the mandibles, and the second (*nmx*) and third (*nl*) the corresponding parts of the maxillæ and labium respectively. The three thoracic ganglia, owing to the voluminous and complicated leg and wing muscles which they innervate, are much larger than the abdominal ganglia. Each gives off a pair of crural nerves to the legs and the prothoracic ganglion also supplies a chordotonal organ near its antero-ventral end (*cho*). From

---

[1] Comparison of my figures of *L. brevicornis* with Forel's of *L. fuliginosus* reveals the fact that the female brain of the latter species is no larger than that of the worker, whereas in *brevicornis* there is a slight difference in size in the corresponding phases. It appears from recent observations of De Lannoy (1908) and Emery (1908) that the queens of *L. fuliginosus* are but little larger than the workers and are probably temporary parasites (see Chapter XXIV). This may at least partially account for Forel's finding the brain of the female ant inferior in organization to that of the worker.

the mesothoracic ganglion arises a pair of so-called alar nerves, which innervate the great longitudinal and transverse vibratory muscles of the wings. The musculature of the epinotum, petiole and postpetiole is supplied by the first to third abdominal ganglia, the two first of which are fused with the metathoracic ganglion. The fourth abdominal (first gastric in the Myrmicidæ) remains in the segment to which it belongs, but lies at its extreme anterior edge. As both this and the succeeding gastric ganglia have been secondarily drawn forward, the pairs of nerves which they give off run obliquely backward, to their innervations. Janet (1902) has found that each of the two nerves arising from each of the four anterior gastric ganglia divides into a dorsal and a ventral trunk. The former sends off a sensory nerve to the corresponding dorsal quadrant of the segment and three motor nerves to its three muscles, the latter a sensory nerve to the ventral quadrant and six motor nerves to as many muscles. The sensory nerves go to the sense-hairs of the integument. The terminal (fifth gastric) ganglion, formed, as we have seen, by a fusion of the eighth to tenth abdominal ganglia, sends off four pairs of nerves, the first to the sense organs and muscles of the stylets of the sting, the second to the sense organs and muscles of the gorgeret, the third to the anal sphincter and papilla and the fourth to the walls of the hind gut.

The Sympathetic.—This consists of several minute ganglia and nerves connected with the central nervous system and supplying the musculature of the alimentary tract. It is, to judge from Janet's account of *Myrmica* (1902), well developed in ants and not unlike that of other insects. It may be said to embrace two systems, one supraintestinal and supplying the dorsal and lateral portions of the digestive tract, the other subintestinal and lying beneath the intestine and above the ventral nerve-cord. The supraintestinal system may be divided into an unpaired and a paired portion. The former begins in the small frontal ganglion (Fig. 27, *fgl*), which lies anterior to the brain, to which it is joined by a pair of connectives. According to Janet, these connectives arise in the protocerebrum, but other authors believe that they are of tritocerebral origin. The frontal ganglion sends a pair of coalesced nerves to the supero-anterior wall of the pharynx and a much stouter unpaired nerve, known as the recurrens (*ren*), downward and backward along the dorsal wall of the pharynx, to a ganglion (the hypocerebral, *hcs*), which lies on the œsophagus just beneath the protocerebrum. Besides innervating the œsophagus this ganglion sends back a pair of long, slender connectives (*sym*) along the sides of the œsophagus and crop to the point where the latter contracts to form the gizzard. Here each connective terminates in a so-called pre-stomachal ganglion, which innervates the surrounding wall of the crop and gizzard. The paired supraintestinal sympathetic has an anterior and a posterior portion. The former consists of the œsophageal ganglia, which lie on each side of the hypocerebral ganglion. They are united with this by commissures and with the tritocerebrum by connectives, and innervate the sides of the œsophagus and crop. The posterior portion of the paired system is very imperfectly known. Janet maintains that the fourth pair of nerves from the terminal ganglion of the ventral cord turns forward and innervates the posterior portion of the digestive tract in somewhat the same manner as the anterior portion is innervated by the brain through the frontal and œsophageal ganglia. He, therefore, calls these the proctodæal recurrent nerves. The subintestinal sympathetic system of *Myrmica* comprises a series of minute, unpaired, metameric ganglia connected with several of the ganglia of the ventral cord. This system, too, both in ants and in other insects, is imperfectly known.

The Sense-Organs.—The sense-organs of ants, like those of insects in general, are modifications of the integument and the terminations of sensory nerves. Hence there can be no sense-organs in the interior of the body unless they have been carried in secondarily on infoldings of the integument. As there are no openings anywhere in the chitinous investment of the insect's body, except those at the anterior and posterior ends of the midgut, the nerve terminations are never freely exposed on the surface, but always covered with at least a very delicate layer of chitin. The number and diversity of sense-organs in insects is very great, but nevertheless, attempts have been made to trace them all back to a common primitive type. One of the most recent of these attempts is that of Berlese (1907) who finds that nearly all these organs admit of hypothetical derivation from a " protæsthesis," a sensilla, or sense-bud, consisting of one or a few chitin-secreting hypodermal cells, a gland cell and a nerve cell. It is possible to show that this type of structure keeps recurring in the various sense-organs of even such highly-specialized insects as the ants.

Tactile (Trichodeal) Sensillæ.—As stated in a previous chapter, ants are usually covered with hairs, which are coarse and long on the body and shorter and denser on the legs and especially on the antennæ. As all of these hairs are movably articulated to the general chitinous integument and are provided with fine nerve terminations, they are universally regarded as tactile sensillæ, although they also aid in the removal of the larval or pupal skin during ecdysis, for they are at first bent at their bases and applied to the chitinous layer to which they belong, but later, in becoming erect, loosen and push the overlying exuvia away from the surface of the body. In section each hair is seen to be a hollow chitinous tube, closed at its apex and open at its base, which is bulbously swollen and fits into a ring-shaped thickening

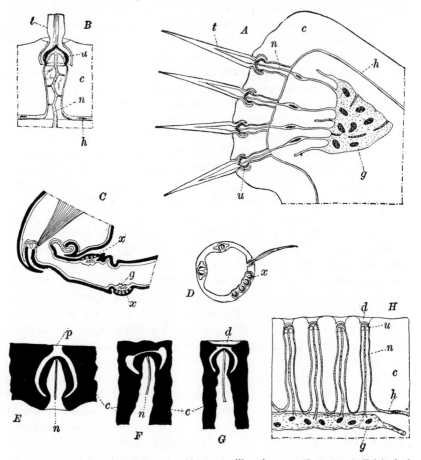

FIG. 31. Trichodeal and campaniform sensillæ of ants. (Janet.) *A*, Trichodeal sensillæ from proximal border of fore coxa of female *Lasius niger*, × 1,000; *B*, single sensilla from the group represented in *A*, × 2,000; *C*, longitudinal section through tip of middle coxa, trochanter and base of femur of *Myrmica rubra* worker, × 100; *D*, cross-section of tip of hind tibia of *M. rubra*, × 200; *E, F* and *G*, sections of campaniform sensillæ from tip of mandibles of *M. rubra*; *H*, campaniform sensillæ near articulation of wing of female *Camponotus herculeanus*, × 500; *t*, chitinous hair; *c*, chitinous integument; *h*, hypodermis; *n*, nerve-termination; *u*, bell, or umbrella, in the center of which the nerve terminates; *x*, groups of campaniform sense-organs; *d*, fossa or pit in the chitinous integument; *p*, pore in same.

of the chitinous integument (Fig. 31, *A, B*, Fig. 32, *b*). This tube is secreted by one or more large hypodermal cells, and a delicate nerve fiber extends up into its base. When the tip of the hair touches an object the tactile impulse is evidently transmitted to the nerve through the movement of the bulbous base in its cup-shaped socket. There is, therefore, no essential difference between the tactile function of the hairs of ants and the analogous structure in mammals.

Olfactory and Gustatory Sensillæ.—It seems to be impossible to distinguish between these organs in insects, although it may be asserted that the organs of smell are situated mainly or exclusively on the antennæ, whereas, those of taste are found on the mouth-parts, especially on the maxillæ and labium and their paipi. The antennary sensillæ of ants have been studied by Hicks (1859), Leydig (1860), Forel (1874, 1884), Lubbock (1877), Kraepelin (1883), and more recently by Krause (1907). From the researches of these authors it appears that in addition to numerous tactile hairs like those described above, there are four more modified types of sensillæ which have been more or less definitely connected with an olfactory function. These do

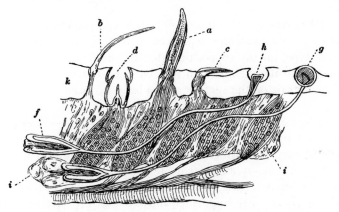

Fig. 32. Subdiagrammatic section of the antennal sense-organs of an ant. (Kraepelin.) *a,* Basiconic sensilla; *b,* trichodeal sensilla, or tactile hair; *c,* cœloconic sensilla; *d,* ampullaceous sensilla; *f,* flask-shaped sensilla; *g* and *h,* openings of same on surface of antenna; *i,* gland cells; *k,* chitinous integument.

not occur on the scape and first funicular joint of the antennæ, but only on the remaining joints and especially on the enlarged terminal joint, which possesses by far the greatest number of all the various sensillæ. The following is a very brief description of these extraordinary structures:

(*a*) *Clubs of Forel* (now called basiconic sensillæ by Berlese).— These resemble the tactile hairs, but are conical and immovable at the base and their chitinous investment is exceedingly thin (Fig. 32, *a*). What corresponds to the cavity of the hair contains a dense bundle of delicate protoplasmic threads, which are prolongations from as many large elliptical cells situated in the hypodermis. These cells form a compact mass, formerly supposed to be a ganglion, but now interpreted as a cluster of unicellular glands that secrete a liquid through the thin chitinous cap of the organ onto the surface of the antennæ. It is, indeed, difficult to conceive such sensillæ as having an olfactory function unless their exposed surfaces are moist like the olfactory organs in the mucous membranes of vertebrates. The nerve termination to the basiconic sensillæ applies itself to the cluster of gland cells and then breaks up into delicate branches that pass around and between the latter and up into the conical portion of the organ.

(b) *Clubs Lying in Elliptical Pits* (cœloconic sensillæ of Berlese). —These may be derived from the preceding type by supposing that the conical hair has come to lie horizontally and to be enclosed in an elongated cavity in the chitinous integument (Fig. 32, c). The cellular structure of the organ is essentially the same as that of the basiconic sensillæ.

(c) *Champagne-cork Organs of Forel* (ampullaceous sensillæ of Berlese).—These evidently represent a further modification of the cœloconic type, on the supposition that the hair becomes smaller and more erect and the pit in which it is enclosed becomes circular, much deeper and opens on the surface of the body by means of a small pore (Fig. 32, d).

(d) *Flask-shaped Organs of Lubbock and Forel.*—Hicks (1859) was the first to describe these extraordinary organs in *Myrmica,* but Forel and Kraepelin have given a more detailed account of their structure. They are really an extreme form of the ampullaceous sensilla, and may be derived from this by supposing that the chitinous ampulla has become enormously lengthened and attenuated till it forms a narrow sac enclosing the conical hair and connected with the pore in the integument by means of a slender tube running more or less parallel with the surface of the antenna (Fig. 32, g, h). That these sensillæ have developed from those of the preceding type (c) is shown by the existence of transitional forms both in ants and in other Hymenoptera. The cellular portions of all these forms of ampullaceous sensillæ are essentially the same as those of types a and b.

The gustatory sensillæ, situated on the mouth-parts and including those in the terminal joints of the palpi, though resembling the antennary sensillæ, in general reproduce only the more primitive of the above-mentioned types, that is, those most like the typical tactile and basiconic sensillæ. The more specialized ampullaceous types are found only in the antennæ.

The Chordotonal Organs.—Recent studies have shown that these structures, which are present in a great many insects, even in the larval stages, are typically compact, spindle-shaped bundles of sensillæ, each consisting of a chitin-secreting gland and a nerve cell. These cells are arranged in a series at an angle to the integument and are stretched, like a tendon, across a cavity between opposite points in the cuticle, or between a point in the cuticle and some internal organ. The gland cell secretes and retains within its cytoplasm a peculiar cone or rod, known as the scolopal body. The chordotonal organs are supposed to be auditory in function, because they are most elaborately developed in the stridulating Orthoptera (crickets and katydids), and because their structure would seem to be adapted to responding like the chords of a musical instrument to delicate vibrations. In ants the development of these sense-organs is greatly inferior to that of the Orthoptera just mentioned, but they are nevertheless very easily seen when one knows exactly where to look for them. They were first detected by Lubbock (1877) in the proximal portion of the fore tibiæ of *Lasius flavus, Myrmica ruginodis* and *Pheidole megacephala.* He pointed out their resemblance to the subgenual chordotonal organs of Orthoptera, discovered by von Siebold in 1844, but al-

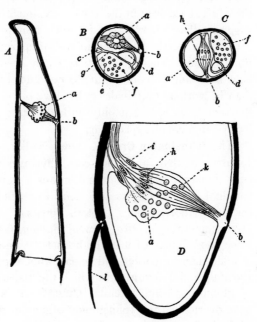

FIG. 33. Chordotonal organs in tibiæ of *Myrmica rubra* worker. (Janet.) *A*, Longitudinal section of fore tibia; *B*, cross-section of same; *C*, cross-section of middle tibia; *D*, cross-section of hind tibia; *a*, chordotonal organ; *b*, internal fossa; *c*, small; *d*, large trachea; *e*, nerve; *f*, muscle; *g*, septum; *h*, scolopal bodies; *i*, ganglion cells; *k*, distal nuclei.

though he fancied he could discern some of their minute structure, his account and figure are very primitive. The matter was re-investigated by Graber (1882), who found the organs in *Solenopsis, Myrmecina* and *Tetramorium,* and showed that they occur not only in the fore but also in the middle and hind tibiæ, that they contain scolopal bodies and are also in other respects typical chordotonal organs.

Janet (1904) has recently studied their structure with great care, and has not only added many details to those seen by his predecessors, but has also discovered a number of less conspicuous chordotonal organs in other parts of the ant's body. He finds a pair in the head at the base of the antennæ (Fig. 27, *acho*), one in the prosternum, just under the prothoracic ganglion (*cho*), with which it is connected by short nerves, a similar pair in the metasternum and two pairs, one in the petiole and another in the postpetiole, which lie near the tracheal stigmata and are innervated by the ganglia of their respective segments. Eight pairs of chordotonal organs have, therefore, been seen in the ant's body, but it is not improbable, as Janet suggests, that others exist, for such minute and recondite objects are very easily overlooked even in well-prepared sections. I find that the tibial organs (Fig. 33) are very easily seen in light-colored ants that have been simply mounted in alcohol, and that they are clearer in males than in workers or females. In clove oil, or Canada balsam, however, the structures are seen only with difficulty and after they have been located in alcoholic specimens.

The Johnstonian Organ.—This peculiar structure, first described by Johnston in 1855, and since carefully investigated by Child (1894), is very similar to the chordotonal organs. It is found only in the second antennal joint of insects and seems to reach its highest development in certain Orthorrhaphous Diptera (gnats). Child found it also in the Hymenoptera (*Formica, Vespa, Bombus*) and Berlese has published some good figures of it in the hornet. I find that it is decidedly larger in male than in worker and female ants, especially in those genera like *Pheidole* and *Solenopsis,* in which the males have an unusually swollen or globular second antennal (first funicular) joint. Janet seems to have overlooked the Johnstonian organs in the *Myrmica,* which he has studied so exhaustively. In section the organ is seen to consist of a variable but considerable number of sensillæ differing but slightly from those of the chordotonal organs, and also containing scolopal bodies. These sensillæ are stretched more or less parallel with the long axis of the funiculus, through the cavity of the second joint. Their distal or hypodermal ends are attached to the articular membrane between the second and third joints, while their proximal ends are innervated by a portion of the antennal nerve. They form a compact cylinder enclosing the remainder of the nerve which passes on into the more distal antennal joints. Both Johnston and Child are inclined to regard the sense-organs under discussion as auditory, although the latter believes that their more primitive function is tactile. As will be shown in

Chapter XXVIII, the auditory and tactile sensations of insects are not sharply distinguishable.

The Campaniform Sensillæ.—These problematic organs have a very simple structure, consisting of a thin, bell- or umbrella-shaped piece of the chitinous cuticle forming the floor of a cavity in the much thicker, undifferentiated chitinous layer of the integument (Fig. 31, *C–H*). This cavity is narrowed externally and usually, but not always, opens on the surface by means of a small pore (*Ep*). A very delicate nerve (*n*) terminates in the middle of the umbrella on its concave inner surface. Organs of this description are found in various parts of the insect body—in the borders of the mandibles, at the bases of the wing membranes, in the balancers of Diptera and in the trochanters and bases of the femora. They have been found in these joints of the legs and in the mandibles of ants by Janet (1904). In the mandibles occur also other organs which may represent modifications of the campaniform sensillæ, although it seems more natural to refer them to the ampullaceous type. The function of the campaniform sensillæ is quite unknown. Morphologically, according to Berlese, they may be derived from a simple protæsthesis, in which the glandular element is lacking and only the chitinogenous and nervous elements are present.

The Lateral Eyes.—Each of the lateral, or compound, eyes, consists of a closely aggregated mass of sensillæ, which are usually called ommatidia and consist of the three elements of the typical protæsthesis: hypodermal cells, which secrete the cornea (facet), gland-cells, which secrete the crystalline cone and nerve-cells known as retinulæ. There seem to be no comparative studies on the minute structure of the ommatidia in ants. It is probable that they differ but little from those of other insects. The great differences in size in the eyes of the different species and castes and their almost universal reduction or degeneration in the workers, induced Forel (1874) to investigate the size and numbers of facets, which, of course, represent the ommatidia. He found the size of the facets varying but little in the different species. The smallest were seen in the male of *Cremastogaster sordidula,* the largest in the worker of *Messor barbarus,* but the latter were only twice as broad as the former. The number of facets is extremely variable—from 1 in the worker of *Ponera punctatissima,* to 1,200 in the male of *Formica pratensis.* The variation in number of the different castes of the same species is also very striking. Thus, in *Tapinoma erraticum,* the worker has 100, the female 260, the male 400 ommatidia in each eye; in *Formica pratensis,* the corresponding numbers are 600, 830 and 1,200, and in *Solenopsis fugax* 6–9, 200, 400. A similar study of certain tropical ants (*e. g., Eciton, Dorylus,* Ponerinæ, etc.) would give an even more surprising range of intraspecific variation in the number of facets. The degeneration of the lateral eyes in the workers has proceeded furthest in the African drivers (*Dorylus*) and American legionary ants (*Eciton*). In the former the eyes have disappeared completely, and the same is true of certain species of *Eciton,* but in many of the latter each eye is reduced to a single facet, which, however, is no longer connected with the brain by an optic nerve. At any rate, in the specimens of *E. schmitti,* which I sectioned, I found the vestigial optic nerve reduced to a small thread depending freely from the inner surface of the eye at some distance from the optic lobe. In some species of *Eciton* and *Ænictus* the eyes are represented only by a pair of small, pale dots in the chitinous cranium. While the females of all these genera have no better eyes than the workers, these organs in the males are extremely large and contain many hundreds of ommatidia. It is obvious, of course, that such enormous differences in the size and development of the lateral eyes in different species and in the various castes of the same species must imply corresponding visual differences.

The Median Eyes, or Stemmata.—These occur in the males and females of nearly all ants and in the workers and soldiers of a number of genera. They are largest in the males and always of very small size in the workers. In the male Dorylii, Ecitonii and Ponerinæ they are unusually well developed. In general, it may be said that they tend to vary in correlation with the lateral eyes: the better these are developed, the larger are the stemmata. Structurally the latter cannot be derived from a simple type of sensilla, like that to which we have referred the lateral eyes and the other sense-organs above described. On this account some authors believe that the stemmata are unique and extremely ancient organs, *i. e.,* relics of eyes that preceded the lateral eyes in the phylogeny of insects. It should be noted, however, that both lateral eyes and stemmata present the same development in the earliest known fossil insects, the Carboniferous Palæodictyoptera, that they do in recent species. The stemmata are supposed to give an indistinct visual image of very near objects. Further consideration of the function of these and the other sense-organs briefly described in the preceding paragraphs is reserved for a future chapter.

CHAPTER V

THE DEVELOPMENT OF ANTS

"Incredibili Στοργῇ et cura Formicæ educant summamque dant operam, ne vel tantillum quod spectet eorum Vermiculorum educationem atque nutritionem omittant."—Swammerdam, "Biblia Naturæ," 1737.

"Ces insectes, si peu timides et qui ne craignent point pour eux-mêmes les intempéries de l'air, sont d'une extrême sollicitude pour leur petits, ils redoutent pour ces êtres, d'une constitution délicate, les plus légères variations de l'atmosphère; s'alarment au moindre danger qui semble les menacer, et paroissent jaloux de les soustraire à nos regards."—P. Huber, "Recherches sur Les Mœurs des Fourmis Indigènes," 1810.

Ants, like other metabolic, or metamorphosing insects, pass through four consecutive stages, or instars, before reaching their adult, or imaginal form. These stages, which are known as the egg, or embryo, the larva, the semipupa, or pseudonymph and the pupa, or nymph, are very similar to those of other Hymenoptera both social and solitary. Such close adherence to an ancient method of development in insects, which, in their adult stage, present so many idiosyncrasies of structure and behavior, must be attributed to a general principle according to which the developmental stages of an organism are much more conservative than the adult. The highly modified behavior of the ants themselves towards their brood certainly contrasts very forcibly with the monotonous repetition in the young of stages essentially like those of solitary wasps and gall-flies. This contrast becomes more intelligible, however, when we follow the various phylogenetic stages through which it has been attained. Even the solitary insects make some provision for their young by placing their eggs in suitable situations, and while, among insects of the lower orders, these situations represent merely an indefinite environment, like the earth or the water, in which the young will have to seek their food, the lower Hymenoptera (saw-flies and gall-flies) deposit their eggs only on certain plants. The solitary wasps and bees make ampler provision in constructing cells for the individual larvæ and in supplying them directly with prepared foods. In all of these cases the relation of parent to offspring is both protective and nutritive, but the protective relation is still incompletely developed, since these insects are unable to remove their brood when the nest is disturbed or destroyed. The ants, however, have entered into much more intimate relations with their progeny. They

never construct elaborate earthen, paper or waxen cells for the individual larvæ, and, unlike the solitary bees and wasps, which never
see their brood, or the social bees and wasps, whose experience is

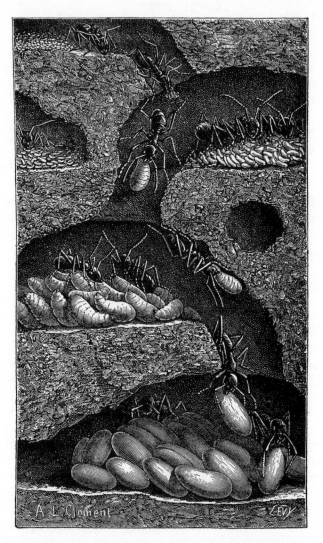

FIG. 34. Interior of a formicary to show the classification of the larvæ and pupæ
according to their stages. (Ern. André.)

largely confined to the heads and gaping mouths of their progeny,
the ants have acquired an extensive and uniform experience with all
the developmental stages of their species from the egg to the adult.

They not only feed, but clean and transport the young from place to place, thus utilizing to the advantage of their development the ever-varying temperature and humidity of the soil. By this means they also protect them from exposure to light and enemies. Moreover, they assist the young to undergo their transformation by embedding them in the earth till the cocoons are woven, and eventually extricate the hatching callows from their envelopes. This freedom in dealing with the brood is certainly one of the most striking manifestations of the plasticity of ants. The remarkable consequences which it entails in their relations with other insects will be considered in future chapters.

As the eggs, larvæ and pupæ develop in the dark recesses of the nest, these stages are always of a pale color, usually translucent white or yellowish, more rarely greenish or roseate, like the corresponding stages of other insects that develop in dark cavities of the soil or in the tissues of plants or animals. Ants rarely or never bring the brood to the surface unless they feel compelled to move to another nest or belong to species like the slave-makers, which kidnap the young of other ants. Occasionally, however, during very warm weather, the young may be brought to the surface after nightfall. In the dry deserts of western Texas, I have seen *Ischnomyrmex cockerelli* bring its larvæ and pupæ out onto the large crater of the nest about 9 P. M. and carry them leisurely to and fro, much as human nurses wheel their charges about the city parks in the cool of the evening.

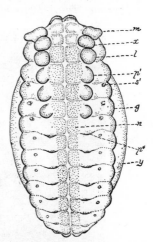

FIG. 35. Embryo of *Formica gnava*. (Original.) *m*, Mandible; *x*, maxilla; *l*, labium; *p¹*, fore leg; *p⁴*, evanescent appendage of first abdominal segment; *s¹*, mesothoracic stigma; *n*, nerve ganglion of future ventral cord; *y*, yolk; *g*, lateral edge of germ-band which advances dorsally to enclose yolk.

Since the brood is always nurtured in darkness we must suppose that the manipulation which this implies depends on highly developed tactile and olfactory senses to the exclusion of vision. Evidence of the exquisite perfection of these senses of contact-odor is seen in the segregation of the brood according to age and condition. The eggs, larvæ and pupæ of different sizes are placed in separate piles in the same or different chambers of the nest, reminding one, as Lubbock (1894, p. 7) aptly says, "of a school divided into five or six classes" (Fig. 34). Inspection of the nests of many species of ants shows that this habit is very prevalent, although it is not so clearly manifested in primitive groups (Ponerinæ) or in species that form small colonies, as in the opulent formicaries of the more highly specialized genera (*Myrmica, Aphænogaster, Formica, Camponotus,* etc.). This classification seems to be an expression of a need for different degrees of moisture and temperature in different developmental stages, as Janet has shown (1904, pp. 38, 39). He says: " In regard to the degree of humidity most favorable for each class of progeny, I have made the following observation on artificial nests of a porous substance, in which the humidity was very regularly graduated, and containing a populous colony of *Myrmica rubra lævinodis,* with extremely numerous offspring. The

Fɪɢ. 36. Larvæ of *Pogonomyrmex molefaciens,* magnified about 5 diameters.
(Original.)

larvæ of medium and large size had been placed on the floor of a very damp chamber. In the less humid neighboring chamber, enormous packets of eggs were found at the bottom of the wall, and above them, attached by their hooked hairs, were all the just-hatched larvæ. All the pupæ were in the even dryer adjacent chamber." As the ants are continually shifting their young about in the nest in response to diurnal changes of moisture and temperature, bringing them nearer the surface during the warm hours of the day and carrying them below during the cooler nights, the classification in wild colonies is best seen only when the weather has been unusually constant for several days.

The eggs of ants are minute bodies, hardly more than .5 mm. long even in the largest species, and usually much smaller. They are commonly overlooked by the casual observer who applies the term " ants' eggs" erroneously to the cocoons or even to the larvæ and pupæ of many of our species. In a few groups, like the Attii, the eggs are nearly spherical or broadly elliptical, but in most species they are elongate elliptical (Fig. 45, *a*). In certain Ponerinæ (*Parasyscia, Lobopelta, Ponera,* etc.) they are unusually long and slender and may be described as cylindrical (Figs. 37, *a,* and 40, *a*). The yolk, like that of the bee's and wasp's egg, is very thin and liquid and is enveloped by a delicate, transparent shell, or chorion. As in other elongated insect eggs, the longitudinal axis of the future embryo and adult insect is clearly pre-determined and corresponds with the long axis of the egg. One of its poles therefore foreshadows the anterior, or cephalic, the other the posterior, or caudal end of the ant. There are said to be no differences in the eggs corresponding to the castes into which they develop, but this matter requires further investigation. It is certain that the eggs deposited by the same female often vary considerably in size and shape, and those laid by the workers are sometimes only half as large as those laid by females of the same species. As the ants frequently lick the eggs it is possible that the saliva may be absorbed by osmosis and increase their volume. This salivary coating is also important in causing the eggs to cohere in packets so that they can be quickly and easily carried away in case of danger. It is prob-able, moreover, that the saliva contains some antiseptic substance which prevents the de-struction of the eggs by fungi.

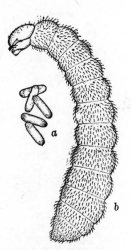

FIG. 37. *Parasyscia augustæ.* (Original.) *a,* Eggs; *b,* young larva, lateral view.

While the eggs are passing out of the oviducts of the female they may be fertilized with some of the spermatozoa stored in the sperma-theca, or they may pass the orifice of this organ and escape from the body without fertilization. The latter, is, of course, always the case in old females whose supply of spermatozoa has been exhausted, or in workers, which usually lack the spermatheca and are not known to mate with males. According to a well-known theory, advanced by Dzierzon for the honey-bee, the unfertilized eggs develop into males, the fertilized eggs into females or workers. Although it has been shown by a number of authors, and especially by Miss Fielde (1905*f*), that unfertilized eggs develop into males, Tanner (1892), Reichenbach (1902), and Mrs. Comstock (see Wheeler, 1903*a*, pp. 835, 836) have recorded observations which indicate that the unfertilized eggs of certain species (*Lasius niger, Atta*) may develop into workers. The Dzierzon theory cannot, therefore, be rigorously extended to the ants till this matter has been more thoroughly investigated.

No complete embryological study of the ants has yet been undertaken. The earliest account of the development of these insects is by Ganin (1869). He studied the eggs of *Lasius flavus, Formica fusca, Myrmica levinodis* and *ruginodis* and *Tetramorium cespitum,* and described the formation of the amnion. This envelope, he maintained, arises by delamination from the blastoderm, but as his investigations were made before modern embryological methods were introduced, it is impossible to attach much importance to his statements. Several years ago Blochmann published two short papers (1884, 1886) on the growth of the ovarian egg, and the formation of the polar bodies and blastoderm in *Camponotus ligniperdus* and *Formica fusca.* I have examined some of the later stages of *F. gnava* and find them to be very similar to those of the bee (*Apis, Chalicodoma*) and wasp (*Polistes*). The accompanying sketch (Fig. 35) of a young embryo of *F. gnava* is interesting as showing some of the conservative traits in the development of ants. Not only are there distinct traces of the antennæ (not seen in the figure, as the head is folded over the anterior pole

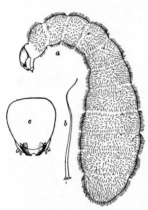

Fig. 38. Larva of *Stigmatomma pallipes.* (Original.) *a,* Larva from the side; *b,* flexuous hair enlarged; *c,* head from above.

of the egg) and three pairs of thoracic legs, but there are also traces of the abdominal appendages, although all of these disappear before the hatching of the larva. The thoracic limbs and antennæ again develop in the larval stage, but the evanescent abdominal appendages, with the exception of those that go to form the parts of the sting of the adult, are mere vestiges, harking back, so to speak, to the legs of ancient larval types like the caterpillar, or eruciform larva of the saw-flies or even to the Palæodictyopteroid ancestors of all insects.

The larva emerges from the egg as a soft, legless, translucent grub, usually shaped like a " crook-necked " squash or gourd, with a broad, straight posterior and narrower, curved anterior end terminating in a small but distinct head (Fig. 36). In some forms (*Eciton, Parasyscia, Lobopelta,* etc.) the body is more cylindrical (Fig. 37). In all cases, however, it consists of a head and thirteen more or less clearly marked segments. Three of these belong to the thorax, the remainder to the abdomen, *i. e.*, to the pedicel plus the gaster of the adult. In a few genera (*Pseudomyrma*) the head, as Emery (1899*e*) has shown, bears minute vestiges of antennæ. The mouth-parts are distinct and consist of a pair of mandibles, a pair of fleshy maxillæ and an unpaired labium. Both maxillæ and labium are furnished with small, conical tactile papillæ (Figs. 38–41), and the latter also bears the opening of the sericteries, or spinning glands. No traces of eyes are visible. There are ten pairs of tracheal openings, a pair each for the meso- and meta-thoracic and the eight anterior abdominal segments.

The transparent chitinous integument is very thin and easily ruptured, so that handling the larvæ must require considerable care on the part of the ants. It is sometimes naked (*Platythyrea*), but much more frequently covered with chitinous hairs which in different species show a bewildering di-versity of form and are most abundant and conspicuous in young individuals. These hairs, which Janet has called "poils d'accrochage," may be long, simple and rigid, or flexuous, helicoid, furcate or tipped with single or double hooks, ramose, plumose or serrate (Figs. 37–43). Some species have hairs of very different kinds on dif-ferent parts of the body. These are all adaptive structures with well-defined functions, at least in certain species. The follow-ing are some of these functions:

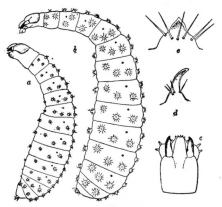

Fig. 39. Larva of *Lobopelta elongata*. (Original.) *a*, Young; *b*, adult larva; *c*, head of adult larva from above; *d*, tubercle of young, *e*, tubercle of adult larva.

1. The hairs may serve to protect the delicate larvæ from the mandibles of their voracious or underfed sister larvæ.

2. They prevent the body of the larva from lying directly in con-tact with the moist soil of the nest.

3. In many Myrmicinæ the pairs of very long, hooked, dorsal hairs which have an S- or C-shaped flexure in their bases (Fig. 43), serve to anchor the larvæ to the walls of the nest, the under surfaces of stones, etc. Janet (1904, p. 32) has shown that the flexure acts like a spring and prevents the rupture of the thin integument when the larva is hastily picked up by the ants, for when the hair is drawn out, the terminal hooks have time to become inclined and release their hold.

4. The hairs hold the young larvæ together in packets and thus

function like the salivary coating of the eggs, in enabling the ants to transport large numbers of their offspring with little effort.   This is a matter of great moment when the colony is disturbed or attacked and the young have to be carried away and concealed with great dispatch.

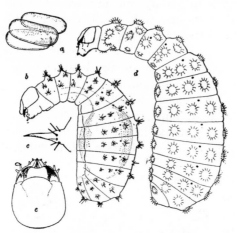

Besides hairs, the larvæ of many Ponerine genera (*Lobopelta, Pachycondyla, Ponera, Diacamma,* etc.) have prominent, pointed, or rounded tubercles which probably have a protective function (Figs. 39–41), and in addition to these, *Ponera* has pairs of glutinous dorsal tubercles (Fig. 41) which, like the flexuous, hooked hairs of many Myrmicinæ, serve to attach the larva to the walls of the nest (Wheeler, 1900*e*).

FIG. 40.   Eggs and larvæ of *Pachycondyla harpax.* (Original.)   *a,* Eggs ; *b,* young larva with pointed tubercles ; *c,* tubercle of same enlarged ; *d,* adult larva with boss-like tubercles ; *e,* head of same from above.

The feeding of the larvæ is of considerable interest owing to the prevailing supposition that the quantity or quality of the food, or both, determine whether the larva hatching from a fertilized egg shall become a worker or a female.   Recent observations have shown that the different species adopt very different methods of nourishing their brood.   Many ants, like most Camponotinæ, Dolichoderinæ and Myrmicinæ, feed their larvæ only on regurgitated liquids, whereas the Ponerinæ, many Myrmicinæ and probably also the Dorylinæ, feed them directly with pieces of the same kind of food that they bring into the nest for their own consumption.   Carnivorous species give their larvæ pieces of insects, and the harvesting ants (*Pogonomyrmex,* some species of *Pheidole*) administer fragments of seeds.   In larvæ that are habitually fed on such resistant substance the mandibles are apt to be more highly developed.   Some species (*Aphænogaster, Lasius, Pheidole,* etc.) undoubtedly feed their brood both with regurgitated and solid food.   Certain groups of ants that have developed a specialized diet in their adult stages show a corresponding specialization in feeding their young.   Thus the larvæ of the fungus-growing Attii of tropical America are nourished with wisps of fungus-hyphæ, and according to Dahl (1901, p. 31) the larvæ of the East Indian *Campo-*

notus quadriceps feed directly on the pith of the plants in which the insects nest (see Fig. 168).

The internal structure of the larva, which is essentially that of the mature embryo, has been described by Ganin (1876), Dewitz (1877, 1878), Nassonow (1886) and Karawaiew (1898, 1900) for *Formica, Myrmica* and *Lasius,* by Berlese (1901) for *Tapinoma,* and by Pérez (1902) for *Formica rufa.* In the following account I have followed Pérez. The alimentary tract of the larva (Fig. 44) is much simpler than that of the adult described in Chapter III. The thin outer integument is folded into the body to form the walls of a slender pharynx and œsophagus, which is, therefore, of ectodermal origin and corresponds to the stomodæum of the embryo. Muscles extend from the walls of the pharynx to the dorsal integument and function as dilators during the sucking or imbibing movements of the larva. At its posterior end the pharynx opens on an elevated, valvular papilla into the chylific stomach, which is equivalent to the embryonic mesenteron, or mid-gut. It is a spacious, ovoid receptacle, somewhat attenuated anteriorly in the future proventricular region and closed posteriorly where it unites with the anterior end of the hind-gut, or embryonic proctodæum. The latter is formed by a tubular invagination of the ectoderm similar to that which forms the œsophagus. Owing to the closure between the chylific stomach and the hind-gut, all the undigested portions of the larval food enclosed in

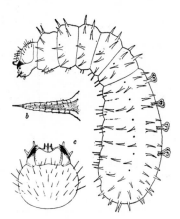

Fig. 41. Larva of *Ponera pennsylvanica.* (Original.) *a,* Larva ready to pupate; *b,* bristle-capped tubercle of same; *c,* head from above.

the series of successively sloughed peritrophic membranes, accumulate in the cavity of the stomach and form a black, elliptical mass, the meconium, which often shows through the translucent body walls of the larva. The hind-gut is differentiated into two regions, a more slender, tubular anterior portion, the small intestine, and a more capacious sac, the large intestine. The latter is constricted behind and opens on the surface as the anus, which has the form of a transverse slit and is provided with a sphincter muscle. Four Malpighian tubules open into the anterior blind end of the small intestine and describe a few convolutions in the dorsal body cavity. In the ventral body cavity lies a pair of less convoluted sericteries, or spinning glands, which unite to form a duct, opening on the tip of the labium. These organs are also present in larvæ that do not spin cocoons. The nervous system consists of a cerebral ganglion, connected by a pair of commissures surrounding the œsophagus, with the most anterior of a series of twelve ganglia, which extend through the body on the ventral side of the alimentary tract. The first, or subœsophageal ganglion, is a fusion of the ganglia of the mandibular, maxillary and labial segments of the embryo. The tubular heart lies just under the dorsal integument and terminates anteriorly beneath the brain. The pericardial cells float out into the body like a velum on each side of the heart. The feebly developed muscular system consists of longitudinal fibres lying in two latero-dorsal and two latero-ventral zones in the various segments. Another set of muscles, which are oblique antero-posteriorly, have their dorsal insertions at the intersegmental constrictions near the stigmata and their ventral insertions at the anterior border of the preceding segment. Segmental groups of œnocytes are suspended near these oblique muscles. The tracheal system consists of a pair of longitudinal trunks which send off short branches to the adjacent stigmata. The greater portion of the spaces between the above-described organs is filled with lobes of the voluminous fat-body which shows through the transparent integument and gives the larva its shining white, greenish or pinkish color. The undeveloped reproductive organs are clearly discernible as small bodies in the postero-dorsal region of the abdomen, and the histoblasts, or imaginal discs, are present as small, paired clusters of formative cells in the hypodermis of the integument. They represent the adult antennæ, legs, wings, copulatory organs, parts of the sting, etc. Each histoblast receives a slender nerve.

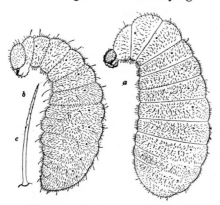

FIG. 42. Larvæ of *Pogonomyrmex molefaciens*. (Original.) *a*, Adult larva; *b*, young larva; *c*, hair of same enlarged.

When the larva approaches its full size important changes occur in both its external and internal structure in preparation for metamorphosis, or pupation. For an account of the internal changes, which are too numerous and intricate to be described here, the reader is referred to the works of Karawaiew, Berlese and Pérez. The external changes may be briefly considered. When full-grown the larva passes on to the semipupa stage, but in certain ants (Ponerinæ and most Camponotinæ) it first spins a cocoon (Figs. 45 and 46). Except for this episode, the development of all ants is essentially the same. The mature larvæ of cocoon-spinning species have to be buried in the earth by the workers or covered with particles of detritus, since the larva cannot spin an elliptical envelope about itself while it lies freely in the nest, but must lie in a cavity so that it can fix the threads from its sericteries to different points in an adjoining wall. The larva moves its head back and forth and lines the cavity in which it lies with a fine web of silk. As soon as this has been accomplished it is unearthed by the workers and the foreign particles adhering to the outer surface of the cocoon are carefully removed. The cocoon is now found to contain a semipupa (Figs. 47, *a,* and 49), which resembles the larva except that the body has become straight and rigid, with its anterior end no longer bent in an arc and with a pronounced constriction behind the epinotal segment. Beneath the cuticle the legs, wings and cephalic appendages, which have developed in the meantime from the histoblasts, are clearly discernible, though still of small size, more or less folded and closely applied to one another and to the surface of the body. The

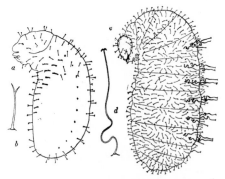

FIG. 43. Larva of *Pheidole instabilis.* (Original.) *a,* Young larva; *b,* bifurcated hair of same; *c,* adult larva; *d,* dorsal spring-like hair of same.

larval skin is soon ruptured along the back (Fig. 47, *b*), stripped from the body and pushed into the caudal pole of the cocoon. The small intestine has meanwhile formed an open communication with the chylific stomach and the mass of meconium and peritrophic membranes is voided through the large intestine and also deposited in the posterior pole where it forms a black or dark brown spot. In the meantime the appendages have been growing rapidly and assuming their adult structure, though they are still bent and closely applied to the body (Fig. 47, *c*). The further external changes in the quiescent pupa, which is now definitely formed, consist in a gradual deposition of pigment. This makes its appearance first in the eyes, which become intensely black before the color spreads over the remainder of the body (Fig. 49). Finally, when all the organs have reached their full development, the workers cut open the antero-ventral

wall of the cocoon, draw forth the young and strip the enveloping
cuticle from its body and appendages. The newly hatched ant which
has not yet acquired its deep adult coloration is known as a callow.
Owing to the absence of wings, the hatching of the workers is somewhat more easily accomplished than that of the males and females.
Dewitz (1878) has shown that the worker larva actually possesses minute histoblasts of these appendages, but they do not develop except in
certain abnormal individuals which I have called pterergates (Fig. 63).

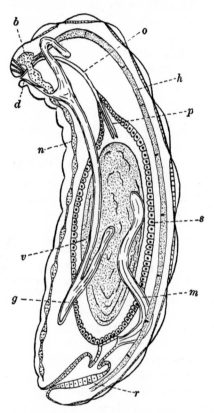

FIG. 44. Anatomy of ant larva.
(Pérez.) *b*, Brain; *n*, ventral nerve
cord; *o*, œsophagus; *p*, proventriculus;
s, midgut (stomach); *v*, mass of substance to be excreted; *r*, rectum; *m*,
Malpighian vessel; *g*, spinning gland;
d, duct of same opening on labium;
h, heart.

In ant larvæ that do not spin
cocoons, development and hatching are, of course, considerably
simplified (Figs. 48 and 49).
In such species the adult larva
passes at once to the semipupa
stage after discharging the meconium. A worker receives the
black pellet in its mandibles, or
even pulls it out of the large intestine and deposits it on the refuse heap of the nest. The fact
that the cocoon is constantly present in the most primitive ants
and as constantly lacking in large
groups of highly specialized
forms, shows that it is an ancient
inheritance from solitary, wasp-
like ancestors. Certain Camponotine genera and subgenera (*Prenolepis*, *Œcophylla*, *Plagiolepis*
and *Colobopsis*) always have
nude pupæ, and in certain species
of *Formica* and *Lasius* the cocoon
may be present or absent in the
brood of the same colony or even
in the male and female pupæ.
Janet (1896c) regards the sudden
elimination of the envelope in
these species as a mutation, or
saltatory variation. I have seen
the nude pupæ of a Dolichoderine
ant (*Iridomyrmex geinitzi*) in the Baltic amber (Lower Oligocene),
so that the complete elimination of the cocoon, in this subfamily at

least, is not a very recent development. The shape and color of
the cocoon differ considerably in different species. In *Leptogenys,*
for example, it is very long and slender and of a dark-brown color,
in *Lasius* and *Formica* it is a pale buff or whitish and broadly elliptical,
in *Ponera pennsylvanica* it is oblong and sulphur yellow.

Fig. 45. *Camponotus americanus* × 2. (Photograph by J. G. Hubbard and Dr.
O. S. Strong.) *a,* Egg; *b,* young larvæ; *c,* older larvæ; *d,* worker cocoons; *e,* female
cocoon; *f,* worker major pupa removed from cocoon; *g,* worker media in the act
of hatching; *h,* major workers; *i,* minor workers; *k,* virgin female; *l,* males.

Little attention has been paid to the coloration of the callows as
compared with the mature ants. In certain species, when the latter

are black, the callows are drab or yellowish (*Formica subsericea*), while in others they may be orange or deep red (*Platythyrea punctata*). The callows of bright red ants are often sulphur yellow or orange (*Polyergus, Pogonomyrmex, Myrmica mutica*), while in the yellow species, like our North American *Lasius* of the subgenus *Acanthomyops,* the callows are sordid white or drab (Fig. 46, *a*).

Fig. 46. *Acanthomyops claviger* workers and cocoons, × 2. (Photograph by J. G. Hubbard and Dr. O. S. Strong.)   *a,* Callow workers; *b,* queen cocoons; remaining cocoons those of workers.

The length of embryonic, larval and pupal life appears to be highly variable and to depend very intimately on temperature. Wasmann (1891c) and Miss Fielde (1905g) have shown that a rise of temperature at once induces both females and workers to lay and accelerates the growth of the larvæ. According to Miss Fielde: " It appears that the time of development may be altered by a change of the prevailing temperature and that an intervening period of recuperation will be maintained in spite of a temperature stimulus. Other factors being equal, the development of the eggs within the ovaries, the deposit of the eggs, the feeding and growth of the larvæ, the pupation and hatching, all appear to be determined by temperature. The degree of heat suiting the species probably varies for the different stages of development. . . Among the ant-young observed by me, none has developed at a temperature below 70° F., while long exposure to a degree of heat above 90° F. manifestly causes injury." Both Miss Fielde and Janet have taken pains to ascertain the duration of the embryonic, larval and pupal stages. Their results are remarkably similar when we consider that they were made on different species and in different countries. For *Aphænogaster fulva* Miss Fielde gives the duration of the embryonic period as 17 to 22 days (usually 19 days), that of the larval period as 24 to 27 and the pupal period as 13 to 22 days, while Janet gives as the corresponding periods for *Myrmica rubra* 23 to 24 days, 30 to 71 days, and 18 to 22 days. This makes the total for the entire development of *A. fulva* 54 to 141 days and of *M. rubra* 71 to 117 days. According to Miss Fielde,

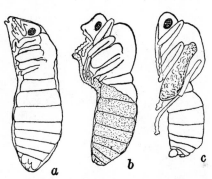

FIG. 47. Semipupa becoming a pupa. (Pérez.) *a,* Semipupa, still covered by larval skin; *b,* larval skin removed from anterior portion of body; *c,* pupa.

the parthenogenetic offspring of workers develop much more slowly than the offspring of females. In wild colonies development is most rapid during the spring and summer months, and undoubtedly in many species the larvæ manage to live from November till the following March without showing any signs of development.

Although the developmental periods above given are unusually long for metabolic insects, the longevity of adult ants is still more remarkable. The male is supposed to be very short-lived and there can be little doubt that in most species it dies soon after the nuptial flight. Still Lubbock (1894) mentions males of *Myrmica ruginodis* which lived in an artificial nest from August 14 till the following April, and Janet (1904, p. 40) kept males of *M. rubra* alive from October 12 till the beginning of April. The males undoubtedly live

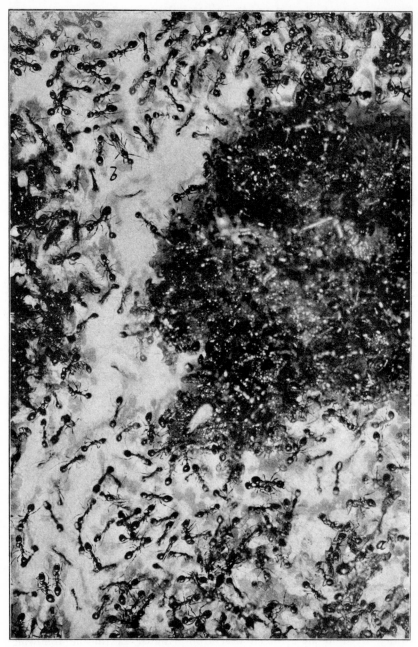

FIG. 48. Colony of *Aphænogaster picea* with naked brood, slightly enlarged.
(Photograph by J. G. Hubbard and O. S. Strong.)   *a*, Mother queen of colony;
b, male.

as long or even longer in many species of *Camponotus* and *Prenolepis*, whose sexual forms do not mate till the following spring. The longevity of the workers is certainly much greater than that of the males. Lubbock (1894, p. 12) had workers of *Formica cinerea* that lived nearly five years, workers of *F. sanguinea* that had lived at least five years, and some individuals of *F. fusca* and *Lasius niger* that attained an age of more than six years. That the workers of the Myrmicinæ are almost or quite as long-lived may be inferred from the fact that Miss Fielde has kept those of *A. fulva* under observation for a period of three years. But even greater than the longevity of the worker is that of the female, as would be expected from the larger size and vigor of this caste. Janet (1904, p. 42–45) records the age of a female *Lasius alienus* as fully ten years, and Lubbock kept a female *F. fusca* alive from December, 1874, till August, 1888, " when she must have been nearly fifteen years old, and, of course, may have been more. She attained, therefore, by far the greatest age of any insect on record."

Closely related to the longevity of adult ants is the question of their resistance to adverse conditions. On this subject, which is of considerable importance in connection with the economic treatment of these insects, Miss Fielde has published (1901 to 1905) a number of interesting and painstaking observations. Although the optimum temperature for our northern ants lies between 70° and 80° F., the minimum and maximum to which they can be subjected and still survive, are very widely separated. Miss Fielde froze females, workers and a brood of *Aphænogaster fulva* for twenty-four hours at — 5° C. (23° F.). The insects were then gradually thawed and all survived. Even the frozen eggs, larvæ and pupæ subsequently developed in a normal manner. When the temperature was raised to 30° C. (86° F.) the ants began to show signs of discomfort, at 35° C. (96° F.) the smallest individuals swooned, and even the most vigorous ants with which she experimented succumbed after two minutes' exposure to 50° C. (122° F.). It has been known for some time that female ants can go without food for the greater part of the year while they are founding their colonies. Miss Fielde has demonstrated that large workers can fast for almost equally long periods. She succeeded in keeping *F. subsericea* and *Camponotus americanus* workers alive without food for from 7 to 9 months. Ants are also able to endure long submergence in cool or cold water. Miss Fielde found that *Lasius latipes* survived 27 hours of this treatment; *C. pennsylvanicus*, 70 hours, and *Aphænogaster fulva* eight days! This explains how ants that sometimes nest in the beds of streams, like the Texan *Pogonomyr-*

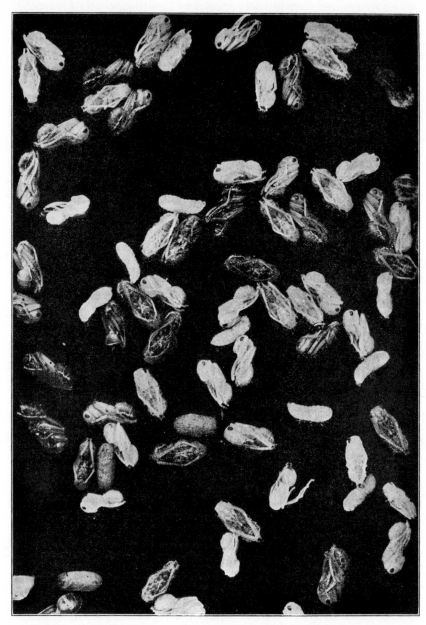

FIG. 49. Adult worker larvæ, semipupæ, and nude and covered pupæ in various stages of pigmentation of *Formica subsericea,* × 2. (Photograph by J. G. Hubbard and Dr. O. S. Strong.)

mex barbatus, can survive a flood of several days' duration. She did not test the resistance of ants to drought, but that this is considerable in many species is shown by the rich ant-fauna of many deserts like the Sahara and the deserts of the Southwestern States and northern Mexico. Miss Fielde also found that ants exhibit considerable resistance to the action of very violent poisons such as corrosive sublimate, potassium cyanide and carbolic acid. Their tenacity is best shown, however, in the number of days they are able to live after severe maiming, like decapitation. Janet (1898*g*, p. 130) kept a beheaded *F. rufa* alive for 19 days, and Miss Fielde kept a beheaded worker of *C. pennsylvanicus* alive for 41 days. And this ant walked about to within two days of its death! In their experiments Janet and Miss Fielde found that the males are least, the females most resistant to adverse conditions, and that the vitality of the workers varies directly as their size.

These facts, with others to be produced in the sequel, show that ants are made of remarkably tenacious protoplasm. Chained to the earth as they are, they have come to adapt themselves perfectly to its great thermal vicissitudes, its droughts and floods, and its precarious and fluctuating food-supply.

CHAPTER VI

POLYMORPHISM

"Ce peuple de Pygmées, de Troglodytes, est, en effet, digne de toute notre admiration. Peut-on voir une société dont les membres qui la composent aient plus d'amour public? qui soient plus désintéressés? qui aient pour la travail une ardeur plus opiniâtre et plus soutenue? Quel singulier phénomène! Je ne vois dans la très-grande majorité de ce peuple que des êtres sourds à la voix de l'amour, incapables même de se reproduire, et qui goûtent néanmoins le sentiment le plus exquis de la maternité, qui en ont toute la tendresse, qui ne pensent, n'agissent, ne vivent en un mot que pour des pupilles dont la Nature les fit tuteurs et nourriciers. Cette république n'est pas sujette à ces vicissitudes de formes, à cette mobilité dans les pouvoirs, à ces fluctuations perpétuelles qui agitent nos républiques, et font le tourment des citoyens. Depuis que la fourmi est fourmi, elle a toujours vécu de même; elle n'a eu qu'une seule volonté, qu'une seule loi, et cette volonté, cette loi ont constamment pour base l'amour de ses semblables."—Latreille, "Histoire Naturelle des Fourmis," 1802.

There is a sense in which the term polymorphism is applicable to all living organisms, since no two of these are ever exactly alike. But when employed in this sense, the term is merely a synonym of " variation," which is the more apt, since polymorphism has an essentially morphological tinge, whereas variation embraces also the psychological, physiological and ethological differences between organisms. In zoölogy the term polymorphism is progressively restricted, first, to cases in which individuals of the same species may be recognized as constituting two or more groups, or castes, each of which has its own definite characters or complexion. Second, the term is applied only to animals in which these intraspecific groups coëxist in space and do not arise through metamorphosis or constitute successive generations. Cases of the latter description are referred to " alternation of generations " and " seasonal polymorphism." And third, the intraspecific groups of reproductive individuals existing in all gonochoristic, or separate-sexed Metazoa are placed in the category of " sex " or " sexual dimorphism." There remain, therefore, as properly representing the phenomena of polymorphism only those animals in which characteristic intraspecific and intrasexual groups of individuals may be recognized, or, in simpler language, those species in which one or both of the sexes appear under two or more distinct forms.

As thus restricted polymorphism is of rare occurrence in the animal kingdom and may be said to occur only in colonial or social species where its existence is commonly attributed to a physiological division of labor. It attains its clearest expression in the social insects, in some of which, like the termites, we find both sexes equally polymorphic, while in others, like the ants, social bees, and wasps, the female alone, with rare exceptions, is differentiated into distinct castes. This restriction of polymorphism to the female in the social Hymenoptera, with which we are here especially concerned, is easily intelligible if it be traceable, as is usually supposed, to a physiological division of labor, for the colonies of ants, bees and wasps are essentially more or less permanent families of females, the male representing merely a fertilizing agency temporarily intruding itself on the activities of the community at the moment it becomes necessary to start other colonies.

FIG. 50. Males of *Aphænogaster picea*. (Photograph by J. G. Hubbard and Dr. O. S. Strong.)

We may say, therefore, that polymorphism among social Hymenoptera is a physical expression of the high degree of social plasticity and efficiency of the female sex among these insects. This is shown more specifically in two characteristics of the female, namely the extraordinary intricacy and amplitude of her instincts, which are thoroughly representative of the species, and her ability to reproduce parthenogenetically. This, of course, means a considerable degree of autonomy even in the reproductive sphere. But parthenogenesis, while undoubtedly contributing to the social efficiency of the female, must be regarded and treated as an independent phenomenon, without closer connection with polymorphism, for the ability to develop from unfertilized eggs is an ancient characteristic of the Hymenoptera and

Fig. 51. Colony of *Acanthomyops claviger*, showing workers, deälated and virgin females, males, worker, male and female cocoons, × 2. (Photograph by J. G. Hubbard and Dr. O. S. Strong).

many other insects, which made its appearance among the solitary species, like the Tenthredinidæ and Cynipidæ, long before the development of social life. Moreover, polymorphism may occur in male insects which, of course, are not parthenogenetic. That parthenogenesis is intimately connected with sexual dimorphism, at least among the

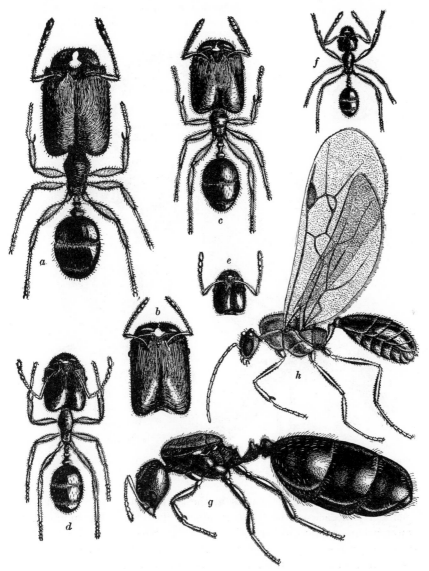

FIG. 52. *Pheidole instabilis.* (Original.) *a*, Soldier; *b–e*, intermediate workers; *f*, typical worker (micrergate); *g*, deälated female; *h*, male.

social Hymenoptera, seems to be evident from the fact that the males usually if not always develop from unfertilized, the females from fertilized eggs.

While the bumble-bees and wasps show us the ancient stages in the development of polymorphism, the ants as a group, with the exception of a few parasitic genera that have secondarily lost this character, are all completely polymorphic. It is conceivable that the

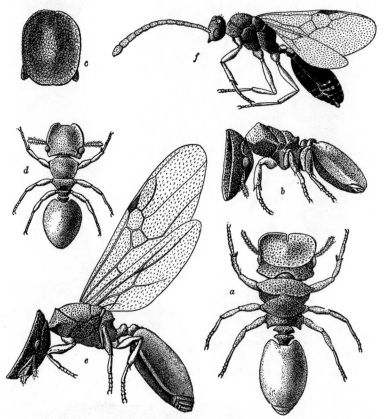

FIG. 53. *Cryptocerus varians.* (Original.) *a,* Soldier; *b,* same in profile; *c,* head of same from above; *d,* worker; *e,* female; *f,* male.

development of different castes in the female may have arisen independently in each of the three groups of the social Hymenoptera, although it is equally probable that they may have inherited a tendency to polymorphism from a common extinct ancestry. On either hypothesis, however, we must admit that the ants have carried the development of the female castes much further than the social bees and wasps, since they have not only produced a wingless form of the worker, in addition to the winged female, or queen, but in many cases also two distinct castes of workers known as the worker proper and the soldier.

Different authors have framed very different conceptions of the phylogenetic beginnings of social life among the Hymenoptera and consequently also of the phylogenetic origin and development of polymorphism. Thus Herbert Spencer (1893) evidently conceived the colony as having arisen from consociation of adult individuals, and although he unfortunately selected a parasitic ant, the amazon (*Polyergus rufescens*), on which to hang his hypothesis, there are a few facts which at first sight seem to make his view applicable to other social Hymenoptera. Fabre (1894) once found some hundreds of specimens of a solitary wasp (*Ammophila hirsuta*) huddled together under a stone on the summit of Mt. Ventoux in the Provence, at an altitude of about 5,500 feet, and Forel (1874) found more than fifty deälated females of *Formica rufa* under similar conditions on the Simplon. I have myself seen collections of a large red and yellow *Amblyteles* under stones on Pike's Peak at an altitude of more than 13,000 feet, and a mass of about seventy deälated females of *Formica gnava* apparently hibernating after the nuptial flight under a stone near Austin, Texas. I am convinced, however, that such congregations are either entirely fortuitous, especially where the insects of one species are very abundant and there are few available stones, or, that they are, as in the case of *F. rufa* and *gnava*, merely a manifestation of highly developed social proclivities and not of such proclivities in process of development.

A very different view from that of Spencer is adopted by most authors, who regard the insect colony as having arisen, not from a chance concourse of adult individuals, but from a natural affiliation of mother and offspring. This view, which has been elaborated by Marshall (1889) among others, presents many advantages over that of Spencer, not the least of which is its agreement with what actually occurs in the founding of the existing colonies of wasps, bumble-bees and ants. These colonies pass through an ontogenetic stage which has all the appearance of repeating the conditions under which colonial life first made its appearance in the phylogenetic history of the species—the solitary mother insect rearing and affiliating her offspring under conditions which would seem to arise naturally from the breeding habits of the nonsocial Hymenoptera. The exceptional methods of colony formation seen in the swarming of the honey bee and in the temporary and permanent parasitism of certain ants, are too obviously secondary and of too recent a development to require extended comment. The bond which held mother and daughters together as a community was from the first no other than that which binds human societies together—the bond of hunger and affection. The daughter insects in the primitive colony became dependent organisms as a result of two factors: inadequate nourishment and the ability to pupate very prematurely. But this very ability seems to have entailed an incompleteness of adult structure and instincts, which in turn must have confirmed the division of labor and thus tended to perfect the social organization.

Before further discussing the problems suggested by this view of the origin of the colony and the general subject of polymorphism, it will be advisable to pass in review the series of different phases known to occur among ants. This review will be facilitated by consulting the accompanying diagram, in which I have endeavored to arrange

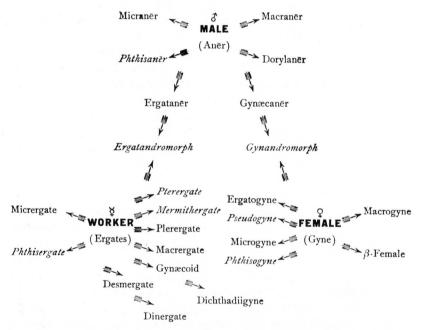

the various phases so as to bring out their morphological relations to one another. The phases may be divided into two main groups, the normal and the pathological. In the diagram the names of the latter are printed in italics. The normal phases may be again divided into primary or typical, and secondary or atypical, the former comprising only the three original phases, male, female and worker, the latter the remaining phases, which, however, are far from having the same dignity or frequency. The three typical phases are placed at the angles of an isosceles triangle, the excess developments being placed to the right, the defect developments to the left, of a vertical line passing through the middle of the diagram. The arrows indicate the directions of the affinities of the secondary phases and suggest that those on the sides of the triangle are annectant, whereas those which radiate outward from its angles represent the new departures with excess and defect characters.

1. The *male* (*anēr*) is far and away the most stable of the three typical phases which are found in all but a few monotypic and parasitic genera of ants. This is best shown in the general uniformity of structure and coloration which characterize this sex in genera whose female forms (workers and queens) are widely different; *e. g.*, in such a series of cases as *Myrmecia, Odontomachus, Cryptocerus* (Fig. 53), *Formica, Pheidole* (Fig. 52), etc. In all of these genera the males are very similar, at least superficially, whereas the workers and females are very diverse. The body of the male ant is graceful in form, one might almost say emaciated (Fig. 50). Its sense-organs (especially the eyes and antennæ), wings and genitalia are highly developed; its mandibles are more or less imperfectly developed, and in correlation with them the head is proportionally shorter, smaller and rounder

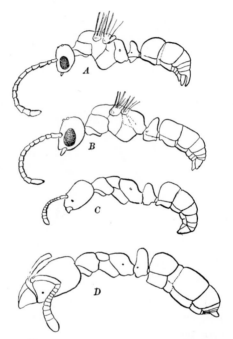

Fig. 54. Males of *Ponera*. (Emery.) *A*, Winged male of *Ponera coarctata*; *B*, winged male of *P. eduardi*; *C*, ergatomorphic male (ergatanēr) of *P. eduardi*; *D*, ergatanēr of *P. punctatissima*.

than in the females and workers of the same species. Even when the latter phases have brilliant or metallic colors, as in certain species of *Macromischa* and *Rhytidoponera*, the males are uniformly red, yellow, brown or black. Yet notwithstanding this monotony of structure and coloration, the male type may present interesting modifications.

2. The *macranēr* is an unusually large form of male which occasionally occurs in populous colonies.

3. The *micranēr* or dwarf male, differs from the typical form merely in its smaller stature. Such forms often arise in artificial nests.

4. The *dorylanēr* is an unusually large form peculiar to the driver

FIG. 55. *Acanthomyops claviger* and *A. latipes.* (Original.) *A,* Deälated female of *A. claviger; B,* α-female of *A. latipes; C.* β-female of same.

and legionary ants of the subfamily Dorylinæ (*Dorylus* and *Eciton*). It is characterized by its large and peculiarly modified mandibles, long cylindrical gaster and singular genitalia (Figs. 141, *E,* and 142). It may be regarded as an aberrant macranēr that has come to be the typical male of the Dorylinæ.

5. The *ergatanēr,* ergatomorphic, or ergatoid male resembles the worker in having no wings and in the structure of the antennæ. It occurs in the genera *Ponera, Formicoxenus, Symmyrmica, Technomyrmex* and *Cardiocondyla.* In certain species of *Ponera* (*P. punctatissima* and *ergatandria*) and in *Formicoxenus nitidulus* the head and thorax are surprisingly worker-like, in other forms like *Symmyrmica chamberlini* these parts are more like those of the ordinary ant, while *P. eduardi* shows a more intermediate development of the head with a

worker-like thorax. Forel (1904*h*) has recently shown that the ergatanēr may coëxist with the anēr, at least in one species of *Ponera* (*P.
eduardi* Forel). In other words, this ant has dimorphic males (Fig.
54, *B* and *C*).

6. The *gynæcanēr,* or gynæcomorphic male occurs in certain parasitic and workerless genera (*Aner-
gates* and *Epœcus*) and resembles
a female rather than a worker form.
The male of *Anergates* is wingless, but has the same number of
antennal joints as the female (Fig.
279). In *Epœcus* (Fig. 278) both
sexes are very much alike and both
have 11–12-jointed antennæ (Emery, 1906*d*).

7. The *phthisanēr* is a pupal male
which in its larval or semipupal
state has its juices partially extracted by an *Orasema* larva. This
male is too much depleted to pass on
to the imaginal stage. The wings
are suppressed and the legs, head,
thorax and antennæ remain abortive.

FIG. 56. *Monomorium floricola.*
(Original.) *a,* Worker; *b,* apterous female (ergatogyne); *c,* same seen from
the side.

8. The female (*gyne*), or queen,
is the more highly specialized sex
among ants and is characterized, as a rule, by a larger stature and the
more uniform development of her organs (Figs. 52, *g,* etc.). The head
is well developed and provided with moderately large eyes, ocelli and
mandibles; the thorax is large (macronotal) and presents all the
sclerites of the typical female Hymenopteron; the gaster is voluminous
and provided with well-developed reproductive organs. The latter
possess a receptaculum seminis. The wings and legs are often proportionally shorter and stouter than in the male.

9. The *macrogyne* is a female of unusually large stature.

10. The *microgyne,* or dwarf female, is an unusually small female
which in certain ants, like *Formica microgyna* and its allies, is the
only female of the species and may be actually smaller than the largest
workers (Fig. 262). In other ants, like certain species of *Leptothorax*
and *Myrmica,* microgynes may sometimes be found in the same nest
as the typical females.

11. The *β-female* is an aberrant form of female such as occurs in
Lasius latipes (Fig. 55, *C*), either as the only form or coëxisting with

the normal female which is then called the α-female. In this case, therefore, the female is dimorphic. The β-female is characterized by excess developments in the legs and antennæ and in the pilosity of the body or by defective development of the wings.

12. The *ergatogyne,* ergatomorphic, or ergatoid female, is a worker-like form, with ocelli, large eyes and a thorax more or less like that of the female, but without wings. Such females occur in a number of species of ants. They have been seen in *Myrmecia, Odontomachus, Anochetus, Ponera, Polyergus, Leptothorax, Monomorium* and *Cremastogaster.* There is nothing to prove that they are pathological in

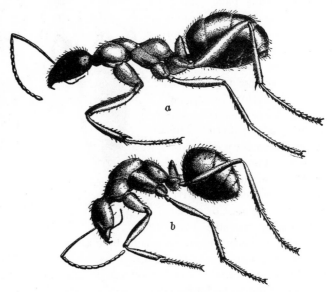

Fig. 57. *Formica incerta.* (Original.) *a,* Normal worker; *b,* pseudogyne drawn to the same scale.

origin. In fact, in *Monomorium floricola* (Fig. 56), and certain species of *Anochetus* they appear to be the only existing females. In other cases, like *Ponera eduardi,* as Forel has shown, they occur with more or less regularity in nests with normal workers. They also occur under similar conditions in colonies of the circumpolar *P. coarctata,* and among other species of the genus.

13. The *pseudogyne* (Fig. 57, *b*) is a worker-like form with enlarged mesonotum and sometimes traces of other thoracic sclerites of the female, but without wings or very rarely with wing vestiges. This form, when it occurs among species of *Formica,* is produced by the presence of Lomechusine beetles in the colony (see p. 407 *et seq.*).

14. The *phthisogyne* arises from a female larva under the same conditions as the phthisaner, and differs from the typical female in the same characters, namely absence of wings, stenonoty, microcephaly and microphthalmy. It is unable to attain to the imaginal instar.

15. The *worker* (ergates) is characterized by the complete absence of wings and a very small (stenonotal) thorax, much simplified in the structure of its sclerites (Fig. 8, *C*, etc.). The eyes are small and the ocelli are usually absent or, when present, extremely small. The gaster is small, owing to the undeveloped condition of the ovaries. A receptaculum seminis is usually lacking, and the number of the ovarian tubules is greatly diminished. The antennæ, legs and mandibles are well developed.

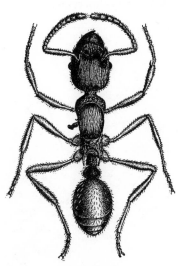

16. The *gynæcoid* is an egg-laying worker. It is a physiological rather than a morphological phase, since it is probable that all the worker ants when abundantly fed become able to lay eggs. Wasmann (1904*a*) observed in colonies of *Formica rufibarbis* that one

FIG. 58. Pseudogyne of *Myrmica sulcinodoides*, with vestige of fore wing on left side. (Original.)

or a few workers became gynæcoid and functioned as substitution queens. In colonies of the Ponerine genus *Leptogenys* (including the subgenus *Lobopelta* (Fig. 137), and probably also in *Diacamma* and *Champsomyrmex*), the queen phase has disappeared and has been replaced by the gynæcoid worker.

17. The *dichthadiigyne,* or dichthadiiform female is peculiar to the ants of the subfamily Dorylinæ and probably represent a further development of the gynæcoid. It is wingless and stenonotal, destitute of eyes or ocelli, or with these organs very feebly developed, and with a huge elongated gaster and extraordinary, voluminous ovaries (Figs. 141, *A,* and 147, *b* and *c*).

18. The *macrergate* is an unusually large worker form which in some species is produced only in populous or affluent colonies (*Formica, Lasius*).

19. The *micrergate,* or dwarf worker, is a worker of unusually small stature. It appears as a normal or constant form in the first brood of all colonies that are founded by isolated females.

20. The *dinergate,* or soldier (Figs. 52, *A* ; 60, *a*), is characterized by

a huge head and mandibles, often adapted to particular functions (fighting and guarding the nest, crushing seeds or hard parts of insects), and a thoracic structure sometimes approaching that of the female in size or in the development of its sclerites (*Pheidole*).

21. The *desmergate* is a form intermediate between the typical worker and dinergate, such as we find in more or less isolated genera

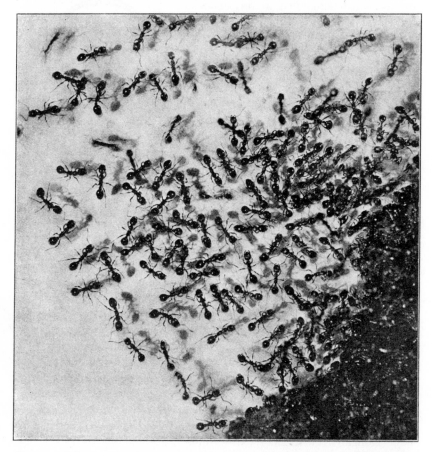

FIG. 59.   *Aphænogaster picea,* an ant with monomorphic workers.   (Photograph by
J. G. Hubbard and Dr. O. S. Strong.)

of all the subfamilies except the Ponerinæ, *e. g.,* in *Camponotus* (Fig. 45, *a*), some species of *Pheidole* (Fig. 52, *b–e*), *Solenopsis* and *Pogonomyrmex, Azteca, Dorylus* (Fig. 62, *b*), *Eciton,* etc.   The term might also be employed to designate the intermediate forms between the small and large workers in such genera as *Monomorium, Formica,* etc.

22. The *plerergate,* " replete," or " rotund," is a worker, which in its callow stage has acquired the peculiar habit of distending the gaster with stored liquid food (" honey ") till it becomes a large spherical sac and locomotion is rendered difficult or even impossible (Figs. 218 and 219). This occurs in the honey ants (some North American species of *Myrmecocystus,* some Australian *Melophorus* and *Camponotus,* and to a less striking extent in certain species of *Prenolepis* and *Plagiolepis*).

23. The *pterergate* is a worker or soldier with vestiges of wings on a thorax of the typical ergate or dinergate form, such as occurs in certain species of *Myrmica* and *Cryptocerus* (Fig. 63).

24. The *mermithergate* is an enlarged worker, produced by *Mermis* parasitism and often presenting dinergate characters in the thorax and minute ocelli in the head (Fig. 254, *B, C*).

25. The *phthisergate,* which corresponds to the phthisogyne and phthisaner, is a pupal worker, which in its late larval or semipupal stage has been attacked and partially exhausted of its juices by an *Orasema* larva (Fig. 252, *B* and *C*). It is characterized by extreme

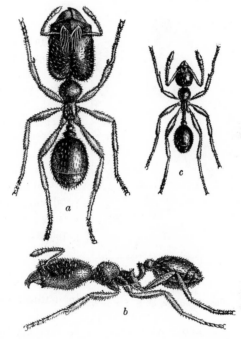

Fig. 60. *Pheidole borinquenensis* of Porto Rico. (Original.) *a,* Soldier; *b,* same in profile; *c,* worker.

stenonoty, microcephaly and microphthalmy, and is unable to pass on to the imaginal stage. It is in reality an infra-ergatoid form.

26. The *gynandromorph* is an anomalous individual in which male and female characters are combined in a blended or more often in a mosaic manner (Figs. 64 and 65).

27. The *ergatandromorph* (Fig. 66) is an anomaly similar to the last but having worker instead of female characters combined with those of the male (Wheeler, 1903*b*).

It is usually conceded that the fertilization or non-fertilization of the egg of the social Hymenopteron determines whether it shall give

rise to a male or a female. And as the queen represents the typical
female form of the species, the problem of polymorphism is to account
for the various worker forms, and those like the soldiers, pseudogynes
and ergatoid females which are intermediate between the worker and
the queen. The ergatomorphic males are usually regarded as inheriting
worker characters. Thus the problem of
polymorphism centers in the development
of the worker. It must suffice in this
place to give the briefest possible statement of the views of the various authors
who have endeavored to account for the
development of this caste. These authors
may be divided into three groups:

1. Those who believe with Weismann
that the various castes are represented in
the egg by corresponding units (determinants). Fertilization is then regarded as
the stimulus which calls the female determinants into activity and meagre feeding
the stimulus which arouses the worker-
producing determinants in young larvæ
arising from fertilized eggs. Such an
explanation is obviously little more than
a restatement or "photograph" of the

Fig. 61. Workers major
and minor of *Camponotus ameri-*
canus. (Photograph by J. G.
Hubbard and Dr. O. S. Strong.)

problem. It seeks to account for the
adaptive characters of the worker forms
by natural selection acting on fortuitous
congenital variations.

2. Those who believe with Herbert Spencer that there is no such
predetermination of the various female castes, but that these are produced epigenetically by differences in the feeding of the larvæ. The
workers simply arise from larvæ that are inadequately fed but are
nevertheless able to pupate and hatch when only a part of their growth
has been completed. This is not, like the preceding view, a restatement
of the problem, since the modifications produced by inadequate feeding
are conceived as somatic and not as germinal, but it fails to explain
how the worker caste acquires its adaptive characters, unless this caste
is supposed to reproduce with sufficient frequency to transmit acquired
somatic modifications to the germ-plasm of the species.

3. A third group of investigators believes with Emery that the
germ-plasm of the social Hymenopteron is indeed implicated in the
problem, not as possessing separate sets of determinants, but as being

in a labile or sensitive condition and therefore capable of being deflected by differences in the trophic stimuli acting on the larva. According to Emery: " The peculiarities in which the workers differ from

the corresponding sexual forms are, therefore, not innate or blastogenic, but acquired, that is somatogenic. Nor are they transmitted as such, but in the form of a peculiarity of the germ-plasm that enables this substance to take different developmental paths during the ontogeny. Such a peculiarity of the germ may be compared with the hereditary predisposition to certain diseases, which like hereditary myopia, develop only under certain conditions. The eye of the congenitally myopic individual is blastogenetically predisposed to short-sightedness, but only becomes short-sighted when the accommodation apparatus of the eye has been overtaxed by continual exertion. Myopia arises, like the peculiarities of the worker ants, as a somatic affection on a blastogenic foundation.

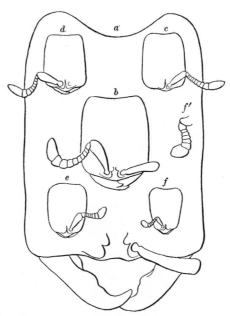

FIG. 62. Heads of workers of *Dorylus affinis* drawn to same scale to show differences in size and in number of antennal joints. (Emery.) *a*, Soldier, or worker maxima, 11 mm. long; *b*, worker major 5 mm. long; *c*, worker minima with 11-jointed antennæ; *d*, worker minima with 10-jointed antennæ; *e*, with 9-jointed antennæ, *f*, with 8-jointed antennæ: *f'*, antenna of same enlarged.

" With this assumption the problem of the development of workers seems to me to become more intelligible and to be brought a step nearer its solution. The peculiarities of the Hymenopteran workers are laid down in every female egg; those of the termite workers in every egg of either sex, but they can only manifest themselves in the presence of specific vital conditions. In the phylogeny of the various species of ants the worker peculiarities are not transmitted but merely the faculty of all fertilized eggs to be reared as a single or several kinds of workers. The peculiar instinct of rearing workers is also transmitted, since it must be exercised by the fertile females in establishing their colonies."

The views above cited show very clearly that authors have

been impressed by very different aspects of the complicated phenomena of polymorphism, and that each has emphasized the aspect which seemed the most promising from the standpoint of the general evolutionary theory he happened to be defending. Escherich (1906) has recently called attention to two very different ways of envisaging the problem; one of these is physiological and ontogenic, the other ethological and phylogenetic. As these furnish convenient captions under which to continue the discussion of the subject, I shall adopt them, and conclude with a third, the psychological aspect, which is certainly of sufficient importance to deserve consideration.

While the ontogeny of nearly all animals is a repetition or reproduction of the parent, this is usually not the case in the social Hymenoptera, since the majority of the fertilized eggs do not give rise to

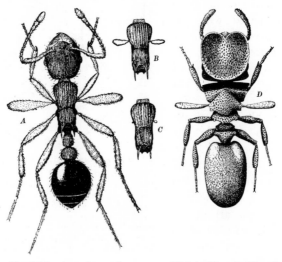

Fig. 63. Vestigial wings in worker ants. (Original.) *A, Myrmica scabrinodis* var., with spatulate wing vestiges on mesothorax; *B,* and *C,* Thoraces of two other individuals from the same colony, showing a more vestigial development of the wings; *D,* Soldier of *Cryptocerus aztecus* with mesothorácic wing vestiges.

queens but to more or less aberrant organisms, the workers. And as these do not, as a rule, reproduce, the whole phenomenon is calculated to arouse the interest of both the physiologist and the embryologist. The former, concentrating his attention on the reactions of the animal to the stimuli proceeding from its environment, is inclined to study its later stages as determined by the reactions to such stimuli, without regard to any internal or hereditary predetermination or disposition, while the embryologist seeks out the earliest moment at which the organism may be shown to deviate from the ontogenetic pattern of its parent. If this moment can be detected very early in the development he will be inclined to project the morphological differentiation back into the germ-plasm and to regard the efforts of the physiologist as relatively unimportant if not altogether futile. Now in his study of the social insects the embryologist is at a serious disadvantage, since he has hitherto been unable to distinguish any prospective worker or queen characters in the eggs or even in the young larvæ. Compelled, therefore, to confine his attention to the older larvæ, whose development as mere processes of histogenesis and metamorphosis throws little or no light on the meaning of polymorphism, he is bound to leave the physiologist in possession of the problem.

The physiologist, in seeking to determine whether there is in the environment of the developing social Hymenopteron any normal

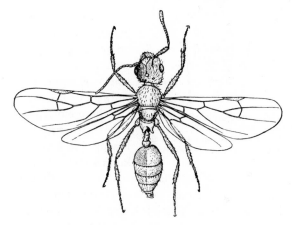

Fig. 64. Gynandromorph of *Epipheidole inquilina;* male on the left, female on the right side. (Original.)

stimulus that may account for the deviation towards the worker or queen type, can hardly overlook one of the most important of all stimuli, the food of the larva. At first sight this bids fair greatly to simplify the problem of polymorphism, for the mere size of the adult insect would seem to be attributable to the quantity, its morphological deviations to the quality of the food administered to it during its larval life. Closer examination of the subject, however, cannot fail to show that larval alimentation among such highly specialized animals as the social insects, and especially in the honey-bees and ants, where the differences between the queens and workers are most salient, is a matter of considerable complexity. In the first place, it is evident that it is not the food administered that acts as a stimulus but the portion of it that is assimilated by the living tissues of the larva. In other words, the larva is not altogether a passive organism, compelled to utilize all the food that is forced upon it, but an active agent, at least to a considerable extent, in determining its own development. And the physiologist might have difficulty in meeting the assertion that the larva utilizes only those portions of the proffered food that are most conducive to the specific, prede-termined trend of its development. In the second place, while experi-ments on many organisms have shown that the quantity of as-similated food may produce great changes in size and stature, there is practically nothing to show that even very great differences in the quality of the food can bring about morphological differ-ences of such magnitude as those which separate the queens and workers of many ants.

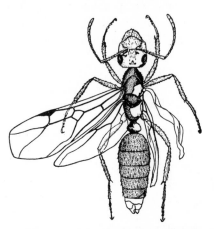

FIG. 65. Gynandromorph of *Formica microgyna;* head almost purely female, gaster male, thorax, petiole and legs male on left, female on right side. (Original.)

These more general consider-ations are reinforced by the fol-lowing inferences from the known facts of larval feeding:

1. There seems to be no valid reason for supposing that the mor-phogeny of the queens among the social Hymenoptera depends on a particular diet, since with the possible exception of the honey- and sting-less bees, to be considered presently, they differ in no essential respect from the corresponding sexual phase of the solitary species. In both cases they are the normal females of the species and bear the same morphological relations to their males quite irrespective of the nature of their larval food. Hence, with the above mentioned exception of the honey- and stingless bees, the question of the morphogenic value of the larval food may be restricted to the worker forms.

2. Observations show that although the nature of the food admin-istered to the larvæ of the various social insects is often very different, even in closely related species, the structure of the workers may be extremely uniform and exhibit only slight specific differences. Among ants, as we have seen (p. 74), the larvæ are fed with a great variety of substances. The quality of the food itself cannot, therefore, be supposed to have a morphogenic value. And even if we admit what seems to be very probable, namely, that a salivary secretion—possibly

containing an enzyme—may be administered by some ants, at least to their younger larvæ, the case against the morphogenic effects of qualitative feeding is not materially altered, as we see from the following considerations:

3. In incipient ant-colonies the queen mother takes no food often for as long a period as eight or nine months, and during all this time is compelled to feed her first brood of larvæ exclusively on the secretions of her salivary glands. This diet, which is purely qualitative, though very limited in quantity, produces only workers and these of an unusually small size (micrergates).

4. In the honey-bees, on the other hand, qualitative feeding, namely with a secretion, the so-called " royal jelly," which according to some authors (Schiemenz) is derived from the salivary glands, according to others (Planta) from the chylific stomach of the nurses, does not produce workers, but queens. In this case, however, the food is administered in considerable quantity, and is not provided by a single starving mother, as in the case of the ants, but by a host of vigorous and well-fed nurses. Although it has been taken for granted that the fertilized honey-bee becomes a queen as the result of this peculiar diet, the matter appears in a different light when it is considered in connection with von Ihering's recent observations on the stingless bees (Meliponidæ) of South America (1903). He has shown that in the species of *Melipona* the cells in which the males, queens and workers are reared are all of the same size. These cells are provisioned with the same kind of food (honey and pollen) and an egg is laid in each of them. Thereupon they are sealed up, and although the larvæ are not fed from day to day, as in the honey-bees, but like those of the solitary bees subsist on stored provisions, this uniform treatment nevertheless results in the production of three sharply differentiated castes. On hatching the queen *Melipona* has very small ovaries with immature eggs, but in the allied genus *Trigona,* the species of which differ from the *Melipona* in constructing large queen cells and in storing them with a greater quantity of honey and pollen, the queen hatches with her ovaries full of ripe eggs. These facts indicate that the large size of the queen cell and its greater store of provisions are merely adaptations for accelerating the development of the ovaries. Now on reverting to the honey-bee we may adopt a similar explanation for the feeding of the queen larva with a special secretion like the "royal jelly." As is well known, the queen honey-bee hatches in about sixteen days from the time the egg is laid, while the worker, though a smaller insect and possessing imperfect ovaries, requires four or five days more to complete her development. That the special feeding of the

queen larva is merely an adaptation for accelerating the development of the ovaries is also indicated by the fact that this insect is able to lay within ten days from the date of hatching. If this interpretation is correct, the qualitative feeding of the queen larva is not primarily a morphogenic but a growth stimulus.

5. The grossly mechanical withdrawal, by parasites like *Orasema* (see p. 418), of food substances already assimilated by the larva, produces changes of the same kind as those which distinguish the worker ant from the queen, *i. e.,* microcephaly, microphthalmy, stenonoty and aptery.

This case is of unusual interest because the semipupa, after the detachment of the parasite, seems to undergo a kind of regeneration and produces a small but harmonious whole out of the depleted formative substances at its disposal. What is certainly a female or soldier semipupa takes on worker characters while the worker semipupa may be said to become infraergatoid as the result of the sudden loss of the formative substances. These observations clearly indicate that the normal worker traits may be the result of starvation or withholding of food rather than the administration of a particular diet.

6. The pseudogynes of *Formica* admit of a similar interpretation if it be true, as I am inclined to believe (see p. 408), that they arise from starved female larvæ. Here too, the organism undergoes a kind of regeneration or regulation and assumes the worker aspect owing to a dearth of sufficient formative substances with which to complete the development as originally planned.

FIG. 66. Ergatandromorph of *Aphænogaster picea;* male on left, worker on right side. (Original.)

7. In the preceding cases the ants take on peculiar structural modifications as the result of tolerating parasites that bring about unusual perturbations in the trophic status of the colony. When ants themselves become parasitic on other ants a similar perturbation ensues, but in these cases the morphological effects are confined to the parasitic species and do not extend to their hosts. This must be attributed to the fact that the parasitic species live in affluence and are no longer required to take part in the arduous and exacting labors of the colony. Under such circumstances the inhibitory effects of nutricial castration on the development of the ovaries of the workers are removed and there is a tendency for this caste to be replaced by egg-laying gynæcoid individuals or by ergatogynes, or for it to disappear

completely. These effects are clearly visible in nearly all parasitic ants. In the European *Harpagoxenus sublevis,* for example, the only known females in certain localities are gynæcoid workers. In the American *Leptothorax emersoni,* as I have shown (1903*f*), gynæcoid workers and ergatogynes are unusually abundant, while the true females seem to be on the verge of disappearing. Among the typical amazon ants (*Polyergus rufescens*) of Europe, ergatogynes are not uncommon. In *Strongylognathus testaceus* the worker caste seems to be dwindling, while in several permanently parasitic genera (*Anergates, Wheeleriella, Epœcus, Epipheidole* and *Sympheidole*) it has completely disappeared. Only one cause can be assigned to these remarkable effects—the abundance of food with which the parasites are provided by their hosts.

8. In the Ponerinæ and certain Myrmicinæ, like *Pheidole, Pogonomyrmex* and *Aphænogaster,* the larvæ are fed on pieces of insects or seeds, the exact assimilative value of which as food can neither be determined nor controlled by the nurses. And while they may perhaps regulate the quantity of food administered, it is more probable that this must fluctuate within limits so wide and indefinite as to fail altogether to account for the uniform and precise morphological results that we witness in the personnel of the various colonies (Fig. 51). Moreover, accurate determination of the food supply by the workers must be quite impossible in cases like that of the *Pachycondyla* larva bearing the commensal *Metopina* (see p. 412).

9. The dependence of the different castes of the social insects on the seasons may also be adduced as evidence of the direct effects of the food supply in producing workers and queens. The latter are reared only when the trophic condition of the colony is most favorable, and this coincides with the summer months; in the great majority of species only workers and males are produced at other seasons. Here, too, the cause is to be sought in the deficient quantity of food rather than in its quality, which is in all probability the same throughout the year, especially in such ants as the fungus-growing Attii.

While these considerations tend to invalidate the supposition that qualitative feeding is responsible for the morphological peculiarities of the worker type, they are less equivocal in regard to the morphogenic effects of quantitative feeding. Indeed several of the observations above cited show very clearly that diminution in stature and, in pathological cases, even reversion to the worker form may be the direct effect of underfeeding. To the same cause we may confidently assign several of the atypical phases among ants, such as the micrergates, microgynes, and micranērs, just as we may regard the macrergates, macrogynes, and macranērs as due to overfeeding. These are, of course, cases of nanism and giantism, variations in stature, not in form. Similarly, all cases in which, as in certain species of *Formica, Campo-notus, Pheidole,* etc., the workers or desmergates vary in size, must be regarded as the result of variable quantitative feeding in the larval stage. Here we are confronted with the same conditions as Weismann observed in prematurely pupating blow-flies, and entomologists have noticed in many other insects. Such variations are of the fluctuating type and are therefore attributable to the direct effects of the environment. The soldier and worker, however, differ from the queen in the absence of certain characters, like the wings, wing-muscles, spermatheca, some of the ovarian tubules, etc., and the presence of other characters, like the peculiar shape of the head and mandibles. In these respects the sterile castes may be regarded as mutants, and Weismann's contention that such characters cannot be produced by external conditions, such as feeding, is in full accord with de Vries's hypothesis. His further contention, however, that they must therefore be produced by natural selection need not detain us, since it is daily becoming more and more evident that this is not a creative but an eliminative principle. It is certain that very plastic insects, like the ants, have developed a type of ontogeny which enables them, not only to pupate at an extremely early period of larval life, but also to hatch and survive as useful though highly specialized members of the colony. It is quite conceivable that this precocious pupation may be directly responsible for the complete suppression of certain organs that require for their formation more substance than the underfed larva is able to accumulate. At the same time it must be admitted that a direct causal connection between underfeeding on the one hand and the ontogenetic loss or development of characters on the other hand, has not been satisfactorily established. The conditions in the termites, which are often cited as furnishing proof of this connection, are even more complicated and obscure than those of the social Hymenoptera. While Grassi and Sandias (1893) and Silvestri (1901) agree with Spencer in regarding feeding as the direct cause of the production of the various castes, Herbst (1901), who has reviewed the work of the former authors, shows that their observations are by no means conclusive; and Heath (1902) makes the following statement in regard to his experiments on Californian termites: "For months I have fed a large number of termite colonies of all ages, with or without royal pairs, on various kinds and amounts of foods—proctodæal food dissected from the workers or in other cases from royal forms, stomadæal food from the same sources, sawdust to which different nutritious ingredients have been added—

but in spite of all I cannot feel perfectly sure that I have influenced in any unusual way the growth of a single individual."

This rather unsatisfactory answer to the question as to whether quantity or quality of food or both, have an ergatogenic value, has led some investigators to seek a solution along more direct lines. Thus O. Hertwig and Herbst suggest that the morphogenic stimulus may be furnished by some internal secretion of the reproductive organs. This, too, is possible, but owing to our very imperfect knowledge of the internal secretions, even in the higher animals, we are not in a position either to accept or reject this suggestion.

We may conclude, therefore, that while the conception of the worker phase as the result of imperfect nutrition is supported by a considerable volume of evidence, we are still unable to understand how this result can take on so highly adaptive a character. Such a concise effect can hardly be due to manifold and fluctuating external causes like nutrition, but must proceed from some more deeply seated cause within the organism itself. Of course, the difficulty here encountered is by no means peculiar to polymorphism; it confronts us at every turn as the all-pervading enigma of living matter.

CHAPTER VII

POLYMORPHISM (CONCLUDED)

"La conservation de ces animaux et la prospérité de leur famille ne pouvoient donc être assurées que par l'établissement d'un ordre particulier et nombreux d'individus qui suppléassent aux fonctions des mères et qui n'en eussent même que les sentimens et les affections. La nature, en formant ici des neutres, s'est vue contrainte de s'écarter de ses lois ordinaires, pour que son ouvrage subsistât, et sa prévoyance a modifié ses ressources selon les circonstances où les êtres devoient être placés."—Latreille, "Considerations Nouvelles et Générales sur les Insectes Vivant en Société," 1817.

An extensive study of the structure and habits of ants must inevitably lead to a certain amount of speculation concerning the phylogenetic development of their colonies. That these insects have had communistic habits for ages is clearly indicated by the fact that all of the numerous existing species are eminently social. There can be little doubt, however, that they arose from forms with habits not unlike those we find to-day in some of the solitary wasps, such as the Bembecidæ, or in the remarkable South African bees of the genus *Allodape*. Unlike other solitary wasps, the females of *Bembex* may be said to be incipiently social, since a number of them choose a nesting site and, though each has her own burrow, coöperate with one another in driving away intruders. *Bembex* has also taken an important step in the direction of the social wasps not only in surviving the hatching of her larvæ, but also in visiting them from day to day for the purpose of providing them with fresh insect food.

At a very early period the ants and social wasps must have made a further advance when the mother insect succeeded in surviving till after her progeny had completed their development. This seems to have led naturally to a stage in which the young females remained with their mother and reared their progeny in the parental nest, thus constituting a colony of a number of similar females with a common and indiscriminate interest in the brood. This colony, after growing to a certain size, became unstable in the same way as any aggregate of like units, and must soon have shown a differentiation of its members into two classes, one comprising individuals devoted to reproduction and another devoted to alimentation and protection. In this division of labor only the latter class underwent important somatic modification and specialization, while the former retained its primitive and more generalized characters. It is more than probable, as I shall attempt to show in the sequel, that this differentiation was manifested in the sphere of instinct long before it assumed morphological expression. The social wasps and bumble-bees are still in this stage of sociogeny. The ants, however, have specialized and refined on these conditions till they have not only a single marked alimentative and protective caste without wings and lacking many other female characters, but in some species two distinct castes with a corresponding further division of labor. In the phylogeny as well as the ontogeny these characters appear as a result of nutricial castration.[1]

If the foregoing considerations be granted the biogenetic law may be said to hold good in the sociogeny of the ants, for the actual ontogenetic development of their colonies conforms not only to the purely conjectural requirements of phylogeny but also to the stages represented by the various extant groups of social insects. It is clear that we cannot include the honey-bee among these groups, since this insect is demonstrably so aberrant that it is difficult to compare it with the other social insects.

Comparison of the different genera and subfamilies of ants among themselves shows that some of them have retained a very primitive social organization, and with it a relatively incomplete polymorphism, whereas others have a much more highly developed social life and a greater differentiation of the castes. Such a comparison, coupled with a study of the natural relationships of the various genera as displayed in structure, shows very clearly that the advance from generalized to highly specialized societies did not follow a single upward course during the phylogeny, but occurred repeatedly and in different phyletic groups. And since the complications of polymorphism keep pace with those of social organization, we may say that the differentiation of the originally single worker caste into dinergates, or soldiers on the one

---

[1] "Nutricial castration" (from *nutrix*, a nurse), as understood by Marchal, must be distinguished from "alimentary castration" (Emery, 1896*k*), although both are responsible for the infertility of the worker. Through alimentary castration the development of the reproductive organs is inhibited in the larva and pupa, and this inhibition is maintained in the adult by the strong nursing instincts which prevent the workers from appropriating much of the food supply of the colony to their individual use. In many of the higher animals also (birds, mammals) reproduction is inhibited by the exercise of the nutricial function. A third method of inhibiting or destroying the reproductive function is known to occur in the "parasitic castration" of certain bees and wasps (*Andrena, Polistes*) by Strepsiptera (*Stylops, Xenos,* etc.). See Pérez, "Des Effects du Parasitisme des Stylops sur les Apiaires du Genre Andrena," *Actes Soc. Linn. Bordeaux,* 1886, 40 pp., 2 pls. Westwood has also described a Strepsipteron (*Myrmecolax nietneri*) which, in all probability, produces this form of castration in certain Formicidæ (1861).

hand, and micrergates, or small workers, on the other, has been several times repeated in remotely related genera. In some genera (*Stenamma sens. str., Leptothorax*) there are also indications of a lapsing of highly specialized into simpler conditions by a kind of social degeneration. In its extreme form this manifests itself as a suppression of castes and a consequent simplification of polymorphism. Beautiful examples of this condition are furnished by the parasitic species that have lost their worker caste. But there are also cases in which the queen caste has been suppressed and its functions usurped by workers.

Not only have these greater changes been effected and fixed during the phylogenetic history of the Formicidæ, but also many subtler differences such as those of stature, coloration, pilosity and sculpture. And although such differences belong to the class of fluctuating variations and are usually supposed to have a greater ontogenetic than phylogenetic significance, they are undoubtedly of great antiquity and must therefore be regarded as more important than many of the minor morphological traits.

Emery was the first to call attention to a number of peculiar phylogenetic stages in the development of stature among ants (1894*d*). We find by comparison with the male, which may be regarded as a relatively stable and conservative form, that the cospecific females and workers may vary in stature independently of each other. The following are the stages recognized by Emery, with some additions of my own:

1. In the earliest phylogenetic condition, which is still preserved in the ants of the subfamily Ponerinæ and in certain Myrmicinæ (*Pseudomyrma, Myrmecina,* etc.), the workers are monomorphic and about the same size as the males and females.

2. The worker becomes highly variable in stature from large forms (dinergates, or maxima workers) resembling the female, through a series of intermediate (desmergates, mediæ) to very small forms (minima workers, or micrergates). This condition obtains in the Dorylinæ, some Myrmicinæ (some species of *Pheidole, Pheidologeton, Atta*), Camponotinæ (*Camponotus*) and Dolichoderinæ (*Azteca*).

3. The worker becomes dimorphic through the disappearance of the desmergates, so that the originally single and highly variable caste is now represented by two, the soldier (dinergate) and worker proper. We find this condition in certain Myrmicinæ and Camponotinæ (*Cryptocerus, Pheidole, Acanthomyrmex, Colobopsis,* etc.).

4. The soldier of the preceding stage disappears completely, so that the worker caste again becomes monomorphic but is represented by individuals very much smaller than the female. Such individuals are

really micrergates. This condition is seen in certain Myrmicine genera, especially of the tribe Solenopsidii (*Carebara, Erebomyrma, Diplomorium,* most species of *Solenopsis,* etc.).

5. The worker form disappears completely leaving only the males and females to represent the species, which thus returns to the condition of sexual dimorphism seen in the great majority of insects and other Metazoa. This occurs in the parasitic ants of the genera *Anergates, Wheeleriella, Epœcus, Sympheidole* and *Epipheidole.*

6. In certain species the workers remain stationary while the female increases in size. This is indicated by the fact that the worker and male have approximately the same stature. Such a condition obtains in certain Myrmicinæ (*Cremastogaster*), Camponotinæ (*Lasius, Prenolepis, Brachymyrmex,* North American species of *Myrmecocystus*) and Dolichoderinæ (*Iridomyrmex, Dorymyrmex, Liometopum*).

7. The worker caste remains stationary while the female diminishes in size till it may become even smaller than the large workers. This occurs in certain parasitic species of North America, like *Aphænogaster tennesseensis* among the Myrmicinæ, and among the Camponotinæ in the species of the *Formica microgyna* group (*F. difficilis, nevadensis, impexa, dakotensis, nepticula*).

8. The female phase disappears completely and is replaced by a fertile, or gynæcoid worker form. This occurs in certain Ponerine genera like *Leptogenys* (including the subgenus *Lobopelta*), and probably also in *Diacamma* and *Champsomyrmex.* The conditions in *Acanthostichus* and certain Cerapachysii (*Parasyscia peringueyi*) indicate that the dichthadiigynes of the Dorylinæ may have arisen from such gynæcoid workers instead of from winged queens.

9. The female shows a differentiation into two forms (α- and β-females) characterized by differences in the structure of the legs and antennæ, in pilosity and coloration (*Lasius latipes*), or in the length of the wings (macropterous and micropterous females of *L. niger*). The macrocephalic and microcephalic females of *Camponotus abdominalis* and *confusus* described by Emery (1896k) may also be regarded as α- and β-forms.

In this series of stages, one to five represent changes in the worker caste while the female remains relatively stationary, whereas stages six to nine represent the converse conditions. Stages one to four probably succeeded one another in the order given, but stage five may have arisen either from the first or fourth. The sixth to ninth stages must, of course, be supposed to have developed independently of one another.

The stature differences described in the above paragraphs are, in most, if not all cases, highly adaptive. This is clearly seen in such forms as the Indo-African *Carebara,* the huge, deeply colored females of which are more than a thousand times as large as the diminutive, yellow workers. This ant dwells in termite nests where it occupies chambers connected by means of tenuous galleries with the spacious apartments of its host. The termites constitute a supply of food so accessible and abundant that the workers are able to rear enormous males and females, while they themselves must preserve their diminutive stature in adaptation to their clandestine and thievish habits. Similar conditions are found in many species of the allied genus *Solenopsis,* which inhabit delicate galleries communicating with the nests of other ants on the larvæ and pupæ of which they feed. In one species of this genus (*S. geminata*), however, which leads an independent life and feeds on miscellaneous insects and seeds, the worker caste is still highly polymorphic.

Another interesting case of adaptation in stature is seen in the ants of the *Formica microgyna* group. The females of these species are temporarily parasitic in the nests of other *Formicæ* and are therefore relieved of the labor of digging nests for themselves and rearing their first brood of larvæ. On this account they need not store up large quantities of food, so that the nourishment which in non-parasitic species goes to produce a comparatively few large females may be applied to the production of a large number of small females. This latter condition is necessary in parasitic species which are decimated by many vicissitudes before they can establish themselves successfully among alien hosts. I have already emphasized the adaptive significance of the disappearance of the worker caste among permanently parasitic species like *Anergates, Wheeleriella,* etc.

There are several cases in which the worker and female differ greatly in color, pilosity or sculpture, and in such cases either caste may be conservative or aberrant according to ethological requirements. Thus in certain temporary parasites like *Formica ciliata, oreas, crinita, specularis* and *difficilis,* the female is aberrant in one or more of the characters mentioned, while the cospecific worker retains the ancestral characters of its caste in the closely allied forms of *F. rufa.* The same condition is seen in a very different ant, *Aphænogaster tennesseensis,* as the result of similar parasitic habits. In all of these species the females alone have developed myrmecophilous characters, like the long yellow hairs of *F. ciliata,* or the mimetic coloring of *F. difficilis,* which enable them to foist themselves on the allied species and thus avoid the exhausting labor of excavating nests and rearing workers.

The foregoing observations indicate that in morphological characters the worker and female of the same species have advanced or
digressed in their phylogeny, remained stationary or retrograded,
independently of each other. The same peculiarity is also observable in
species with distinct worker and soldier castes. It thus becomes impossible, even in closely related species of certain genera, like *Pheidole,* to predict the characters of the worker from a study of the cospecific soldier or *vice versâ.* And while adaptive characters in stature, sculpture, pilosity and color must depend for their ontogenetic
development on the nourishment of the larvæ, it is equally certain that
they have been acquired and fixed during the phylogeny of the species.
In other words, nourishment, temperature, and other environmental
factors merely furnish the conditions for the attainment of characters
predetermined by heredity. We are therefore compelled to agree with
Weismann that the characters that enable us to differentiate the castes
must be somehow represented in the egg. We may grant this, however,
without accepting his conception of representative units, a conception
which has been so often refuted that it is unnecessary to reconsider it in
this connection.

Having touched on this broader problem of heredity it will be necessary to say something about the inheritance or non-inheritance of
acquired characters, especially as Weismann and his followers regard
the social insects as demonstrating the non-transmissibility of somatogenic traits. In establishing this view and the all-sufficiency of natural
selection to which it leads, Weismann seems to have slurred over the
facts. While he admits that the workers may lay eggs, and that these
may produce male offspring capable of fertilizing females, he nevertheless insists that this is altogether too infrequent to influence the
germ-plasm of the species. I venture to maintain, on the contrary,
that fertile workers occur much more frequently in all groups of social
insects than has been generally supposed. As this fertility is merely a
physiological state it has been overlooked. Marchal has shown how
readily the workers of the social wasps assume this state, and the
same is true of the honey-bees, especially of certain races like the
" Egyptians " and " Cyprians " (*Apis mellifica-fasciata* and *cypria*).
In the hives of these insects fertile workers are either always present
or make their appearance within a few days after the removal of the
queen. In the termites fertile soldiers have been observed by Grassi
and Sandias and fertile workers by Silvestri. Among ants fertile
or gynæcoid workers occur so frequently as to lead to the belief that
they must be present in all populous colonies. Their presence is also
proved by the production of considerable numbers of males in old

and queenless colonies. In artificial nests Wasmann, Miss Fielde and myself have found egg-laying workers in abundance.

Now as the males that develop from worker eggs are perfectly normal, and in all probability as capable of mating as those derived from the eggs of queens, we are bound to conclude, especially if we adopt the theory of heredity advocated by Weismann himself, that the characters of the mother (in this case the worker) may secure representation in the germ-plasm of the species. Weismann is hardly consistent in denying the probability of such representation, for when he is bent on elaborating the imaginary structure of the germ-plasm he makes this substance singularly retentive of alteration by amphimixis, but when he is looking for facts to support the all-sufficiency of natural selection the germ-plasm becomes remarkably difficult of modification by anything except this eliminative factor. Certainly the simplest and directest method of securing a representation of the worker characters in the germ-plasm would be to get them from the worker itself that has survived in the struggle for existence, rather than through the action of natural selection on fortuitous constellations of determinants in the germ-plasm of the queen. If we grant the possibility of a periodical influx of worker germ-plasm into that of the species, the transmission of characters acquired by this caste is no more impossible than it is in other animals, and the social insects should no longer be cited as furnishing conclusive proof of Weismannism.

Plate has attempted to overcome the difficulties presented by the normal sterility of the worker by supposing that the distinguishing characters of this caste arose prior to their inability to reproduce. He recognizes the following stages in the phylogeny of the social insects:

" 1. The presocial stage with but a single kind of male and female.

" 2. The social stage with but a single kind of male and female. The peculiarities in nesting, caring for the brood, and other instincts were already developed during this stage.

" 3. The social stage with one kind of male and two or several kinds of females, which were all fertile, but in consequence of the physiological division of labor became more and more different in the course of generations. The division of labor took place in such a manner that the sexual functions passed over primarily to a group A, while the construction of the nest, predatory expeditions and other duties devolved mainly on another group of individuals (B), which on that account used their reproductive organs less and less.

" 4. The present stage with one kind of male, a fertile form of female, which arose from group A, and one or several kinds of sterile females, or workers (group B)."

Plate assumes that the differentiation into sterile and fertile forms did not take place until stage 3, and if I understand him correctly, not till after " the races had become differentiated morphologically." This view, as he admits, resembles Spencer's (p. 100). The two views, in fact, differ merely in degree, for the underlying contention is the same, namely that sterility is one of the most recently developed characters among the social insects. There can be little doubt, however, that the smaller adaptive characters, for example those of the families of certain species of *Formica* above mentioned, must have made their appearance in the fourth stage of Plate's scheme. The view which I have advocated differs from Plate's in admitting that even in this stage the workers are fertile with sufficient frequency to maintain a representation of their characters in the germ-plasm of the species. Conclusive evidence of the presence or absence of such representation can be secured only by experimental breeding, and especially by hybridizing the male off-spring of workers of one species (*a*), with females of another (*b*) that has workers of a different character.

In the foregoing discussion attention has been repeatedly called to adaptation as the insurmountable obstacle to our every endeavor to explain polymorphism in current physiological terms. Of course, this is by no means a peculiarity of polymorphism, for the same difficulty confronts us in every biological inquiry. As the type of polymorphism with which we are dealing has been developed by psychically highly endowed social insects, it cannot be adequately understood as a mere morphological and physiological manifestation apart from the study of instinct. This has been more or less clearly perceived by nearly all writers on the subject. However various their explanations, Spencer, Weismann, Emery, Forel, Marchal and Plate all resort to instinct. Emery especially has seen very clearly that a worker type with its peculiar and aberrant characteristics could not have been developed except by means of a worker-producing instinct. In other words, this type is the result of a living environment consisting of the fostering queen and workers which instinctively control the development of the young in so far as this depends on external factors. Only under such conditions could a worker caste arise and repeat itself generation after generation. This caste may be regarded as a mutation comparable with some of De Vries's *Œnothera* mutations, but able to repeat and maintain itself for an indefinite series of generations in perfect symbiosis with its parent form, the queen, because, notwithstanding its relative infertility, it can be put to very important social use. Among ants this social use not only pervades the activities of the adult worker but extends even to the more inert larval stages. Thus the latter represent a rich and ever-fresh supply of food that can be devoured whenever a temporary famine overtakes the colony. In certain species, like the East Indian *Œcophylla smaragdina* and the South American *Camponotus senex,* the larvæ are more humanely employed as spinning machines for constructing the silken nest inhabited by the colony (see p. 216). These examples also illustrate the purposive manner in which an organism can satisfy definite needs by taking advantage of ever-present opportunities.

In the lives of the social insects the threptic, or philoprogenitive instincts are of such transcendent importance that all the other instincts of the species, including, of course, those of alimentation and nest-building, become merely tributary or ancillary. In ants, especially, the instincts relating to the nurture of the young bear the aspect of a dominating obsession. Their very strength and scope render the insects more susceptible to the inroads of a host of guests, commensals and parasites. Besides the parasitic larvæ of Chalcidids, Lomechusini and *Metopina,* to be described in Chapter XXII, there are many adult beetles and other insects on which the ants lavish as much attention as they do on their own brood. And when the ants themselves become parasitic on other ants, it is always either for the sake of having their own brood nurtured, as in the temporarily and permanently parasitic forms, or for the purpose of securing the brood of another species, as in the slave-making species.

The philoprogenitive instincts arose and were highly developed among the solitary ancestral insects long before social life made its appearance. In fact, social life is itself merely an extension of these instincts to the adult offspring, and there can be no doubt that once developed it reacted rapidly and powerfully in perfecting these same instincts. It is not so much the fact that all these activities of the social insects converge towards and center in the reproduction of the species, for this is the case with all organisms, as the elaborate living environment developed for the nurture of the young, that gives these insects their unique position among the lower animals. A full analysis of the threptic instincts would involve a study of the entire ethology of the social insects and cannot be undertaken at the present time. Nevertheless the bearing of these activities on the subject of polymorphism can hardly be overestimated and deserves to be emphasized in this connection.

All writers agree in ascribing polymorphism to a physiological division of labor among originally similar organisms. This is tantamount to the assumption that the phylogenetic differentiation of the castes arose in the sphere of function before it manifested itself in structural peculiarities. Although this view implies that the female, or queen was the source from which the instincts and structures of the worker were derived, it has been obscured by an improper emphasis on the instincts of the honey-bee, in which the female is clearly a degenerate organism, and on certain specialized instincts, supposed to belong exclusively to worker ants like those of the slave-makers (*Polyergus* and *Formica sanguinea*). We have therefore to consider first the instincts of the queen, and second, any evidence that may go to show that instinct-changes precede morphological differentiation in the phylogeny of the species.

It is evident that the social insects may be divided into two groups according to the instinct rôle of the queen. In one group, embracing the social wasps, bumble-bees, ants and termites, the female is the complete prototype of her sex. Even the queen of the slave-making ants, manifests in the founding of her colonies all the threptic instincts once supposed to be the exclusive prerogative of the worker caste. These may be called the primary instincts. After the colony is established, however, and she no longer needs to manifest these instincts, she becomes a mere egg-laying machine and her instincts undergo a corresponding change and may now be designated as secondary. She thus passes through a gamut of instincts successively called into activity by a series of stimuli which in turn arise in a definite order from her changing social environment. The workers, however, are capable of repeating only a portion of the female gamut, the primary series. In gynæcoid individuals there is also a tendency to take up the secondary series, but in most workers this has been suppressed by countless generations of nutricial castration. The social insects of this type may be called *gynæcotelic,* to indicate that the female preserves intact the full series of sexual attributes inherited from her solitary ancestors. In these the primary and secondary series are simultaneous or overlap completely, in the gynæcotelic social insects they are extended over a longer period of time and overlap only in part, as social life permits the extension of the secondary long after the primary series has lapsed into desuetude. It will be seen that the division of labor which led to the special differentiation of like females into workers and queens is clearly foreshadowed in the consecutive differentiation of instincts in the individual queen. The second group of social insects is represented by the honey-bees and probably also by the stingless bees (Meliponidæ). In these only the secondary instincts are manifested in the queen, while the worker retains the primary series in full vigor and thus more clearly represents the ancestral female of the species. This type may therefore be called *ergatotelic*. The suppression of the primary instincts in the queen honey-bee was undoubtedly brought about by the change in the method of colony formation. When the habit of swarming superseded the establishment of colonies by solitary queens, as still practiced by the gynæcotelic insects, the primary instincts of the female lapsed into abeyance or became latent. This change took place so long ago that it has had time to express itself in the structure of the queen honey-bee as compared with the worker (shorter tongue and wings, feebler sting, degenerate structure of hind legs, etc.).

The first of the following examples, which seem to indicate the occurrence of instinctive prior to morphological differentiation, shows at the same time how the ergatotelic type of the honey-bee may have arisen from the gynæcotelic type of the social wasps and bumble-bees.

1. The queens of certain species of *Formica* (*F. rufa, exsectoides,* etc.), are no longer able to establish colonies without the coöperation of workers. The common method of colony formation among these insects is by a process of swarming like that of the honey-bees: a certain portion of the colony emigrates and founds a new nest with one or more queens. When this method is impracticable the young queen seeks the assistance of an allied species of *Formica* (*F. fusca*), the workers of which are willing to take the place of her own species in rearing her brood. In *F. rufa* and *exsectoides* there is nothing in the stature or structure of the queen to indicate the presence of these parasitic instincts, but, in many of the allied species like *F. ciliata, microgyna,* etc., the colonies of which are smaller and no longer swarm, or do so only to a very limited extent, the queens have become more dependent on the workers of other species of *Formica* and have developed mimetic characters or a dwarf stature to enable them to enter and exploit the colonies of their hosts.

2. In many ants the callows, or just hatched workers, confine themselves to caring for the larvæ and pupæ and do not exhibit the foraging instincts till a later period. But even adult workers may perform a single duty in the colony for long periods of time, if not indefinitely. Thus Lubbock (1894) and Viehmeyer (1904) have observed in certain *Formica* colonies that only certain individuals forage for the community. The latter has also noticed that certain individuals, indistinguishable morphologically from their sister workers, stand guard at the entrances. In other genera, like *Camponotus, Atta, Pheidole,* etc., with species that have desmergates, the morphological differentiation between foragers and guardians is still unsettled. It becomes com-

pletely established, however, in certain genera and species with the suppression of the desmergates. A remarkable example of division of labor, without corresponding structural differentiation, is seen also in the *Œcophylla* above mentioned, an ant which inhabits nests of leaves sewn together with fine silk. According to the observations of Dodd (1902) and Doflein (1905), when the nests are torn apart the monomorphic workers separate into two companies, one of which stations itself on the outside of the nest, draws the separated leaves together and holds them in place with the claws and mandibles, while the other moves the spinning larvæ back and forth within the nest till the rent is repaired with silken tissue (see p. 216).

3. An interesting case is presented by the honey-ants (*Myrmecocystus melliger* and *mexicanus*). All the workers of these species, though variable in size, are structurally alike. Among the callows, however, and quite independently of their stature, certain individuals take to storing liquid food, as I have found in my artificial nests of the latter species, and gradually, in the course of a month or six weeks, become repletes, or plerergates. Except for this physiological peculiarity, which gradually takes on a morphological expression, the plerergates and ordinary workers are indistinguishable. We must assume, therefore, that the desire to store food represents an instinct specialization peculiar to a portion of the callow workers. There can be no doubt that as our knowledge of the habits of ants progresses many other cases like the foregoing will be brought to light.

It may be maintained that in these cases physiological states must precede the manifestation of the instincts, and that these states, however inscrutable they may be, are to be conceived as structural differentiations. There is undoubtedly much to justify this point of view. The elaborate sequence of instincts in the queen ant, for example, is accompanied by a series of physiological changes so profound as to be macroscopical. After the loss of her wings, the wing muscles degenerate and the fat-body melts away to furnish nourishment for the ovaries, which in the old queen become enormously distended with eggs as the breeding season approaches. Such changes would seem to be amply sufficient to account for the changing instincts. I have found that mere artificial deälation at once alters the instincts of the queen, probably through a stimulus analogous to that which leads to the atrophy of a muscle when its nerve is severed, and in the case under consideration leads to the degeneration of the wing-muscles and to changes in the ovaries. In the mermithergates and pseudogynes we also have peculiarities of behavior which are attributable to peculiar physiological states.   Similarly, nutricial castration may be said to be a physiological state, namely that of hunger.

We may conclude therefore that the worker, both in its ontogenetic and phylogenetic development, is through and through a hunger-form, inured to protracted fasting.   Miss Fielde has shown (1904f) that the workers of *Camponotus americanus* may live nearly nine months without food, which is as long as the much larger and more vigorous queens are known to fast while establishing their colonies.   The larvæ of ants, too, are known to remain alive in the nests for months without growing.   And even when food is abundant the workers appropriate very little of it to their individual maintenance, but distribute it freely among their sister workers, the brood and queen.   It is not improbable, moreover, that the single instinct peculiar to workers, the instinct to leave the nest and forage, is the direct result of a chronic state of hunger.

CHAPTER VIII

THE HISTORY OF MYRMECOLOGY AND THE CLASSIFICATION OF ANTS

" Les mœurs des fourmis sont si variées qu'il est important de connoître à quelle espèce se rapporte chaque trait d'industrie, chaque particularité de leur histoire."—P. Huber, " Recherches sur les Mœurs des Fourmis Indigènes," 1810.

Myrmecology has been more fortunate than many other branches of entomology in the men who have contributed to its development. These have been actuated, almost without exception, not by a mania for endless multiplication of genera and species, but by a temperate and philosophical interest in the increase of our knowledge. The reason for this fortunate circumstance is probably to be sought in the *ingenium formicæ male habitat,* the fact that ants are small, homely organisms with nothing to attract the amateur who cares only for size and beauty of form and color. This is, perhaps, regrettable as it has

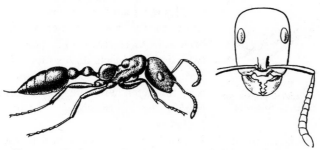

Fig. 67. Worker of *Sima allaborans* of India. (Bingham.)

certainly retarded the accumulation of study materials in our museums and private collections, and has left the subject in the hands of a few devotees. But this disadvantage is not so great as might be supposed, because the species of ants, though far less numerous than those of butterflies and beetles, are nevertheless more abundant in individuals and hence more easily obtained. Undoubtedly the great difficulty of the study has had much to do with limiting the number of myrmecologists, especially in America. Here the literature of descriptive myrmecology, which is widely scattered through somewhat obscure serials and is written very largely in the German, French and Italian languages, has remained quite inaccessible to the average student. Even a knowledge of the literature, however, does not overcome all of the difficulties of the subject, for the species of ants often differ from one another by characters too subtle and intangible to be readily put in words. The "habitus" of a species, as every taxonomist knows, is something one may take in at a glance, but be quite unable to express without wearisome prolixity. Hence the importance of large collections, thoroughly studied and identified and accessible to every student. Such collections have been lacking in America and those interested in ants have had to send their specimens abroad for identification. This is time-consuming, to say nothing of the inconvenience to which it often puts the overworked specialist.

Ants, like other organisms, may be studied from at least three different points of view, according as the observer is most interested in their classification, or taxonomy (including geographical distribution), their morphology (anatomy and development) or their ethology, that is, their functional aspect (physiology and psychology). Even in such a small group of insects these various subjects are so extensive and intricate that very few observers have been able to cultivate them all with equal success. This has, perhaps, been accomplished only by

FIG. 68. Worker of *Trigonogaster recurvispinosa* of Western India. (Bingham.)

Emery and Forel, each of whom has devoted more than forty years of unremitting study to the ants. Other workers have been able to cultivate only one or at most two of the subjects above mentioned. Before considering the classification it may be well to sketch with the utmost brevity the history of myrmecology in its various branches.

The foundations of the taxonomy of ants were laid in the closing years of the eighteenth and the opening years of the nineteenth century by Linné, Fabricius and Latreille. Linné (1735) in his "Systema Naturæ" briefly described eighteen species, eight from Europe, eight from South America and two from Egypt as belonging to the single genus *Formica*. Some of these, like other well-known Linnæan species of animal and plants, are collective species, that is, they embrace several of what would now be regarded as distinct species. Fabricius (1804), besides describing a number of additional species, created five more genera: *Lasius, Cryptocerus, Atta, Myrmecia* and *Dorylus*. Of course, none of these corresponds fully to the genus bearing the same name at the present time. He still retained the great majority of the species in the Linnæan genus *Formica*, but divided it into two purely artificial categories, one for the species with, and one for the species

without spines on the thorax. Neither Linné nor Fabricius seems to
have paid much attention to the habits of the ants.

The third and by far the most important of the pioneers in myrmecography was Latreille (1798*b*, 1802*b*). He collected the ants of
Europe, studied their habits assiduously and described many species
that had been overlooked by his predecessors, including a number of interesting forms. He produced good descriptions of nearly a hundred
species which he had himself examined. All of these he placed in the
single genus *Formica* which he divided into nine " families ": the *Formicæ arcuatæ* (corresponding to our present genera *Camponotus* and
Polyrhachis), *camelinæ* (our *Formica, Lasius, Myrmecocystus, Œcophylla* and *Dolichoderus* in part), *atomariæ* (our *Dolichoderus* in part,
Tapinoma and *Acantholepis*), *ambiguæ* (*Polyergus*), *chelatæ* (*Odontomachus*), *coarctatæ* (*Ponera, Pachycondyla, Neoponera, Ectatomma,
Myrmecia*, etc.), *gibbosæ*
(*Atta, Pheidole, Messor,
Pogonomyrmex*, etc.),
punctoriæ (*Eciton, Myrmica, Tetramorium, Myr-
mecina, Leptothorax, Solenopsis*, etc.) and *caperatæ*
(*Cryptocerus, Œcophylla*).
It is impossible to run over
this arrangement without
admiring Latreille's acu-

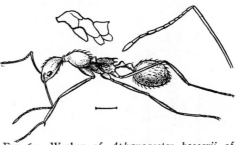

FIG. 69. Worker of *Aphænogaster beccarii* of
the Indomalayan region. (Bingham.)

men in so clearly forecasting the limits of many of our modern subfamilies, tribes and genera.

For nearly fifty years after the publication of Latreille's work systematic myrmecology stagnated, till a revival of interest in the subject
began to set in about the middle of the past century with the work of
Nylander and Mayr. Both of these authors devoted themselves to a
careful study of the European species, Nylander to the boreal, French
and Mediterranean, and Mayr to the Austrian and eventually to the
whole European fauna. Both authors, but especially Mayr, defined
the genera and species more accurately than any of their predecessors. Later Mayr extended his studies to the faunas of foreign
countries and published several important works on the ants of Asia,
Africa, Australia, and North and South America. Forel, in comment-
ing on his work says: " His remarkable perspicacity in creating genera,
and in general in the distinction of the comparative value of zoölogical
characters, and the minute exactitude of all his writings, which represent a vast amount of labor, have raised myrmecology to the rank of

the best known portions of entomology." A well-known English hymenopterist of the same period, Frederick Smith, undertook a similar universal study of the ants, basing his descriptions on the numerous specimens from all parts of the world in the collections of the British Museum. Many of his species are so inadequately described that the writers of today are obliged either to discard them or to make pilgrimages to the British Museum for the sake of consulting the types from which they were drawn, and while some of his species bear appropriate or even elegant names, and have been identified after much labor with a fair degree of certainty, his generic distinctions give evidence of deficient classificatory sense.

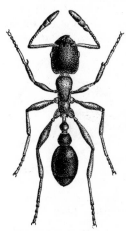

FIG. 70. Worker of *Cardiocondyla venustula* of Porto Rico. (Original.)

During the latter half of the nineteenth century a considerable number of local European ant faunas were published and our knowledge of the ants of other lands grew apace. Adlerz studied the ants of Sweden; Ernest André of France, Europe and North Africa; Bos, Meinert and Wasmann of the Netherlands; Curtis, Saunders and F. Smith of England; Forel of Switzerland; Emery of Italy; Gredler of Tyrol; Nassonow and Ruzsky of Russia; Schenck and Förster of Germany, while some accomplished entomologists like Roger, Gerstaecker, Shuckard and Westwood evinced a greater interest in the exotic genera and species. Nor was this activity confined to the recent ants. Heer, Mayr, Emery, Ernest André and others published descriptions of many fossil species preserved in the Baltic and Sicilian ambers and in the strata of Oeningen and Radoboj.

Among this group of diligent investigators two are *facile principes,* Emery and Forel. In 1874 Forel published at a remarkably early age what must always be regarded as one of the finest natural histories of any group of insects, the " Fourmis de la Suisse," a work to which the student must constantly turn both for information and encouragement. Emery and Forel, who both began to publish in 1869 and have continued ever since to make important contributions to our knowledge, combine an excellent zoölogical and philosophical training with rare judgment and acumen. Building on the excellent foundations laid by Latreille, Nylander and Mayr, they have been able to make our knowledge of the ants more complete than that of any other family of the vast Hymenopteran order. Not only have they perfected the system of the European species, but they have published excellent monographs and revisions of the faunas of other continents, so that the student of today finds it a comparatively easy task to continue the work.

Although the ant-fauna of North America is vastly richer than that of Europe, few of our entomologists have cared to study its taxonomy and as a rule these few have been poorly prepared to undertake the work. Species have been described by Buckley, Cresson, Fitch, Haldeman, McCook, Norton, Pergande, Provancher, Scudder, Viereck and Walsh, but the really valuable work on our fauna has been accomplished by Mayr, Emery and Forel.

FIG. 71. Worker of *Stereomyrmex horni* of Ceylon. (Bingham.)

The study of ant ethology has had a more continuous, though perhaps slower, development than the taxonomy. It is also much older, and may be said to date back to the seventeenth and eighteenth centuries, to authors like Wilder (1615) Bonnet (1779–'83), Swammerdam (1682), Leuwenhoeck (1695), Gould (1747), De Geer (1778) and Christ (1791). The subject does not begin to assume definite form, however, till we reach the writings of Latreille (1802) and especially of Pierre, the son of the celebrated François Huber. P. Huber's work entitled " Recherches sur les Mœurs des Fourmis Indigènes " published in 1810, is perhaps the most remarkable of all works on the habits of ants. It has been widely quoted and has never ceased to be an inspiration to all subsequent workers. It covers much of the subject of the habits of ants in an attractive and luminous style and abounds in accurate and original observations. The most interesting portions of the work treat of the slave-making habits of the sanguinary ant (*Formica sanguinea*) and the amazon (*Polyergus rufescens*). Huber was not only the first to discover and interpret the symbiotic relations of these species but his account is so complete that even Forel could add to it little that was really new. Huber also observed the relations of the ants to the aphids and of the various castes to one another and correctly interpreted the origin of colonies.

Since the publication of Huber's work the habits of ants have been studied by an ever increasing number of investigators. The most comprehensive contributions have been made by Forel and Emery, but important work has been done by Adlerz, Ernest André, Bates, Belt, Bethe, Brauns, von Buttel Reepen, Ebrard, Escherich, Goeldi, Heer, J. Huber, von Ihering, Janet, Karawaiew, Lameere, Lespes, Lubbock, Mayr, Moggridge, Reichenbach, Reuter, Rothney, Santschi, Sykes,

Tanner, Trimen, Ule, Urich, Viehmeyer, Wasmann, Wroughton, and
Yung, and in the United States by Buckley, Miss Fielde, Leidy,
Lincecum, McCook, Pricer, Mrs. Treat and Turner.

The study of myrmecophily, or the relations of the numerous
guests and parasites to the ants, and of the plants frequented by
ants, has developed into a very interesting and important branch
of ethology which must be mentioned in this connection.   An extra-

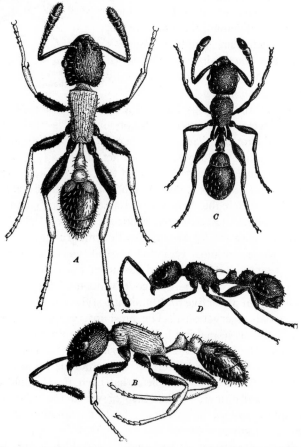

FIG. 72. Species of *Macromischa*. (Original.)   *A* and *B*, Worker of *M. isabellæ* of
Porto Rico ; *C* and *D*, worker of *M. albispina* of Culebra.

ordinary number of articles has been published on animal myrmecophily, especially by Wasmann, who since 1886 has devoted himself
to this subject with great ardor, and has brought to light many curious
facts which have a bearing not only on the ethology of ants but of

many other groups of insects. Other students of this subject are Casey, Donisthorpe, Escherich, von Hagens, Kraatz, Lespes, George Lewis, Lichtenstein, Lucas, Raffray, Reuter, de Saulcey, Joh. Schmidt, Sharp, Trimen, Viehmeyer, and in the United States Cockerell, Brues, Hamilton, Haldemann, King, Schwarz and Wickham. The relation of plants to ants has been studied by many botanists, notably by Delpino, Huth, Holmgren, A. Mœller, Fritz Mueller, Schimper, Treub, von Ihering, Rettig and Ule.

Although the history of ant morphology also goes back to such investigators as Swammerdam and Leuwenhoek, little headway could be made with the study of structure and development in such small organisms till the microscope and the technique of sectioning and staining had been perfected, and this was accomplished only within the last quarter of a century. Forel and Emery, and more recently Janet, have done very important work on the anatomy of ants. Other authors worthy of mention in this hasty review, are Adlerz, Berlese, Bos, Dewitz, Fenger, Karawaiew, Leydig, Lubbock, Meinert, Nassonow, Pérez and Sharp. As yet American zoölogists have accomplished little in this interesting and accessible field of investigation. After this hasty sketch of the history of myr-

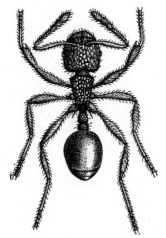

FIG. 73. Worker of *Pristomyrmex japonicus*. (Original.)

mecology we may take up a somewhat more detailed consideration of the taxonomy of the Formicidæ.

Inasmuch as the generic and specific characters of ants are to be derived not only from a male and female, but also from a worker caste, the classification of these insects presents certain difficulties and peculiarities not encountered in classifying most other animals. The exact status of a species can, of course, be determined only when all of its phases are known. The worker, as the most abundant, is usually first to fall into the hands of the systematist, and many years may elapse before the corresponding female and male are discovered. There are still a great many exotic and even several European species that are known only from one or at most two of the castes. Moreover, the resemblances between the different phases of the same species are often so remote that it is impossible to correlate workers and females, workers and males, or males and females, unless they have been taken from the same nests. It is, therefore, largely a matter of convenience that the soldier or worker is selected as the paradigm of the species and takes precedence of the other forms in systematic descriptions. It is obvious that the female, as presenting more numerous and complete characters, would occupy this position, were it not that this caste is, as a rule, less easily obtainable. Except for the same reason, the male would also occupy a more important place in generic and specific diagnosis, since this sex is very stable and often presents important characters, especially in the structure of the genitalia. It is probable, therefore, that at some future time, when large numbers of male and

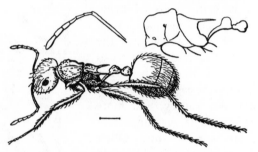

FIG. 74. Worker of *Myrmicaria brunnea* of India. (Bingham.)

female specimens have accumulated in our collections and have been carefully studied, the present classification of the Formicidæ will undergo considerable alteration. Until this time arrives, however, it will be prudent to move slowly in establishing new genera. Mayr, Forel and Emery have all shown admirable conservatism and a laudable absence of the "mihi-itch" in dealing with this aspect of the subject.

Another difficulty arises from the great variability of ants, both among members of the same colony and hence among the progeny of a single or a very few mothers, and among colonies of the same species in different stations or localities. In the former case we have what are known as "nest varieties," in the latter "local or geographical varieties." The danger of basing species on mere nest varieties is often considerable and can be overcome only by studying large series of specimens collected from the same colony. Probably many of the "species" of exotic ants included in our faunistic lists are nothing more than nest varieties. The local varieties are of peculiar interest. Like other animals, certain species of ants may be very stable though widely distributed, others highly variable though very restricted in their range. Some widely distributed species may be stable in some portions of their range and highly variable in others. And finally, some widely distributed species seem to be decidedly variable wherever they occur. Such a species is *Camponotus maculatus,* which occurs on every continent and many islands, and varies *ad infinitum.* In studying such species we are often presented with two sets of variable characters, one of which is adaptive and largely morphological, while the other comprises small indifferent traits of no considerable value to the organism in its struggle with its environment, such as slight peculiarities in size, sculpture, pilosity and color. These characters, which remind one of the De Vriesian "unit characters," are relatively stable in particular races or varieties and have a tendency to combine and recombine in endless permutation. Besides *C. maculatus,* many of the species of the large genera *Formica* and *Pogonomyrmex* are admirable examples of this phenomenon.

FIG. 75. Head of female *Epitritus emmæ* of the West Indies. (Original.)

Characters of importance in classification may be drawn from all parts of the ant's body, but the most useful are furnished by the number of palpal joints, shape of the clypeus, mandibles, shape and comparative length of the antennal joints, shape of the thorax, petiole, postpetiole, spurs of the middle and hind tibiæ, tarsal claws, genitalia of the male, the venation of the wings of both sexes, the structure of the gizzard, larva and pupa. The tribes, genera and species are built on combinations of these characters. But as there are many minor characters, especially in sculpture, pilosity and color, which though constant for all the members of a caste, may nevertheless vary in colonies in different localities, it becomes necessary to recognize smaller divisions than that of the species. These subdivisions are of different rank for the reason that slight differences in form or sculpture are more important, because less variable, than pilosity and coloration. Myrmecologists have therefore recognized two categories within the species, one more important and called the *race* by Forel, the *subspecies* by Emery, and another less important category which has been called the *variety* by both of these authorities. Subspecies may be regarded as small or incipient species in the De Vriesian sense. They are much less frequently connected by transitional forms than the varieties.

The recognition of these various categories necessitates the employment of a quadrinomial nomenclature. Thus one of our common carpenter ants is known as *Camponotus herculeanus* Linn. subsp. *ligniperdus* Latreille var. *noveboracensis* Fitch. This is a strictly North American variety, with red head and thorax, of a smooth race, or subspecies, of the dark-colored, opaque, circumpolar species *herculeanus,* the typical form of which is confined to Europe. This method of

naming ants has great advantages and some disadvantages. It shows
the relationships of the different forms very clearly and this is an
admirable trait in nomenclature, but it is also very cumbersome. For
ordinary purposes it is sufficient to treat the varietal name as if it
were specific and designate the ant mentioned above simply as *Camponotus noveboracensis* Fitch. This is the more justifiable as the variety
among ants is very nearly equivalent to the species among many
other groups of animals, such as birds and mammals. In the present
work I shall use the binomials as a rule and refer the reader for the
full terminology of our North American ants to the catalogue in
Appendix C.

This chapter may be concluded with a conspectus of the present
classification of the Formicidæ compiled very largely from the works

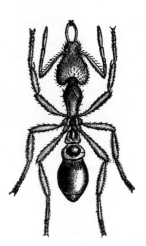

FIG. 76. Worker of
*Strumigenys obscuri-
ventris* of Porto Rico.
(Original.)

FIG. 77. Worker of
Strumigenys lewisi of Japan. (Original.)

of Emery and Forel. Concerning the important details of this classification these authorities are unanimous but there are certain points on
which they differ, and many which they have left undecided till more
material is forthcoming and profounder studies of whole groups of
genera have been undertaken. They differ mainly on the limits of two
of the five subfamilies, the Ponerinæ and Dorylinæ, Emery maintaining that the tribe Cerapachysii belongs with the Dorylinæ whereas
Forel assigns it to the Ponerinæ. The tribe in question certainly
possesses peculiarities which ally it with both subfamilies, but the

development and habits of its species are so imperfectly known that its exact position cannot be determined at the present time. I have followed Forel in placing it with the Ponerinæ though I appreciate Emery's reasons for dissenting from this procedure.[1] Some of the tribes, especially the Ponerii and Myrmicii still embrace very heterogeneous groups of genera, and many of the genera, especially those which are known only from specimens of a single caste, are probably

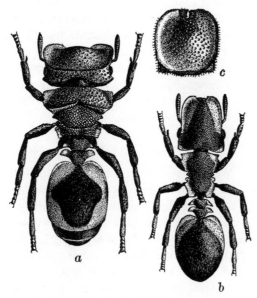

Fig. 78. *Cryptocerus angulosus* of Central America. (Original.) *a,* Soldier; *b,* worker; *c,* head of soldier from above.

placed in the wrong tribes. Ashmead (1905c) recently undertook to construct a new arrangement of the genera, but as Emery has shown (1906a), it is anything but an improvement on the existing classification. What we need for the present as not a new arrangement, the erection of a lot of new genera on superficially aberrant species and the raising of every subgenus to generic rank, but a painstaking study of all the species in the existing groups. Until such studies have made appreciable headway, the existing avowedly imperfect classification should not be discarded without at least as much thought as has been devoted to its construction.

[1] Since these remarks were written, Emery (*Deutsch. Ent. Zeitsch.,* 1909, p. 355) has changed his views on the position of the Cerapachysii. He now places them under the new caption Prodorylinæ, but within the subfamily Ponerinæ.

Family FORMICIDÆ (Heterogyna)

Subfamily I. *PONERINÆ* Mayr

Worker always with highly developed sting. Frontal carinæ vertical, oblique or forming horizontal lobes partly covering the antennal insertions. Antennæ 12-, rarely 9-, 10- or 11-jointed. Palpal joints nearly always reduced. Clypeus well-developed. Pedicel nearly always 1-jointed; first gastric segment usually narrowed behind where it encloses the basally constricted second segment, which bears a stridulatory organ on its dorsal surface.—Female usually winged and but little larger than the worker; ergatoid, apterous or gynæcoid in some forms.—Male usually with long gaster; genitalia partially exserted or in a few tribes (Cerapachysii and Proceratii), completely retractile. Pedicel like that of the worker. Wings usually with 2 closed cubital cells. Wingless, ergatoid males occur in a few species.—Pupæ always enclosed in cocoons.

Tribe 1. MYRMECII

Australian.—Worker and female: Pedicel distinctly 2-jointed as the second abdominal (first gastric segment of other Ponerinæ) is narrower than the succeeding segment and strongly constricted behind. Frontal carinæ as in the Ectatommii. Eyes large. Mandibles narrow, with bicuspidate teeth. Palpi with the full number of joints. Females winged, barely larger than the corresponding workers.—Male pedicel like that of the workers. Genitalia bulky, of complicated structure; stipes with dorsal and terminal branches, volsella with a well-developed lamina.

Myrmecia (Fig. 3, *B*).

Tribe 2. AMBLYOPONII

Cosmopolitan.—Pedicel 1-jointed, articulating over its whole posterior surface with the first gastric segment. Mandibles usually narrow, inserted at the corners of the head. Palpal joints reduced. Eyes of worker vestigial. Posterior tibiæ with double spurs.

Amblyopone, Stigmatomma (Fig. 131), *Mystrium* (Fig. 129), *Prionopelta, Myopopone.*

Tribe 3. ECTATOMMII

Cosmopolitan.—Worker and female: Pedicel 1-jointed, often scale-like, with slender insertion usually at half the height of the first gastric segment. Palpal joints reduced in number. Frontal carinæ diverging behind or feebly converging, their anterior ends rarely dilated to form narrow lobes, but then their posterior ends are widely separated.

> *Typhlomyrmex, Paraponera, Ectatomma* (with subgenera: *Ectatomma, Acanthoponera, Stictoponera, Mictoponera, Rhytidoponera, Holcoponera* and *Gnamtogenys*), *Thaumatomyrmex* (Fig. 3, *I*), *Alfaria, Emeryella.*

Tribe 4. PONERII

Cosmopolitan.—Pedicel of worker and female 1-jointed, usually scale-like, with slender articulation usually at the ventral side of the first gastric segment. Palpal joints reduced in number. Frontal carinæ converging posteriorly, often closely approximated behind and usually forming a flattened plate anteriorly into which the posterior end of the

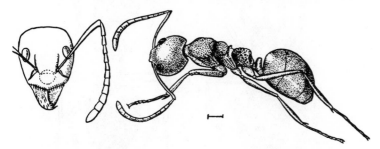

FIG. 79. Worker of *Dolichoderus bituberculatus* of the Indomalayan region. (Bingham.)

clypeus is inserted like a wedge. (*Odontoponera* is transitional to *Ectatomma* in the structure of its frontal carinæ.)

> *Odontoponera* (Fig. 136), *Diacamma, Ophthalmopone, Dinoponera* (Fig. 132), *Megaloponera* (with subgen. *Megaloponera* and *Hagensia*), *Paltothyreus, Plectroctena, Neoponera* (Fig. 134; with subgen. *Neoponera* and *Eumecopone*), *Pachycondyla* (with the subgenera *Pachycondyla* (Fig. 133), *Bothroponera* and *Ectomomyrmex*), *Ponera* (Fig. 131), *Euponera* (with the subgenera *Euponera, Mesoponera, Pseudoponera* and *Brachyponera* (Fig. 135)), *Trapeziopelta, Cryptopone, Streblognathus, Belonopelta, Centromyrmex, Psalidomyrmex, Platythrea, Rhopalopone, Myopias, Onychomyrmex, Prionogenys, Leptogenys* (with the subgen. *Leptogenys* and *Lobopelta*, Fig. 137), *Harpegnathus.*

Tribe 5. ODONTÓMACHII

Cosmopolitan.—Worker and female characterized by the peculiar configuration of the head and mandibles (Fig. 3, *K*).

Anochetus (with the subgen. *Anochetus* and *Stenomyrmex*), *Champsomyrmex, Odontomachus* (Fig. 3, *K*).

Tribe 6. PROCERATII

Cosmopolitan, but not yet known from the Indian and Ethiopian regions.—Worker with vestigial eyes and sutureless thorax. Tip of large first gastric segment turned downward and the succeeding seg-

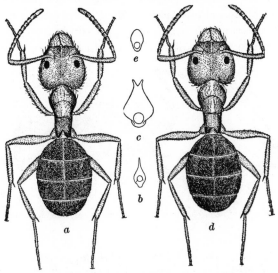

FIG. 80. Species of *Liometopum*. (Original.) *a*, Worker of *L. apiculatum* of Southwestern North America; *b*, petiole of same seen from behind; *c*, petiole of female; *d*, worker of *L. microcephalum* of Southern Europe; *e*, petiole of same.

ments forming a cone with its tip directed anteriorly.—Females winged and with well-developed eyes. Male genitalia completely retractile.

Sysphincta (Fig. 128, *a*), *Proceratium* (Fig. 128, *b*), *Discothyrea*.

Tribe 7. CERAPACHYSII

Cosmopolitan.—Workers blind or with vestigial eyes. Antennæ 9–12 jointed. Frontal carinæ erect. Males and females imperfectly known; in some cases the latter are apterous and dichthadiiform (*Acanthostichus*). Males with furcate subgenital plate.

Subtribe (*a*) *Acanthostichii*

Acanthostichus, Ctenopyga.

Subtribe (*b*) *Cerapachysii* s. str.

Cerapachys (with the subgenera *Cerapachys, Parasyscia* (Fig. 125), *Oöceræa, Syscia* and *Cysias*), *Phyracaces, Lioponera, Sphinctomyrmex* (with the subgen. *Sphinctomyrmex* (Fig. 126) and *Eusphinctus*), *Probolomyrmex.*

Subtribe (*c*) *Cylindromyrmii*

Cylindromyrmex (Fig. 127), *Simopone.*

Subfamily II. *DORYLINÆ* Shuckard

Worker with sting, sometimes vestigial. Frontal carinæ vertical or subvertical, closely approximated or even fused, usually leaving the antennal insertions completely uncovered and curved anteriorly around the antennal foveæ. Clypeus usually much reduced or even fused with the frontal carinæ. Pedicel 1- or 2-jointed. Stridulatory organ im-

FIG. 81. Worker major of *Pseudolasius familiaris* of India. (Bingham.)

perfectly developed.—Female apterous, much larger than the worker but like the worker blind or with vestigial eyes. Pedicel always 1-jointed.—Male large, with 1-jointed pedicel; anal segment without cerci (penicilli); genitalia completely retractile.—Pupæ naked or enclosed in cocoons.

Tribe 1. DORYLII

Paleotropical.—Worker eyeless; strongly polymorphic in *Dorylus*. Pedicel 1–2-jointed. Antennal joints usually reduced in number — Female eyeless, with gaping end to the gaster and peculiarly formed hypopygium. Sting vestigial.—Male with one cubital cell in wings. Genitalia with very narrow lamina annularis; subgenital plate furcate.

Dorylus (with subgen. *Dorylus* (Fig. 141), *Anomma, Typhlopone, Dichthadia, Alaopone, Rhogmus, Shuckardia*), *Ænictus* (Fig. 143), *Ænictogeton.*

Tribe 2. Ecitonii

Neotropical.—Workers eyeless or usually with vestigial eyes; poly-morphic. Antennæ 12-jointed. Pedicel 2-jointed (1-jointed in *Chelio-myrmex*).—Female resembling that of *Dorylus* but with vestigial eyes. Gaster not gaping at the tip. Sting vestigial.—Male with 2 closed cubital cells in the wings. Genitalia with strongly developed lamina annularis; subgenital plate furcate.

> *Eciton* (with subgen. *Eciton* (Fig. 145) and *Acamatus* (Fig. 147)), *Cheliomyrmex* (Fig. 148).

Tribe 3. Leptanillii

Paleotropical.—Worker minute, monomorphic, eyeless. Antennæ 12-jointed, inserted further apart than in the preceding tribes. Labial palpi 1-jointed.—Female resembling that of *Dorylus,* eyeless. Gaster gaping at the tip.—Male minute, with small eyes, ocelli and mandibles and no veins in the wings.

> *Leptanilla* (Fig. 149).

Subfamily III. *MYRMICINÆ* Mayr

Worker with a sting. Frontal carinæ and clypeus usually as in the Ectatommii. Palpal joints commonly reduced in number. Pedicel dis-tinctly 2-jointed; very rarely the postpetiole is campanulate and as

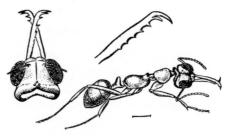

Fig. 82. Worker of *Myrmoteras binghami* of Tenasserim. (Bingham.)

broad as the succeeding segment. A stridulatory organ is present in at least many of the genera.—Female usually winged, often very different from the worker and much larger; very rarely ergatoid.—Male with cerci (absent in *Anergates*). Genitalia usually partly concealed, rarely completely retractile (*Carebara*). Gaster usually short. In some genera there are wingless, ergatoid males.—Pupæ always naked, with-out cocoons.

Tribe 1. PSEUDOMYRMII

Tropicopolitan.—Characterized by the closely approximated frontal carinæ in the worker and female (in *Pseudomyrma* even recalling the conditions in the Dorylinæ). Clypeus not distinctly wedged in between the frontal carinæ.

Sima (Fig. 67), *Pseudomyrma.*

Tribe 2. MYRMICII

A cosmopolitan, negatively characterized group comprising all the genera that have the clypeus produced back between the frontal carinæ and that are not at present assignable to the other tribes.

Myrmecina, Pristomyrmex (Fig. 73), *Acanthomyrmex, Podomyrma, Lordomyrma, Dacryon, Odontomyrmex, Atopomyrmex, Rogeria, Leptothorax* (with the subgen. *Leptothorax, Temnothorax, Goniothorax* and *Dichothorax*), *Trigono-*

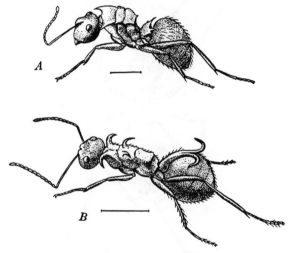

FIG. 83. Two species of *Polyrhachis* of the Indomalayan region. (Bingham.) *A, P. mayri; B, P. bihamata.*

gaster (Fig. 68), *Macromischa* (Fig. 72), *Harpagoxenus, Vollenhovia, Stereomyrmex* (Fig. 71), *Megalomyrmex, Ocymyrmex, Sifolinia, Myrmoxenus, Monomorium* (with the subgen. *Monomorium, Adlerzia, Martia* and *Holcomyrmex*), *Cardiocondyla* (Fig. 70), *Emerya, Xenomyrmex, Huberia, Phacota, Epœcus, Anergates, Wheeleriella, Liomyrmex, Machomyrma, Symmyrmica, Formicoxenus, Pheidole* (with

the subgen. *Pheidole* and *Cerætopheidole*), *Epipheidole,*
Sympheidole, Stenamma, Aphænogaster (with the subgen.
Aphænogaster and *Ischnomyrmex*), *Messor, Oxyopomyr-*
mex (with the subgen. *Oxyopomyrmex* and *Goniomma*),
Myrmica, Pogonomyrmex (with the subgen. *Pogonomyr-*
mex, Janetia and *Ephebomyrmex*), *Cratomyrmex, Tricho-*
myrmex.

Tribe 3. CREMASTOGASTRII

Cosmopolitan.—With the characters of the single genus: *Cremasto-*
gaster (with the subgen. *Cremastogaster* and *Oxygyne*).

Tribe 4. SOLENOPSIDII

Cosmopolitan.—Workers often highly dimorphic, or very small
when monomorphic. Antennæ with a reduced number of joints and

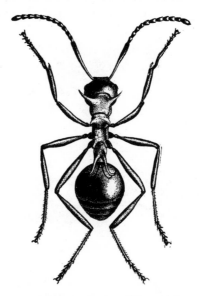

FIG. 84. Worker of *Polyrhachis lamellidens* of Japan. (Original.)

usually 2-jointed club. Male and female often very large compared
with the workers, always winged. Male genitalia sometimes completely
retractile. Many of the species are decidedly subterranean, or hypogæic.

Pheidologeton (with the subgen. *Pheidologeton* and *Ancleus*),
Aëromyrma, Solenopsis, Oligomyrmex, Carebara, Care-
barella, Erebomyrma, Tranopelta, Rhopalomastix, Allo-

merus, Lophomyrmex, Diplomorium, Melissotarsus (Fig. 139).[1]

Tribe 5. MYRMICARII

Indo-African.—With the characters of the single genus:

Myrmicaria (Fig. 74).

Tribe 6. TETRAMORII

Cosmopolitan.—Usually characterized by the 10-jointed antennæ in the male, with 9–12-jointed antennæ in the worker and female, in the latter the frontal carinæ are often moved a great distance towards the sides of the head and form deep grooves for the antennæ.

> *Tetramorium* (with the subgen. *Tetramorium, Tetrogmus* and *Xiphomyrmex*), *Eutetramorium, Triglyphothrix, Mayriella, Calyptomyrmex, Meranoplus, Strongylognathus, Rhoptro-myrmex, Wasmannia, Ochetomyrmex.*

Tribe 7. DACETONII

Cosmopolitan.—Antennæ of worker 5–12-jointed, in the male always 13-jointed.

> *Daceton, Acanthognathus, Orectognathus, Strumigenys* (Figs. 76 and 77), *Epitritus* (Fig. 75), *Rhopalothrix, Ceratobasis.*

Tribe 8. ATTII

Neotropical.—Antennæ of worker and female 11-jointed, with a tendency to form a 1-jointed club; 13-jointed in the male. All the known species cultivate fungi for food.

> *Apterostigma, Myrmicocrypta, Sericomyrmex, Cyphomyr-mex, Atta* (with the subgen. *Atta, Acromyrmex, Mœllerius, Trachymyrmex, Mycetosoritis* and *Mycocepurus*).

Tribe 9. CRYPTOCERII

Neotropical.—Characterized mainly by the peculiar mushroom-shaped gizzard. Frontal carinæ in the worker and female prolonged backward above the eyes to form deep scrobes for the antennæ.—Male very different from the female.

> *Procryptocerus, Cryptocerus* (Figs. 53 and 78).

[1] This aberrant genus, known only from the peculiar dimorphic workers, has been recently assigned to the Ponerinæ by Emery.

Tribe 10. Cataulacii

Paleotropical.—Worker and female with deep antennal scrobes on the sides of the head but formed by the true frontal carinæ only in front; further back they are bounded by special prolongations.—Male very similar to the female. Antennæ in both sexes 11-jointed.

Cataulacus (with the subgen. *Cataulacus* and *Otomyrmex*).

Subfamily IV. *DOLICHODERINÆ* Forel

Gizzard with a 4-sepaled, reflected calyx, completely enclosed within the crop, or without a calyx. Pedicel 1-jointed. Poison gland of worker and female without pulvinus, invaginating the cuticle of the vesicle, becoming enclosed within this organ and terminating in a knob. Tube of gland straight throughout, and furnished with lateral

Fig. 85.   Worker of *Hemioptica scissa* of Ceylon.   (Bingham.)

tubules for each cell. Poison vesicle variable in form, usually small, sometimes like the gland itself, highly vestigial. Sting very small (except in *Aneuretus*), vestigial, but not transformed into an organ to support the orifice of the vesicle. Cloacal orifice large, forming a nonciliated, transverse slit, usually ventral to the tip of the gaster. Pygidium commonly vertical or oblique antero-posteriorly and concealed under the fourth gastric segment. Antennæ 12-jointed. Anal glands almost always present and secreting an aromatic product of characteristic odor (Tapinoma odor).—Pupæ naked, never enclosed in cocoons.

Cosmopolitan.

> *Aneuretus* (Fig. 140), *Dolichoderus* (with subgen. *Dolichoderus* (Fig. 79), *Hypoclinea* and *Monacis*), *Leptomyrmex*, *Liometopum* (Fig. 80), *Azteca, Semonius, Tapinoma* (with the subgen. *Tapinoma, Ecphorella* and *Doleromyrma*), *Turneria, Technomyrmex, Dorymyrmex, Forelius, Iridomyrmex* (Fig. 86), *Engramma, Bothriomyrmex, Linepithema*.

Subfamily V. *CAMPONOTINÆ* Forel

Gizzard with a 4-sepaled straight, recurved or reflected calyx, which however, is always covered with circular muscles that separate it from the cavity of the crop. Pedicel 1-jointed. In the worker and female the poison gland forms a flat or oval cushion in the back of the vesicle, with a large tube but without accessory tubules for each cell. Poison vesicle large and elliptical. Sting transformed into a small vestigial apparatus which serves to support the orifice of the vesicle. All the gastric segments visible from above. Terminal segment conical, bearing at its apex the small, round, ciliated cloacal orifice. Anal glands lacking.—Pupæ usually enclosed in cocoons, but sometimes naked.

The following tribes are established mainly on peculiarities in the structure of the gizzard.

Tribe 1. PLAGIOLEPIDII

Cosmopolitan but mostly paleotropical.

> *Plagiolepis* (Fig. 87), *Acropyga, Rhizomyrma, Acantholepis* (with subgen. *Acantholepis* and *Stigmacros*), *Brachymyrmex, Myrmelachista, Melophorus* (with subgen. *Melophorus* and *Lasiophanes*), *Notoncus, Aphomomyrmex, Rhopalomyrmex*.

Tribe 2. DIMORPHOMYRMII

Paleotropical.

> *Dimorphomyrmex* (Fig. 98).

Tribe 3. MYRMOTERATII

Paleotropical.

> *Myrmoteras* (Fig. 82).

Tribe 4. ŒCOPHYLLII

Tropicopolitan.

> *Œcophylla* (Fig. 123), *Gigantiops, Gesomyrmex* (Fig. 100).

Tribe 5. FORMICII

Cosmopolitan.

> *Prenolepis* (with the subgen. *Prenolepis, Euprenolepis* and *Nylanderia*), *Pseudolasius* (Fig. 81), *Lasius* (with the subgen. *Lasius, Prolasius* and *Acanthomyops*), *Polyergus, Formica* (with the subgen. *Formica* and *Proformica*),

Myrmecocystus (with the subgen. *Myrmecocystus* and *Cataglyphis*).

Tribe 6. CAMPONOTII

Cosmopolitan.

Camponotus (with the subgen. *Camponotus* and *Colobopsis*), *Rhinomyrmex, Mayria, Myrmecopsis, Calomyrmex, Myrmecorhynchus, Dendromyrmex, Opisthopsis, Echinopla, Polyrhachis* (Figs. 83 and 84), *Hemioptica* (Fig. 85).

CHAPTER IX

THE GEOGRAPHICAL DISTRIBUTION OF ANTS

"These craggy regions, these chaotic wilds,
  Does that benignity pervade, that warms
  The mole contented with her darksome walk
  In the cold ground; and to the emmet gives
  Her foresight, and intelligence that makes
  The tiny creatures strong by social league;
  Supports the generations, multiplies
  Their tribes, till we behold a spacious plain
  Or grassy bottom, all, with little hills—
  Their labour, covered, as a lake with waves;
  Thousands of cities, in the desert place
  Built up of life, and food, and means of life!"
      —Wordsworth, "The Excursion," Book IV.

Few circumscribed groups of animals have a more significant geographical distribution than the ants. As colonies they are fettered to the soil or vegetation, but their winged females, though feeble flyers, may be wafted long distances by the wind and thus overcome mountain and water barriers of considerable magnitude. In these respects ants resemble plants, which, though rooted in the ground, are able nevertheless greatly to extend the range of their species by means of wind- or animal-borne seeds. That ants are often carried by air currents to great distances beyond their normal range is attested by a number of facts. Annually numbers of female ants are wafted out to sea or into our great lakes to be drowned and eaten by fishes, or conveyed to desolate mountain summits where they perish in futile attempts to found colonies. Occasionally however such widely dispersed females do succeed in establishing themselves and in rearing their offspring. According to Forel (1901*m*) the occident ant (*Pogonomyrmex occidentalis*), a species peculiar to the Great Plains, has been taken in Hawaii, and King (1901*a*) has found in Massachusetts a single colony of *Formica neoclara,* an ant restricted, so far as known, to the mountain valleys of Colorado.

This method of dispersal is, of course, denied to all ants like the Dorylinæ, certain Ponerinæ and Myrmicinæ, whose females are wingless, since these insects cannot cross bodies of water nor high mountain ranges. But as the Dorylinæ are migratory ants, and, as a rule, do not inhabit permanent nests, their colonies compensate, to a certain extent, for the apterous condition of their females. There is, however, a passive displacement or dissemination of whole colonies in certain species like the fire-ant (*Solenopsis geminata*), which often nests in low-lands subject to frequent and sudden inundations. Von Ihering (1894) has made the interesting discovery that when a nest of these ants is flooded, they agglomerate to form a ball 16–25 cm. in diameter, which encloses the brood in the center. This ball is borne along on the surface of the water while its living units keep shifting their position to avoid too prolonged immersion, till the shore or some projecting rock or tree-trunk is reached, when the colony scrambles out of the uncongenial element. I am informed by a gentleman from Louisiana that this same ant resorts to the same method of saving its colonies in the flooded bayous of the Southern States. Similar observations have been made by Savage (1847) on the African driver ants (*Anomma arcens*) and by Ern. André (1885) on European ants.

Finally, ant colonies or fertile female ants are often transported by man from land to land as stowaways in the cargoes of ships and railway trains. Every botanical garden annually receives several species of these insects from the tropics in the pseudobulbs of orchids, among the leaves of aroids or tillandsias, or in the soil and moss adhering to the roots of plants, and some of the smaller species thus unintentionally imported manage to establish themselves permanently in the hot-houses.

Owing to these various means of dissemination, the species of ants have become more widely distributed than any other insects, with the possible exception of the Diptera. Some of our American forms, for example, *Dorymyrmex pyramicus,* range from Illinois to Argentina. Many species, like *Eciton cæcum* and *Solenopsis geminata,* are coëxtensive with the tropical and subtropical portions of America, and the latter also occurs in the tropics of the Old World. The former, being a Doryline ant, does not occur in the West Indies. Still other species, like *Camponotus herculeanus, Formica fusca* and *sanguinea,* extend over the whole north temperate portion of the globe, and *C. maculatus* is represented by subspecies or varieties on every continent and on many of the outlying islands.

The distribution of ants may be studied either from a faunistic or from an ethological point of view. In faunistic studies the emphasis is placed on the areas or ranges covered by the various species, subspecies and varieties and on the bearing of such distribution on the genesis or descent of taxonomic groups as units. And since the existing fauna is unquestionably derived from previous faunas, which must have determined its character and composition, we are compelled to seek for antecedent explanatory conditions in geology and paleontology. In ethological studies, on the other hand, one turns at once to the adaptations of the living forms to their specific environment and works back from these adaptations to the geographical and geological conditions by which they are influenced. Of these two methods, which necessarily supplement each other, the latter leads to more detailed and positive results, since our knowledge of previous faunas is in all cases more or less vague and problematic. A résumé of what has been ascertained concerning fossil ants will be given in the next chapter, but owing to its fragmentary character, will be used rather as a confirmation than as a foundation for inferences drawn from our existing fauna.

Emery (1893–'94) and von Ihering (1894) have shown that there is a very significant parallelism between the distribution of mammals and that of ants. Both groups appear to have arisen simultaneously during the Triassic or possibly during some previous period, and to have spread over the earth's surface in much the same manner, although, if we except the bats, few mammals have possessed such power of dispersal as the ants. A study of the mammals indicates that during the Mesozoic era there were extensive land connections between the present continents of Eurasia, Africa, America and Australia, and that these various regions were inhabited by a primitive, widely-distributed but now extinct fauna. During this era New Zealand was cut off from Australia and during the following Eocene epoch Africa, South America and Australia were in turn separated from the great continental mass. During the Oligocene a boreal and Indian fauna became differentiated in Eurasia and their separation was emphasized during the Miocene and Pliocene periods by an upheaval of the boundaries between the respective regions. During the early Tertiary, also, the connection between North and South America was severed and was not restored, according to some paleontologists, till the Pliocene epoch. It is highly probable, as Emery has suggested, that the Ponerinæ correspond to the primitive, widely-distributed mammals of the Mesozoic era, and together with certain Myrmicinæ, like *Solenopsis, Pheidole*, etc., represent an ancient cosmopolitan ant-fauna. Ponerinæ occur even in New Zealand, which appears to have been isolated ever since the Jurassic. Since the Dorylinæ are well developed in the tropics of both hemispheres, these ants must have arisen before Africa was separated from South America, probably from some primitive and widespread Ponerine forms like the Cerapachysii. The almost complete absence of Dolichoderinæ in Africa shows that this subfamily must have made its appearance after Africa had been separated from Eurasia. That the Dolichoderinæ came from Ponerine ancestors is indicated by the annectant genus *Aneuretus,* still living in Ceylon, and the genera *Protaneuretus* and *Paraneuretus,* which I have detected in the Baltic amber.   The Camponotinæ are a thoroughly cosmopolitan group, though represented by the greatest variety of types in the Old World. They must have arisen from the Ponerinæ at a very remote period during Mesozoic times.   It is very probable that the separation of the Indian from the South American region preceded the development of certain peculiar tribes among the Myrmicinæ and Camponotinæ since we find the singular Cryptocerii and Attii confined to the American tropics, whereas, the Indian region has the Cataulacii, *Polyrhachis,* and several remarkable Camponotine genera.   The Tetramorii, too, are almost exclusively Indo-African, being represented in America only by a few more or less aberrant species.

The north temperate regions both in Eurasia and America seem to have remained long enough in connection with the Indian region to acquire an admixture of types from this source.   Purely north temperate elements are the genera *Formica, Polyergus, Lasius, Myrmica, Stenamma s. str.* and certain species of *Leptothorax* (*acervorum*) and *Camponotus* (*herculeanus*).   Europe acquired its species of *Monomorium, Tetramorium, Cremastogaster, Plagiolepis, Acantholepis* and *Bothriomyrmex* from southern Asia, and North America received its species of *Monomorium* and *Cremastogaster* from the same source.

The history of the North American ant-fauna deserves somewhat fuller treatment.   This fauna, which during preglacial times was probably exceedingly rich in genera and species, must have been largely exterminated when the northern portion of our continent was buried under the great ice-sheet.   Further southward a few of the more warmth-loving forms managed to survive, where they have persisted as relicts, while somewhat more numerous remnants of the ancient preglacial arctic fauna survived along the edge of the ice-sheet or possibly on small non-glaciated islands farther north.   South of the ice-sheet the survival of the old forms was greatest in the Sonoran province, *i. e.,* in Northern Mexico and the Southwestern States.   This seems to have been an arid region even at that time and was, therefore, warmer than the more humid southeastern portion of the continent. The recession of the ice-sheet at the close of the glacial epoch was followed by a northward migration of the ants.   This appears to have taken place in much the same manner as Adams has described for other North American animals and plants: " The returning biota followed, in all probability, a definite successional relation and was composed of three general belts or ' waves,' concentrically distributed south of the ice margin.   The first one was of the barren ground type, the second was represented by distinct eastern and western coniferous forest types, and the third by the biota of the southeastern and southwestern states. The first wave was of a trans-continental extent, the second while coniferous and transcontinental was composed of two distinct types, the eastern, represented by the biota of northeastern North America, and the western by that of the Rocky Mountains and the Pacific Coast. The northeastern biota overflowed to the north, to the northwest into the Mackensie basin and even a few forms into the Yukon valley and to the Rocky Mountains. The northwestern biota spread from the Rocky Mountains and Pacific Coast region in the United States north to British Columbia and Alaska. The third wave spread from the southeastern centre of dispersal northward to the conifers and west to the Great Plains. From the southwestern centre the life spread north on each side of the Rocky Mountains into Canada, and only stragglers spread eastward into the humid region."

Besides the three waves recognized by Adams it is necessary to recognize a fourth or tropical wave of species, which have been moving up into North America from South America. As this has come over two distinct routes, namely by way of the West Indies and Mexico, we may recognize an eastern and a western center as in the second and third waves.

At present our knowledge of the ants of British America and Alaska is so incomplete that it is impossible to state whether there is a distinct tundral fauna, that is, a fauna living beyond the coniferous tree-belt. Observations in the mountains of Colorado, however, indicate that ants do not occur far above timber-line, which is there at an altitude of about 4,000 meters. Isolated females may sometimes be found under stones at a greater elevation, but these have been borne aloft by air-currents and perish without being able to establish formicaries. This is also the case at more moderate elevations above the timber-line, as, for example, on the summit of Mt. Washington (Wheeler, 1905*h*).

Even the non-glaciated portion of North America, however, has retained an ant-fauna composed very largely of well-known Eurasian genera and relicts of a more southerly type which have been unequally preserved in the eastern and western portions of the United States. The eastern portion retained a very small number of these ancient genera, probably on account of its much colder climate during the glacial epoch. Nevertheless, the eastern and western centers of the areas covered by Adams's second and third waves each retained a certain number of relicts, which seem to have formed as many constellations of species, subspecies and varieties within comparatively recent

times. Although these have spread from their centers of origin and
intermingled with the northern circumpolar fauna, they have not been
sufficiently displaced to prevent the recognition of the four centers of
dispersal which Adams calls the northeastern, northwestern, southeastern and southwestern respectively. Of these the first has contributed very little, the last more considerably to our ant-fauna, and
the northeastern and northwestern have more species in common than
the other two centers. The former, in addition to the subboreal types
above mentioned, is characterized by the following: *Stigmatomma
pallipes, Cremastogaster lineolata, Camponotus fallax, Prenolepis
imparis, Polyergus* and the species of *Lasius* of the subgenus *Acanthomyops*. These species, however, are often represented by distinct
eastern and western subspecies and varieties and usually the western
are more closely related to the Eurasian than to the eastern forms of
the species. This difference in relationships is even more striking when
distinct but allied species are compared in the two centers. Thus the
western *Stenamma nearcticum* is more closely related to the European
S. westwoodi than to the eastern *S. brevicorne;* the eastern *Aphænogaster fulva* is represented in the west by *A. occidentale* which is
merely a variety or subspecies of the European *A. subterranea;* the
eastern *Camponotus fallax, Formica rufa* and *Polyergus lucidus*
are represented in the western region by subspecies or varieties very
much like the Eurasian forms. The northeastern center retains at
least three relicts, *Myrmecina graminicola, Ponera coarctata* and
Harpagoxenus common to the Eurasian fauna, but apparently absent
from the northwestern center; whereas *Myrmica mutica,* which is
hardly more than a subspecies of the European *M. rubida,* occurs
only in the mountain valleys of the northwest. This center also has
three genera, *Symmyrmica, Sympheidole* and *Epipheidole,* not known
to occur elsewhere. These are, however, parasitic species and have
probably developed from *Lepthothorax-* and *Pheidole*-like forms within
comparatively recent times. Although several species of *Acanthomyops* occur in the Rocky Mountains, representatives of this subgenus are far more abundant in the northeastern center from which
they probably radiated. On the other hand, the species of *Formica*
allied to the European *F. rufa* have had their center of origin and dispersal in the northwest.

    The southeastern and southwestern centers contain more relicts of
the southern preglacial fauna and have, moreover, received many accessions from the fourth, or tropical wave which started in South America, probably in Archiguiana, and reached North America by way of
Central America and Mexico on the one hand, and the Antilles on the

other.   The southeastern and southwestern centers exhibit some blending of forms through an eastward migration from Mexico across the Gulf States and a counter westward migration of forms from the southeastern center.

The southeastern center is characterized by several species of *Dolichoderus* of the subgenus *Hypoclinea,* closely related to the Eurasian *H. 4-notata.*   This group is not represented in the southwest.   The species of *Sysphincta* and *Proceratium* have been retained as relicts. The latter genus seems not to occur in Eurasia.   Several peculiar species of *Aphænogaster* (*treatæ, mariæ* and *lamellidens*) have evidently had their origin in the southeastern center, to which we must also assign *Pogonomyrmex badius,* a single genus, *Epœcus,* and a subgenus of *Lepthothorax* (*Dichothorax*).

In the arid southwestern center there are a number of relicts which seem to have been actively producing new forms since they were relegated to this area.   Such are the genera *Liometopum, Myrmecocystus, Messor* and the subgenus *Ischnomyrmex* and the sections of the genus *Camponotus* which comprise the species allied to *C. maculatus* and *fallax.*   These forms are closely related to Old World species of Indian origin.

The admixture of adventitious tropical forms both in the southeastern and southwestern centers is considerable.   In the latter these have nearly all arrived by way of Mexico, in the former many are of Antillean provenience, but a certain number seem to be Mexican.   The genus *Eciton, e. g.,* is well represented in Texas and there are a few species in the Southeastern States.   As this genus is not represented in the West Indies or even in Florida, the eastern forms must have immigrated from the southwest.   The same is true of species like *Odontomachus clarus* which is said to occur as far east as Georgia. *O. hæmatodes, Xenomyrmex stolli, Cryptocerus varians, Pseudoponera stigma* and *Camponotus abdominalis,* however, must have entered Florida directly from the West Indies.   It is equally clear that *Cryptocerus angustus,* the species of the Ponerine genera *Pachycondyla, Platythyrea, Neoponera, Acanthostichus* and *Cerapachys,* the Myrmicine forms *Macromischa* and *Xiphomyrmex* and the Attiine genera and subgenera *Atta, Mœllerius, Mycetosoritis, Trachymyrmex* and *Cyphomyrmex* (in part) reached the southwestern center from tropical Mexico.   Other genera widely distributed in the American tropics, like *Iridomyrmex, Dorymyrmex, Pseudomyrma, Strumigenys,* certain species of *Ponera* (*ergatandria, trigona, opaciceps*) and *Camponotus* (*maculatus* and *planatus*) may have reached the adjacent portions of the United States both from Mexico and the West Indies.   This is clearly the case with *C. planatus,* which occurs in the United States only at the southern tip of Florida and in southwestern Texas.

It is not so easy to account for the distribution of species of a few tropical and subtropical genera like *Pogonomyrmex, Erebomyrma* and *Pheidole* within the United States. *Pogonomyrmex* is a peculiarly American genus ranging from Montana to Argentina. It is represented in the Southwestern States by a number of species, one occurs in Florida and Georgia and at least one in the West Indies. The southeastern species (*P. badius*) differs from all the others in having polymorphic workers, the West Indian form belongs to the subgenus *Ephebomyrmex,* which is also represented in Brazil, Mexico, Texas and Arizona. Recently the number of known South American species of *Pogonomyrmex* has been considerably augmented (Emery, 1905*b*). The question arises as to whether this genus had its center of origin in South America and radiated its species northward or whether it arose in the southwestern center of North America and extended thence southward to Argentina. The former supposition is supported by analogy with the advent of so many South American forms in North America, the latter by the fact that *Pogonomyrmex* is closely related in structure, though not in habits, with the boreal genus *Myrmica.* Of *Erebomyrma* only a single species (*E. longi* of Texas) was known till recently, when Emery described another (*E. peruviana*) from Peru. This genus, too, is probably of South American origin. This may be inferred from the fact that the allied genera *Tranopelta* and *Carebarella* are exclusively neotropical. Moreover, the allied genus *Solenopsis* is represented by a much greater number of species in South than in North America. The genus *Pheidole* is widely distributed and represented by numerous species in the Southeastern and Southwestern States and a few species (*Ph. vinelandica, tysoni, pilifera*) have spread into the Northern States. Most of the North American species are quite distinct and may be regarded as endemic. I know of no species common to the West Indies and the southeastern center, and although many southwestern species occur in northern Mexico they seem to be for the most part quite distinct from the southern Mexican and South American species. As the genus is cosmopolitan it is not improbable that our species may be derived from relicts of Mesozoic forms that were preserved in the southeastern and southwestern centers during glacial times. Perhaps further studies of the Mexican and West Indian, and especially of the Cuban and Haytian species may throw some light on the American distribution of this interesting genus.

A few words must be said about the ants that have been imported into North America by commerce, for although these comprise a comparatively small number of species, they have considerable economic importance. The following have been brought to our shores and have succeeded in gaining a foothold, especially in dwellings where they do

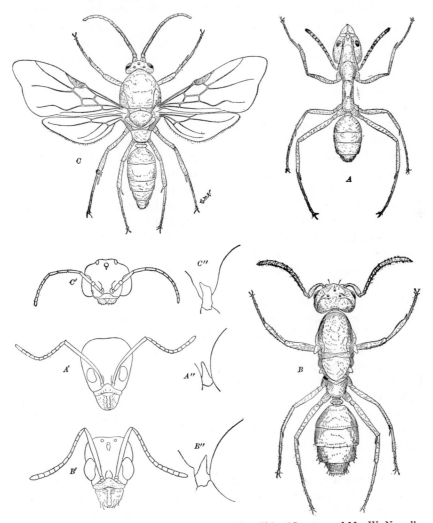

FIG. 86. The Argentine ant (*Iridomyrmex humilis*). (Courtesy of Mr. W. Newell, drawing by Miss Charlotte M. King.) *A*, Worker; *A'*, head; *A''*, petiole of same in profile; *B*, deälated female; *B'*, head; *B''*, petiole of same; *C*, male; *C'*, head; *C''*, petiole.

not come into competition with our native species: *Monomorium pharaonis, salomonis, destructor* and *floricola, Solenopsis rufa, Pheidole megacephala* and *flavens, Tetramorium cespitum, guineense* and *simillimum, Prenolepis fulva* and *longicornis, Plagiolepis longipes, Tapinoma melanocephalum* and *Iridomyrmex humilis.* All of these, with the exception of the pavement ant (*T. cespitum*), are of tropical origin, and nearly all of them have come from the Old World. *T. cespitum* of Europe is now common about New York, Washington and Philadelphia, but it is so sporadic that we must conclude either that it is of comparatively recent importation, or is prevented from spreading by competition with our native ants.[1]

All of the other species cited above require considerable warmth and even *Monomorium pharaonis,* the tiny yellow house-ant, which is often a pest in ships or in the dwellings of sea-port towns, does not nest out of doors except in southern latitudes. Some of our tropical ants (*Neoponera villosa, Camponotus floridanus* and *Pheidole flavens*) manage to live for considerable periods of time in our northern hot-houses. At least one species from the American tropics (*Iridomyrmex humilis* (Fig. 86)) has acquired a much wider range, having recently made its appearance in New Orleans. In this locality, where its habits have been carefully studied by Titus (1905) and Newell (1908*a*), it has become a serious pest and is driving out the native ants. That it is spreading rapidly over the warmer portions of the globe is shown by the fact that I have recently received specimens from various localities in California and from Cape Colony. It has also become a pest in Portugal (Martins, 1907), and, according to Stoll (1898) has been imported into Madeira where it has supplanted another previously introduced species, *Pheidole megacephala,* which was *the* house-ant of the island in the days of Heer (1852).

Some idea of the abundance of this ant in the middle of the last century may be gained from the following extract from Heer's work: " It occurs throughout the southern portion of the island of Madeira up to an elevation of 1,000 feet in prodigious numbers, especially in hot, sunny places, where it is to be found under eight out of every ten stones that may be overturned. In the city of Funchal there is probably not a single house that is not infested with millions of these insects. They climb to the top stories, issue in swarms from the cracks in walls and floors and keep crossing the rooms in regular files in all directions. They creep up the legs of tables, along their edges and into cupboards, chests, etc·" This ant is very common in the Bermudas and West Indies and will probably be found in Florida. There can be little doubt that wherever it gains a foothold in tropical or

[1] According to Marlatt (1898) this species has long been a resident of the Eastern States. He believes that it may be the species referred to by Kalm as occurring in the houses of Philadelphia as early as 1748.

subtropical countries it is able to propagate very rapidly and to exterminate the indigenous ant-fauna. This seems to be the case in Bermuda, and I have recently seen a good illustration of its habits in the Virgin Islands. During March, 1906, I devoted ten days to a careful study of the ant-fauna of the little island of Culebra, off the eastern coast of Porto Rico, without seeing a single specimen of *Ph. megacephala.* This island is, however, completely overrun with a dark variety of the vicious fire-ant (*Solenopsis geminata*). One day, on visiting the island of Culebrita, which is separated by a shallow channel hardly a mile in width from the eastern coast of Culebra, I was astonished to find it completely overrun with *Ph. megacephala.* This ant was nesting under every stone and log, from the shifting sand of the seabeach to the walls of the light-house on the highest point of the island. The most careful search failed to reveal the presence of any other species, though the flora and physical conditions are the same as those of Culebra. It is highly probable that *Ph. megacephala,* perhaps accidentally introduced from St. Thomas, a few miles to the east, had exterminated all the other ants which must previously have inhabited Culebrita. The absence of *megacephala* on Culebra is perhaps to be explained by the presence of the equally prolific and pugnacious fire-ant.

The recent displacement of *Ph. megacephala* in Madeira and of our native ants in Louisiana by *Iridomyrmex humilis* is analogous to the

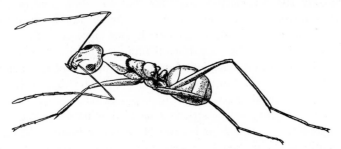

FIG. 87. Worker of *Plagiolepis longipes,* now spread over the tropics of both hemispheres. (Bingham.)

well-known displacement in Europe and America of the black house-rat (*Mus rattus*) by the brown species (*M. decumanus*). In a similar manner, according to Stoll, another ant, *Plagiolepis longipes* (Fig. 87), introduced into the island Reunion from its original home in Cochin China, has driven out some of the primitive autochthonous species. We may also look forward to the appearance of this same ant within the warmer portions of the United States, since it has already been recorded by Pergande (1894) from Todos Santos, in Lower California.

Still another ant that has acquired a footing in tropical Florida, and probably also in other localities in the Gulf States, is *Prenolepis longicornis*. It has long been a common species in the green-houses of temperate Europe and America. In some of these, as in the Jardin des Plantes in Paris, it has been a permanent resident for more than forty years. In the city of New York it may sometimes be found even on the top floors of the great apartment buildings. Wasmann (1905g) and Assmuth (1907) give good reasons for believing that the original home of this ant is India, and that it has been carried to all parts of the tropics in ships. They show that it has been accompanied in its wanderings by two myrmecophiles, a Lathridiid beetle (*Coluocera maderæ*) and a small cricket (*Myrmecophila acervorum* var. *flavocincta*). The peregrinations of *Tapinoma melanocephalum,* which also occurs in northern dwellings and green-houses, are similar to those of *P. longicornis.*

The foregoing sketch of the distribution of North American ants shows that our fauna is very rich in comparison with that of Europe. Nevertheless it must be admitted that we have few distinctive types—apparently only the specialized parasitic genera *Epœcus, Symmyrmica, Sympheidole* and *Epipheidole,* the subgenera *Dichothorax* and *Acanthomyops* and the ancient relict *Proceratium.* Kobelt has been led by his studies on the distribution of other animals to the conclusion that our existing North American fauna, like that of other countries, " apart from the introduced and feral domestic animals and the English sparrow—has shown no evidence of enrichment since the diluvial period. The present is a depauperate diluvial fauna. America, too, proves that we are not living in an incipient, but in a declining geological epoch, not at the beginning of a youthful, creative Quaternary, but at the close of the Tertiary period, whose generative power has been extinguished." This statement may not be strictly true of dominant insect groups like the Formicidæ. Not only is it probable that our fauna is being slowly but continually enriched by accessions from the tropics, but a comparison of the list of North American ants at the end of this volume with the lists of European species compiled by Mayr, Forel, Emery, Ern. André and others, shows that the related and identical species of both continents have a greater number of subspecies and varieties in North America. This would seem to force us to the conclusion that many of our ants are actually in a mutational or premutational phase.

Turning from this more general, faunistic account to the ethological distribution of ants, we observe considerable differences in the frequency with which the colonies occur within the range of each species. When we thus concentrate our attention on a single form, we find that the colonies are not uniformly distributed over their whole range, but only in particular stations, or habitats, showing that these insects, like plants and many other animals, depend very intimately for their welfare on precise physical and organic environments, such as the nature of the soil and vegetation, the amount of moisture and the exposure to sunlight. Colonies that happen to be established in unfavorable localities take on a more or less depauperate appearance. This is indicated by their scarcity and the small size of the colonies and individuals, and is particularly noticeable at the very limits or just beyond the limits of the normal range of a particular form. I find that according to the station inhabited by the various species, subspecies and varieties, at least in North America, we may distinguish the following ethological groups, or associations:

1. The *woodland,* or *silvicolous association,* comprising the species that inhabit our moist, shady northern and eastern forests. With the extinction or drainage of these forests or the removal of the undergrowth, this characteristic, and in many respects, very primitive fauna rapidly disappears.

2. The *glade,* or *nemoricolous association,* comprising the ants that prefer open, sunny woods, clearings or the borders of woods. A portion of this fauna maintains itself even in the gardens and parks of our cities.

3. The *field,* or *cespiticolous association,* comprising the ants that prefer to nest in grassy pastures and lawns, in situations exposed to the full warmth and light of the sun.

4. The *meadow,* or *pratincolous association,* comprising the ants which inhabit low, grassy meadows or bogs.

5. The *heath,* or *ericeticolous association,* comprising the ants that inhabit rather poor, sandy or gravelly soil exposed to the sun and covered with a sparse growth of weeds or grasses.

6. The *sand,* or *arenicolous association,* comprising the ants that prefer to nest in pure sand.

7. The *desert,* or *deserticolous association,* comprising the ants that inhabit the dry, open deserts and plains.

A few of our species, like *Lasius americanus* and *Formica subsericea,* are so adaptable that they occur more or less abundantly in all or nearly all of the above stations. Owing to intergradation of these stations in some places, there is, of course, a corresponding mingling of forms. Thus certain species, like *Monomorium minimum,* seem to belong indifferently either to the heath or sand fauna. In the deserts of the Southwestern States these two faunas may either mingle or be sharply separated from each other. In the Northeastern and

Middle States a similar relation obtains between the glade and field
faunas, which it is often impossible to separate by a hard and fast line.
Formica schaufussi, for example, seems to occur indifferently in
either station.

With the exception of the sand and desert associations, which depend very largely on physical conditions, like soil, warmth and moisture, the above list comprises mainly adaptations to particular types
of vegetation.   Other associations of a similar character undoubtedly
exist in other countries, especially in the tropics, where the relations
between ants and plants are often more intimate than in temperate
regions·   A very striking ethological association, depending on relations to the soil and consisting of species common to many of the above
groups, is represented by the so-called hypogæic ants.   These occur
in all parts of the world, and, owing to their exclusively subterranean
life, have acquired a peculiar adaptive facies.   They are aptly described by Emery (1875a) as " the inhabitants of the most remote and
obscure hiding places of the soil, dwellers in the narrow crannies
beneath the heaviest rocks, in the very pores of the earth, blind and
amblyopic pygmies of slow gait and strangely varied forms, microscopic remnants, so to speak, of extinct genera, that have found in the
bosom of the earth a respite from the invasion of more robust and
prolific types."   As a rule these hypogæic ants are of small size, pale
color and have no eyes or only vestiges of these sense-organs, although
all of these peculiarities may be found in certain epigæic species.   We
find, indeed, all gradations in habits between ants that live in exposed
situations and extremely hypogæic forms, and there can be no doubt
that the latter ethological group has been recruited from unrelated
genera among the former.   As nearly all ants live much of the time
in dark subterranean galleries and chambers, the transition to a completely hypogæic habit is easily effected, especially when food is more
accessible in the soil than on the surface, or when larger and more
pugnacious ants make life at the surface intolerable.   But no matter
how hypogæic a species may become, it always retains enough of its
ancestral habits to come to the surface for the nuptial flight of the
males and females.   At such times the blind and etiolated workers
excavate a gallery to the surface and conduct the winged sexes to the
opening.   In North America there are hypogæic species of *Eciton,*
Stigmatomma, Cerapachys, Sysphincta, Proceratium, Ponera, Sole-
nopsis, Erebomyrma, Strumigenys and *Lasius,* and in other parts of
the world species of the genera *Dorylus, Leptanilla, Aëromyrma, Dip-*
lomorium, Epitritus, Rhopalothrix, etc., have very similar habits,
although these in most cases are very imperfectly known.   Facts of

great interest will surely be brought to light, when hymenopterists devote as much attention to these insects as the coleopterists have bestowed on hypogæic beetles. Many of the species (*Eciton cæcum, Stigmatomma,* etc.) feed on larvæ and subterranean arthropods in general; others, like some of the small species of *Solenopsis, Aëromyrma, Erebomyrma,* etc., live in cleptobiosis with other ants or termites and feed on their brood; still others, like our yellow species of *Lasius s. str.* and all the species of the subgenus *Acanthomyops,* pasture droves of aphids and coccids on the roots and subterranean stems of plants.

In conclusion it should be noted that the habitat of a particular species, subspecies or variety is selected in the first instance by the fertile female ant when she establishes her colony. If the physical and living environment is congenial and moderately stable, the colony, in the great majority of cases, remains stationary, but if the conditions become unfavorable, it migrates to another site. In such cases the workers not only select the new habitat, but also determine and bring about the change of dwelling.

CHAPTER X

FOSSIL ANTS

Dum Phaëthontea formica vagatur in umbra
Implicuit tenuem succina gutta feram,
Sic modo quæ fuerat vita contempta manente
Funeribus facta est nunc pretiosa suis.
—Martial, " Epigrammata," Liber VI, 15.

Before proceeding further with our account of existing ants, it will be advisable to review what is known of the extinct species. And as the Formicidæ are one of the most specialized families of the Hymenoptera, which are themselves a highly specialized order, this review may properly begin with a few remarks on the paleontological history of the order as a whole.

The Hymenoptera first make their appearance during Mesozoic time, but concerning the families to which the few fossil remains belong, there is considerable difference of opinion. Heer in 1865 described from the Lower Liassic of Aargau, Switzerland, a specimen which he regarded as an ant and named *Palæomyrmex prodromus.* This has long been regarded as the most ancient not only of known ants but also of Hymenoptera. According to Handlirsch (1906–1908), however, who has recently subjected our knowledge of extinct insects to a critical revision, this fossil " certainly does not belong to the Hymenoptera, but presumably to the Homoptera." In 1854 Westwood described two wing impressions from the Lower Purbecks of Durdlestone Bay, England (Jurassic), as those of a couple of huge ants, *Formicium brodiei* and *Myrmicium heeri.* These are now shown by Handlirsch to belong to saw-flies of the genus *Pseudosirex,* which also comprises thirteen other species from the Solenhofen deposits of the same age. This singular genus is the most primitive of known Hymenoptera and has been assigned by Handlirsch to a special family, the Pseudosiricidæ, differing from the Siricidæ and other recent Hymenoptera in having numerous longitudinal veins in the wings, a distinctly Orthopteroid character which, like many other peculiarities of the Hymenoptera, points to a derivation of the order from Blattoid, or cockroach-like ancestors. The only other Hymenopteron known from the Mesozoic is *Ephialtites jurassicus,* based on a specimen from the Kimmeridge (Malm) of Spain. This insect is evidently a member of

the higher, or apocrital division of the order, but its affinities are very
obscure. We are thus led to the conclusion that, although both the
lower and higher divisions of the Hymenoptera are represented in the
Mesozoic, no ants are included in the number. But so many genera
and species of these insects appear full-fledged in the early Tertiary
that we are compelled to believe that they must have existed in the
Trias or even in the Lias, but belonged to so few genera and species
or lived in such small communities that they left no remains.

The numerous species of Tertiary ants not only belong to many
different genera but often to living genera, and even the extinct types
are readily referable to the recent subfamilies and to no others. The
extinct genera, moreover, are of such a character that one would not
be surprised to discover any of them alive today in some of the unex-
plored portions of the Old World tropics. Among these Tertiary ants
the male, female and worker phases were as sharply differentiated as
they are today. Joseph Le Conte ("Elements of Geology," p. 511) is,
therefore, mistaken when, from the fact that nearly all the fossil ants

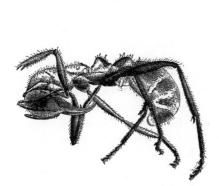

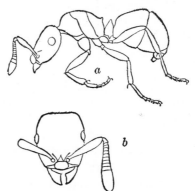

FIG. 88. Worker of *Prionomyrmex longiceps,* a primitive Ponerine ant from the Baltic Amber. (Original.)

FIG. 89. Worker of *Bradoponera meieri* from the Baltic Amber. (Mayr.) *a,* From the left side; *b,* head from above.

of Oeningen and Radoboj are males and females, he infers that " the
wingless condition, the neutral condition, the wonderful instincts and
organized social habits, have been developed together *since the Miocene
epoch.*" I shall show presently that had he consulted Heer's work on
these insects (1847), he would not have made this statement.

Tertiary ants have been found in both Europe and North America
in some 23 localities, representing several geological periods and formations. The following are the European formations: Baltic amber, beds
of Aix in the Provence and Gurnet Bay, Isle of Wight (Lower Oligo-

cene); Schossnitz in Silesia, Krottensee in Bohemia and Rott in the Rhinelands (Upper Oligocene); Radoboj in Croatia, Falkenau and Kutschlin in Bohemia and Cape Staratschin, Spitzbergen (Lower Miocene); Sicilian amber and the beds of Brunnstatt in Alsacia (Middle Miocene); Oeningen in Baden, Parschlug in Styria, Tallya and Thalheim in Hungary, Gabbro in Italy (Upper Miocene); Sinigallia in Italy (Pliocene). The age of the North American deposits has not been accurately determined. Ants have been seen in the amber of Nantucket (Goldsmith, 1879) which is attributed to the Tertiary. Other

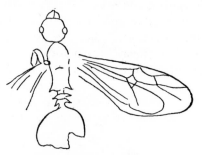

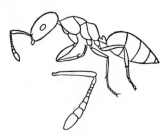

Fig. 90. Female of *Lonchomyrmex heyeri,* a Myrmicine ant from the Radoboj formation. (Mayr.)

Fig. 91. Worker of *Rhopalomyrmex pygmæus* from the Baltic Amber. (Mayr.)

localities are Green River, Wyoming; White River, Colorado and Quesnel, British Columbia, which are referred to the Oligocene, and Florissant, Colorado, which is said to belong to the Miocene.

The Baltic and Sicilian ambers and the beds of Radoboj, Oeningen and Florissant have yielded far and away the greatest number of ants. The most beautiful specimens are those of the amber, which are often so perfectly preserved that they may be as readily studied as recent ants mounted in Canada balsam. Most of these specimens are workers and belong to more or less arboreal species, but there are also quite a number of males and females. As nearly all of the latter have wings they must have been caught in the liquid resin just before or after their nuptial flight. The preservation of the Oeningen, Radoboj and Florissant specimens is very inferior to those of the amber. The deposits in these localities are lacustrine, that is, they consist of fine sand or volcanic ashes laid down in fresh water lakes. This accounts for the fact that nearly all the specimens are males and females, for as Heer says: " With few exceptions only winged individuals are found, because the wingless individuals, in this case the workers, were drowned less frequently than the others. Both males and females occur, but the former are much rarer than the latter, probably because the females, having a much larger and heavier abdomen, fell into the water more often than the males." The fossil ants of Florissant show the same peculiarities, except that the males are not much rarer than the females. Thus the condition which Le Conte interpreted as indicating an absence of the worker caste during Miocene and premiocene times, is easily and naturally explained. It is strange that he failed to see this, especially as in the paragraph immediately preceding the remark above quoted, he calls attention to the following interesting resemblance between modern

FIG. 92. Male of *Aëromyrma* sp. from the Baltic Amber. (Original.)

FIG. 93. Worker of *Propodomyrma samlandica* sp. nov. from the Baltic Amber. (Original.)

lacustrine conditions and those which must have prevailed at Oeningen: "On Lake Superior, at Eagle Harbor, in the summer of 1844, we saw the white sands of the beach blackened with the bodies of insects of many species, but mostly beetles, cast ashore. As many species were here collected in a few days, by Dr. J. L. Le Conte, as could have been collected in as many months in any other place. The insects seem to have flown over the surface of the lake; to have been beaten down by winds and drowned, and then slowly carried shoreward and accumulated in this harbor, and finally cast ashore by winds and waves. Doubtless at Oeningen, in Miocene times, there was an extensive lake surrounded by dense forests; and the insects drowned in its waters, and the leaves strewed by winds on its surface, were cast ashore by its waves."

The conditions described by Le Conte for Lake Superior are common to all our Great Lakes. The insects drowned in them are often buried in the sand of the beaches and might eventually fossilize, but the Tertiary lakes of Oeningen, Radoboj and Florissant must have been much smaller, shallower and calmer bodies of water, and the insects that dropped into them or were swept into them by streams, were probably imbedded in the mud under water. Many of them were, of course, devoured by fishes. Professor Cockerell has sent me from Florissant several specimens of fossil fish excrement consisting almost entirely of the hard indigestible heads of ants. It is very unfortunate for the student that so few of the workers of the Oeningen, Radoboj and Florissant ants have been preserved, for our knowledge, as we have seen, is largely based on the worker caste and the males and females even of recent forms are so imperfectly known that fossils of these sexes are very difficult to classify, especially when the characters of most taxonomic value, such as the shape of the head, mouth-parts and abdominal pedicel are obliterated by flattening and distortion. Another great difficulty is encountered in attempting to correlate the

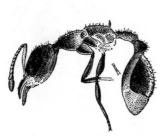

FIG. 94. Worker of *Electromyrmex klebsi* sp. nov. from the Baltic Amber. (Original.)

FIG. 95. Worker of *Stigmomyrmex venustus* from the Baltic Amber. (Mayr.)

males, females and workers of the same species. This is no easy task with carelessly collected recent ants, but with fossils, except those of the amber, it becomes almost impossible.

The ants of Oeningen and Radoboj were first studied by Heer (1849, 1856, 1867) before the taxonomy of recent ants had been placed on a firm basis by the researches of Mayr. It is therefore impossible to assign most of Heer's species to their proper genera, and although Mayr (1867b) was able to examine a number of the Swiss paleontologist's species, he did not have access to the types. Hence the whole ant-fauna of Oeningen and Radoboj must be reinvestigated by some one thoroughly acquainted with the recent ants. The species of the Baltic amber have been studied in a masterly manner by Mayr (1868*a*). A few additional species from the same formation were subsequently described by Ern. André (1895*a*) and Emery (1905*e*), and the latter has also described fourteen species from the Sicilian amber (1891*e*).

According to Handlirsch's list of fossil insects, of the 600 species of Hymenoptera that have been described from the Tertiary, 307 or more than half are ants. These insects must therefore have been very numerous in individuals, just as they are to-day. This is true alike of the Baltic amber and the shales of Radoboj, Oeningen and Florissant. Mayr examined 1,460 ants from the amber, Ern. André 698 and through the kindness of Prof. R. Klebs, of the Royal Amber Museum of Königsberg and Prof. W. Tornquist of the Königsberg University, I have been able to study nearly 5,000 of these beautiful specimens. Heer says: " The ants are among the commonest fossil animals of Oeningen and Radoboj. In the latter locality they predominate even more in proportion to the other insects than they do at Oeningen. Altogether I have examined 301 specimens, representing 64 species; from Oeningen 151 specimens of 30 species, from Radoboj 143 specimens of 37 species and from Parschlug 7 specimens belonging to 4 species." According to Scudder (1890), " the ants are the most numerous of all insects at Florissant, comprising, perhaps four-fifths of all the Hymenoptera; I have already about four thousand specimens of perhaps fifty species (very likely many more); they are mostly Formicidæ, but there are not a few Myrmicidæ and some Poneridæ." I have recently made a rapid preliminary study of the 4,000 specimens of the Scudder collection belonging to the Museum of Comparative Zoölogy, and of nearly 3,000 more found at Florrisant by Prof. T. D. A. Cockerell, Mrs. W. P. Cockerell, S. Rohwer and myself, and am able to confirm Scudder's statement. There are probably not more than 50 species in both collections, many of them being represented by a great number of specimens, and hardly 70, or one per cent., of the 7,000 specimens are workers.

Of the described Tertiary ants that can be unmistakably assigned to their respective subfamilies, 139 species are Camponotinæ, 25 are Dolichoderinæ, 85 Myrmicinæ and 27 Ponerinæ. A single species (*Anomma rubella*) is referred to the Dorylinæ by F. Smith (1868). I have not seen his description and figure of this insect, but his generic determinations of recent ants were often so erroneous that his competence to assign a fossil species to its proper genus may be doubted. The proportion of species in the other subfamilies is interesting because it is not unlike that obtaining at the present day. The number of individuals belonging to each subfamily can be satisfactorily given only for the ants of the Baltic amber. Of the 2,158 specimens examined by Mayr and André, 764 were Camponotinæ, 1,310 Dolichoderinæ, 59 Myrmicinæ and 25 Ponerinæ. The great preponderance of Dolichoderinæ is due to two species, *Bothriomyrmex gœpperti* (889 specimens) and *Iridomyrmex geinitzi* (248 specimens), which are represented by 1,137 specimens, or more than half of the total number. The species of Myrmicinæ and Ponerinæ are each represented by only a few individuals. From these facts Mayr concludes " that the Ponerinæ of the Tertiary exhibited the weakest development and have reached their full efflorescence in recent times." He advances a similar opinion in regard to the Myrmicinæ. Emery, however, has shown that this inference is erroneous, for the Ponerinæ—and the same is true of the Myrmicinæ—are much less arboreal in their habits than the Dolichoderinæ and Camponotinæ, and would therefore be much less frequently entrapped in the liquid exudations of succiniferous trees. Then, too, the Ponerinæ probably formed small colonies as they do at the present time. I have found several undescribed Ponerinæ and Myrmicinæ both in the Baltic amber and in the shales of Florissant, showing that these groups must have been at least as highly diversified in the Miocene and lower Oligocene as the other two subfamilies.

Only in the amber species have the genera been at all satisfactorily established. Those described from other formations are very largely guesswork. This is especially true of such genera as Heer's *Imhoffia, Attopsis* and *Poneropsis*. Other species were placed by him and Scudder in the recent genera *Lasius, Formica, Dolichoderus, Camponotus, Myrmica* and *Aphænogaster,* but probably many of these allocations are erroneous. The only genera not represented in the amber, but occurring in the Tertiary strata, are *Lonchomyrmex* (Fig. 90) and *Liometopum.* We may divide the genera of the Baltic and Sicilian ambers into two groups, the extinct and recent, and the latter may be subdivided into those still represented by species in Europe (palearctic), which are nearly all common to the nearctic region as well (circumpolar), and those now confined to the tropics of the Old World (paleotropical). Grouping the genera thus, we have the table on page 167.

Of the 40 genera included in this table, 13 are extinct and 27, or more than two thirds, are still living. Of the latter, a little more than half (14) are still represented in Europe and a little less than half (13) in the Old World tropics. It will also be seen that the ratio (7:4) of exclusively paleotropical to palearctic genera in the Sicilian amber is nearly twice that of the Baltic amber (11:13), although very few specimens of the former have been examined. But it should

BALTIC AMBER   SICILIAN AMBER

1. Extinct Genera

Prionomyrmex   *Acrostigma*
Bradoponera   *Hypopomyrmex*
Propodomyrma gen. nov.
Nothomyrmica gen. nov.
Electromyrmex gen. nov.
Stigmomyrmex
Lampromyrmex
Enneamerus
Paraneuretus gen. nov.
Protaneuretus gen. nov.
Rhopalomyrmex

2. Recent Genera

(a) Palearctic

Ponera   *Ponera*
Monomorium   *Cremastogaster*
Aphænogaster   *Tapinoma*
Myrmica   *Plagiolepis*
Leptothorax
Dolichoderus
Bothriomyrmex
Tapinoma
Plagiolepis
Prenolepis
Lasius
Formica
Camponotus

(b) Paleotropical

Ectatomma   *Ectatomma*
? Anomma   *Aëromyrma*
Sima   *Cataulacus*
Oligomyrmex   *Leptomyrmex*
Aëromyrma   *Technomyrmex*
Cataulacus   *Œcophylla*
Iridomyrmex   *Gesomyrmex*
Œcophylla
Dimorphomyrmex
Gesomyrmex
? Polyrhachis

be noted that all the palearctic genera enumerated for the Sicilian amber are also common to the paleotropical fauna of the present day. This will explain the following quotation from Emery (1893–'94) : " My studies on the ants of the Sicilian amber have demonstrated that at the beginning of the Tertiary, Europe had an ant-fauna of Indoaustralian character, still living and exclusively of this character in Sicily during

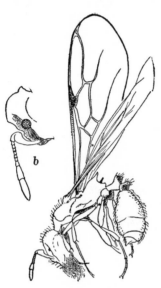

FIG. 96. *A*, Female of *Hy-popomyrmex bombiccii,* a singular Myrmicine ant from the Sicilian Amber. (Emery.) *b*, Side of head, showing eye and antenna more enlarged.

the formation of the amber; while to the north of the sea which at that time extended across Europe, representatives of this fauna, mingled with *Formica, Myrmica* and other recent holarctic types, lived in the forests of the Samland. After the disappearance of this sea the northern fauna pushed its way southward as far as the Mediterranean. Then came the Glacial epoch, which extinguished the Indian fauna in the north and drove its feeble remnants, mingled with arctic forms to the warmer localities of southern Europe. From these regions the present ant-fauna wandered back, with the disappearance of the ice, into the middle and northern portions of the continent. But the tropical forms had difficulty in returning, because the Mediterranean, the African deserts and the steppes to the eastward were so many barriers to their progress. The European ant-fauna therefore remains comparatively poor."

The mixture of arctic and tropical forms in the amber, a peculiarity which characterizes the other insects and the plants no less than the Formicidæ, has not been satisfactorily explained. Heer endeavored to account for it on the following assumption: " It is probable that the succiniferous forests also covered Scandinavia and that the conifers were able to grow even on the high mountains. As the amber region extended from Scandinavia to Germany, where a sea separated it from the remainder of the Germanic continent, we may see in this natural barrier the cause of the peculiar facies of the amber flora. It presents to our view the Scandinavian type of the Tertiary, mixed, in all probability, with a mountain or subalpine type. It is, in fact, conceivable that the plants and animals, embalmed as they were in their elegant amber sarcophagi, could be carried long distances without sustaining the slightest injury and could, therefore, present this exceptional appearance, which is seen nowhere else in the plants and animals of the ancient world. If we suppose that a river flowed down from the Sweden of that day and opened into the Tertiary sea near Dantzig, there would be nothing irrational in admitting that this stream might easily carry the amber in the resinous state from the distant localities and mountains of Sweden, so that the organic remains enclosed in the amber may have been gathered together from an extensive territory, from low as well as from mountainous countries, and may even belong

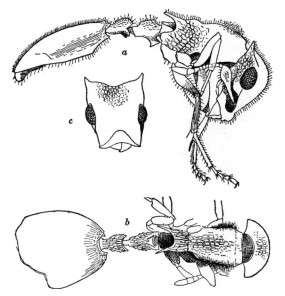

FIG. 97. Worker of *Cataulacus silvestrii* from the Sicilian Amber. (Emery.)   *a,* From the right side; *b,* from above; *c,* head from above.

to different Tertiary periods. . . . If we admit that the amber does not belong to one and the same epoch, we can explain why in the plants and animals of this formation the mixture of northern and southern types is so much more striking than it is in the remainder of the European Tertiary, and why among these we find several types peculiar to high latitudes or even to mountains."

At first sight Heer's assumptions are plausible and would seem to be supported by the fact that although ants of different genera are occasionally found enclosed in the same block of amber, these never, to my knowledge, belong to both arctic and tropical types. On the other hand, the fact that the tropical, like the extinct genera of the above table, are represented by very few specimens compared with the boreal genera, is not readily explained by assuming that a river brought down lowland and mountain forms from Tertiary Scandinavia and deposited them together in the beds of northern Germany, for on this assumption we should expect to find the lowland or tropical greatly in excess of the boreal specimens. It seems more natural to suppose that during the Lower Oligocene both the extinct and the tropical genera were already reduced to dwindling relics, though co-existing with the circumpolar ant-fauna which had taken possession of the amber forests. In other words, even at that time the modern genera were far and away the more vigorous and prolific in the Samland, which was to become their exclusive heritage after the glacial epoch had wiped out the tropical genera that were leading a precarious existence in the warmer and more sheltered spots. We may assume, therefore, that the greatest development of these southern genera in this northern region occurred during the Eocene or even during the

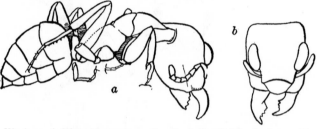

Fɪɢ. 98. Worker of *Dimorphomyrmex theryi* of the Baltic Amber. (Emery.) *a,* From the right side; *b,* head from above.

Mesozoic and that the adverse conditions, which culminated in the glacial epoch, were already beginning to destroy the older, tropical components of the Lower Oligocene fauna.[1]

To this consideration of the amber ants a few remarks on some of the more interesting genera and species may be appended:

1. *Ponerinæ.*—The most conspicuous of these is the large *Prionomyrmex longiceps* (Fig. 88) of the Prussian amber. Mayr described this species from a single specimen and I have found several more in the collections loaned me by Professors Klebs and Tornquist. This ant is allied to the Australian *Myrmecia,* the most primitive of living Formicidæ, but is even less specialized in the structure of the mandibles and abdominal pedicel. Another interesting but much smaller species is *Bradoponera meieri* (Fig. 89), which foreshadows our modern species

[1] Since these lines were written, I have found in one of the Königsberg collections a single block of amber containing a tropical *Dolichoderus* and a specimen of *Formica flori.* These ants, therefore, not only nested in the same locality, but foraged on the same tree.

of *Sysphincta, Proceratium* and *Discothyrea.* I have also found in the Prussian amber two new Ponerine genera related to the Indian *Diacamma* and *Lioponera.*

2. *Myrmicinæ.*—Of this subfamily there are several genera which show a wide range of organization and specialization in both the Baltic and Sicilian ambers. *Hypopomyrmex bombiccii* (Fig. 96), a singular ant described by Emery from the latter formation, although possessing 10-jointed antennæ and a well-developed venation in the wings, seems to represent a generalized type from which the modern Dacetonii may have sprung. In the Baltic amber *Stigmomyrmex* (Fig. 95), with 10-jointed, and *Enneamerus* with only 9-jointed antennæ, are remarkable forms. The latter, except in the small number of antennal joints, resembles the paleotropical *Pristomyrmex.* Several species referred by Mayr

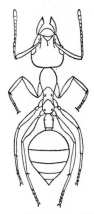

FIG. 99. *Œcophylla brischkei,* an arboreal Camponotine ant from the Baltic Amber. (Mayr.)

FIG. 100. Worker of *Gesomyrmex hærnesi,* a large-eyed, arboreal Camponotine ant from the Baltic Amber. (Mayr.)

to the genus *Macromischa,* because they lack spurs on the middle and hind tibiæ, do not belong to this genus, which is exclusively neotropical and largely West Indian, but must be placed in a new genus, which may be called *Nothomyrmica.* Much more like the true *Macromischa* than any of Mayr's species, especially in the structure of the thorax and petiole, is the extraordinary ant which I shall call *Electromyrmex klebsi* (Fig. 94). This and many other amber Myrmicinæ are as exquisitely sculptured as any of our modern species. *Propodomyrma* (Fig. 93) from the Baltic and *Acrostigma* from the Sicilian amber are related to the paleotropical *Podomyrma* and *Atopomyrmex,* but are simpler and more primitive in their structure.

3. *Dolichoderinæ.*—This subfamily is represented by a number of

interesting forms, many of which Mayr originally assembled in the genus *Hypoclinea*. Among these it is now possible to recognize species of *Dolichoderus*, *Iridomyrmex* and *Bothriomyrmex*. I have already called attention to the great abundance of two of the species of *Bothriomyrmex* and *Iridomyrmex*. In the material sent me by Professors Klebs and Tornquist there are single specimens of two new genera (*Protaneuretus* and *Paraneuretus*) of unusual interest. Both of these are closely allied to *Aneuretus*, a genus which is now represented by a single species, *A. simoni*, described by Emery from Ceylon (Fig. 140). This ant combines both Dolichoderine and

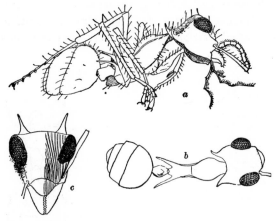

Fig. 101. Worker of *Gesomyrmex corniger* from the Sicilian Amber. (Emery.)
a, From the right side; *b*, from above; *c*, head of same from above.

Ponerine characters, having the head of the former, and the petiole and sting of the latter subfamily. In the Sicilian amber Emery has recognized a male *Leptomyrmex* (*L. maravignæ*), a genus now confined to Australia and New Guinea, an extremely small *Tapinoma* (*T. minutissimum*) and a *Technomyrmex* (*T. deletus*). As the Dolichoderinæ are practically absent from the African continent, the great development of this subfamily in the two ambers shows that the complexion of the European Tertiary ant-fauna was decidedly Indo-australian.

4. *Camponotinæ.*—The amber species of *Œcophylla*, *Gesomyrmex*, *Dimorphomyrmex* and *Rhopalomyrmex* are worthy of note. *Œcophylla* and *Gesomyrmex* occur both in the Baltic and Sicilian ambers, *Œ. brischkei* and *G. hœrnesi* (Fig. 100) in the former and *Œ. sicula* and *G. corniger* (Fig. 101) in the latter. These species of *Œcophylla* are closely related to *Œ. smaragdina*, the well known red tree ant of the

Old World tropics. *Gesomyrmex* was supposed to be an extinct genus till Ern. André (1892c) described a species (*G. chaperi*) from Borneo. In the same paper and from the same locality he described the type of another interesting Camponotine genus, *Dimorphomyrmex janeti.* This has polymorphic workers with large reniform eyes and 8-jointed antennæ. Some years later (1905e) Emery found a species (*D. theryi*, Fig. 98) of this same genus in the Baltic amber. *Rhopalomyrmex* (Fig. 91) resembles the neotropical *Myrmelachista.* It has 10-jointed antennæ, with 4-jointed clubs. Only a few species of the recent genera *Lasius, Formica* and *Camponotus* have been described from the Baltic

amber. The workers of one of the *Camponoti, C. constrictus* (Fig. 102), are peculiar in possessing ocelli and in having a thorax like *Formica.* Of this latter genus Mayr described only a single species, *F. flori*, which is very closely related to the existing *F. fusca.*

FIG. 102. Worker of *Camponotus constrictus,* with ocelli and sellate thorax, from the Baltic Amber. (Mayr.)

Our knowledge of the fossil ants of North America is insignificant. Scudder (1890) described *Lasius terreus* and a *Myrmica* sp. from the Green River Oligocene, *Camponotus vetus* and *Liometopum pingue* from the White River Oligocene and *Formica arcana, Dolichoderus obliteratus* and *Aphænogaster longæva* from the Quesnel formation, but neither the descriptions nor the figures make it at all certain that these ants are assigned to their proper genera. He also described and figured (p. 606, pl. III, fig. 32) the wing of an ant as that of a Braconid, *Calyptites antediluvianus.* Cockerell (1906) has described a *Ponera hendersoni* from the Florissant shales but the size of the specimen shows that it cannot be a true *Ponera.* My own studies on the Florissant ants are not yet completed.

Very few ants are known from the Quaternary, or Pleistocene. Some Camponotinæ and Dolichoderinæ are recorded by Handlirsch as having been found in the interglacial deposits of Re, Italy by Benassi (1896) and a number of unidentified species are enumerated from the copal, an amber-like fossil resin found in several tropical countries (Africa, Brazil, New Zealand, etc.). One of the earliest accounts of copal ants is that of Blochs (1776) who describes and figures specimens of what he calls *Formica saccharivora, salomonis, nigra* and *Formica* sp. In a fine series of copal specimens from Zanzibar in the American Museum of Natural History, I find well-preserved specimens belonging to the following genera: *Camponotus, Polyrhachis, Myrmicaria, Cremastogaster, Pheidole, Cataulacus, Atopomyrmex, Ponera* and *Anomma,* and to species very closely related to living forms of the same territory if not identical with them. In a specimen of copal from Demerara in the same collection there is a worker *Azteca.*

In reviewing the Tertiary and Quaternary ants one is impressed with two facts that have not been emphasized in the preceding pages. One of these is the close similarity of some of the ants of the Baltic amber to species now living in the same region. So intimate is this similarity that it may, in a few cases at least amount to identity, *e. g.,* in *Ponera atavia, Lasius schiefferdeckeri* and *Formica flori* which neither Mayr nor myself have been able to distinguish by any satisfactory characters from the living *Ponera coarctata, Lasius niger* and *Formica fusca!* Such cases bring home to us very forcibly the enormous age and stability of species which the student, dealing exclusively with living forms, would be inclined to regard as of very recent origin.

The second fact is one to which attention seems not to have been called by previous authors, namely, the absence of polymorphism in the workers of the Tertiary ants. There are, indeed, differences in stature between workers of the same species, but I have seen no specimens with sufficient differences in the size and shape of the head to indicate the existence of soldiers and workers proper. This is the more noticeable, because there are recorded from the amber several genera whose living species have polymorphic workers, such as *Anomma, Aëromyrma, Oligomyrmex, Camponotus* and *Dimorphomyrmex.* The known specimens of *Aëromyrma* and *Oligomyrmex* are all males and females, so that nothing is known concerning the workers, which may have been monomorphic. To the former genus belongs also, according to Emery, the *Pheidologeton antiquus* described by Mayr from a female specimen. The occurrence of *Anomma* in the amber is very doubtful. There remain then only the genera *Camponotus* and *Dimorphomyrmex* in which we might expect to find polymorphic workers. I have examined a number of specimens of the three species of *Camponotus* (*mengei, igneus* and *constrictus*) described by Mayr, but all of them have the form of the minor workers of our existing *Camponoti.* *Dimorphomyrmex theryi* was based on a single specimen, but several others which I have seen are monomorphic and in this respect unlike the living type of the genus from Borneo. It may be objected, of course, that no conclusions as to the presence or absence of polymorphism in the workers can be drawn from the amber material, both because it is too meager and because the soldiers do not forage like the workers and would not therefore be caught in the liquid resin.

This is certainly true of some genera, but not of *Camponotus,* to judge from our modern species. The fact remains that no polymorphic workers have been seen in the amber, that the great majority of the species certainly had only monomorphic workers, and that genera like *Pheidole* and *Pheidologeton,* so prominent in the Old World tropics to-day, are conspicuous by their absence. In the Pleistocene, however, genera like *Pheidole* and *Anomma* have their worker polymorphism fully developed, as I have observed in the Zanzibar copal, so that this condition must have made its appearance during the late, if I am right in concluding that it was absent during the early Tertiary.

CHAPTER XI

THE HABITS OF ANTS IN GENERAL

"La fourmi, qui n'est point dédaigneuse et accepte toute nourriture, est, pour cela même, moins inquiète et moins égoiste. C'est bien a tort qu'on l'appelait *avare*. Loin de la, elle ne semble occupée qu'a multiplier dans sa ville la nombre des copartageants. Dans sa maternité généreuse pour ceux qu'elle n'a pas enfantés, dans sa sollicitude pour ces petits d'hiers qui deviennent aujourd'hui de jeunes citoyens, naît un sens tout nouveau fort rare chez les insectes, celui de la fraternité."—Michelet, " L'Insecte," 1857.

Before proceeding to a more detailed account of the extraordinary habits and instincts exhibited by certain groups of ants, it will be advisable to say something about the activities that are more generally manifested by these insects as a group. And as the ants, like all other living organisms, pursue the three-fold aim of securing food, perpetuating their species, and shielding themselves and their offspring from enemies and the inclemencies of a changing physical environment, I may properly include my remarks under the general heads of nutrition, protection and reproduction. The activities implied by these terms, which must, of course, be taken in an elastic sense, necessarily coimplicate and supplement one another in the most manifold and intimate manner.

Permanent social life is, generally speaking, possible only for animals that have access to an abundant food supply. Species that have great difficulty in securing food or succeed in finding only a scanty and precarious amount, are compelled to lead solitary lives, or at any rate, can never form populous communities of long standing. It is evident, moreover, that only vegetable food is ever really abundant and that animal food is in the majority of cases limited in amount, difficult to obtain, or abundant only during certain seasons or in circumscribed localities. Predatory animals like the mammals, birds and insects of prey, are, therefore, solitary in their habits, whereas vegetarians, like the rodents, ruminants and many plant-eating insects, are prone to be more or less social. Ants, at first sight, would seem to be an exception to this rule, but this is only conditionally true. Although primitively carnivorous, these insects are unreservedly such only in the lower subfamilies like the Ponerinæ and Dorylinæ. The colonies of the former are usually rare, like those of the social wasps, and of small size, and the colonies of the Dorylinæ, though often very populous, lead a nomadic existence, since they must continually seek fresh hunting grounds in order to obtain the requisite amount of food. The ants of the three remaining subfamilies, though often predatory, have adapted themselves to a more varied diet and many of them have come to rely almost exclusively on vegetable food. The following are the sources from which these insects as a family derive their nourishment:

1. The original food of ants consists of other insects, especially helpless larvæ and other terrestrial arthropods such as spiders, myriopods and isopods, the dying imagines of the countless insects which fall to the earth when their life-work is completed, those which are just leaving their pupa-cases, and the fragments rejected by insectivorous birds and mammals.

2. The larvæ and pupæ of ants are a favorite food of certain species of *Eciton* and *Formica,* which are sufficiently intrepid to pillage the nests of other species. And, in fact, in times of need many species will eat their own offspring, which may, therefore, be considered as an ever-present and available food-supply stored up against periods of famine.

3. The excretions of plants, such as the sweet liquids exuding from the leaves and especially from the floral and extrafloral nectaries, the sap escaping from wounded stems, etc.

4. The honey-dew excreted by plant-lice (aphids), mealy bugs (coccids) and leaf-hoppers (membracids), and the secretions of the caterpillars of the butterfly family Lycænidæ. These liquids are, of course, plant juices that have undergone certain changes in the alimentary tract or glands of the insects.

5. The seeds of plants, especially of grasses and berries, drupes and fruits of all kinds, that have been injured by birds or other insects or by falling to the ground, for the ants are unable to gnaw through the tense skins or rinds of fruits. Some hypogæic species also feed on bulbs or tubers, the tender bark of roots, or the cotyledons of germinating seeds.

6. One tribe of ants, the *Attii* of tropical America, lives exclusively on fungus hyphæ, which they cultivate on vegetable substances carried into the nests.

Probably no single species of ant is able to draw on all of these sources of nutrition, but many species are sufficiently adaptable to utilize several of them. The fungus-growing ants are the most highly specialized in their diet and next to these some of the seed-storing, or harvesting species. Many ants, however, are more or less omnivorous, and many find it an easy matter to pass from one kind of food to another, if only it will yield to their mouth parts, that is, if it can be imbibed directly as a liquid or rasped off in minute particles from which the liquid can be expressed in the hypopharyngeal pocket. Ants with a specialized diet are described in detail in several of the chapters of this volume.

The protective habits are always very complex in colonial organisms, and this is particularly true of ants. These embrace nidification, to which Chapters XII and XIII are devoted, the care of the young, which has already been briefly considered, their personal care, and that of one another, their methods of defending themselves against enemies, of keeping their nests clean, of preserving the colony free from admixture with other species, etc.

The care which ants lavish on their young is the manifestation of an instinct so all-pervasive and obsessional that we are not surprised to find it embracing the adult members of the colony as well. That it extends even further and envelopes a motley multitude of alien arthropods, enabling them to live as guests or parasites in the ant colonies, will be shown in the chapters on myrmecophiles. Many observers, especially McCook, have dwelt on the exquisite care bestowed by ants on their own bodies and those of their comrades. Much of the time spent by these insects in the dark recesses of their nests is devoted to cleansing the surfaces of their bodies with their tongues and strigils. This process is not only necessary for removing all particles of the earth in which the ants work so much of their lives, but it also invests their bodies with a coating of slightly oleaginous saliva, which probably protects them from moisture and may be sufficiently antiseptic to prevent the growth of lethal moulds and bacteria.

This care of one another, however, does not cease with mutual cleansing and feeding, but is also exhibited in their habit of deportation. There can be little doubt that this peculiar habit has developed out of the instinct to carry the brood from place to place. It may be observed under certain conditions, as when a colony is moving to a new nest, or towards nightfall when inexperienced or weary workers have strayed some distance from the nest. In the former instance the workers that initiate the change of quarters carry their indifferent or recalcitrant companions bodily to the new nest. Of deportation under the latter conditions I once saw a beautiful example on the sandy deserts about Monahans, in western Texas. The straggling workers of the slow-moving harvesting ant, *Ischnomyrmex cockerelli,* were returning from all directions to their nests just as the cold December twilight was setting in. Each worker bore in her slender jaws a fellow worker that she had picked up while on her way home. In a similar manner the amazons are carried back to the nest by their slaves. In all cases the deported, on being seized by the deporting ant, assumes a quiescent attitude with her body curled and her legs drawn up as if she were dead. The position in which she is carried seems to be characteristic of certain species, though this matter has not been studied in any great detail. In *Formica* the deporting ant seizes the ant to be deported by the mandibles and holds her with back directed forward and downward and head uppermost. The deporting Texas harvester (*Pogonomyrmex molefaciens*), as McCook has shown (1879c), seizes her companion by the back of the pedicel and holds her head uppermost and ventral surface facing forward. These ants also have a peculiar habit of walking " tandem," sometimes in threes, the middle ant holding the pedicel of the first with her mandibles and the hind ant doing the same with the middle individual. In this position I have occasionally seen them returning to the nest and have wondered whether this strange performance could be a manifestation of the play-instinct, which Huber and Forel believe they have detected in certain species of *Formica*. In *Leptothorax* another position is assumed by the deported ant, which is held by her mandibles and curls herself up over the head of her carrier with dorsal surface directed forward. Still another position is adopted by *Leptogenys,* at least by the deported males, which are held by the neck and lie stretched out under the body and between the long legs of the deporting worker. The long slender cocoons of this ant are carried in the same manner.

The care of the nest is an important matter with all ants, for convenience no less than sanitation requires that the galleries and chambers be kept scrupulously clean. All species, therefore, remove any refuse food, empty cocoons, pupal exuviæ, meconial pellets, dead members of the colony, etc., to a proper distance from the living apartments. Veritable kitchen middens are established for this purpose, either in the open air or, if the colony is nesting under a large stone, in one of the deserted surface galleries.

A peculiar reaction is exhibited by nearly all ants in the presence of some substance that they cannot remove, such as a strong-smelling liquid. They throw pellets of earth or any other débris on the substance, sometimes in sufficient amount to bury it completely. The origin of this reaction which is often manifested in artificial nests, is very obscure. The fact that it is more frequently called forth by the presence of liquids would seem to indicate that it may be a normal method of staying the invasion of water into the galleries of the nest. It certainly has all the characters of a pure reflex, although, curiously enough, its manifestation under certain conditions has been regarded

as a demonstration of reasoning power. One observer who placed
tobacco juice across the path of some ants that were attending aphids
on a tree and saw the workers cast pellets of earth on the liquid, concluded that they were intentionally building a bridge, and therefore
credited them with a high degree of intelligence, whereas they were
merely exercising one of their customary reflexes and happened to
use enough earth to enable them to cross the obstacle and reach their
charges.

When a colony is attacked by alien ants or disturbed by larger
organisms, the character of the reaction varies with the species and the
size of the community. The workers of large colonies are usually aggressive, those of small colonies are timid and resort to more passive
means of defence. Usually the most immediate response, at least on
the part of a considerable portion of the colony, is precipitate flight
into the surrounding vegetation. This is invariably the resort of small
colonies of fleet-footed ants. Others, like *Myrmecina* and the smaller
species of the slow-footed Attii, " feign death " after the manner of
weevils or " skip-jack " beetles. They roll themselves up and remain
motionless for a time. In this posture the opaque, rough-bodied species
of *Cyphomyrmex, Trachmyrmex* and *Mycocepurus* are almost indistinguishable from particles of earth or sand.

Several species with peculiar mandibles manage to escape from
their enemies by leaping. In *Odontomachus,* the " tic-ant " of the
tropics, for example, the linear mandibles are inserted close together
at their bases and provided along their inner edges with a few sense-
hairs which are nearly as long as the mandibles. When the ant is
excited it opens its mandibles to their utmost extent, till they form
together a straight line at right angles with the long axis of the body.
Then as soon as a hard object is touched by the sense-hairs the blades
are suddenly closed, striking the object with their tips with sufficient
force to throw the insect backwards into the air for a distance of
several inches. This habit is also exhibited by other genera and species
with similar mandibles, for example by *Anochetus sedilloti* (Wroughton, 1892), *Strumigenys saliens* (Mayr, 1892a, 1893a) and probably
also by *Daceton* and *Acanthognathus.* According to Emery (1893*h*)
the large-eyed Brazilian *Gigantiops destructor* is able " to leap from
twig to twig," and an Indian ant with extraordinary mandibles, *Harpegnathus cruentatus,* is said to leap forward like a grass-hopper to a
distance of eighteen inches (Wroughton).

In many species the tough integument or specially developed spines
are an important means of defense. The workers of the large species
of *Atta* and *Acromyrmex* bristle with hard spines and tubercles, and

many other Myrmicinæ have at least a single pair of spines on the
epinotum, apparently to protect the vulnerable pedicel from the mandibles of their enemies. Other species (*Cryptocerus, Cataulacus, Strumigenys* and *Meranoplus*) can conceal their sensitive antennæ in deep
grooves or under broad projecting ridges along the sides of the head.

But ants do not have to rely altogether on such passive means of
defence. The means of direct attack on their enemies are almost as

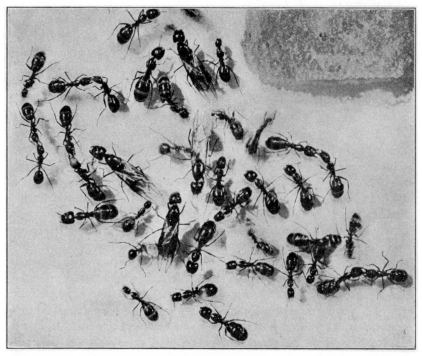

Fig. 103. Virgin females and workers of *Camponotus americanus*, showing five
pairs of the latter in the act of feeding by regurgitation. (Photograph by J. G.
Hubbard and O. S. Strong.)

varied and usually more efficacious. The mandibles are the principal
weapons and these alone in the larger species of *Camponotus* and *Atta*
are sometimes employed with telling effect. In the Myrmicinæ and
Ponerinæ their action is often supplemented by that of a well-developed sting. Many species of *Formica* spray their enemies with formic
acid, or inject it into their victim by moving the gaster forward and
centering its tip on the wound made by their mandibles. In battles
with other species or aliens of their own species they pull their opponents legs or antennæ with their mandibles and spray the tense mem-

branes between the joints. Enough of the acid is absorbed by the victim's blood to cause temporary paralysis or even death. The Dolichoderinæ and some Myrmicinæ (*Ischnomyrmex, e. g.*) smear their victims
with a malodorous secretion from the anal glands, which seems to have
an equally irritating and noxious effect. While in many species some or
all of these aggressive measures may be adopted by the workers in
general, other species have a specially protective caste in the soldiers
(*Camponotus, Atta, Pheidole,* etc.). In the subgenus *Colobopsis* the
soldiers guard the circular nest-entrance which they may even plug up
completely with their peculiarly modified heads (see p. 210). In *Polyergus* and *Leptogenys* all the workers have sickle-shaped mandibles
adapted to piercing the heads or bodies of their victims.

Since many species of ants often live together in the same stations,
means have been developed for preventing the fusion or mixture of
colonies and the consequent exploitation of one species by another.
The general truth of this statement is not invalidated by the existence
of a small number of interesting species that have developed symbiotic
or parasitic instincts. As a rule, members of different colonies, even of
the same species, are so hostile to one another that they cannot meet in
numbers without a pitched battle. This hostility tends to restrict the
feeding grounds of certain species within very narrow limits. It is
generally admitted that this segregation of colonies is due to the presence of characteristic odors which vary with the species, colony and
caste, and, according to Miss Fielde, also with the developmental stages
of the individual. The specific odor may be readily detected even by the
blunted human olfactories. Thus the odor of *Formica rufa* is pungent and
ethereal, of *Hypoclinea gagates* and *mariæ* smoky, of *Acanthomyops*
like the lemon geranium or oil of citronella, of the species of *Eciton*
and some *Pheidole,* like mammalian excrement, of *Cremastogaster lineolata* fainter but equally unpleasant, of *Tapinoma* like rotten cocoa-nuts,
etc. Undoubtedly ants are very quick to react to these various odors as
well as to the " nest-aura," or odor which every colony derives from
its immediate environment, brood, etc. For interesting accounts of
this important subject the reader is referred to the recent papers of
Bethe (1898) and Miss Fielde (1905c to e).

While the protection of the colony centers in the activities of the
workers, the reproduction both of the individual ants and of the colony
as a whole centers in the males and females. The mating of the sexes
differs according to whether only one or both of the sexual forms
possess wings. No species are known in which both sexes are apterous. In forms like *Anergates, Symmyrmica, Formicoxenus* and some
species of *Cardiocondyla* and *Ponera* the male is wingless, whereas this

is the case with the female in the Dorylinæ and in *Leptogenys*. In these cases mating must take place either within the nest or on the ground outside. When only the female is winged, unless it be possible for sisters and brothers of the same colony to mate,—and this is actually the case in *Anergates*—she must enter strange nests or meet the male while she is wandering about in the open. Observations on this subject are, unfortunately, very meager.

When both sexes are winged mating nearly always takes place in the air on what is called the nuptial, or marriage flight. Even among these species however, mating or attempts to mate have been observed in artificial nests, but this is certainly exceptional and its normal occurrence in wild colonies is rather doubtful. Apparently there are provisions for favoring cross fertilization between the sexes of different colonies. In the first place, it is rare to find colonies at the breeding season containing equal numbers of males and females. Usually one or the other sex greatly predominates and often only one is represented in a colony. Then, too, the nuptial flight for all the colonies of a particular species in the same neighborhood usually takes place on the same day or even at the same hour, so that the males of one colony have an opportunity of mating with the females from others. It is certain that the workers forcibly detain the impatient sexes in the nests till the propitious hour arrives. Why this should be the same for all the colonies in a given locality is not easily determined, but it is generally conceded to be due to meteorological conditions. This, indeed, seems to be the most natural explanation of the phenomenon.

Fig. 104. Winged and deälated female of *Camponotus americanus*, somewhat enlarged. (Photograph by J. G. Hubbard and O. S. Strong.)

When the hour for the nuptial flight draws near, a strange excitement pervades the ranks of the workers. At such times even the blind and etiolated workers of the hypogæic species venture out into the sunlight and accompany the males and females to the entrance of the nest. The winged forms move about in tremulous indecision, but, finally venture forth, run about on the stones or climb about on the grass-blades till they have filled their tracheæ with a plentiful supply of oxygen. Then they spread their wings and are soon lost to view high in the air. Their evolutions, so far as they can be observed, resemble those of the honey-bee so vividly described by Maeterlinck: " She, drunk with her wings, obeying the magnificent law of the race that chooses her lover, and enacts that the strongest alone shall attain her in the solitude of the ether, she rises still; and, for the first time in her life, the blue morning air rushes into her stigmata, singing its song, like the blood of heaven, in the myriad tubes of the tracheal sacs, nourished on space, that fill the center of her body. She rises still. A region must be found unhaunted by birds, else that might profane the mystery. She rises still; and already the ill-assorted troop below are dwindling and falling asunder. The feeble, infirm, the aged, unwelcome, ill-fed, who have flown from inactive or impoverished cities, these renounce the pursuit and disappear in the void. Only a small, indefatigable cluster remain, suspended in infinite opal. She summons her wings for one final effort; and now the chosen of incomprehensible forces has reached her, has seized her, and bounding aloft with united impetus, the ascending spiral of their intertwined flight whirls for one second in the hostile madness of love."

It must be noted, however, that there are several important differences between the nuptial flights of ants and honey-bees. In the case of the bees there is a single female for whom the males compete, whereas among ants there may be hundreds of females. Moreover the pairs of ants often descend to the earth in copula and always separate without the female tearing away the male genitalia. Nor does the female ant as a rule, return to the colony in which she was born. In both cases the males die soon after mating.

In the European literature there are many accounts of great nuptial swarms of ants, visible from afar like clouds of smoke. Similar swarms have also been witnessed in the United States. The species usually concerned in producing this phenomenon are the common *Lasius niger* and *Myrmica rubra*. The nuptials of our other species take place, as a rule, without attracting particular attention.

On descending to the earth the fertilized female divests herself of her easily detached wings, either by pulling them off with her legs and jaws or by rubbing them off against the grass-blades, pebbles or soil. This act of deälation is the signal for important physiological and psychological changes. She is now an isolated being, henceforth restricted to a purely terrestrial existence, and has gone back to the ancestral level of the solitary female Hymenopteron. During her life in the parental nest she stored her body with food in the form of masses of fat and bulky wing-muscles. With this physiological endowment and with an elaborate inherited disposition, ordinarily called instinct, she sets out alone to create a colony out of her own substance. She begins by excavating a small burrow, either in the open soil, under some stone, or in rotten wood. She enlarges the blind end of the burrow to form a small chamber and then completely closes the opening to the outside world. The labor of excavating often wears away all her mandibular teeth, rubs the hairs from her body and mars her burnished or sculptured armor, thus producing a number of mutilations, which, though occurring generation after generation in species that nest in hard, stony soil, are, of course, never inherited. In her cloistered seclusion the queen now passes days, weeks, or even months, waiting for the eggs to mature in her ovaries. When these eggs have reached their full volume at the expense of her fat-body and degenerating wing-muscles, they are laid, after having been fertilized with a few of the many thousand spermatozoa stored up in her spermatheca during the nuptial flight. The queen nurses them in a little packet till they hatch as minute larvæ. These she feeds with a salivary secretion derived by metabolism from the same source as the eggs, namely, from her fat-body and wing-muscles. The larvæ grow slowly, pupate prematurely and hatch as unusually small but otherwise normal workers. In some species it takes fully ten months to bring such a brood of minim workers to maturity, and during all this time the queen takes no nourishment, but merely draws on her reserve tissues.   As soon as the workers mature, they break through the soil and thereby make an entrance to the nest and establish a communication with the outside world. They enlarge the original chamber and continue the excavation in the form of galleries. They go forth in search of food and share it with their exhausted mother, who now exhibits a further and final change in her behavior. She becomes so exceedingly timid and sensitive to the light that she hastens to conceal herself on the slightest disturbance to the nest. She soon becomes utterly indifferent to her progeny, leaving them entirely to the care of the workers, while she limits her activities to laying eggs and imbibing liquid food from the tongues of her attendants. This copious nourishment restores her depleted fat-body, but her disappearing wing-muscles have left her thoracic cavity hollow and filled with air which causes her to float when placed in water. With this circumscribed activity she lives on, sometimes to an age of fifteen years, as a mere egg-laying machine. The current reputation of the ant queen is derived from such old, abraded, toothless, timorous queens found in well-established colonies. But it is neither chivalrous nor scientific to dwell exclusively on the limitations of these decrepit beldames without calling to mind the charms and sacrifices of their younger days, for to bring up a family of even very small children without eating anything and entirely on substances abstracted from one's own tissues, is no trivial undertaking. Of the many thousands of ant queens annually impelled to enter on this ultra-strenuous life, very few survive to become mothers of colonies. The vast majority, after starting their shallow burrows, perish through excessive drought, moisture or cold, the attacks of parasitic fungi or subterranean insects, or start out with an insufficient supply of food-tissue in the first place. Only the very best endowed individuals live to preserve the species from extinction. I know of no better example of the survival of the fittest through natural selection.

It is certain that the colonies of most species are founded in the manner here described. It is certain, moreover, that all this is rendered possible by the nutritive endowment of the queen. As the winged germ of the species she has all the advantages that a yolk-laden has over a comparatively yolkless egg. Now among the 5,000 known species of ants we should expect to find considerable differences in the quantity of nutriment stored up in the young queen. And this is unquestionably the case. In some species the queens are of enormous size, in others they are very small compared with the workers. And since the queens of average dimensions are able to start colonies by themselves alone, we should expect unusually large queens to accomplish even more, and very small ones less. This, too, is borne out by observation.

Unusually large queens are found in the genus *Atta,* a group of American ants that raise fungi for food, and are, so far as known, quite unable to subsist on anything else. The female *Atta* on leaving the parental nest is so well endowed with food-tissue that she not only can raise a brood of workers without taking nourishment, but has energy to spare for the cultivation of a kitchen garden.

Very different is the condition of certain queen ants poorly endowed with food-tissue, especially of some whose bodies are actually smaller than the largest workers of their species. Such queens are quite unable to bring up colonies unaided. They are, therefore, compelled after fertilization to associate themselves with adult workers either of their own or of a closely allied species. In the former case the queens may either remain in the parental nest and omit the nuptial flight, or return to the parental or to some other colony of the same species. In either case they add to the reproductive energy of an already established colony and thus prolong its life. If one of these poorly endowed queens, however, happens to alight from her nuptial journey far from any colony of her own species, she is obliged to associate with alien workers. And in this case, according to the species to which she belongs, one of three courses is open to her:

First, she may secure adoption in a small queenless colony of an allied species. Here she is fed, lays her eggs, and the resulting larvæ are reared by the strange workers. Eventually the alien workers die off and leave the queen and her own workers as an independent and sufficiently established colony, capable of rapid and often enormous multiplication. This I have called temporary social parasitism.

Second, the poorly endowed queen may establish herself in a colony of another species, but be unable, even after the workers have matured, to survive the death of the host colony, except, perhaps, by migrating to another nest of the same species. This is permanent social parasitism.

Third, the queen may enter a small colony of alien workers, and, when attacked, massacre them, appropriate their larvæ and pupæ, carefully secrete and nurse them till they hatch and thus surround herself with a colony of young and loyal workers that can bring up her brood for her without any drain on her food-tissues. This is the method of colony formation adopted by queens of *Formica sanguinea.* These queens thus manifest an instinct, hitherto supposed to be exclusively peculiar to the workers, namely, the instinct to rob the larvæ and pupæ of another species and bring them up as auxiliaries, or slaves.

Pierre Huber (1810) was the first to call attention to the method of colony formation adopted by the great majority of ants, but while we must still admire, in the light of our present knowledge, the accuracy of his statements, we must not forget that he did not actually observe the female ant bringing her firstling brood of workers to maturity. Subsequent authors have not failed to notice this important hiatus in the work of that gifted naturalist. Although Mayr in 1864 observed isolated female ants with eggs, the actual founding of a colony by a single queen was first witnessed by an American of somewhat doubtful reputation as a myrmecologist, Dr. Gideon Lincecum (1866, 1874a). Essentially the same account is repeated in McCook's larger work on the Texan agricultural ant (1879c).

The first to witness the founding of a colony in an artificial nest, that is, under conditions accurately controlled, was Sir John Lubbock. His account, originally published in 1879, is reproduced in the various editions of his well-known book on ants, bees and wasps. August 14, 1876, he isolated two pairs of *Myrmica ruginodis* and succeeded in keeping them in a perfectly healthy condition through the winter. The males died during the following April and May. The females laid during the latter part of April. Some of the young had pupated by the first of July and the firstling workers appeared and began to care for the remainder of the brood by the end of that month and the first week in August. This demonstrated, as Lubbock said, " that the queens of

Myrmica ruginodis have the instinct of bringing up larvæ and the power of founding communities."

McCook (1883*a*) published several careful observations by Edward Potts to show that young females of *Camponotus pennsylvanicus* "when fertilized, go solitary, and after dispossessing themselves of their wings, begin the work of founding a new family. This work they carry on until enough workers are reared to attend to the active duties of the formicary, as tending and feeding the young, enlarging the domicile, etc. After that, the queens generally limit their duty to the laying of eggs."

To any one who has given even a little attention to the insect life of our northern woods, it must seem strange that the founding of colonies by this ant should not have been recorded till 1883. Certainly no observation could be more easily made, for in many localities it is hardly possible to tear a strip of bark from an old log without finding one or more females of *C. pennsylvanicus* or of the allied varieties *ferrugineus* and *noveboracensis,* each in her little cell brooding over a few eggs, larvæ, cocoons or minim workers. Usually the cell is carefully excavated just under the loose bark in the decayed wood, but where pine logs are abundant these females often prefer to take possession of the deserted pupal cavities of a longicorn beetle (*Rhagium lineatum*). These cavities are surrounded by a regular wall of wood fibers arranged like the twigs in a bird's nest (Fig. 105).

Within more recent years the observations of Lincecum, Lubbock, McCook, and Potts have been repeatedly confirmed by continental authors. Blochmann (1885), Forel (1902*d*), Janet (1904), von Buttel-Reepen (1905*a*), Emery (1904*d*) and Mrázek (1906) have all published interesting notes on colony formation by isolated females of ants belonging to the common genera *Myrmica, Cremastogaster, Formica, Lasius* and *Camponotus.*

On more than one occasion during the past ten years I myself have been able, both in the field and in the laboratory, to test the truth of these observations. In fact, a catalogue of the North American species, in which I have seen evidence of the founding of colonies by isolated females, would comprise nearly all of our common ants. I have observed it in members of all the subfamilies except the Dorylinæ. Even the Ponerinæ, which I at one time supposed to be an exception, conform to the general rule, for I have found isolated females of *Odontomachus clarus* and *hæmatodes* in the act of establishing their formicaries. During May, 1895, I observed an unusually striking case of colony formation by queens of the Californian harvester (*Pogonomyrmex californicus*) on the edge of the Mojave Desert. This recalls the above cited observation of Lincecum on the Texan harvester. I arrived at Needles, California, May 23, a day or two after the nuptial flight of *P. californicus*. This was proved by the thousands of isolated females of this species, in the act of establishing their formicaries. The country in which I observed them was the sandy bottom on the

Fig. 105. *Camponotus pennsylvanicus* queen with incipient colony in abandoned cocoon of *Rhagium lineatum* under pine bark, slightly enlarged. (Original.)

right bank of the Colorado River and the adjacent low escarpment of the desert. The latter is interrupted by numerous short "draws," which are more or less sandy like the river bottom into which they open. The surface of the escarpment, however, is very hard and stony, but it, too, is furrowed by very small draws, often only a few inches wide and containing sand washed from the surrounding surfaces by the winter showers. After their nuptial flight myriads of *Pogonomyrmex* females had rained down over the whole hot, dry country for a distance of at least three miles to the south and as many to the west of the Needles. After losing her wings, each female sought out the regions of pure sand, avoiding the hard surfaces, and set to work digging a hole. The earth was brought out to one side of the

burrow so as to form a diminutive mound, which when completed was
about two inches in diameter. On May 23, during the hot morning
hours the females could be seen at work everywhere in the draws
and river bottom, often within a few inches of one another. Many
had already completed their burrows, which extended down obliquely
to a depth of three to four inches, and had closed the opening behind
them. It was an easy matter to dig a deälated female from each spot
indicated by a small fan-shaped mound or to tempt her to the surface
by inserting a straw into her burrow. A wind- or rain-storm would
have obliterated at once all traces of the whereabouts of these insects.
That they actually sought the pure sand, which is also the substance
in which the adult colonies are found, was seen on the top of the
escarpment. There each tiny draw was literally filled with incipient
nests, although none could be found on the hard intervening spaces
often hundreds of feet wide. The ants would, in fact, be quite unable
to excavate the hard soil. The comparatively small number of adult
colonies in the vicinity proved that but few of these isolated females
ever succeed in rearing a colony. They are doomed to rigid, all but
catastrophic, elimination, which only the best endowed and most favor-
ably situated can survive.

In the foregoing paragraphs attention has been repeatedly called
to the fact that an ant colony is started by a single isolated female.
This requires some qualification, since under very exceptional circumstances a couple of females from the same maternal nest may meet
after their marriage flight and together start a colony. During August,
1904, I found two deälated females of *Lasius brevicornis* occupying
a small cavity under a clump of moss on a large boulder near Colebrook, Conn. They had a few larvæ and small cocoons and a couple of
small callow workers. The colony was transferred to an artificial nest
and kept for several days. Both females were seen to take part in
feeding and caring for the single packet of larvæ and freeing the remaining callows from their cocoons. Without doubt these twin females
were sisters that had accidentally met under the same bit of moss and
had renewed the friendly relations in which they had lived before
taking their nuptial flight. June 16, 1907, I found a very similar colony
consisting of two deälated queens of *L. flavus* near Sion in the valley
of the Rhone. They were in a small earthen cavity under a stone and
had eggs and young larvæ, which they hastened to conceal when the
nest was uncovered. These cases are of considerable interest because,
as a rule, sister ants seem to be averse to such postnuptial partnerships.

Among certain ants the females may be retained and deälated by
the workers in the parental nest, or carried in and readopted just after

they have descended from the nuptial flight, for we often find more than one queen in a colony. In some species of *Formica* a single colony may thus accumulate more than fifty deälated queens. Certain observations also show that colonies may multiply by fission, the offshoots migrating to new nests and taking with them some of the queens. These nests may remain connected with the parental colony by runways, but in some cases (*Formica exsectoides*) they probably become independent commonwealths. This whole subject, however, is in urgent need of careful investigation, as it has important bearings on some of the cases of symbiosis to be described in future chapters.

The number of ants in a colony varies greatly according to the species, and evidently depends on the number and fertility of the queens and the nature and amount of the available food. In many species, like most Ponerinæ, and the ants of the genera *Leptothorax, Cardiocondyla, Xenomyrmex,* etc., among the Myrmicinæ, the colony, even at the apogee of its development, comprises only a few dozen, or at most, a few hundred individuals. But the average number for most species is much greater and may exceed a thousand or ten thousand. It is, however, very easy to overestimate the population of a colony. Forel (1874) estimated that a *Formica pratensis* mound of medium size contains 114,000 ants and that the largest formicaries may contain as many as 500,000. But Yung (1899, 1900) who has actually counted the ants in several hills of *F. rufa,* an ant which has larger colonies than *pratensis,* found the numbers to vary between 19,933 and 93,694. These numbers are not proportional to the size of the nest. He, therefore, believes that Forel's estimates are excessive. Pricer (1908) has recently given valuable statistics of *Camponotus pennsylvanicus* colonies from their inception to their adult stage, which is marked by the throwing off of males and virgin females. He finds that such adult colonies contain from 1,943 to 2,500 workers, and that they must be from three to six years old before they produce the sexual phases. It is very probable that the population of the adult ant colony, which is, after all, merely an enlarged family, fluctuates about a specific average or mean. With the exception of Pricer's work, no attempts have been made to determine this mean for our various species or its relation to the ethological environment. Here is a promising field for statistical study.

CHAPTER XII

ANT-NESTS

"Le premier objet qui frappe nos sens en commençant à étudier les mœurs des fourmis, c'est l'art avec lequel elles construisent leur habitation, dont la grandeur paroît souvent contraster avec leur petitesse; c'est la variété de ces bâtimens, tantôt fabriqués avec de la terre, tantôt sculptés dans le tronc des arbres les plus durs; ou composés simplement de feuilles et de brins d'herbe ramassés de toutes parts; c'est enfin la manière dont ils répondent aux besoins des espèces qui les construisent."—P. Huber, "Les Mœurs des Fourmis Indigènes," 1810.

Nothing is better calculated to illustrate the marvellous plasticity of ants than the study of their nesting habits. Not only may every species be said to have its own plan of nest construction, but this plan may be modified in manifold ways in order to adapt it to the particular environment in which the species takes up its abode. Even the same colony may adopt very different methods of building at different periods in its growth and development. Hence the study of formicine architecture becomes one of bewildering complexity and defies all attempts at rigid classification. Owing to this complexity it is impossible to form a correct conception of the general plan of architecture in a particular species without studying its nesting habits throughout its whole geographical range. In such a subject recourse to laboratory methods is of little avail, whereas careful and extensive observation in the field is all-important.

One remarkable peculiarity of ant-nests impresses us at the very outset when we compare them with the nests of the social wasps and bees, namely, their extreme irregularity. The ants have abandoned, if indeed they ever acquired, the habit of constructing regular and permanent cells for their brood. The advantages of such cells to the ants evidently do not outweigh the disadvantages of being unable to move their larvæ and pupæ from place to place when danger threatens or in response to the diurnal variations of warmth and moisture. In its essential features the typical nest is merely a system of intercommunicating cavities with one or more openings to the outside world (Fig. 106). Even these openings, or entrances, as they are called, are absent in the nests of hypogæic species, except at the time of the nuptial flight. The intercommunicating cavities may be excavated in the soil or in plants, and even preëxisting cavities often answer every purpose and save labor. The irregular form of the cavities is a characteristic so universal in ant-nests that it would seem to be preferred to a monotonous regularity. It may be important, in fact, in enabling the ants to orient themselves readily. The nest entrance is sometimes peculiarly modified to suit the needs of the various species. It may be left permanently

FIG. 106. Superficial galleries of *Acanthomyops latipes* as they appear on removing the stone that covers them. About ¼ natural size. (Original.)

open and guarded by workers or soldiers, or it may be closed at night; it may be enlarged or constricted for the purpose of regulating the ventilation of the cavities and preventing the inroads of enemies, it may be adroitly concealed or exposed to view and surrounded by conspicuous earth-works.

Even in this prevailing and opportunistic irregularity, however, there are singular differences of degree. The more primitive ants, like the Ponerinæ, build with a certain irregularity devoid of character. The Dorylinæ may hardly be said to build nests at all, but merely to bivouac in some convenient cavity under a stone or log, or they may temporarily occupy the nests of other ants or dig irregular runways beneath the surface of the soil. The higher ants, however, which form stationary and populous formicaries, devote a great deal of attention to architecture and work according to a more or less definite plan, which they skilfully modify to suit the conditions of a specific environment.

The nests of nearly all ants are the result of two different activities, excavation and construction. Both of these may be simultaneously pursued by the workers, or either may predominate to the complete exclusion of the other, so that some nests are entirely excavated in soil or wood, whereas others are entirely constructed of soil, paper or silk. As the nests of the latter type resemble those of the social wasps, one might be led to suppose that they represent the original ancestral form and that the excavated are degenerate types, but the prevalence of earthen nests among ants of the most diverse genera in all parts of the world, as well as the occurrence of similar nests among the solitary bees, wasps and Mutillids, would seem to indicate that even the most

Fig. 107. Crater of *Myrmecocystus semirufus* of the Mojave Desert; ⅓ natural size. (Original.)

ancient ants practiced both methods of nesting. In other words, the variable architecture of ants may be an inheritance from presocial ancestors and may have been well-established before these insects came to live in communities.

The methods employed by worker ants in making their nests are easily observed, and have been described in detail by Huber (1810) and Forel (1874). According to Forel, "They use their mandibles in two ways. When closed these organs form a kind of trowel, convex in front and above, concave beneath and behind, and pointed at the tip. This trowel is used for raking up the soft earth and also for moulding and compressing their constructions and thus rendering them more solid and continuous. This is accomplished by pushing the anterior portion of the closed mandibles forward or upward. In the second place, the mandibles, when open, constitute a veritable pair of tongues with toothed edges, at least in all of the workers of our native ants that do any excavating. They thus serve not only for transporting but also for moulding or comminuting the earth." The forelegs are used for scratching up the soil, in moulding pellets and patting them down after they have been placed in position by the mandibles, and are of so much assistance in this work that when they are cut off the insects are unable to excavate or build without great difficulty and soon abandon their work altogether.

Ants dislike to excavate in soil that is too dry and friable. When compelled to do this in artificial nests they will sometimes moisten it with water brought from a distance, as Miss Fielde (1901) has observed. She says that the workers of *Aphænogaster picea*, "like the Termites, are able to carry water for domestic uses. They probably lap the water into the pouch above the lower lip [the hypopharyngeal pocket] and eject it at its destination. A hundred or two of ants that I brought in and left in a heap of dry earth upon a Lubbock nest, during the ensuing night took water from the surrounding moat, moistened a full pint of earth, built therein a proper nest, and were busy depositing their larvæ in its recesses when I saw them on the following morning."

As even the most extensively excavated nests represent little labor compared with the nests of social wasps and bees, ants are able to leave their homes and make new ones without serious inconvenience. Such changes are often necessitated by the habit of nesting in situations exposed to great and sudden changes in temperature and moisture or to the inroads of more aggressive ants and larger terrestrial animals. Barring the intervention of such unusual conditions, however, most ants cling to their nests tenaciously and with every evidence of a keen sense of proprietorship, although there are a few species, besides the nomadic Dorylinæ, that seem to delight in an occasional change of residence. Wasmann has shown that *Formica sanguinea* often has summer and winter residences analogous to the city and country homes of wealthy people. The ants migrate from one to the

other during March and April and again during late summer or early
autumn (September). The summer nests are built in open, sunny
places where food is abundant and the conditions most favorable to
rearing the brood, whereas the winter nests are built under stumps and

Fig. 108. Nest of *Pogonomyrmex occidentalis* at Las Vegas, New Mexico; showing
the basal entrance on the southeastern side. (Original.)

rocks usually in protected spots in the woods, and are used as hiber-
nacula, or, very rarely, for protection from excessive heat during the
summer.

The migration of ants from one nest to another is determined upon
and initiated by a few workers which are either more sensitive to
adverse conditions or of a more alert and venturesome disposition than
the majority of their fellows. These workers, after selecting a site,
begin to deport their brood, queens, males, fellow workers and even
their myrmecophiles. The deported workers are at first too strongly
attached to their old quarters to remain in the new ones and therefore
keep returning and carrying back the brood. The enterprising workers,
however, obstinately persist in their endeavors to move the colony till
their intentions are grasped and become contagious. The indecision or
indifference of many of the workers may last for days or even for
weeks, during all which time files of ants move back and forth between
the two nests carrying their larvæ and pupæ in both directions. But

more and more workers keep joining the ranks of the radicals till the conservative individuals constitute such a helpless minority that they

FIG. 109. Large nest of *Formica exsectoides*, at Scotch Plains, N. J. Height 1 meter, basal diameter 3.25 m., circumference 10.21 m. (Original.)

are compelled to abandon the old nest and join the majority. I once observed a colony of agricultural ants (*Pononomyrmex molefaciens*) which for at least two years had occupied a nest directly in front of my house in Austin, Texas. In the autumn of the third year when certain workers decided to establish a new nest in a vacant lot about seventy feet away, I observed that it required nearly three weeks to overcome the attachment of all the workers to their old home.

Forel and Escherich (1906) distinguish two types of ant-nests, the temporary and the permanent, but this does not involve corresponding differences in architecture. The same is true of Forel's convenient distinction of monodomous and polydomous colonies. The nest of a monodomous colony is a circumscribed unit, whereas a polydomous colony, as the name implies, spreads over several nests, the inhabitants of which remain in communication with one another and may visit back and forth. This may lead to the development of accessory structures, like covered runways, but in other respects the architecture is merely a repetition of that of the simple nest. For convenience we may adopt the following classification:

A. Nests in the Soil.
    a. Small crater nests.
    b. Large crater nests.
    c. Mound or hill nests.
    d. Masonry domes.
    e. Nests under stones, logs, etc.
B. Nests in the Cavities of Plants.
    1. Nests in preformed cavities of living plants.
        a. In hollow stems.
        b. In hollow thorns.
        c. In tillandsias.
        d. In hollow bulbs.
    2. Nests in woody plant-tissues, often in cavities wholly or in part excavated by other insects.
        a. In or under bark.
        b. In twigs.
        c. In tree-trunks.
        d. In galls, pine-cones, seed-pods, etc.
C. Suspended Nests.
    a. Suspended earthen nests.
    b. Carton nests.
    c. Silken nests.
D. Nests in Unusual Sites (in houses, etc.).

E. Accessory Structures.
        a. Succursal nests.
        b. Covered runways.
        c. Tents, or pavilions.

Accurate delimitation of the foregoing categories is, of course, impossible, since two or more of them may be combined in the same nest. Thus some ants construct carton nests in dead logs or under stones, others extend their galleries from dead logs into the underlying soil. Then there are also transitional forms between the various categories, as, for example, between the small and large crater nests, and between the latter and mound nests. And lastly, a single formicary may gradually pass through a series of these categories during its growth and development.

Nests in the Soil.—These always consist of a subterranean portion comprising a number of more or less irregular excavations and may or may not have a definite superstructure surmounting the entrance or entrances (Fig. 106). The excavations, which are usually widely separated but are occasionally compactly branching or anastomosing, may be divided into chambers and galleries. The former are more spacious, with flattened floors and vaulted roofs, but of extremely variable size and outline; the latter are more tenuous, being more or less tubular connections between the chambers themselves and between these and the nest openings. Chambers and galleries are most sharply differentiated from each other in the fungus-growing ants, especially in the typical genus *Atta*. These nests will be described in greater detail in a future chapter. Suffice it to say in this place that the chambers of ants of the subgenera *Trachymyrmex* and *Mycetosoritis* are large spherical cavities, whereas the galleries are uniform, tubular passages entering and leaving the chambers at rather definite points. In several species the chambers have the appearance of being strung along a single vertical gallery like beads on a thread. The chambers in most ant-nests are used as nurseries for the brood and for the assemblage of the ants themselves. In species which store seeds several of the chambers near the surface may be set apart as granaries, and in the Attii nearly all the chambers of the nest are given up to fungus gardens. In the nests of the honey-ants the replete workers, or honey-bearers, hang from the hard, vaulted roofs of the chambers furthest removed from the surface, while the brood is reared in the small and more superficial apartments.

The incipient nests of all soil-inhabiting species are essentially alike in presenting only the subterranean excavations. Ants in this stage of colonial development are exceedingly timid and take the greatest care to conceal the situation of their nests. The excavated soil pellets are therefore carried some distance from the nest opening and scattered about irregularly, and the entrance itself is often kept closed with a few pebbles or so adroitly concealed in a tuft of grass or under a prostrate leaf that it is impossible to find the nest without carefully following some worker that happens to be returning from a foraging excursion. This habit of concealment is retained even by adult colonies of timid species (*Dichothorax* and *Leptothorax*). Sometimes the earthen pellets are scattered over a wide circular area so as to produce what may

FIG. 110. *Formica rufa* nest 2.15 meters high and 9.8 meters in diameter; pine forests of Belgium. (Photograph by G. Severin.)

be called a rudimental crater (*Myrmecocystus mojave* and *Aphæno-gaster treatæ.*) Another form of rudimental crater is seen in species like *Trachymyrmex septentrionalis,* which dumps all the excavated soil in an elliptical or crescentric heap at a distance of several inches from the opening, and in *Pogonomyrmex occidentalis* and *californicus,* which, on first establishing their nests, arrange the soil in a fan-shaped sector at the opening (Fig. 165, *A*). In older nests of these ants the crater is completed by the gradual enlargement of the sector along its radii and arc till it becomes a circle (Fig. 165, *B*). The typical crater which is the commonest form of ant-nests in regions devoid of stones and is best developed in light soil or pure sand, is often constructed with exquisite care. It is at once restored or rebuilt after destruction by rain or wind. In sandy regions most ants carry out the sand-grains one by one and deftly lay them on the walls of the crater. Among the Attii, however, the excavated sand is moulded into large polygonal pellets of uniform size in which the grains are agglutinated by moisture.

What I have called small craters vary from a couple of centimeters to 10 or 15 cm. in diameter. They are constructed by many of our species of *Pheidole, Myrmica* and *Prenolepis*, by *Lasius americanus, Dorymyrmex pyramicus, Monomorium minimum, Camponotus americanus* and by the smaller species of *Pogonomyrmex, Myrmecocystus* (Fig. 107), etc. These craters vary greatly in size and shape, some being very flat and ring-like, with a clear space between the central opening and the crater wall (*Nylanderia arenivaga*), others very high and narrow, and almost chimney- or tower-shaped, with the opening on the summit (*Trachymyrmex turrifex, Mycetosoritis hartmani* and *Lasius americanus*). In some species there are numerous craters corresponding to as many nest entrances, and the walls of these craters may be strung along in a series (*Pheidole vinelandica*) or more or less fused with one another (*Ph. dentata* and *morrisi, Solenopsis geminata*).

Large craters, from 20–50 cm. or even more in diameter, are constructed by several of our North American ants, notably by *Atta texana, Mœllerius versicolor, Ischnomyrmex cockerelli* (Fig. 156), *Messor pergandei* (Fig. 152), *Pogonomyrmex badius, comanche* and *californicus, Myrmecocystus melliger* and *hortideorum,* and several species of *Formica* (*F. schaufussi, munda, subpolita,* etc.). These craters, especially in *Formica,* may be multiple and fused with one another like the small craters, and thus form extensive flattened elevations, perforated with openings (*F. subsericea, neoclara, neocinera,* etc.). It has been suggested that the craters, though consisting of materials brought to the surface and rejected during excavation, may nevertheless be of use to the ants in protecting their nest entrances from the wind. Forel has observed that the walls of the craters of certain desert ants, like *Messor arenarius* of the Sahara, are raised to a greater height on the windward side.

Just as it is difficult to make anything more than a purely artificial distinction between small and large crater nests, so it is by no means easy to distinguish certain large craters from mound, or hill nests. The latter are usually much larger than the craters, not because they represent more extensive excavation in the underlying soil, but because they represent a large amount of material collected by the workers from the territory surrounding the nest. This accumulation is perforated throughout with galleries and chambers and consists of earth, small pebbles and vegetable detritus such as straws, twigs, pine-needles, leaves, etc. The proportions of these various constituents differ greatly in the different species. In our eastern *Formica exsectoides* (Fig. 109) which constructs conical mounds sometimes a metre in height and two to three in diameter at the base, earth greatly predominates, whereas in the European *F. rufa* (Fig. 110) and our western subsp. *obscuripes*

Fig. 111. Mound of thatching ant (*Formica obscuripes*) of Colorado, made of coarse twigs and grasses. (Original.)

(Fig. 111) the dome-shaped nest consists of a mass of sticks or pine-needles resting on a large crateriform earthen base. In *Pogonomyrmex molefaciens* and *occidentalis* (Fig. 108) the mound consists very largely of pebbles. The number and position of the nest openings is also highly variable. In *F. rufa* the numerous openings are scattered over the whole surface of the mound, in *F. exsectoides* they are mostly aggregated in a broad belt around the base, in *molefaciens* there is a single opening at or near the summit, whereas in *P. occidentalis* the single entrance is situated at the base, and almost invariably on the southern or eastern side (Fig. 108). There can be little doubt that the mound nests of the species of *Pogonomyrmex* mentioned above have arisen from the large crater, which is the only form of nest in most species of the genus, through stages like those shown in Fig. 165. In *F. rufa* and *exsectoides,* however, the mound seems to have developed from multiple fused craters like those of *F. sanguniea, neocinerea* and *subsericea,* species which are also in the habit of accumulating a certain amount of detritus about the openings. This habit in the various mound-building ants is most easily observed when their nests are constructed near railway tracks. In such situations the *Pogonomyrmex* and *Formica* workers bring together great quantities of locomotive cinders and place them on their nests, so that the latter stand out as black hillocks in striking contrast with the surrounding soil and vegetation. In certain localities in Arizona, *P. occidentalis* also covers its mounds with the dung-pellets of spermophiles, and Wasmann has noticed that the European *F. pratensis* employs rabbit dung and the dried flower-heads of *Centaurea* in the same manner.

Forel has shown that the mounds of *F. rufa* serve the important purpose of incubators for the brood. During the breeding season the leaves and sticks of which they consist tend to acquire the high temperature of a compost heap, and thereby accelerate the development of the larvæ and pupæ. Escherich has found that the temperature of the mounds is sometimes 10° C. higher than that of the surrounding air and must be much higher than that of the galleries in the subjacent soil. Undoubtedly the gravel mounds of *Pogonomyrmex barbatus, molefaciens* and *occidentalis* are equally useful as incubators.

Other mound nests, differing from the foregoing in their smaller size and compact earthen structure, have been designated by Forel as masonry domes (domes maçonnés). This authority, who in 1900 made a hurried myrmecological excursion through the Atlantic States, was surprised to find that many circumpolar ants (*Lasius niger* and *flavus, Formica fusca* and *sanguinea*), which construct masonry domes in Europe, fail to exhibit this peculiarity in the United States. He concluded that these structures, which, like the large mounds, serve as incubators, must be unnecessary in this country on account of its great annual extremes of climate. This inference is certainly premature, for although it is true that many of the circumpolar species do not make domes in the Atlantic States, they have this habit in the Mississippi Valley and Rocky Mountains, where the annual extremes of temperature are even greater. *Formica subsericea* and many species of *Lasius* and *Acanthomyops* become dome builders in Illinois and Wisconsin, although it must be admitted that the term "masonry domes" is not always strictly applicable to their nests, since the earth of which they consist is not firmly compacted but carried up rather loosely around grass and plant stems. I have frequently seen such mounds of *Lasius aphidicola, Acanthomyops interjectus* and *claviger* and *F. subsericea*

fully 30 cm. in height and 60 cm. to 1 m. in diameter. In the Rocky
Mountain region large mound nests of *Pogonomyrmex occidentalis,
Formica obscuripes, opaciventris* and *argentata* abound, and in these
regions they are much needed for maturing the brood, as the nights are
cold in the summer and the heat of the daylight hours must be utilized.
Formica glacialis, one of the varieties of *F. fusca,* in Maine, makes

Fig. 112. Nest of *Formica integra* in a huge pine stump, showing vegetable detritus accumulated by the workers in the crevices of the bark and about the roots. (Original.)

true masonry domes like the European ants, and in this region such
nests must be very useful as incubators since the summers are short and
comparatively cool.

I am able to confirm Forel's statement that in hilly or mountainous
regions ant-nests are most abundant on the eastern and southern
slopes. He says: " I have observed this repeatedly and also more recently here in America. Here, too, the same explanation applies: The
morning sun awakens and urges the ants to work. During the afternoon it is sufficiently warm so that this stimulus is unnecessary. Hence

the advantage of an eastern exposure which lengthens their daily activity. On a western slope, on the contrary, they lose the early morning hours, are too warm in the afternoon and are unable to do much after nightfall." Those nests, therefore, have the most favorable position which are exposed to the sun in the morning and shaded in the afternoon. Not only is this advantage apparent in the greater abundance of nests on southern and eastern slopes, but the nests themselves may show structural adaptation to the position of the sun. I have already called attention to the constant position of the nest opening at the base of the southern or eastern slope of the mounds of *Pogonomyrmex occidentalis*. Huber says that the yellow ants (*Lasius flavus*) of Switzerland " serve as compasses to the mountaineers when they are enveloped in dense fogs or have lost their way at night; for the reason that the nests, which in the mountains are much more numerous and higher than elsewhere, take on an elongated, almost regular form. Their direction is constantly from east to west. Their summits and more precipitous slopes are turned towards the winter sunrise, their longer slopes in the opposite direction." These remarks of Huber have been recently confirmed by Tissot (Wasmann, 1907*a*) and Linder (1908). The latter has shown that the elongate shape of the mounds is due to the fact that the ants keep extending them in an easterly direction in such a manner that only the extreme easterly, highest and most precipitous portions are inhabited by the insects. I have observed a similar and equally striking orientation of the mounds of *Formica argentata* in the subalpine meadows of Colorado.

By far the greatest number of ant-nests, at least in many parts of the world are excavated in the soil under stones, logs, boards, etc. Most of our ants, including even those that construct large mounds, are very fond of nesting in such places during the younger colonial stages. In fact only two of our terricolous species—*Dorymyrmex pyramicus* in the Southern, and *Prenolepis imparis* in the Northern States—are so rarely found under stones as to indicate that they have a pronounced aversion for such sites. The advantage of nesting under stones is considerable, for these not only protect the entrances, galleries and chambers from rain and wind and enable the ants to dispense with the labor of roofing over their surface excavations, but they are of even greater service in conserving the moisture in the underlying soil while rapidly taking up the sun's heat and thus accelerating the incubation of the brood. Nearly all ants prefer flat stones of moderate dimensions and not too deeply buried in the soil. Many *Formicæ* of the *rufa* and *sanguinea* groups (*nepticula, difficilis, consocians, microgyna, obscuriventris, oreas, ciliata, dakotensis, integra, rubicunda,* etc.) bank the edges of the stones with earth or plant detritus into which they often extend their galleries and chambers for the aëration and incubation of the brood. Even the mound-building forms frequently start their nests in this way and gradually heap the detritus up over the stones till they are concealed under typical domes and the original lapidicolous habit of the colony is no longer recognizable. In the North American forests the logs and branches strewn about on the ground afford a substitute for stones and cover the nests of many glade ants, such as *F. rubicunda, integra, hæmorrhoidalis, Aphænogaster fulva,* etc., *F. integra* (Fig. 112) in the Eastern and *hæmorrhoidalis* in the Western States fill out the spaces in and under logs with vegetable detritus. Ants are not fond of nesting under cow dung, but in Texas I have found *Solenopsis geminata* and *Camponotus fumidus* resorting to such nesting sites in regions where stones were scarce and moisture and protection from the intense heat of the sun nowhere else to be found. Forel has made similar observations in the high mountain pastures of Switzerland (1874).

the interior has been eaten out by the Cynipid larva, the imago of which leaves the gall by a circular aperture in its side. Hundreds of recently fertilized females of several different species of ants annually take up their homes and start their formicaries in these hollow spheres. On examining several thousands of these galls in the vicinity of Austin, Texas, I found a considerable percentage of them inhabited by colonies of the following ants which are here enumerated in the order of increasing frequency: *Leptothorax fortinodis, Leptothorax obturator, Colobopsis etiolata, Cremastogaster clara, Camponotus decipiens, Cam-*

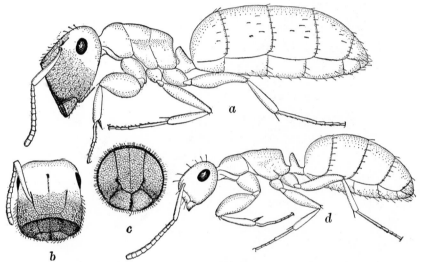

Fig. 115. *Colobopsis etiolata* of Texas. (Original.) *a,* Soldier in profile; *b,* head of same, dorsal view; *c,* head from anterior end; *d,* worker.

ponotus rasilis. The species of *Leptothorax* and *Colobopsis,* which never form large colonies, inhabit the galls permanently, the *Cremastogaster* and *Camponotus* use them mainly during the incipient colonial period. Two of the species, *L. obturator* and *C. etiolata* are especially interesting on account of their methods of modifying and guarding the nest entrance. The former ant is very small, and the solitary female on entering the gall finds the opening made by the gall-fly inconveniently large. She therefore plugs it up with wood-fillings mixed with saliva. When the small workers of her first brood hatch, they perforate the middle of the diaphragm with an opening just large enough to permit their bodies to pass in and out (Fig. 113). Occasionally this same ant nests in twigs of the hop-tree (*Ptelea trifoliata*) that have been hollowed out by a small carpenter bee (*Ceratina nana*). In such nests the larger opening at the end of the twig is occluded and then perforated in the

FIG. 116. Gall of *Holcaspis cinerosus* on live oak, showing soldier of *Colobopsis etiolata* closing the round hole in the gall with its head. (Original.)

same manner. The same habit is also seen in other ants, for example in *Camponotus sexguttatus* of the American tropics. Fig. 114 shows the ends of a couple of twigs of the sea-grape (*Coccoloba uvifera*) which I found at San Juan, Porto Rico. They have been plugged with ligneous carton by the nest-founding queens and subsequently perforated by the workers.

Even more interesting is the behavior of *Colobopsis etiolata* when it nests in *Holcaspis* galls. This ant (Fig. 115) has strongly marked soldiers, with peculiar truncated, roughened, stopper-shaped heads which

Fig. 117. *Holcaspis cinerosus* gall opened to show ants and their galleries in its woody substance. Two workers and three soldiers are shown; one of the latter in the act of closing the hole which serves as an entrance. (Original.)

exactly fit the circular holes in the galls (Figs. 116 and 117). These individuals are, therefore, told off to act as animated portals to the nest. When a worker wishes to forage on the branches of the oak, it approaches the stationary soldier from behind and palpates its gaster.

The soldier moves aside to let the worker pass out and then at once moves its head back into the circular aperture. In order to enter, the returning worker has to stroke the soldier's truncated forehead, and the guardian again steps aside for a moment. Though most abundant in the oak-galls, *C. etiolata* occasionally nests in the hard wood of tree trunks and branches (*Carya myristicæfolia*), apparently in preformed larval burrows. This seems to be the usual method of nesting of *C. pylartes* of Texas. Forel has described very similar nests and habits for the European *C. truncata* (1874, 1893*h*, 1894*e*, 1903*f*) which nests in twigs of the walnut tree. More recently I have seen another species (*C. culmicola*) nesting in the hollow culms of sedges (*Cladium jamaicense*) in the "swashes" of the Bahamas. In this case the nest often extends over several internodes of the plant and each is perforated with a circular opening occluded by the head of a soldier (Fig. 118). The slightly truncated heads of the soldiers of many wood-inhabiting species of *Camponotus* suggest very similar habits. The same inference may be drawn from the structure of the head in the soldiers of a peculiar Texan *Pheidole* (*Ph. lamia*) which nests in slender galleries under stones. In this insect the anterior surface of the head is remarkably like that of *Colobopsis* and may be said to present a striking case of convergence (Fig. 3*H*).

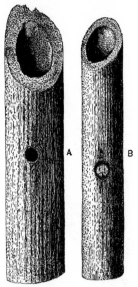

FIG. 118. Pieces of culms of a sedge (*Cladium jamaicense*) inhabited by the Bahaman *Colobopsis culmicola*. (Original.) *A*, Showing the perfectly circular nest opening; *B*, same closed with the truncated head of the soldier *Colobopsis*.

The old galls on our northern oaks, and especially those of *Eurosta solidaginis* and *Gelechia gallæsolidaginis* on the stems of golden rod (*Solidago*) are often tenanted by colonies of *Leptothorax curvispinosus* (Patton, 1879). This ant, however, is more frequently found in hollow twigs, especially in those from which the pith has been removed by small carpenter bees (*Ceratina dupla*). Even dried seed-pods, nuts and pine-cones may furnish convenient quarters for ant colonies. *Leptothorax longispinosus* occasionally nests in hickory nuts from which the kernel has been removed by squirrels. Professor C. H. Eigenmann sent me from Cuba some dried bean-pods containing colonies of the pale yellow *Camponotus inæqualis;* and Mr. William T. Davis has given me a couple of cones of *Pinus rigida* from Lakehurst, N. J., each inhabited by a colony of *C. nearcticus.*

Suspended Nests.—The suspended nests, like the majority of epiphytic plants, are found only in the forests of the tropics. They are true constructions throughout, consisting of earth, carton or silk, built so as to enclose anastomosing chambers and galleries. Earthen suspended nests, or "ant-gardens," were recently discovered by Ule (1905) in the forests of Brazil (Fig. 179). They are constructed by several species of ants (*Azteca olithrix, ulei* and *traili* and *Camponotus femoratus*), which

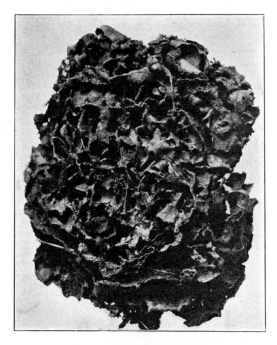

FIG. 119. Nest of *Cremastogaster lineolata,* made of carton and leaves; Colorado. ½ natural size. (Original.)

carry up particles of earth and build them into spherical masses, sometimes of the size and appearance of bath-sponges around the branches of trees. According to Ule, the ants even plant the seeds of epiphytes in this earth, so that it may be held together by the roots and thus acquire greater consistency for the support of the enclosed galleries. This statement is open to some doubt, as it is evident that such suspended earth-masses in a humid tropical forest may easily become seeded with epiphytes without the intervention of the ants. Even in temperate regions there is a slight approach to this kind of nest in the masses of earth which are sometimes built up around the stems of herbaceous plants by certain European species of *Lasius, Myrmica* and by *Tapinoma erraticum.* I have seen similar nests fashioned by *Myrmica canadensis* in the bogs of New England.

Although a few ants in temperate regions are able to make carton nests, the majority of carton-builders are found in the tropics and it is

Fig. 120. Carton nest of *Azteca trigona* on branch of *Cecropia adenopus;* Santa Catharina, Brazil, ¼ natural size. From a specimen in the American Museum of Natural History. (Original.)

only in these regions, as I have said, that the nests are suspended from trees. In Europe *Lasius fuliginosus* and *Liometopum microcephalum* construct carton nests in hollow logs, and in the Western and Southwestern States *Liometopum apiculatum* and *Cremastogaster lineolata* (Fig. 119) make similar nests under stones. In the tropics suspended carton nests are built by ants belonging to the genera *Camponotus,*

Polyrhachis, Azteca (Fig. 120), *Dolichoderus* (Fig. 121), *Cremastogaster, Macromischa, Myrmicaria* and *Tetramorium,* representing the three more specialized subfamilies. The genera *Azteca* and *Cremastogaster,* the former a cosmopolitan, the latter an exclusively neotropical group, seem to contain the greatest number of carton-building species. Certain Indian and African species of *Cremastogaster* have long been known to construct large spherical or egg-shaped paper formicaries. Sykes (1836) and Kirby (1837) described and figured those of *C. kirbyi* of India. Later Mayr (1878), Wroughton (1892) and Rothney (1895) published accounts of the similar nests of *C. rogenhoferi* and *ebeninus.* Another species (*C. artifex*) according to Mayr, builds carton nests in Siam and Singapore. In Madagascar, according to Forel (1891*b*), the carton nests of *C. ranavalonæ* may reach a diameter of 30 cm., and *C. tricolor* makes similar structures. In the same island the nests of *C. schencki* are said to be large enough to enclose the body of a man. In Africa, according to Mayr (1896, 1901), *C. inconspicua, marginata, stadelmanni, opaciceps, hova* and *peringueyi* all make carton nests. Tropical America is also rich in species with similar proclivities. F. Smith

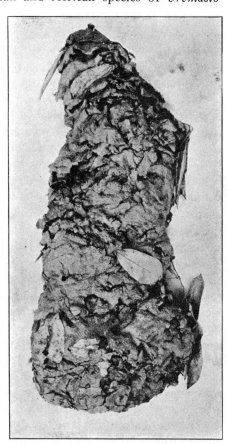

Fig. 121. Carton nest of *Dolichoderus quadrispinosus* of Colombia, ¼ natural size. From a specimen in the American Museum of Natural History. (Original.)

(1858) figured and described the paper nests of the Mexican *C. montezumia,* and Forel (1899*a*) has more recently shown that similar structures are built by *C. sulcata, ramulinida* and *stolli.* Even in North America *C. lineolata,* which usually nests in logs or in paper nests under stones (Fig. 119), occasionally makes suspended nests on bushes (Atkinson, 1887).

Many species of the highly arboreal genus *Azteca* build carton nests, and these show considerable range of variation in form and structure. The suspended nests of *A. aurita, mathildæ trigona, multinida, lallemandi, schimperi,* etc., are more or less egg-shaped or cylindrical and resemble the carton nests of termites and *Cremastogaster.* Other species (*Azteca barbifex, stalactitica, decipens* and *lanians*) build their paper nests in the form of long pendant stalactites. *A. hypophylla* lives under leaves whose edges are attached to tree-trunks by means of carton, *A. xysticola* lives in meandering carton galleries on the surface of large stones in forests, and *A. muelleri, constructor* and *nigriventris* use more or less carton in the construction of their galleries in plant cavities.

The interesting paleotropical genus *Polyrhachis* contains several carton-building species. These ants like the African *Tetramorium aculeatum* and certain species of *Dolichoderus* attach their small, and often very symmetrical nests to the surfaces of leaves. Forel has examined the condition of the carton in the different genera above mentioned and finds that it varies greatly in its consistency, from the hard ligneous substance of *Lasius fuliginosus* to the finest, thinnest and most pliable paper. It consists of vegetable particles glued together with a secretion of the maxillary glands, which are enormously developed in the workers of some of the species. When the nests are built in hollow logs (*Lasius fuliginosus, Limometopum microcephalum*) wood filings are used in making the carton. In some species like the South American *Dolichoderus attelaboides* cow-dung is employed. According to Forel (1893*h*), *D. bispinosus* of tropical America uses the seed-hairs of the silk-cotton tree (*Bombax ceiba*). *Tetramorium africanum* and *aculeatum* of the Congo line their nests with a thin layer of carton consisting of vegetable detritus and fungus hyphæ (Santschi, 1908). The flexibility of the carton in all cases depends on the amount of glandular secretion mixed with the vegetable particles.

The most extraordinary ant-nests are undoubtedly the silken structures inhabited by certain species of *Œcophylla, Camponotus* and *Polyrhachis,* all genera belonging to the same subfamily. The following description of several silken nests of *Polyrhachis* and the nests of *Œcophylla* is taken from Forel (1894*e*):

" The nest of the *Polyrhachis jerdonii* Forel which I received from Ceylon through Major Yerbury is very interesting. This species builds upon leaves small nests, the wall of which greatly resembles in appearance the shell of many Phryganeidæ larvæ. Pebbles, and especially small fragments of plants, are cemented together by a fine web or

woven together, and form a rather soft, tough web-like nest wall of a
greyish-brown color. . . . We see here unmistakable small fragments
of plants bound together in a web by peculiar silk threads. These silk
threads are found, upon close examination, to be of very irregular
thickness, often branching, and in many cases issuing from a thicker
crosspiece. . . . *Polyrhachis dives*, however, no longer needs any foreign materials. It makes its nest wall out of pure silk web, exactly like
coarse spun yarn or the web of a caterpillar. The web is of a brown-
ish-yellow color and is fixed between leaves, which are lined with it and
are bound together. Mr. Wroughton, of Poonah, India, sent me such a
nest, simply between two leaves. A still finer, softer silk web, finer and
thicker than the finest silk paper, very soft and as pliable as the finest
gauze, though much thicker, of a brown color, is produced by *Polyrhachis spinigera* Mayr. . . . Here we find no more crosspieces but only
silk webs. They are, however, still irregular, of varying thickness, spun

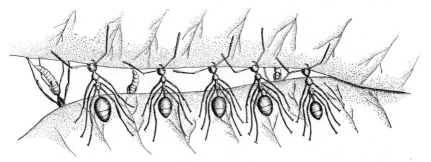

Fig. 122. Brigade of *Œcophylla smaragdina* workers drawing edges of leaves
together while other workers bind them together with the silk spun by the larvæ.
(Doflein.)

across each other into a web. This web is fixed in a wonderful manner
in the ground, where it forms the lining of a funnel-shaped cave which
is widened out into a chamber at the bottom. . . . The large nest constructed in the foliage of trees, between the leaves by *Œcophylla
smaragdina* Fabr., one of the most common ants of tropical Africa,
forms, however, the prototype of spun ant-nests. A great number of
leaves are fastened together by a fine white web, like the finest silk
stuff. This web, apart from the color, has exactly the same appearance,
both to the naked eye and under the microscope, as that of *Polyrhachis
spinigera*. The leaves are usually fastened together by the edges. The
nest is larger, and the large, long, very vicious, reddish or greenish
worker ants live in it, with their grass-green females, their black males,
and the whole brood. They form very populous colonies in the

branches of the trees." A similar nest is constructed by *Camponotus senex* in the forests of Brazil.

As no adult insects are known to produce silk, the question naturally arises as to how the ants manage to make these nests. Misled by some inadequate observations on *Œcophylla* published by Aitken in 1890, Forel concluded that the silk was spun by the workers from the maxillary glands. In other words, he believed it to be equivalent to the glandular component of the carton manufactured by other ants. Subsequent observations, however, have shown that it has a very different and more remarkable origin. Ridley (1890) discovered in Singapore that *Œcophylla* uses its larvæ for spinning the silk of its nest. His observations were confirmed by Holland and Green (1896, 1899) and Dodd (1902). Chun in 1903 observed that the spinning glands or sericteries of *Œcophylla* larvæ are enormously developed and Saville Kent is said to have figured the spinning larvæ of *Œcophylla* from specimens found in Australia (1897). More recently (1905) Doflein has published some interesting observations on the nest-building habits of this ant. I here reproduce his account together with three of the accompanying figures. On opening a nest for the purpose of studying its reconstruction Doflein observed "that while the majority of the workers betook themselves to defending their home, a small troop went to work to repair the rent I had made in its wall. They lined up in a very peculiar manner in a straight row as shown in the figure. They seized the edge of the leaf on one side of the rent while they fastened themselves by means of the claws on their six feet to the surface of another leaf (Fig. 122). Then they began to pull, slowly and cautiously, carefully placing one foot behind the other, while the edges of the rent were seen gradually to approach each other. It was a bizarre sight to see the animals thus working side by side with their bodies in a regular parallel series.

"Now others came and began to cut away very carefully the remnants of the old web along the edges of the rent. They bit through the web with their mandibles and tugged at it till it came away in shreds. These shreds they carried off in their mandibles to an exposed part of the nest and let them fly away in the wind, opening their mandibles whenever there was a gust. I also saw a whole row of ants carry a big piece of web to the tip of a leaf, open their mandibles as if at command and permit the piece to flutter away.

"These operations lasted nearly an hour when suddenly a strong gust of wind tore the edges of the rent out of the ants' mandibles and frustrated all their efforts. But the ants were not discouraged. Again a long row of them lined up along the slit and in half an hour they had again brought the edges pretty close together.

"I was about to despair of seeing the important part of the performance, when several workers emerged from the interior of the nest, each with a larva in its mandibles. And they did not run away with the larvæ in order to deposit them in a place of safety, but came right up to the exposed opening of the slit. There they were to be seen climbing about behind the row of workers making very odd motions with their heads. With their mandibles they held their larvæ so tightly that the bodies of the latter appeared to be compressed in the middle. Perhaps this pressure is necessary in order to excite the function of the spinning glands. It was a strange sight to see them passing between the ranks of the workers that were holding the leaves. While the latter remained on the outside, the former carried on their

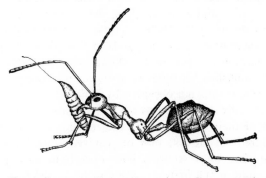

Fig. 123. *Œcophylla smaragdina* worker using a larva as a shuttle in weaving the silken tissue of the nest. (Doflein.)

work within the nest. This made it more difficult to observe what was going on. But after some time I could see very clearly that the larvæ were carried with their anterior ends directed forward and upward (Fig. 123) and were kept moving from one side to the other of the rent. At the same time each worker waited an instant on one side of the rent, as if it were gluing fast the thread spun by the larva by pressing its head against the leaf, before the head of the larva was carried across the rent and the same process repeated on the other side. Gradually, while they tirelessly pursued their task, the rent was seen to be filled out with a fine, silken web.

"There could be no doubt that the ants were actually using their larvæ both as spools and shuttles. As several workers toiled close together, they were able to cross and re-cross the threads and thus produce a rather tenacious tissue. This could be cut with the scissors and the small pieces presented a singular appearance under the microscope.

A lot of threads were seen crossing one another and in some places a number of the threads had a common direction. This agrees very well with my observations on the origin of the web. The ants are in the habit of moving to and fro with the larvæ many times in the same place before changing their position and running the thread crosswise. In this way strands are soon formed on the outside of the web and evidently save labor on the part of the ants that are holding the leaves together. Under the microscope the threads appear to be glued together at many points. This condition is very easily explained when we consider that each thread is moist and sticky for a few moments after leaving the sericteries of the larva.

" I was unable to see the thread itself while it was being spun as it is too delicate and transparent to be visible to the unaided eye. I tried to see it with a strong lens, but in a twinkling dozens of ants had covered my eyelids and after brushing them away I was only too glad to be able to see at all." Doflein (1906) has recently described and figured the voluminous spinning glands of *Œcophylla* (Fig. 124, *D*).

Dodd's account of the nest-building of *Œcophylla virescens* in Queensland, published in 1902, is also worth quoting, as it contains some interesting details not observed by Doflein:

" It is decidedly interesting to observe the insects engaged upon the construction of their domiciles. If the foliage is large or stiff, scores or even hundreds of the ants may be required to haul a leaf down and detain it in place until secured, both operations taking considerable time. It is quite a tug-of-war matter to bring the leaf into position and keep it there. The insects holding it have a chain of two or three of their comrades fastened on to them, one behind the other, each holding its neighbor by its slender waist, and all at full stretch and pulling most earnestly. What a strain it must be for poor number one! When the leaf is far apart the ants form themselves into chains to bridge the distance and bring it down; many of these chains are frequently required for a single leaf. I have seen a large colony at work upon a new nest, and several of these chains were from three to four inches long; altogether there were many of them in evidence, some perpedicular, others horizontal. Up or along these living bridges other ants were passing.[1]

" Now for the web material used to build the nests. It is furnished in fine and delicate threads by the larvæ; moreover, I have only seen what appears to be half-grown examples used for the work—I have

[1] There can be no doubt of the accuracy of this extraordinary observation. During the summer of 1909 Prof. Ed. Bugnion showed me some fine drawings of these chains of *Œcophylla* workers, which he had recently observed in Ceylon. Prof. Bugnion did not know of Dodd's observations.

never seen a large larva being made use of. The soft and tiny grubs are held by the larger ants, who slowly move up against those pulling. Each grub is held by the middle, with head pointing forward, its snout is gently made to touch the edges of the leaves where they are joined, it is slowly moved backwards and forwards and is undoubtedly issuing a thread during the operation, which adheres to the leaf edges, and eventually grows into the web. When this web is completed it must be composed of several layers to be strong enough for the purpose of securing the leaves. Whether the larva is an unwilling instrument or not in its captor's mandibles is a point which cannot be ascertained. Maybe it is, for it cannot be comfortable in such a position. However, it supplies the web; perhaps if it were not robbed of the web for the benefit of the community it would be able to spin a cocoon for itself, in which to undergo the delicate change into the pupa state, for I have never seen a cocoon, all pupæ being quite naked.

" When contemplating the work done in these nests one cannot but marvel at the wonderful ingenuity displayed, or in endeavoring to form some idea of the vast number of larvæ which must be utilized to supply the connecting web even for a moderately sized nest, for with trees with narrow leaves, like *Eucalpytus tesselaris* for instance, many scores of leaves are required to form a nest, and each must be sewn."

Without knowing of these various observations on the Old World *Œcophylla,* Goeldi discovered the same method of nest-weaving in the Brazilian *Camponotus senex.* His observations together with a figure of a nest of this ant, have been published by Forel (1905*d*). Similar observations made by Jacobson (1905) on *Polyrhachis dives* (edited by Wasmann, 1905) and by Karawaiew (1906) on *P. muelleri* and *alexandri* prove that the silken nests of the ants of this genus are also spun by the larvæ. The latter author has described the complicated and voluminous sericteries in the larvæ of *P. muelleri* (Fig. 124*A*). Thus we have indisputable proof that the ants of three different genera, inhabiting the tropics of both hemispheres, have acquired the extraordinary habit of employing their young as instruments, or utensils, in the construction of their nests. Here, as in so many other instances, organs and functions originally developed for a very different purpose —in this particular case for spinning the pupal cocoon—have been adapted and transferred to a very different purpose.

Nests in Unusual Situations.—In this category we may include antnests in human dwellings, ships, etc., tenanted by such species as *Monomorium pharaonis* and *destructor, Pheidole megacephala, Solenopsis molesta* and *Prenolepis longicornis.* These, of course, originally lived in nests in the soil, but on becoming house-ants they took to the crevices of the walls and woodwork. According to Forel (1874), certain European ants (*Lasius emarginatus* and others) often nest in stone masonry. In our Atlantic States *Leptothorax longispinosus,* which originally nested under small stones lying on boulders or in old nuts lying on the ground, frequently nests between the stones of the rough stone walls that enclose woods or pastures.

Accessory Structures.—Ant colonies do not always confine their constructive activities to the nest in which they are rearing their brood, but may extend their influence over the wider area on which they are accustomed to seek their subsistence. Evidences of this influence are seen in the great, bare clearings, sometimes 3–10 meters in diameter, with which *Pogonomyrmex occidentalis, P. barbatus* and its several varieties surround their gravel cones or discs. In addition to these clearings, *P. barbatus* also makes paths that radiate out into the surrounding vegetation, sometimes to a distance of 20 to 30 meters. These

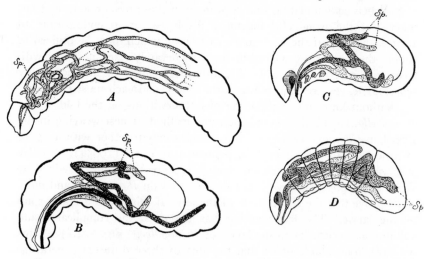

Fig. 124. The spinning glands (sericteries) of ant larvæ. (Karawaiew and Doflein.) *A,* Larva of *Polyrhachis muelleri; B,* of *Lasius flavus; C,* of *Tetramorium cespitum; D,* of *Œcophylla smaragdina;* the spinning glands (*sp*) are most highly developed in the two forms (*A* and *D*) which are used as shuttles in weaving the nest.

are most beautifully developed on the high plateau not far from the City of Mexico, where they are sometimes 10–20 cm. broad and resemble footpaths. More boreal species, like *Formica pratensis* of Europe and *F. integra* of the United States, often make tenuous paths which are roofed over along much of their extent with vegetable detritus and connect the different nests of a colony with one another. These and other species of *Formica* are also fond of constructing along their pathways, what Forel (1874) has called succursal nests, small excavations often resembling true nests, but used by the workers merely as places in which they can rest while foraging or escape from the heat of the sun or the pelting rain.

The tendency to construct such succursals or to establish several nests connected by run-ways is also apparent in many arboreal ants like the species of Œcophylla, Polyrhachis, Cremastogaster and Liometopum. To this habit must also be traced the construction of aphid or coccid tents, sheds or pavilions, as they are variously called. Though often at some distance from the true nests in which the brood is reared, these structures, which are usually made of carton or agglutinated earth may be regarded, nevertheless, as vestigial nests adapted to a specific purpose. Huber (1810) and Forel (1874) have described the aphid and coccid tents of European ants. Similar structures may also be seen in the tropics. On the island of Culebra I found carton tents that had been built by a variety of Cremastogaster victima over coccids on the lower surfaces of the leaves of Cordia macrophylla, and in the mountain forests of Porto Rico a yellow Iridomyrmex (I. melleus) was seen to make similar structures along the prominent ribs on the under sides of the gigantic reniform leaves of the ortegon (Coccolobis rugosa). Titus (1905) has shown that in Louisiana Iridomyrmex humilis occasionally makes coccid sheds on the surfaces of fruits like the persimmon. In our Northern States the versatile little Cremastogaster lineolata builds earthen or carton sheds which have been described by Osten Sacken (1862), Couper (1863), Trelease (1882) and myself (1906b). These structures are of small size, rarely more than 4 cm. long, more or less cylindrical or fusiform, enclosing some twig covered with plant-lice or mealy bugs (Figs. 205–209). A small round opening is left in the wall of the tent for the ingress and egress of the workers. Even the ants which spin silken nests among leaves often construct pavilions for their aphids, coccids, membracids and Lycænid caterpillars. Jacobson has observed this in Polyrhachis dives and Dodd gives the following description of these tents in Œcophylla virescens: " Not only do these strangely used larvæ provide the web to build up the nests, but they are carried considerable distances to various branches, generally near the ends, and they are there induced to furnish material for forming shelters and retreats for various scale insects, ' hoppers' and caterpillars with which the ants fraternize. Upon a tree may be seen several of these enclosures, or a dozen, occasionally many more; as a rule a few leaves joined together. Upon large-leaved trees, like Careya australis or Eucalyptus platyphylla a single leaf doubled over and fastened down will form a sufficient

cover. Upon pulling any of these apart a small flat scale in great
numbers will be found adhering to the leaf. Upon another species
of tree, *Acacia* say, perhaps ' hoppers ' only of a particular kind, with
horned head, and their larvæ and pupæ may be found."

The striking character of the tents described in the preceding paragraph leads naturally to the question of their function and of the
instincts of which they are an expression. There are several possible
answers to such a question. We may suppose that the tents are built,
first, for the purpose of preventing the escape of the aphids and
coccids to other plants or to other parts of the same plant; second,
for the purpose of protecting these insects and the ants themselves from
exposure to cold, air-currents, moisture, or light; third, for the purpose of protecting the aphids and coccids from their natural enemies
or from other ants. For some or all of these purposes the tents would
seem to be admirable contrivances. It is probable that the aphids and
coccids make the same appeal to the ants' sense of ownership as their
own larvæ and pupæ. This is certainly true of some ants, like our
species of *Lasius* which are fond of cultivating snow-white root aphids
and coccids in their subterranean galleries. Whenever the stones covering the nests are overturned, the workers seize their charges in their
mandibles and hurry away with them to a place of safety. It is natural, therefore, that ants should try to prevent the escape of their
charges from a sense of proprietorship such as all ants display towards
their own brood. Protection of the ants themselves from the air, and
especially from the sunlight, is of great importance while they are
waiting among the plant-lice for the accumulation and excretion of the
honey-dew. Indeed, few of the species known to construct pavilions
are at all fond of the open sunlight. This is certainly true of many of
those mentioned in the preceding paragraphs. We may infer, therefore, that the ants probably build tents primarily for their own comfort
and protection.

In concluding this chapter attention must be called to the fact that
ants which have become parasitic on other species tend to lose completely the ability to excavate or construct nests. It is believed that
even *Formica sanguinea,* which is only slightly dependent on its
slaves, shows an inclination to neglect the labors of excavating. More
completely parasitic genera, like *Polyergus,* though still possessing
worker forms, are able to dig in the earth with their fore feet when
opening up the galleries of the ants whose brood they are robbing, but
they leave the construction of the nest entirely to the slaves. In highly
parasitic genera, such as *Anergates, Wheeleriella,* etc., which have no
worker forms, nest-building is, of course, a long-lost art.

CHAPTER XIV

THE PONERINE ANTS

"Si tout est matière en ce monde, on surprend ici le mouvement le plus immatériel de la matière. Il s'agit de passer de la vie égoiste, précaire, et incomplète à la vie fraternelle, un peu plus sûre et un peu plus heureuse. Il s'agit d'unir idéalement par l'esprit ce qui est réellement séparé par le corps, d'obtenir que l'individu se sacrifie à l'espèce et de substituer ce qui ne se voit pas aux choses qui se voient. . . . Aussi est-il curieux, presque touchant, de voir comme l'idée nouvelle tâtonne d'abord dans les ténèbres qui enveloppent tout ce qui naît sur cette terre. Elle sort de la matière, elle est encore toute matérielle. Elle n'est que du froid, de la faim, de la peur transformés en une chose qui n'a pas encore de figure. Elle rampe confusément autour des grands dangers, autour des longues nuits, de l'approche de l'hiver, d'un sommeil équivoque qui est presque la mort."—Maeterlinck, "La Vie de L'Abeille."

The doubtful or indifferent attitude which investigators have assumed of late towards phylogeny, partly through abuse of the historical method on the part of some of its advocates, who have failed to emphasize the provisional and highly problematical character of their speculations, and partly through the attacks of a few experimentalists, who would make us believe that they alone possess the key to all biological knowledge, can hardly be regarded as more than temporary—a silence without complete acquiescence in the prevailing fashion of scientific thought. Although biologists now rarely undertake phylogenetic speculations on a grand scale, they are, perhaps, more active than ever in pursuing such speculations within the more modest confines of species, genera and families, where comparatively slight differences between organisms restrict the problem and the investigator moves with surer touch and deeper conviction. It may, indeed, be confidently asserted that no one can undertake the study of any small group of animals or plants in all its aspects without feeling the need of an historical explanation of the manifold relationships which he constantly witnesses. This is particularly true of such compact groups as the Formicidæ, which are represented by a sufficient number of closely related genera and species to show, both in structure and habits, certain definite, progressive tendencies of development.

Of the five subfamilies of Formicidæ only one, the Ponerinæ, comprises unmistakably primitive and generalized forms and therefore constitutes a group of two-fold interest, first, as the ancestral stirp of the higher subfamilies, and second, as the oldest existing expression of

social life among the Formicidæ—the stage in which we have just
passed, to use Maeterlinck's words, from the "precarious and incomplete egoistic to a social life with its slight accession of certainty and
happiness." In order to appreciate this prospective and retrospective
value of the Ponerinæ, it will be necessary to consider the taxonomy
and especially the habits of these insects. Unfortunately many of the
species are rare and live only in the inaccessible portions of the tropics,
so that little is known of their habits. I have published some observations (1900*a*, 1900*b*, 1903) on our North American species, representing several of the tribes (*Parasyscia augustæ, Stigmatomma pallipes,
Lobopelta elongata, Pachycondyla harpax, Pseudoponera stigma, Neoponera villosa, Ponera pennsylvanica, Platythyrea punctata, Odonto-*

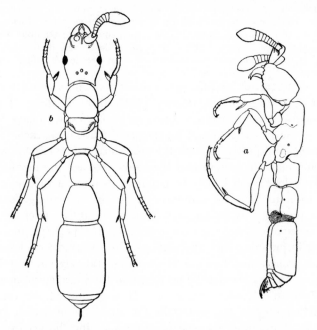

FIG. 125. *Parasyscia augustæ* of Texas. *a,* Worker; *b,* apterous female. (Original.)

machus clarus and *hæmatodes*). Cook has observed the habits of the
Guatemalan kelep (*Ectatomma tuberculatum*), recently introduced into
Texas for the purpose of exterminating the cotton-boll weevil, and
there are some notes on other forms scattered through the literature.

The classification on pages 134–137 shows that the Ponerinæ comprise a number of different tribes, and this number will undoubtedly be augmented, when the subfamily has been carefully studied,
beyond that of any of the other subfamilies. So much differentia-

tion would seem to contradict the statement that the Ponerinæ represent the ancestral stirp of the Formicidæ, but when we stop to consider that we are dealing with a very ancient group, the surviving relicts of a great cosmopolitan and probably Mesozoic fauna, this differentiation is what we should expect. The more recent and specialized subfamilies, with the exception of the Myrmicinæ, though very rich in species, have not yet been able to develop an equal variety of generic and tribal types, whereas the Ponerinæ have had time and opportunities to advance and retrograde along many different lines and to attain a high degree of specialization in certain genera. We may roughly divide the genera of this subfamily into three groups: those which are eminently primitive and generalized (*Myrmecia*), those which exhibit a mingling of primitive and degenerate traits (*Cerapachys, Acanthostichus, Stigmatomma, Amblyopone, Proceratium, Sysphincta,* etc.), and those in which primitive are more or less overlaid by highly specialized characters (*Odontomachus, Anochetus, Leptogenys, Prionogenys, Harpegnathus, Thaumatomyrmex, Ectatomma,* etc.).

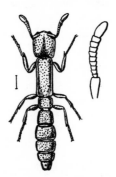

Fig. 126. Worker of *Sphinctomyrmex taylori* of India. (Bingham.)

Although the Ponerinæ represent a much larger portion of the ant-fauna in tropical than in temperate regions, they are nowhere a dominant group, except in Australia. There these ancient insects occupy a position among ants analogous to that of the monotremes and marsupials among mammals, and the Rhynchocephalia among reptiles. And it is especially the genus *Myrmecia,* comprising the "bull-dog ants," which may be said to characterize this fauna and at the same time to represent the prototype of all ants.

This genus *Myrmecia* contains a number of species, nearly all of large size (2–2.5 cm.). They are often conspicuously colored, have long, lithe bodies, long legs, well-developed ocelli and large eyes even in the worker phase, and the full number of palpal joints. The structure of the base of the abdomen differs from that of other Ponerinæ in the powerful constriction between the postpetiole and first gastric segment, so that there is marked off a true postpetiole as in the Myrmecinæ and worker *Eciton.* Our knowledge of the habits of these remarkable insects is still very imperfect and conflicting for they bite and sting with such ferocity that few observers have cared to study them at close quarters. According to Froggatt (1901) the species of *Myrmecia* are largely confined to the Australian littoral, "only one being common inland." According to Sharp (1899) the nests of these ants are "said to be sometimes five feet high," but it is probable that this statement refers either to unusual nests of *Iridomyrmex pur-pureus* or to certain termite nests which Froggatt has recently described and figured. Barker (1903) has published some observations on the black bull-dog ant (*M. forficata*) and a red species (*M. sanguinea*) in Victoria. The colonies of the former number from 500–1,000, of the latter from 200–500 individuals. Externally the nests of both species

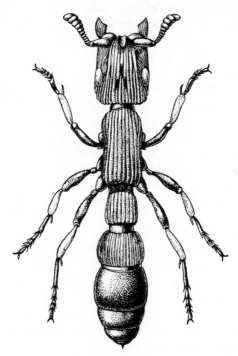

FIG. 127.   Worker of *Cylindromyrmex whymperi* of Ecuador.   (Cameron.)

show only a little loose earth and few holes.   " Both nests go down to two to four feet through the surface soil into yellow clay, and I have found these where the clay was particularly hard, so that considerable labor with pick and shovel is required in taking them out. There are exceptional cases where the form of the nest is modified, which it may be from the strength of the colony, the time it has been established, the nature of the soil, or the advantage taken of its local surroundings." Barker found that "the Blacks show a greater preference for old tree roots, and in one case they had made a nest near a fallen tree, one of the limbs of which dipped into the ground; where it had rotted away, the ants had returned up the limb, so that the nest was not only below but also two feet above ground, and larvæ were found in the portion above the ground level." *M. forficata* is unusually fierce and will " follow an intruder for quite thirty feet from the nest in the hope of getting a parting bite." This ant is also more nocturnal in its habits, *F. sanguinea* more diurnal and of a gentler disposition, although both species are fond of the light and inhabit spots exposed to the sun. The bulldog ants, according to Barker, are very fond of water. They not only drink it but bathe and swim in it. He frequently saw them " voluntarily leave one side of a six-inch dish and swim across to the other." Sharp cites Lowne as saying " that *M. gulosa* attacks large beetles of the genus *Anoplognathus* and buries them; and he also adds the statement that *M. nigrocincta,* when running, is able to take leaps of a foot in length." Froggatt (1905) has published on *Myrmecia forficata,*

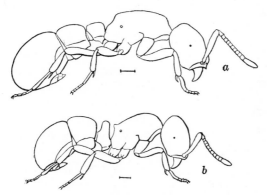

FIG. 128. North American Proceratii. *a, Sysphincta pergandei,* worker; *b, Proceratium silaceum.* (Emery.)

gulosa, tarsata and *nigrocincta,* a number of notes which confirm many of the statements of previous observers. *M. nigrocincta* he designates as the " jumper " and says that " at the first alarm they come jumping out from the side door of their raised mound, which is generally on the ground level, one after the other, like a pack of dogs, and fasten on to the first thing they come across; as there is usually a large opening in the top of the nest, the unwary investigator, who has not learned about the side door, generally discovers it through a rear attack when the jumpers swarm up his legs and begin their investigations." The jumping habit of this ant is not surprising when we consider that several other Ponerinæ (*Harpegnathus, Odontomachus*) also have the power of leaping (see p. 180). The establishment of colonies by species of *Myrmecia* has not been observed, but that they have a nuptial flight

seems to be proved by the observations of Tepper (1882) who came
upon a swarm of these ants early in April. " This was rather a formidable affair, owing to many hundreds of the large creatures (the
female above an inch in length while alive) flitting about one's head,
all armed with a sting about a quarter of an inch in length, while the
shrubs near the nest were covered with scores of pairs and single ones."

The majority of Ponerine genera, in their structural characters at
least, stand in rather marked contrast to *Myrmecia* in exhibiting certain
degenerative or highly specialized traits in combination with a rather
low organization. The Cerapachysii,
Proceratii and Amblyoponii are all
very timid, lead a hypogæic life and
have greatly reduced eyes, at least in
the worker caste. On the other hand,
genera like *Odontomachus* (Fig. 3*K*),
Mystrium (Figs. 3*A* and 129), *Emer-
yella, Leptogenys* (Fig. 3*O*), *Harpegnathus* (Figs. 3*D* and 138), *Thaumatomyrmex* (Fig. 3*I*) and their
allies, have a very highly specialized
development of the head and mandibles. They are undoubtedly very
old forms, some of which have managed to survive as conservative relicts
in remote and protected corners of the
tropics, whereas others, like *Odontomachus* and *Anochetus,* are widely
distributed and have not altogether
lost the ability to produce local races and varieties.

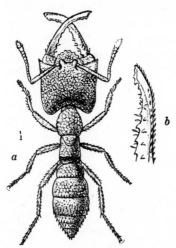

FIG. 129. Worker of *Mystrium
camillæ* of Burma. (Bingham.) *a.*
worker; *b,* mandible from ventral
side.

With the exception of *Myrmecia* and certain species of *Lobopelta*
to be considered presently, all Ponerinæ form small colonies, often of a
few dozen individuals. This indicates either a low degree of fertility
in the females or shortness of life on the part of the individual workers,
or both. It also accounts for the rare or local occurrence of these
insects.

As a rule the females are but little larger, the males but little smaller
than the workers. The similarity of stature of the workers and females
indicates a low degree of fertility on the part of the latter. These
phases also differ very little in other characters such as color, pilosity
and sculpture. The possession of wings, the consequent modification
of the thorax, the larger eyes, ocelli and slight differences in the shape
of the petiole, usually constitute the only peculiarities of the female

This sex, moreover, does not occupy a privileged position in the community, like the females of the higher ants. She is not attended by a body-guard of workers as she moves about the nest but seems to receive only the same attentions as the workers. And as the latter are often fertile, there is little to distinguish the queen from the other members

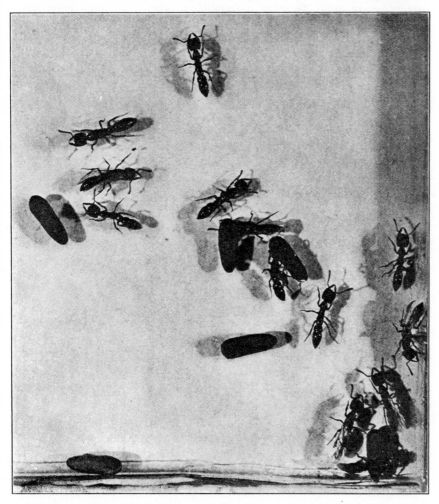

FIG. 130. Workers and winged females of *Stigmatomma pallipes,* with cocoons × 2. (Photograph by J. G. Hubbard & O. S. Strong.)

of the colony. This is true at least of the species of *Odontomachus, Stigmatomma, Pachycondyla* and *Ponera* which I have studied. Cook says, however, that the queens of *Ectatomma tuberculatum,* " even when young are distinctly less active than the workers. Isolated queens have shown no ability or inclination to excavate nests and very little interest in eggs or larvæ which have been entrusted to them."

The workers of the various species of Ponerinæ are monomorphic and do not exhibit the singular polymorphism seen in the workers of many genera in all the other subfamilies of ants. The only exception is *Melissotarsus,* an aberrant genus somewhat doubtfully referred to the Ponerinæ and unique among all ants in having worker and soldier forms of the same size (Fig. 139).

Owing to the small size of the colonies, the nests are usually small and obscure. They are, moreover, even in the tropics, excavated in the soil or in old logs. Few of the species ascend trees and most of

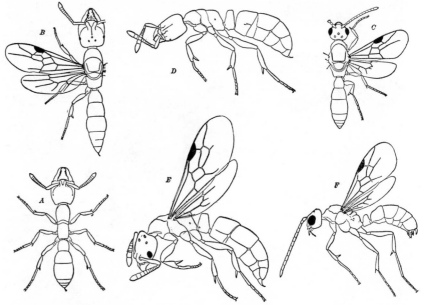

FIG. 131. Ponerine ants. (Original.) *A, B* and *C,* Worker, female and male of *Stigmatomma pallipes; D, E* and *F,* worker, female and male of *Ponera pennsylvanica.*

these, like *Myrmecia, Neoponera* and *Ectatomma,* nest in the ground. The nests are simply and rudely excavated, without smoothly finished chambers and galleries or carefully constructed craters around their entrances. As a rule the colonies are strictly monodomous, but Cook has made the interesting observation that *Ectatomma tuberculatum* is polydomous. In this ant a single colony often extends over several nests, and he is of the opinion that new colonies are formed by a process of budding, like that seen in several of the higher ants, and not by

isolated females.   I had previously reached this conclusion from a study
of *Ponera* and *Stigmatomma,* but later, on finding an incipient colony
of *Odontomachus clarus* in Texas and several isolated females of *O.
hæmatodes* in cells under stones in the West Indies, I concluded that
the Ponerinæ probably resemble the great majority of ants in their
method of founding colonies.   That *Myrmecia* has a nuptial flight is
shown by the passage quoted from Tepper (p. 230).   A proneness to
subdivision of colonies as in the case observed by Cook would account
for the small number of ants found in the nests of most Ponerinæ and
may, perhaps, as in some of the higher ants, coëxist with the formation
of colonies by isolated females.

The Ponerinæ are eminently entomophagous.   *Ectatomma tuberculatum,* according to Cook, also visits the extrafloral nectaries of
plants, but none of the species is known to attend aphids, garner seeds,
or raise fungi.   There is, however, a marked specialization in diet in
certain species.   I have shown that the Texan *Lobopelta elongata* (Fig.
137) feeds mainly, if not ex-
clusively, on land-isopods, or
slaters, and certain species of
*Leptogenys, Lobopelta, Oph-
thalmopone* and *Diacamma* are
much given to preying on termites.   I have never seen any
of our North American Po-
nerinæ feed one another by
regurgitation, but Cook's observations on *Ectatomma tuberculatum* leave little doubt that
this ant practices a similar, if

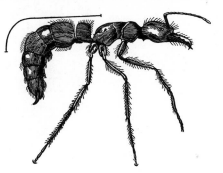

FIG. 132.   Worker of *Dinoponera grandis*
of Brazil.   (Sharp.)

not identical, method of distributing ingluvial food to different members of the colony.

The great differences between the various tribes of Ponerine ants
are reflected in the structure of their larvæ.   At least three different
types may be distinguished among the species that have been studied by
Emery (1899*e*) and myself (1900*b*, 1900*e*, 1903*i*, 1907*d*) :

1. Smooth, thickset larvæ, with short, sparse hairs and peculiar
unpaired tubercles on the midventral surface of some of the abdominal
segments (*Platythyrea*).

2. Smooth, slender larvæ, with a rather dense covering of hairs
(*Myrmecia, Stigmatomma, Parasyscia, Ectatomma*).

3. Larvæ furnished with rows of tubercles which may be pointed
or boss-like, tipped or merely encircled with stout hairs (*Pachycondyla,*

Ponera, Pseudoponera, Leptogenys, Diacamma, Odontomachus, Anochetus). Some of the species of *Ponera* also have long cylindrical dorsal tubercles which are glutinous at their ends and serve to anchor the larva to the walls of the nest.

The bristly tubercles of the third group of Ponerine larvæ are so prominent as readily to suggest the question of their function. Professor L. Biró, who made some observations on the larvæ of *Pseudoponera stigma,* which he sent to Professor Emery, believes that the pointed tubercles are organs of defence. He saw these larvæ, when disturbed by some termites, move their long necks back and forth with

Fig. 133. Female, male and worker of *Pachycondyla harpax* × 2. (Original.)

sufficient force to drive away the intruders. It is possible that the tubercles, at least in the younger larvæ, may function as " poils d'accrochage " in assisting the workers to carry their brood in packets instead of singly. Possibly, too, they are used in defending the larvæ from one another, for the larvæ, like the adults, are highly carnivorous and when food is scarce probably attack one another.

All Ponerine larvæ, so far as observed, are fed with pieces of insect food. This method, which is undoubtedly very primitive, is also adopted by many specialized ants, but as a rule their larvæ are given regurgitated food. My first observation on this singular method of feeding the larvæ was made on a colony of *Pachycondyla harpax* found May 5 under a stone at the foot of Mt. Bonnell, near Austin, Texas. Before the ants could carry them away, I scooped up a fine lot of larvæ, together with the earth in which they were lying. Among these were several pieces, one or two segments long, of a recently killed

Myriopod (*Scutigera*). Into these pieces the larvæ, some of which were nearly full-grown, had inserted their heads and were devouring the softer tissues. This could be distinctly seen with the pocket lens through the glass of the vial to which the larvæ had been transferred. In another nest of the same species, uncovered May 16, I observed the

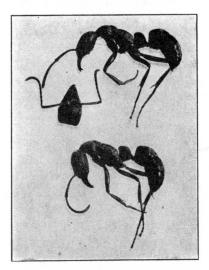

FIG. 134. Workers of *Neoponera villosa* of Tropical America × 2.
(Original.)

larvæ lying on their backs, devouring pieces of some insect which I could not identify.

The former of these observations made in the field led me to observe the feeding of the larvæ in my artificial nests of *Lobopelta elongata*. I had frequently wondered at the way in which these ants decapitated termite nymphs or cut off their abdomens and scattered these about among their larvæ. It was all quite clear to me now; examination with the lens showed that the larvæ had inserted their long necks through the cut surfaces into the soft parts of the termites and were feeding exactly like the larvæ of *Pachycondyla*.

During the month of May I had frequent opportunity to see *Odontomachus clarus* feeding its larvæ in my artificial nests. These larvæ are placed by the ants on their broad backs, and their heads and necks are folded over onto the concave ventral surface, which serves as a table or trough on which the food is placed by the workers. The following observations are transcribed from my note-book:

May 13.—This evening several house-flies, placed in the Janet nest of *Odontomachus,* were at once shorn of their legs, then decapitated, and finally their thoraces and abdomens cut into smaller pieces and distributed among the larvæ. One was given a fly's head, which it kept twirling around in a comical manner, while it devoured the brain through the small cervical orifice. Another was given a piece of a thorax with one of the wings still attached, another a piece of an abdomen, still another, a leg with a mass of muscle at its coxal end, etc.

May 16.—This evening a small Homopterous insect was placed in the *Odontomachus* nest. One of the ants (A) snapped at it, disabled and then left it. A few moments later it was picked up by another ant (B) and carried into the chamber containing the larvæ and pupæ. Thereupon a third ant (C) took hold of it and began to tug at it with B till it was torn open, but not into pieces. B then placed it on the

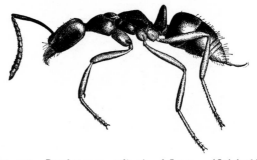

Fig. 135. *Brachyponera solitaria* of Japan.   (Original.)

flat ventral surface of a medium-sized larva, which began to feed at once, moving the Homopteron around with its jaws. After four minutes had elapsed, another ant (D) that had been standing nearby, apparently much interested in the feeding, suddenly tore the morsel away and placed it on a small larva. This larva was permitted to feed ten minutes, closely watched during all this time by ant D and another (E) which had come up in the meantime. Then ant D tried to tear the morsel away from the small larva, but apparently unable to do so, took up the larva with the morsel and dumped both on the ventral surface of a large larva. This creature seized the Homopteron and forced the small larva to release its hold and to drop to the ground. The large larva fed for fully twenty minutes, closely watched by the ant D and two others (E and F). All of these ants tried at different times to wrench the morsel away from the larva, but failed. Suddenly a small ant (C) rushed up, tore it away and ran off with it. By this time very little was left of the Homopteron and I lost track of it.

May 23.—A few crumbs of cake moistened with water were placed in the *Odontomachus* nest at 11.07 P. M. A worker soon carried one of the crumbs into the breeding chamber and gave it to a large larva at 11.20. This larva fed only a few moments, but the cake was not removed till 11.35 when it was carried into another chamber, then at once brought back and placed between three larvæ, from one of which it had just been taken. The smallest of these three larvæ nibbled at it for a short time, beginning at 11.40. But one minute later this larva was carried away by a worker and the cake was taken by another worker and given to a small larva at 11.43. This larva, too, was carried away (at 11.48), and the cake was taken to a large larva, which would have none of it. It was not removed, however, till 11.50. Then it was given by another worker to a large larva, which did eat some of it. At 11.51 the piece of cake, but little diminished in size after all its peregrinations, was taken to another large larva. The ant remained over the larva holding the cake in place till 11.58, when another worker came up and ran away with the larva. While the larvæ were feeding, the ants themselves could be plainly seen to partake of the cake from time to time. During the whole period of the above observations, and for some minutes later, *i. e.,* for over an hour, one little larva was permitted to feed without interruption on what seemed to be a piece of a house-fly.

I have cited these observations at length because of the doubt they cast on the usually accepted view that the workers are able to determine the character of the adult ant by the quantity or quality of the food administered to the larvæ. It is evident not only that the morsels set before the larvæ must be of very unequal nutritive value, but that the very method of their distribution is far too capricious and irregular to produce such clean-cut results as the adult worker and female.

The pupæ of the Ponerinæ, so far as known, are always enclosed in cocoons. This is undoubtedly the primitive ancestral condition from which the absence of a cocoon in the Myrmicinæ, Dolichoderinæ, Dorylinæ and many Camponotinæ has been derived by a suppression of the spinning habit of the larvæ, or as in *Œcophylla* by the use of the silk for other purposes (building nests and aphid-tents).

There is some evidence to indicate that certain Ponerinæ are more negligent of their brood than other ants. Forel (1899c) who observed our North American *Ponera pennsylvanica,* was of the opinion that this ant neglects its cocoons when the nest is uncovered and makes no attempt to assemble or save them. I am convinced, however, from frequent observation of *Ponera,* that Forel's account is incomplete. It is true that the sudden admission of light into the nest causes the ants to forsake their cocoons, but when one stops to watch the nest

for a few moments, one is sure to see the ants returning one by one
and stealthily removing their charges.   This they do rather awkwardly,
walking backwards and dragging the cocoons away without lifting
them from the ground, in marked contrast with *Lobopelta elongata,*
which straddles the cocoon with its long legs and carries it away with
surprising dexterity.   A simple experiment with the artificial nest
shows that the cocoons of *Ponera,* when removed to a distance of three
or four inches from the chamber in which the ants have stored them,
are taken back in the space of ten to thirty minutes.   Forel deserves
credit for directing attention to this matter of the care of the cocoons,
for when one has observed the way in which a large and highly specialized ant, like *Formica schaufussi,* for example, when its nest is uncov-

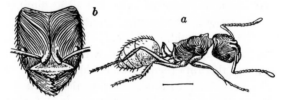

FIG. 136.   *Odontoponera transversa* of the Indomalayan Region.   *a,* Worker ; *b,* head
of same from above.   (Bingham.)

ered, rushes out in the very face of danger to rescue its cocoons, the
slow and awkward movements of *Ponera* certainly indicate a more
primitive, or possibly degenerate condition quite in harmony with its
other habits.   Further evidence that it cares for its cocoons is seen in
its habit of continually creeping in and out among them, and in the
time which it devotes to licking and cleansing them when there are no
longer any larvæ to require its attention.

Forel is also of the opinion that *Ponera* callows, unlike those of
higher ants, may be able to escape from their cocoons without the
assistance of the workers.   I have not observed the hatching of *P.
pennsylvanica,* but in another Ponerine of similar habits, *Stigmatomma pallipes,* I have surprised the callows in the act of escaping from
their cocoons.   Several cocoons were isolated in a watch-glass, and I
had an opportunity of seeing a female, two males and several workers
emerge entirely by their own efforts.   The ant gnaws through the wall
of the cocoon at a short distance behind the anterior pole.   The shape
of the incision at once indicates whether a male or female (or worker)
is about to emerge.   In the latter case the opening, which is produced
by the huge mandibles, has the form of a transverse slit, extending half
way around the cocoon.   The small, sharp mandibles of the male,
however, make a hole with irregular edges and of a much smaller size.

The insect, after periods of struggling, alternating with periods of rest, succeeds in getting first one antenna, then the other, and then the fore legs through the orifice, and finally, with considerable effort, creeps out. After making this observation on isolated cocoons I had an opportunity of making it in the artificial nests. In these the hatching cocoons were often carried about and placed on or under the stack of other cocoons, while the callows, struggling to emerge, seemed to hold out their antennæ and fore legs in a supplicating attitude to the completely indifferent workers. In a few instances the callows died while halfway out of the cocoons and were carried to the refuse-heap in this condition. Occasionally, when the young callows had emerged with their hind legs still enswathed and encumbered by the white pupal skin, the workers would pull this away. They also occasionally licked and

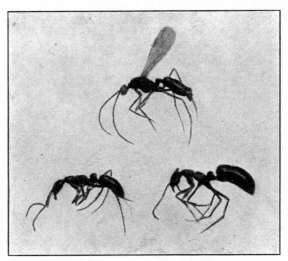

FIG. 137. Male, worker and gynæcoid female of *Lobopelta elongata* × 2. (Original.)

fondled the newcomers as if their bodies were covered with some pleasant secretion, but beyond these acts their helpfulness did not extend. The same workers, however, frequently opened cocoons and extracted dead, immature pupæ, cut them up, and then placed them on the refuse heap.

The newly hatched *Stigmatomma,* as we should naturally expect from the above observations, is not as feeble as the callows of the more specialized ants. The males and females issue with their wings fully expanded; the former have their bodies completely pigmented and are able to run about briskly; the latter, as well as the worker callows, although of a rich yellowish red color, which they retain for several days, are nevertheless soon able to run about and to join in the labors of the colony. The queens show no tendency to leave the nest and usually lose their wings (after copulation?) while still in the red, callow condition.

In none of our North American Ponerinæ have I seen any tendency to deport adult members of the colony, except in *Lobopelta elongata,* the workers of which, when the nest is disturbed, carry the males away as if they were cocoons or larvæ. Nor have I seen any tendency on the part of the workers to hunt in files. But both of these habits, which are so conspicuous in more specialized ants, appear to be developed in some of the tropical Ponerinæ. Forel (1894*f*) quotes the following observations of Ilg on *Ophthalmopone ilgii* of southern Abyssinia: "One day my servants came to tell me that if I wished to see a great many ants at one time, there was a fine opportunity, as every evening, about an hour before sunset, a whole compact army crept out of a hole to disappear into it half an hour later. Having had my attention called to the matter and wishing to know what was going on, I posted a servant in front of the hole, where not a single ant was to be seen, and hurried to the spot as soon as I was told that the performance was about to begin. I saw, in fact, a dense procession of large black ants issuing from the hole and collecting in front of it till they formed a stately assemblage. Suddenly the whole mass, headed by a leader, hurried forward in a dense file, while one company of barely fifty individuals stood for a few moments in front of the hole and then disappeared into it. Curious to know what the little fellows were about, I followed them cautiously, in order not to disturb them, for a distance of about fifty meters. They directed their course towards my traveling bags, and I began to suspect that they were going to steal my rice. To my great astonishment, however, they crept under the covers of my water-bags and I surmised that they might be thirsty. Nothing of the kind. When I carefully raised the covers, I found my rascals fighting fiercely with the white ants (termites) which make their appearance in the desert wherever water has soaked into the ground. Notwithstanding the valiant opposition they encountered, each of the black rascals eventually seized a poor little termite between its shining mandibles, bore it aloft and hurried back as fast as the grass, stones, etc., would permit. I was surprised to see a rather large fellow about two meters from the battle-field halt each termite-laden robber as he came up, till nearly all of them, each with his poor victim, were assembled on the same spot. But this was not all. About thirty or forty of the ants dropped their booty and returned to the battle-field. This time, to my astonishment, they did not look for their little white opponents, but for their black comrades, each of whom they bore back in their mandibles to the company still assembled and waiting on the same spot. When there were no more stragglers the troop hurried back to the hole and disappeared into it with their booty and what I took to be their wounded."

It is very probable that the "wounded" individuals mentioned by Ilg were merely stragglers forcibly deported in the same manner as many of the higher ants carry home belated members of their colonies (see p. 178). Cook has actually witnessed the deportation of queens and workers in *Ectatomma tuberculatum.* He says: "If the kelep

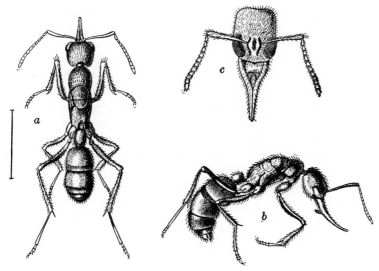

FIG. 138. A Jumping Ponerine Ant. *a,* Female of *Harpegnathus rugosus* of Hong-kong. *b,* Same in profile; *c,* head of same from above. (Mayr.)

queen does not follow at once to the new nest a worker seizes her by her mandibles, raises her in the air, and carries her over bodily. This has been observed repeatedly in connection with the prompt transfers which many of the imported colonies made from their cages into the ground. The queen submits to this treatment as though it were a regular occurrence, and remains quiet and rigid while being carried about. In one instance several workers also remained behind, but were caught and carried by their sisters into the new burrow."

The habit of foraging in files has also been observed by Wroughton (1892) and Aitken in two Indian species of *Lobopelta* (*L. distinguenda* and *chinensis*). Concerning the former Wroughton writes as follows:

"This species is fairly common from Poona westward to the Ghats. The idea of a disciplined army has been fairly developed in this genus. *L. distinguenda* may sometimes, it is true, be found loafing about singly, but these individuals are probably only scouts; ordinarily, she is met, in the early morning or late in the afternoon, travelling in an unbroken column four to six or eight abreast, straight, or rather by the easiest road, to the scene of operations. This is usually a colony of white ants whose galleries have been broken open by the hoof of a passing beast, or some similar accident. Arrived at their destination each worker seizes her termite prey, tucks it under her thorax in the orthodox ponerine fashion, and the column then returns (but marching 'at ease' and much less regularly than on the outward journey) to the nest." Bingham (1903) confirms Wroughton's observations on the termitophagous habits of *Lobopelta* and its methods of foraging in files. He says that "*L. chinensis*, *L. birmana* and *L. kitelli* seem always to march in columns of four; while *L. binghami* and *L. aspera* I have only seen in single or double file, and very often singly, wandering about foraging like *Diacamma*." Dahl (1901) also has seen a troop of about fifty *Lobopelta bismarckensis* workers marching in file in the Bismarck Archipelago, and *Dinoponera grandis* of Brazil, the largest of all Ponerine ants, is described by Bates (1892) as "marching in single file through the thickets." These observations are of unusual interest because they are suggestive of the concerted forays of the Dorylinæ and slave-making *Polyergus* and *Formica sanguinea*.

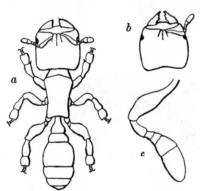

FIG. 139. *Melissotarsus beccarii* of the Sudan. (Emery.) *a*, Soldier; *b*, head of worker; *c*, antenna.

The ants of the genus *Leptogenys* (including the subgenus *Lobopelta*) are also interesting in another respect. The Texan *L. elongata* has no winged females, but instead a single gynæcoid worker usurps this rôle in each colony. This individual is indistinguishable from the workers except for the more rounded petiolar node and more voluminous gaster. As the difference in the petiole is not always constant the question arises as to whether the gynæcoids are not merely workers that have assumed the reproductive rôle. Conclusive evidence in favor of this supposition has been furnished by my former pupil, Miss M. Holliday (1903), who found the gynæcoids to possess a well-developed receptaculum seminis. The number of ovarian tubules is the same as in the workers, which also occasionally possess a receptaculum. Of course, there can be no nuptial flight, and the gynæcoids must be fertilized either by the males of their own or other colonies, and either in the nest or while traveling over the ground.

That the same peculiar usurpation of the queen function by gynæcoid workers obtains among other species of *Leptogenys* is indicated, first, by the fact that winged *Leptogenys* females have never been seen, although the genus is a very large one and widely distributed through the tropics of both hemispheres, and second by Wroughton's observations on the Indian *L. diminuta* (Forel, 1900–'03). At Forel's request Wroughton carefully excavated an enormous formicary of this species, "but looked in vain for a female among the many thousands of workers. All he could find was a worker whose abdomen was conspicuously distended with the ovaries. This worker differed in absolutely no particular from the others, and there was nothing very extraordinary even about its abdomen." It is probable that several other *Ponerine* genera are in the same condition, for example the paleotropical *Diacamma* and *Champsomyrmex,* of which the winged females have never been seen. Wasmann (1904*a*) has recently shown that even in the highly specialized genera *Formica* and *Polyergus* single gynæcoid workers may assume the rôle of queens that have been removed from the colony. It seems probable, therefore, that the Ponerinæ above mentioned present a degenerate, or, at any rate, secondary stage of colonial development in which the true female form has disappeared and is supplanted by a worker, elected, so to speak, to the reproductive office. If this be true, we may be able, as I shall endeavor to show in the next chapter, to account for the peculiar dichthadiiform females of the Dorylinæ.

The habits of the Ponerinæ reviewed in the preceding paragraphs present a mingling of primitive and specialized features, both very interesting, the former because they throw light on the more intricate ethological conditions in the higher ants, the latter because they suggest the enormous antiquity of certain formicine instincts, which must have persisted with little change since Mesozoic or early Tertiary times. Several peculiarities, such as the highly entomophagous habits of the adults, the feeding of the larvæ with pieces of insect food, the retention of the cocoon, the ability of the callows to hatch unaided, the small size of the colonies and the slight fecundity of the females in many species, coupled with many morphological characters, leave little doubt that the Ponerinæ arose from solitary wasps. Emery, who has studied this subject (1895), believes that the immediate ancestors of the ants are to be sought in the group of wasp-like forms represented by the Scoliidæ, Thynnidæ and Mutillidæ.   He leaves the Scoliidæ and Thynnidæ out of consideration on account of the un-antlike structure of their male genitalia, and regards the Mutillidæ, or velvet ants, as having many points of resemblance to the Ponerinæ and especially to the Cerapachysii.   Existing Mutillids, however, present two highly specialized characters which would seem to eliminate them also from the hypothetical ancestral series: they are, so far as known, parasitic and their females are wingless.   Emery does not attach much weight to these considerations, for it is not from the modern Mutillidæ that he would derive the ants, but from their more ancient, entomophagous and non-

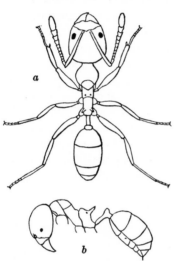

a,

b

FIG. 140. Worker of *Aneuretus simoni* of Ceylon. (Emery.) *a,* From above; *b,* from the side.

parasitic precursors. He believes, however, that the ancestral female ants were wingless and have re-acquired wings by inheritance from the males. For reasons to be given in the next chapter, in connection with the wingless females of the Dorylinæ, I am unable to accept this view and am, therefore, inclined to regard the apterous condition of the female Mutillids as a very serious obstacle to Emery's hypothesis. Handlirsch (1908) has shown that in seeking the ancestors of ants it is necessary to turn to forms in which both sexes are winged. In this respect, and also in being non-parasitic and in hunting their prey under ground, the Scoliidæ seem to present a more faithful picture of the ancestral ants than the existing Mutillidæ.

That the phylogenetic relations of the Ponerinæ to the four other formicine subfamilies are capable of rather satisfactory formulation is evident from Forel's statement (1903*b*) that if, as can hardly be doubted, the Ponerinæ represent the living remnants of the primitive formicine stock, a stock in turn derived from the Scoliids, "the four other subfamilies must all be considered as specialized and more or less parallel derivatives of the Ponerinæ, *i. e.,* as all arising from this common stock, but without connection among themselves.

"The Dorylinæ, arising directly from the Cerapachyii (a tribe of Ponerinæ), have no direct points of relationship with the three other subfamilies, notwithstanding the convergent character presented by the pedicel of certain workers (*Eciton, Ænictus* and the Myrmicinæ).

"The Myrmicinæ have no direct connection either with the Camponotinæ or with the Dolichoderinæ. This is evident. On the contrary, the connection of the Myrmicinæ and the Ponerinæ through groups like *Myrmecia,* the Cerapachyii, and perhaps *Pseudomyrma,* admits of no doubt. The structure of the Myrmicine gizzard and poison apparatus remains the same.

"The Dolichoderinæ were derived directly from the Ponerinæ through a gradual transformation of the gizzard and a shortening and reduction of the poison apparatus, which has become rudimental and almost replaced by the anal glands. Nevertheless, the fundamental plan of the poison apparatus remains the same as in the Ponerinæ. . . . The discovery of the genus *Aneuretus* Emery (Fig. 140) has enabled us to put our finger on the direct derivation of the Dolichoderinæ from the subfamily Ponerinæ. Indeed the genus *Aneuretus* constitutes a true connecting link between these two subfamilies, as is shown by the fact that Emery first placed it among the Ponerinæ, but later came to accept my opinion that it should be attributed to the Dolichoderinæ.

"There remain the Camponotinæ, of which we have been speaking. The transformation of the gizzard is explained by the intermediate forms in the inferior genera of this subfamily (*Myrmoteras, Dimorphomyrmex,* etc.). But it is very difficult to understand the complete transformation of their poison apparatus. Here the series is incomplete. Let us hope, nevertheless, that the future discovery of some extant relict of paleontological times will give us the key to this enigma, as has been done by the genus *Aneuretus* for the Dolichoderinæ."

CHAPTER XV

THE DRIVER AND LEGIONARY ANTS

"When we see these intelligent insects dwelling together in orderly communities of many thousands of individuals, their social instincts developed to a high degree of perfection, making their marches with the regularity of disciplined troops, showing ingenuity in the crossing of difficult places, assisting each other in danger, defending their nests at the risk of their own lives, communicating information rapidly to a great distance, making a regular division of work, the whole community taking charge of the rearing of the young, and all imbued with the strongest sense of industry, each individual labouring not for itself alone but also for its fellows—we may imagine that Sir Thomas More's description of Utopia might have been applied with greater justice to such a community than to any human society. 'But in Utopia, where every man has a right to everything, they do all know that if care is taken to keep the public stores full, no private man can want anything; for among them there is no unequal distribution, so that no man is poor, nor in any necessity, and although no man has anything, yet they are all rich; for what can make a man so rich as to lead a serene and cheerful life, free from anxieties, neither apprehending want himself, nor vexed with the endless complaints of his wife? He is not afraid of the misery of his children, nor is he contriving how to raise a portion for his daughters, but is secure in this, that both he and his wife, his children and grandchildren, to as many generations as he can fancy, will all live both plentifully and happily.'"—Thomas Belt, "The Naturalist in Nicaragua," 1874.

The driver and legionary ants are the Huns and Tartars of the insect world. Their vast armies of blind but exquisitely coöperating and highly polymorphic workers, filled with an insatiable carnivorous appetite and a longing for perennial migrations, accompanied by a motley host of weird myrmecophilous camp-followers and concealing the nuptials of their strange, fertile castes, and the rearing of their young, in the inaccessible penetralia of the soil—all suggest to the observer who first comes upon these insects in some tropical thicket, the existence of a subtle, relentless and uncanny agency, directing and permeating all their activities. These marvellous insects have been studied by many travellers—for they are among the most conspicuous creatures in the tropics—but although our knowledge of them has been notably increased within recent years, we still have much to learn concerning their habits and development.

By its latest and most careful student, Professor Emery, the subfamily Dorylinæ was taken in a broad sense to include not only the drivers (Dorylii) of tropical Africa and Asia, and the legionary, or visiting ants (Ecitonii) of the warmer portions of America, but also

the tribes Leptanillii, Cerapachysii, Proceratii and Acanthostichii. I
have followed Forel in including the last three tribes among the
Ponerinæ, while admitting that they have close and important genetic

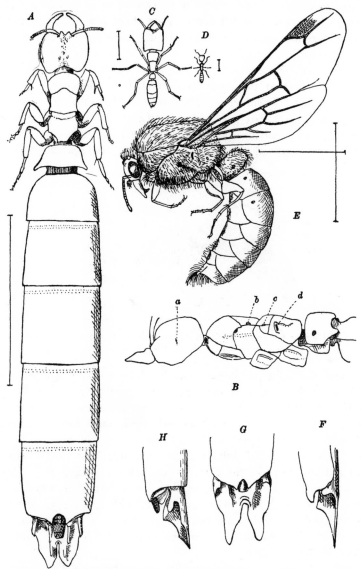

FIG. 141. Castes of *Dorylus helvolus* drawn under same magnification. (Emery.)
A, Female (dichthadiigyne) in dorsal view ; *B*, profile view of same ; *a*, vestige of
eye ; *b* and *c*, vestiges of wings ; *d*, metathoracic stigma ; *C*, worker major ; *D*, worker
minima ; *E*, male ; *F*, tip of gaster of female in profile ; *G*, tip of gaster of female
D. furcatus in dorsal view ; *H*, same in profile.

affinities with the Dorylinæ. Little is known of the minute Leptanillii (Fig. 149) except that they are hypogæic and probably live in small colonies. In the present chapter I shall consider only the Dorylii and Ecitonii, treating the two groups in succession in an endeavor to bring out their similarities and differences, even at the risk of some repetition.

The Dorylinæ seem to have undergone much greater morphological differentiation in the Old than in the New World, for although Emery recognizes only three genera of Dorylii, *Dorylus, Ænictus* and *Ænictogeton,* the first of these covers a number of subgenera (*Anomma, Dorylus s. str. Typhlopone, Dichthadia, Alaopone, Rhogmus* and *Shuckardia*), several of which have been regarded by other authors as distinct genera. All the species of *Dorylus s. lat.,* some two dozen in number, are confined to Africa (excluding Madagascar), southern

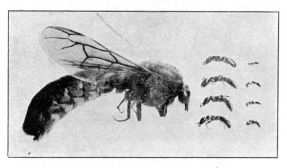

FIG. 142. *Dorylus fimbriatus* of South Africa. Male and workers of different sizes; natural size. (Original.)

Asia and the adjacent larger islands. The workers are completely blind, without vestiges of eyes, and vary greatly in size in the same colony, from large soldiers with toothed mandibles and excised clypeus, through intermediates to small workers with small heads and mandibles, more convex clypeus and sometimes fewer antennal joints (Fig. 62). The females (dichthadiigynes) are huge, unwieldy creatures, blind and wingless like the workers, and with a peculiar pygidium and an enormous gaster to accommodate the voluminous ovaries. The males (dorylaners) are also very large, with great eyes and ocelli, sickle-shaped mandibles and peculiar genitalia. The wings have only one cubital cell. All three of the phases have but a single joint in the pedicel of the abdomen.

Owing to the extraordinary differences between the phases, the nomenclature of the species of *Dorylus* has been in great confusion. At first only the male of one of the African forms, *D. helvolus,* was known and this was consigned by Linné to the genus *Vespa* (1764).

Later Fabricius erected the genus *Dorylus* for it and a few other species (1793). The worker of this species was first described by F. Smith sixty-five years later (1858) as *Typhlopone punctata*. In 1880 Trimen discovered the female which proved to be similar to a couple of insects that Gerstaecker (1872) had previously placed in the genus *Dichthadia*. In 1887 Emery described and figured all three phases of *D. helvolus* (Fig. 141), and in a later paper (1895b) gave good reasons for supposing that *Typhlopone levigata* F. Smith, *Dichthadia glaberrima* Gerst., and *Dorylus klugi* Emery are merely the worker, female and male respectively of a single species, which should be known as *D. levigatus*. These forms have all been taken in Java, Sumatra and Borneo. Recently Ern. André (1900) and Brauns (1903) have discovered the dichthadiigynes of *Dorylus* (*Anomma*) *nigricans* and *D.* (*Rhogmus*) *fimbriatus* respectively, two African species of which the males and workers were previously known. As nothing but males or workers of many of the other species have been described, it is probable that the discovery of the remaining phases will lead to considerable changes in the synonymy.

The habits of *Dorylus* have been observed by Smeathman, Savage (1845), Trimen (1880), Unger, Green (1900b), Forel 1890c), Peringuey, Emery (1905b), Marshall, Brauns (1901), Vossler (1905, 1906), Santschi (1908) and others. Most of the species are hypogæic in their habits, but those of the subgenus *Anomma* live a more exposed life, and one of these, *A. arcens*, a subspecies of *nigricans*, was made the subject of the earliest and most detailed observations by Savage near Cape Palmas, in West Africa. Smeathman, who first saw the armies of these ants, concluded that they had no fixed habitation, but wandered from place to place in long files. Savage confirms this supposition and describes the temporary nest in which they bivouac—a shallow depression under the roots of trees, shelving rocks or in any situation that will afford shelter. They seem to construct no chambers or galleries but merely take advantage of fissures in rocks or the crevices under stones or in the soil. Their sorties are made only on cloudy days or in the night, preferably in the latter, for they cannot endure the direct or even the reflected rays of the sun. "If they should be detained abroad till late in the morning of a sunny day by the quantity of their prey, they will construct arches over their path, of dirt agglutinated by a fluid excreted from their mouth." While running under thick grass, sticks, etc., they dispense with the arch. "In cloudy days, when on their predatory excursions, or migrating, an arch for the protection of the workers, etc., is constructed of the bodies of their largest class (soldiers). Their widely extended jaws, long slender limbs and projecting antennæ intertwining, form a sort of net-work that seems to answer well for their object. Whenever an alarm is given the arch is instantly broken, and the ants, joining others of the same class on the outside of the line, who seem to be acting as commanders, guides and scouts, run about in a furious manner in pursuit of the enemy. If the alarm should prove to be without foundation, the victory won or the danger passed, the arch is quickly renewed, and the main column marches forward as before in all the order of an intellectual military discipline." This habit of hanging together in clusters by means of their hooked claws and slender legs is very striking. Savage saw a colony camping on a tree: "From the lower limbs (four feet high) were festoons or lines of the size of a man's thumb, reaching to the plants and ground below, consisting entirely of these insects; others were ascending and descending upon them, thus holding free and ready communication with the lower and upper portions of

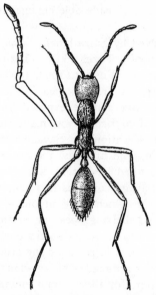

this dense mass. One of these festoons I saw in the act of formation; it was a good way advanced when first observed: ant after ant coming down from above, extending their long limbs and opening wide their jaws, gradually lengthened out the living chain till it touched the broad leaf of a *Canna coccinea* below. It now swung to and fro in the wind, the terminal ant the meanwhile endeavoring to attach it by his jaws and legs to the leaf; not succeeding, another ant of the same class (the very largest) was seen to ascend the plant, and, fixing his hind legs with the apex of the abdomen firmly to the leaf under the vibrating column, then reaching with his fore-legs and opening wide his jaws, closed in with his companion from above, and thus completed the most curious ladder in the world." These living chains are also

Fig. 143. Worker of *Ænictus aitkeni* of India. (Bingham.)

made for the purpose of bridging small streams. The peculiar clustering habit was also observed by Savage during inundations when these insects resort to the same means of survival as *Solenopsis geminata* in tropical America. "In such an emergency they throw themselves into a rounded mass, deposit their ' feebler folk,'' pupæ and eggs in the center, and thus float upon the water till a place of safety is reached, or the flood subsides."

Savage describes the predatory habits of *Anomma* at considerable length. "They will soon kill the largest animal if confined. They attack lizards, guanas, snakes, etc., with complete success. We have lost several animals by them—monkeys, pigs, fowl, etc. The severity of their bite increased to great intensity by vast numbers, it is impossible to conceive. We may easily believe that it would prove fatal to almost any animal in confinement. They have been known to destroy the *Python natalensis,* our largest serpent. When gorged with prey it lies motionless for days; then, monster as it is, it easily becomes their victim. . . . Their entrance into a house is soon known by the simultaneous and universal movement of rats, mice, lizards, Blapsidæ, Blattidæ and of the numerous vermin that infest our dwellings. Not being agreed, they cannot dwell together, which modifies in a good measure the severity of the driver's habits, and renders their visits sometimes (though very seldom in my view) desirable. Their ascent into our beds we sometimes prevent by placing the feet of the bedsteads into a basin of vinegar, or some other uncongenial fluid; this will generally be successful if the rooms are ceiled, or the floors overhead tight; otherwise, they will drop down upon us, bringing along with them their noxious prey in the very act of contending for victory. They move over the house with a good degree of order, ransacking one point after another, till, either having found something desirable, they collect upon it, when they may be destroyed ' en masse' by hot water; or, disappointed, they abandon the premises as a barren spot, and seek some other more promising for exploration. When they are fairly in we give up the house, and try to await with patience their pleasure, thankful, indeed, if permitted to remain within the narrow limits of our beds or chairs. They are decidedly carnivorous in their propensities. Fresh meat of all kinds is their favorite food; fresh oils also they love, especially that of *Elais guiniensis,* either in the fruit or expressed. Under my observation they pass by milk, sugar, and pastry of all kinds, also salt meat; the latter, when boiled, they have eaten, but not with the zest of fresh. It is an incorrect statement, often made, that ' they devour everything eatable' by us in our houses; there are many articles which form an exception. If a heap of rubbish comes within their route, they invariably explore it, when larvæ and insects of all orders are borne off in triumph—especially the former." That the hypogæic species of *Dorylus* are very fond of foraging for larvæ in compost heaps has also been shown by Forel (1890c), Peringuey, Emery (1905b) and Brauns (1901).

Savage has also recorded some observations on the behavior of the various castes of *Anomma* workers. The large soldiers with falcate, unidentate mandibles defend the colony or seize and rend the prey. The latter office is also performed by the intermediates, which have multidentate jaws. The small workers, however, confine themselves to carrying the brood and other burdens. " They carry their pupæ and prey longitudinally under their bodies, held firmly between their mandibles and legs, the latter of which are admirably calculated by their length and slenderness for this purpose." The pupæ are nude, at least in nearly all the species of Dorylii.

The large males and females have been very rarely observed in the nests. Savage saw a number of deälated males of *Anomma nigricans* marching in file with the workers. He endeavored to divert some of them from their companions but they kept returning. This observation is of considerable interest, because the males of all other ants show no ability to return to the colony or the nest, nor do they voluntarily accompany the workers on their foraging expeditions or migrations. It is said that the males of *Dorylus* leave the nests at night as they are often found about lights, but according to Marshall and Brauns the males of *D. fimbriatus* (Fig. 142) and *brevipennis* are expelled by the workers and at once take flight. This expulsion requires several days and does not necessarily take place at night. Marshall succeeded in finding a nest of *fimbriatus* containing a female and several males. It con-

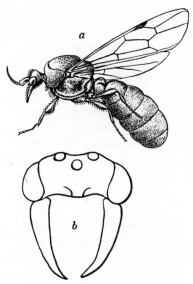

FIG. 144.   *Ænictus grandis* of Lower Burma.   (Bingham.)   *a*, Male; *b*, head of same.

sisted of a broad, spheroidal cavity in the earth, about 70 cm. in diameter and completely filled with a damp, friable mass of earth perforated throughout with tenuous galleries. The cavity was connected with the surface by means of five or six galleries 15 to 25 mm. in diameter. Brauns believes that such nests are excavated and occupied only during the breeding season. There seems to be only a single female to each *Dorylus* colony and she is dragged along by the workers when they migrate. Evidences of this habit are seen in the scratched ventral surface and the absence of some of the tarsal joints in all the various dichthadiigynes of this genus that have come under the observation of myrmecologists.

Some recent observations indicate that certain species of *Eciton* and *Dorylus* may have permanent nests and that their expeditions are of two kinds, predatory and migratory. According to Vosseler (1905) *Anomma molestum* of German East Africa occupies the same nest till it has destroyed all the available prey in a locality. This requires some eight or ten days. Then the colony migrates to a new nest. He observed one of these migrations which continued without interruption for twenty-four hours. Santschi (1908) recently discovered under an oven in a dye-shop in Tunis, a large *Typhlopone fulvus* nest from which hundreds of males took flight about four o'clock in the afternoon of six consecutive days. The dyer stated that he had observed this flight at the same season for four years. "This indicates," as Santschi remarks, "that even if the migrations of *Dorylus* are of general occurrence, they are not obligatory and that under certain circumstances these ants may inhabit the same nest for long periods of time."

The majority of species of *Dorylus* are undoubtedly carnivorous or entomophagous, but Green (1900b) has shown that at least one species, *D. orientalis* of India, is herbivorous, that is, feeds on the bark of trees and the tubers of plants such as the potato.

The genus *Ænictus* comprises more than thirty species, the majority of which are south Asiatic, whereas most of the species of *Dorylus* are African. The workers of *Ænictus* (Fig. 143) have two joints in the abdominal pedicel although the males and females have only one. Wroughton and Forel (1890e) first identified the males of *Ænictus* (Fig. 144) as belonging to workers that had been placed in the genus *Typhlatta,* so that this latter name had to be abandoned. More recently Emery (1901h) has described and figured the female of *Æ. abeillei.* It differs from the dichthadiigynes of *Dorylus* in its smaller stature and in having a very small, pointed pygidium. The genus *Ænictogeton* is known only from a single male specimen from the Congo, on which Emery (1901h) founded the species *fossiceps.*

The habits of *Ænictus* have been observed by Wroughton (1892) and Brauns (1901). It is much less hypogæic than *Dorylus.* Of an undetermined Indian species Wroughton says: "This is the only species of worker I have ever met; but it is far from uncommon in the Dekhan. Notwithstanding the possession by the *Ænictus* worker of two knots in the pedicel like the Myrmicidæ, she is distinctly ponerine in character and carries her booty exactly as do the Poneridæ. She has brought the military organization to perfection. Perhaps on account of her small size (single-handed she does not seem to be able to cope with a *Pheidole,* as small as or smaller than herself), she cannot afford to relax discipline, like *Lobopelta,* even in the moment of victory. Whatever the reason, a column of *Ænictus* (five or six abreast), so long as it is above ground, never shows the slightest irregularity. The destination of the column is not fixed before hand by scouts, as is apparently the case with *Lobopelta.* It starts, and proceeds at a long slinging trot, until a likely hole, crevice or ant's nest is met with, when it pours in, until enough having entered, the remainder of the column goes on, in search of another hole. Moreover, at times, when on the march, the column at a certain point in its length, turns off at an angle, striking out a new line, and, though this menœuvre is often repeated, so far as I have seen, it never happens a few files from the head of the column, but always so that each column shall be strong enough to cope with any ant community likely to be met with. Indeed, this manœuvre seems often to be of the nature of a flanking movement. I have seen a strong column, marching on a white ant heap, detach in this way, columns right and left, and the several detached columns enter the heap from different points of the compass. The notion irresistibly forced on anyone, watching these manœuvres, is that they are either the result of preconcerted arrangement, or are carried out by word of command."

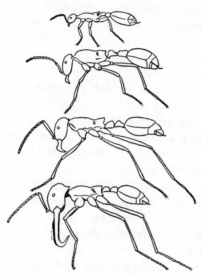

Fig. 145. Workers and soldier of *Eciton hamatum* drawn to the same scale. (Sharp.)

Brauns makes a similar observation on the South African species: "*Ænictus* is not as sensitive to sunlight as *Dorylus* and therefore moves over ground for considerable distances, especially after rain and when twilight is setting in, or even in the bright sunshine. The files resemble those of *Anomma,* in miniature, of course, and are narrow, regular columns. Of several expeditions of *Ænictus eugenii* which I have witnessed in the Orange Free State, one was noteworthy. In this instance the ants carried their brood on the under side of their bodies, just as it is borne by the Ponerinæ, especially by *Leptogenys,* according to my observations."

Wroughton has seen the workers of the Indian *Æ. wroughtoni* expelling the males from the nest. These males escaped on two consecutive days from " a small hole in the floor of a mudwashed verandah, and it did not appear to be a hole used for the regular traffic of the nest." It is an interesting fact that the males of the Dorylii have nearly always been found escaping from holes in the floor or foundations of human dwellings.

In tropical and subtropical America the Dorylinæ are represented by two genera, *Eciton* and *Cheliomyrmex*. Of the former about seventy species are known, of the latter but one, *C. nortoni*. The genus *Eciton* is so homogeneous that it has been split into only two subgenera, *Acamatus* and *Eciton s. str.* It resembles the Old World *Ænictus* in having the pedicel two-jointed in the worker, and in the structure and smaller size of the female. Both worker and female usually have vestiges of eyes, consisting of a single ommatidium on each side of the head, but not connected with the brain by means of optic nerves, so that they must be useless as visual organs. In some species (*E. hamatum* (Fig. 3*C* and 145), *lucanoides* and *foreli*) the largest workers, or soldiers, have peculiarly elongated and hooked jaws of unknown function. The males of *Eciton* resemble those of *Dorylus* (Figs. 146 and 147*d*), but they are smaller, have two complete cubital cells in the wings, and their mandibles are usually longer and more falcate.

As in the case of *Dorylus*, the three phases of *Eciton* have been placed in as many different genera, the worker in *Eciton*, the female in *Pseudodichthadia* and the male in *Labidus*. Hetchko, Mayr (1886*b*) and W. Müller (1886) first showed that the insects which entomologists had been in the habit of calling *Labidus* were the males of *Eciton*, and Ern. André has recently found that the insect which he described as *Pseudodichthadia incerta* is the female of *E. cœcum*. Although the males of several species are known, few have been taken with their workers, and are described in the literature under independent names. In addition to that of *E. cœcum* the females of only three species are known, that of *E. opacithorax*, discovered by Schmitt in North Carolina, that of *E. carolinense* taken by Forel in the same state, and that of *E. schmitti* (Fig. 147*c*) taken by myself in Texas. All the phases are known only of *E. cœcum, opacithorax* and *schmitti*.

The genus *Cheliomyrmex* is confined to the warmest parts of America and appears to be rare except in certain localities. I have recently received a number of specimens of *C. nortoni* (Fig. 148) from British Honduras, but it is recorded also from Colombia and Mexico. Only the worker form is known, and that is remarkable for the hooked and bidentate mandibles of the soldier form, and in having only a single joint in the pedicel like the Old World *Dorylus*. *Eciton* has a much wider distribution, ranging from North Carolina and Colorado to Patagonia, but the largest and most numerous species are found only within the tropics. According to von Ihering (1894) the prominent species do not extend southward beyond the Cebus-line in Brazil, and in Mexico they probably cease with the northern limit of the *terra caliente* on the eastern coast. No species are known from the West Indies.

Observations on the habits of *Eciton* are more numerous than those on *Dorylus*. They have been made in Brazil by Lund (1831), W. Müller (1886), Hetchko, Bates (1892) and von Ihering (1894), in Trinidad by Urich (1893–'94), in Guiana by Bar, in Colombia by Forel (1901*h*), in Nicaragua by Belt (1874), in Mexico by Sumichrast (1868) and myself (1901*a*), in North Carolina by Schmitt and Forel (1899*c*), in Texas, New Mexico and Colorado by Long and myself (1900*a*, 1901). All residents in the American tropics are familiar with these ants, which are variously designated as "padicours," "tuocas," "tepeguas," "soldados" army, foraging, legionary, or visiting ants. Their habits are similar to those of *Dorylus* and *Ænictus,* but there are interesting differences among the various species. Some, like the widely distributed, eyeless *E. cæcum,* are completely hypogæic, or subterranean, others like *E. crassicorne,* are subhypogæic, or creep along under cover of the dead leaves and other vegetable detritus on the surface of the soil. Most species, however, carry out their expeditions in full view and often exposed to the sunlight (*E. prædator, hamatum, pilosum, schmitti,* etc.). Bates has described differences in the methods of making forays in the various Brazilian species, and some of these same species have been studied by Belt. His description of a foray of *E. prædator* may be regarded as typical of all the epigæic forms: "One of the smaller species (*Eciton prædator*) used occasionally to visit our house, swarm over the floors and walls, searching every cranny, and driving out the cockroaches and spiders, many of which were caught, pulled, or bitten to pieces and carried off. . . . I saw many large armies of this, or a closely allied species, in the forest. My attention was generally first called to them by the twittering of some small birds, belonging to several different species, that followed the ants in the woods. On approaching to ascertain the cause of the disturbance, a dense body of the ants, three or four yards wide, and so numerous as to blacken the ground, would be seen moving rapidly in one direction, examining every cranny, and underneath every fallen leaf. On the flanks, and in advance of the main body, smaller columns would be pushed out. These smaller columns would generally first flush the cockroaches, grasshoppers and spiders. The pursued insects would rapidly make off, but many, in their confusion and terror, would bound right into the midst of the main body of ants. . . . The greatest catch of the ants was, however, when they got amongst some fallen brushwood. The cockroaches, spiders and other insects, instead of running right away, would ascend the fallen branches and remain there, whilst the host of ants were occupying all the ground below. By and by up would come some of the ants, following every branch, and driving before them their prey to the ends of the small twigs, when nothing remained for them but to leap, and they would alight in the very midst of their foes, with the result of being certainly caught and pulled to pieces. Many of the spiders would escape by hanging suspended by a thread of silk from the branches, safe from the foes that swarmed both above and below."

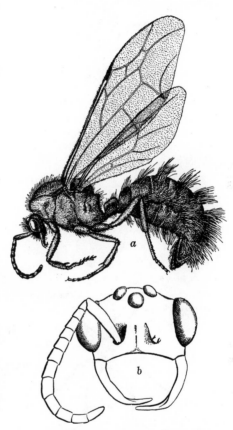

FIG. 146. *Eciton esenbecki.* (Original.) *a,* Male in profile ; *b,* dorsal aspect of head.

In regard to another species, *E. hamatum,* which has large, light-colored soldiers with very long hook-shaped jaws (Fig. 3C), Belt says : " I think *Eciton hamata* does not stay more than four or five days in one place. I have sometimes come across the migratory columns. They may easily be known by all the common workers moving in one direction, many of them carrying the larvæ and pupæ carefully in their jaws. Here and there one of the light-colored officers moves backwards and forwards directing the columns. Such a column is of enormous length, and contains many thousands, if not millions, of individuals. I have sometimes followed them up for two or three hundred yards without getting to the end."

Belt succeeded in finding the temporary nest of an army of these ants: "They make their temporary habitation in hollow trees, and sometimes underneath large fallen trunks that offer suitable hollows. A nest that I came across in the latter situation was open at one side. The ants were clustered together in a dense mass, like a great swarm of bees, hanging from the roof, but reaching to the ground below.

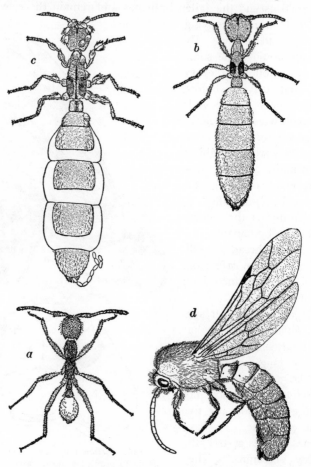

FIG. 147. Castes of *Acamatus schmitti;* drawn under the same magnification. (Original.) *a,* Worker; *b,* young female (dichthadiigyne) ; *c,* old female with enlarged ovaries, in the act of ovipositing; the anterior portion of the body is covered with mites (*Cillibano hirticoma*) ; *d,* male.

Their innumerable long legs looked like brown threads binding together the mass, which must have been at least a cubic yard in bulk, and contained hundreds of thousands of individuals, although many columns were outside, some bringing in the pupæ of ants, others the legs and dissected bodies of insects. I was surprised to see in this living nest tubular passages leading down to the center of the mass, kept open just as if it had been formed of inorganic material   Down these holes the ants who were bringing in booty passed with their prey.   I thrust a long stick down to the center of the cluster and brought out clinging to it many ants holding larvæ and pupæ which were probably kept warm by the crowding together of the ants.   Besides the common dark-colored workers and light-colored officers, I saw there many still larger individuals with enormous jaws.   These they go about holding wide open in a threatening manner, and I found, contrary to my expectation, that they could give a severe bite with them, and that it was difficult to withdraw the jaws from the skin."   These observations recall the clustering habit of the African *Anomma* as described by Savage, a habit which seems to be common to a number of Ecitons.   I have seen it in *E. sumichrasti, schmitti* and *opacithorax*.

Excellent observations on the Mexican species were made by Sumichrast (1868) from whom I quote the following: " The most characteristic trait of the ants of this genus consists in the inroads or migrations which they undertake at undetermined epochs, but in relation, it appears to me, with the atmospheric changes.   What traveller, passing over the *tierra caliente,* has not encountered the phalanxes of *tepeguas* upon the path of the primitive forests?   What inhabitant of these countries has not, at least once, been unpleasantly torn from the arms of sleep by the invasion of his domicile by a black army of *soldados?*

" The purpose of these expeditions of *Eciton* is, without doubt, multiple, for the circumstances that these sorties, as one may call them, coincide more offen with a change of season, hardly permits one to consider them exclusively as simple razzias undertaken at the expense of other insects.   One can believe them to be sometimes expeditions of pillage, sometimes changes of domicile, veritable migrations.   I believe that the following facts, which passed under my observation at the hacienda of Potrero, near Cordova, at the end of September of the past year, show proof of this.   During about three months, a colony of *soldados* [*E. prædator*] had been domiciled under a little bridge formed by some rough trunks of trees bound together by a heap of vegetable mould.   The continued excavation which engaged the ants on the under side of the bridge, threatened to cause the disappearance of all the earth which covered the flooring.   Every day I watched these labors in the hope of discovering at last the interior of the formicary, but this hope was disappointed, for on the thirtieth of September, in the morning, I found the nest completely abandoned.   Its inhabitants did not return until about four months later, and this reappearance, which was of short duration, was followed almost immediately by a visit which these insects made to my habitation, on the twelfth of February, in the night. I have similar observations in regard to another species [*E. foreli*] and I think I can conclude that the *Eciton*, at least the two species in question, are in the habit of forming temporary nests or habitations for themselves, which they abandon from time to time, distinct from those where are found the reproducing sexes, and where is the place of the growth of the larvæ and their metamorphoses.

"The nests are found in cool, shady places in great woods or

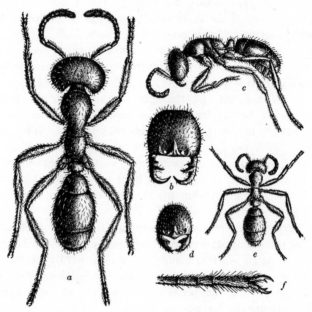

Fig. 148. *Cheliomyrmex nortoni* of Central America. (Original.) *a,* Soldier; *b,* head of same from above; *c,* worker media; *d,* head of same; *e,* worker minima; *f,* tarsus to show toothed claws.

among rocks and are tunneled more often at the foot of, and among the roots of, old trees. The earth or the fragments of wood, which the ants cast out, sometimes form a dome above, but at times only an irregular opening indicates the existence of a colony.

"The extraction of one such nest, beside the difficulty of penetrating to the center through the entangled roots of the tree, is not an easy thing, for at the first alarm, the *soldados* sally forth in myriads and attack the aggressor with fury.

" Besides the changes of domicile, which are so generally in relation with the atmospheric variation as to serve as a rule to the inhabitants of the country, the *Eciton* devotes itself every season to excursions for pillage, destined to supply the larvæ with nourishment. Nothing is more curious than these *battues* executed by an entire population. Over an extent of many square meters, the soil literally disappears under the agglomeration of their little black bodies. No apparent order reigns in the mass of the army, but behind this many lines or columns of laggards press on to rejoin it. The insects concealed under the dry leaves and the trunks of fallen trees fly on all sides before this phalanx of pitiless hunters, but, blinded by fright, they fall back among their persecutors and are seized and despatched in the twinkling of an eye. Grasshoppers, in spite of the advantage given them by their power of leaping, hardly escape any more easily. As soon as they are taken, the *Eciton* tears off the hinder feet and all resistance becomes useless.

" If some heap of dry leaves, some tree or bush presents itself upon the path of the columns, a party of hunters separates itself from the mass of the army, and, after having ransacked it in every part, retakes its place in the advance guard. I have observed, sometimes, that little flies, of the family Syrphides, follow, flying above them, the column of *Eciton,* but cannot give any account of the evolution of these Diptera.[1]

" It is probable that the Ecitons attack the larvæ and pupæ of other ants to make them serve as food for the nourishment of their own larvæ or for sustaining themselves. I surprised, one day, in the first hours of a sombre and rainy morning, a considerable assemblage of *tepeguas* [*E. foreli*] fastened one upon another like a swarm of bees and entirely still. Having dispersed them I perceived in the place which they covered with their bodies a quantity of little white larvæ, brought away doubtless, from the nests of some Myrmicidæ. At another time I witnessed the pillage of a nursery of other ants by a quite enormous band of workers minores [*E. hamatum*] ; alarmed by the reprisals which I made on their account, they took to flight, some of them carrying between their mandibles as many as three larvæ at once. Among the Mexican species of the genus *Eciton,* that to which they apply more specially the name of *soldados* [*E. prædator*], may be noticed for the habit which it has of invading the habitations of the country. These visits ordinarily take place at the beginning of the

---

[1] These " Syrphids " probably belong to the Conopid genus *Stylogaster,* of which Townsend (1897) found three species hovering over troops of *Eciton* in the lowlands of the Rio Naubla, in the state of Vera Cruz, Mexico.

rainy season, and almost always during the night. The expeditionary
army penetrates the habitation which it proposes to visit at many points
at once, and for this purpose divides itself into many columns of
attack. One is apprised very soon of their arrival by the household
commotion among the parasitic animals. The rats (*Mus tectorum*),
the spiders, the cockroaches (*Periplaneta australasiæ* Fab.), abandon
their retreats and seek to escape from the attacks of the ants by flight.

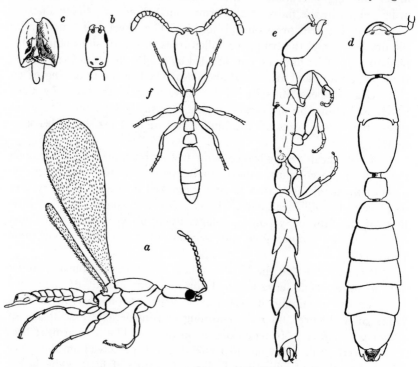

Fig. 149. Castes of *Leptanilla*. *a, L. minuscula*, male; *b*, head; *c*, copulatory
organs of same. (Santschi.) *d, L. revelieri*, dichthadiiform female, dorsal view; *e*,
same in profile; *f*, worker. (Emery.)

Alimentary substances the *soldados* hold in no esteem, and they disdain
even sugary things, to which the ants in general are so partial. Dead
insects even do not seem to invite their covetousness. It has often
happened to me to be obliged to abandon my abode, without having
time to carry away my collection, to which they have never done the
least injury. The trouble occasioned by these insects in entering
houses is more than compensated by the expeditious manner in which
they purge them of vermin, and in this view their visit is an actual
benefit."

Bates appears to have been the first to observe the habits of the hypogæic *E. cæcum.* The armies of this ant move " wholly under covered roads, the ants constructing them gradually but rapidly as they advance. The column of foragers pushes forward step by step under the protection of these covered passages, through the thickets, and on reaching a rotting log, or other promising hunting ground, pour into the crevices in search of booty. I have traced their arcades, occasionally for a distance of one or two hundred yards; the grains of earth are taken from the soil over which the column is passing, and are fitted together without cement. It is this last mentioned feature that distinguishes them from the similar covered roads made by Termites, who use their glutinous saliva to cement the grains together. The blind *Ecitons,* working in numbers, build up simultaneously the sides of their convex arcades, and contrive in a surprising manner, to approximate them and fit in the keystones without letting the loose, uncemented structure fall to pieces."

To the foregoing observations of other authors I may add some of my own on the Texan species, dwelling on certain points not noticed in the above descriptions. The workers of all the Ecitons I have seen have a peculiar nauseating, fecal odor, which is also found in a few carnivorous species of *Pheidole* (*Ph. antillensis* and *ecitonodora*). The males and females, however, have a sweet and pleasant odor, which probably accounts for the strong attraction they have for the workers, for in the living colonies the latter always form a mass enveloping the sexual phases. The males are produced in great numbers. Towards nightfall on one occasion I witnessed the escape of the males of *E. schmitti* from a nest in the dry limestone soil near Austin. Throughout the spring and summer months these insects fly to the lights at night in great numbers. There is only a single mother queen to a colony, but the workers readily adopt queens from other colonies of the same species. I have never seen these females dragged along during the expeditions, but it is probable that this is the case. Owing to their smaller size they are undoubtedly more easily moved from place to place than the huge *Dorylus* queens, and this may account for the fact that none of the numerous females of *E. schmitti* and *opacithorax* which I have seen was mutilated or abraded. The eggs are very small and exceedingly numerous. The worker larvæ are slender, and the pupæ are never enclosed in cocoons.

None of the Texan Ecitons forms very large or conspicuous armies though they hunt in files like the large tropical species. Their food consists very largely of the larvæ and pupæ of other ants. On many occasions I have seen *E. schmitti, opacithorax* and *crassicorne* plundering formicaries and carrying the brood to their temporary nests. This habit is also well-known in the tropical species and is expressly mentioned by nearly all the authors above cited. The kidnapped larvæ and pupæ are stored for a time and then eaten like any other insect prey. All the species I have seen, with the exception of *E. cœcum,* are exclusively entomophagous.

E. cœcum is, as Bates observed, exclusively hypogæic in its habits and never appears in the open, but tunnels along just beneath the surface of the soil or under clusters of stones. I have never been able to find even its temporary nests, although it is one of the most abundant ants in central Texas. It may often be found ferreting out larvæ in or under old logs, under cow-dung, or the dead bodies of cats and dogs. Sometimes on these subterranean forays, it chances to enter the galleries of other ants and then a fierce battle ensues. On one occasion I found a number of dead *E. cœcum* workers on the refuse heap of a large nest of the Texan harvester (*Pogonomyrmex molefaciens*) and on examining the workers of this colony, which were running about on the denuded nest area, I found each of them carrying the head of an *E. cœcum* immovably attached by the closed mandibles to the antennal scape. This told the story of a fierce subterranean conflict in which the harvesters had come off victorious, though compelled to carry about the detached heads of their assailants. *E. cœcum* is also very fond of certain vegetable substance, especially of nuts. I have sometimes attracted and trapped great numbers of workers by burying a few walnut or pecan kernels in the lawns near Austin.

The *Ecitons* carry their larvæ and pupæ under their bodies like the Dorylii and the Ponerinæ. They move very rapidly and orient themselves with surprising alacrity for animals that are quite blind and have to rely entirely on their contact-odor sense. This was observed by Forel (1899c) in *E. carolinense* and I have noticed it in a number of species. Forel says: "Throw a handful of Ecitons with their larvæ on a spot with which they are absolutely unacquainted. In such circumstances other ants scatter about in disorder and require an hour or more (sometimes less) to assemble and bring their brood together and especially to become acquainted with their environment, but the Ecitons do this at once. In five minutes they have formed distinct files which no longer disintegrate. They carry their larvæ and pupæ, marching in a straight path, palpating the ground with their antennæ and exploring all the holes and crevices till they find a suitable retreat and enter it with surprising order and promptitude. The workers follow one another as if at word of command, and in a very short time all are in safety."

In captivity Ecitons are remarkably restless, at least at certain times during the day. Part of a fine colony of *E. schmitti* which I kept some years ago, exhibited this restlessness in a striking and ludicrous manner. The colony was at first confined in a tall glass jar on a square board surrounded by a water moat. The ants kept going up and down the inside of the jar in files for many hours. Finally I removed the lid. The file at once advanced over the rim and descended on the outer surface till it reached the circular base of the jar where it turned to the left at a right angle and proceeded completely around the base till it met the column at the turning point. To my surprise it kept right on over the same circumference which was long enough to accommodate all the individuals. They continued going round and round the circular base of the jar, following one another like so many sheep, without the slightest inkling that they were perpetually traversing the same path. They behaved exactly as they do on one of their predatory expeditions. They kept up this gyration for forty-six hours before the column broke and spread over the board to the water's edge and clustered in the manner so characteristic of this and the allied species (*E. opacithorax, sumichrasti,* etc.). I have never seen a more astonishing exhibition of the limitations of instinct. For nearly two whole days these blind creatures, so dependent on the contact-odor sense of their antennæ, kept palpating their uniformly smooth, odoriferous trail and the advancing bodies of the ants immediately preceding them, without perceiving that they were making no progress but only wasting their energies, till the spell was finally broken by some more venturesome members of the colony.[1]

In conclusion attention may be called to certain problems that are suggested by our present meager knowledge of the Dorylinæ. Besides the investigation of the species with a view to obtaining all the phases and thus clearing up the taxonomy, we are in great need of a fuller insight into the domestic economy of these singular insects. As yet no one has been able to observe the methods of rearing the brood and the mating of the sexual forms, which must, of course, take place without a true marriage flight. Nor has it been possible to plot the

[1] I have found a remarkable observation of the same kind recorded by Fabre in the sixth volume of his incomparable " Souvenirs Entomologiques." He describes an army of caterpillars of the " processionaire du pin " (*Cnethocampa pityocampa*) going round and round the outside of a large vase 1.35 m. in circumference for seven days! During this period the caterpillars were on the march 84 hours altogether, stopping to rest on their path only when overtaken by the cold of the night, and not actually deviating till the eighth day. Fabre estimates that the caterpillars crawled around the vase 335 times. In this case the insects were not guided by contact-odor like the Ecitons, but by the silken thread spun by each individual over the surface traversed.

territory covered by the annual migrations of any of the species, to determine the time spent in the bivouacs or in the presumably more permanent breeding nests, or the precise relations which these nomadic ants bear to their myrmecophiles. Curiously enough, these seem to be more numerous both in species and in individuals than the myrmecophiles of the non-migratory ants of other subfamilies.

Another problem of more theoretical interest is presented by the dichthadiigynes, which are so unlike typical female ants. To Emery these forms seemed to indicate that the females of ancestral ants were wingless and that the alate condition represented a secondary inheritance from the male sex within comparatively recent times. He was confirmed in this opinion by his discovery of apterous dichthadiiform females in the very primitive species of *Acanthostichus* and *Parasyscia*. There is, however, another possibility, which seems not to have been considered. The occurrence in certain Ponerinæ (*Leptogenys* and probably also in *Diacamma* and *Champsomyrmex*) of gynæcoid workers that have supplanted the winged females, suggests that the dichthadiigynes may also be highly modified gynæcoids. It must be admitted that this view is beset with serious difficulties. First, we must suppose, on such a hypothesis, that the gynæcoids are phylogenetically fixed forms of very ancient origin, since in *Ænictus* and *Eciton* they are quite unlike the existing workers in having only a single joint in the pedicel. Hence they cannot be compared directly with the gynæcoids of *Formica,* which are merely workers that usurp the queen's place and function during the ontogenetic development of the colony. Second, Emery has figured in the female *Dorylus helvolus* minute "rudiments of wings" and a conformation of the thoracic sclerites suggestive of the typical winged form. If he has correctly interpreted these various structures we are bound to suppose that the dichthadiigyne is a highly degenerate, alate female and both his hypothesis and the one I have suggested must be abandoned. The females of *Eciton* and *Ænictus,* however, certainly have a much simpler and more worker-like thorax, and I am by no means certain that Emery has correctly interpreted the conditions in *Dorylus.* Too few female Dorylinæ are known at the present time to enable us to decide this question, which must be left to future students.

CHAPTER XVI

THE HARVESTING ANTS

" Verrit tetra boum gratos formica labores
    Et caveis fruges turba nigella locat,
Quamlibet exiguo videatur pectore, sollers,
    Quo legat hibernæ commoda grana fami.
Hanc juste famulam nigri jam dixeris Orci,
    Quam color et factum composuit domino.
Namque ut Plutonis rapta est Proserpina curru,
    Sic formicarum verritur ore Ceres."
                              —" Anthologia Latina," 104.

The two preceding chapters contain an account of the primitive and carnivorous species which represent the savage and hunting stages in the development of ant societies. In this and the following chapter I shall endeavor to sketch the habits of certain ants that have largely abandoned entomophagy and have taken to a benigner, vegetarian diet. I have called attention (p. 176) to the fact that abundance of food is necessary to the maintenance of social life and that the fullest expansion and development of such life is possible only to animals that have learned to draw on the vegetable kingdom for a large part of their sustenance. Hence we are not surprised to find that in warm, arid countries, where, during many months of the year, insect food is either very scarce, or where the competition for food among ants and other animals is very keen, a number of the former have become confirmed vegetarians as their last resource in the struggle for existence. Under such circumstances the seeds of herbaceous plants obviously furnish the most accessible and nutritious food. The harvesting habit thus developed is only one of many indications of an ever-increasing dependence of ants on the vegetation, a subject which will occupy us in several of the succeeding chapters. Even a few of the eminently terrestrial and carnivorous Ponerinæ and Dorylinæ, as we have seen, show indications of vegetarianism. The three higher subfamilies, however, have a much more varied and unstable diet, with an increasing tendency to imbibe plant-juices, either directly from the floral and extrafloral nectaries, or indirectly after they have passed through the bodies of aphids and other Homoptera, or to feed on fungi, seeds or fruit. Among these subfamilies certain tribes and genera have become so addicted to specialized diets as to be of unusual interest.

It is easy to conceive of the origin and development of the graniv-

orous habit, for a carnivorous ant, used to collecting insects and crushing their hard integuments with its powerful mandibles, is already fully
equipped with the apparatus necessary for dealing with seeds.   And
although many harvesting ants have more convex mandibles and blunter
teeth than carnivorous species, it is impossible merely from examination of the mouthparts to ascertain whether an ant is granivorous or
not.   It may be doubted, furthermore, whether there is such a thing
as a purely granivorous ant.   There is clearly no advantage in an ant's
losing its taste for the succulent tissues of other insects, although there
is an obvious advantage in its supplementing this diet with seeds during
certain seasons of the year.
Indeed, many, if not all, of
the species mentioned in the
following pages are quite as
eager to secure insect food as
seeds, especially while they
are raising their brood, and
unquestionably many ants that
are supposed to be exclusively
predaceous will, on closer
study, be found to be more
or less granivorous.

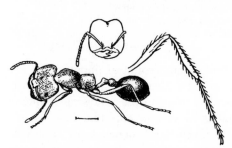

Fig. 150.   Worker of the Indian harvester,
Holcomyrmex scabriceps.   (Bingham.)

If the foregoing considerations are correct, we should expect to
find the harvesting ants arising sporadically and often in distantly
related genera and species.   This appears to be the case, for although
these insects belong to a single subfamily, the Myrmicinæ, they occur
in at least three of the tribes, the Solenopsidii, the Tetramorii and the
Myrmicii.   Among the Solenopsidii, however, only a single species of
Solenopsis (*S. geminata*) is known to be granivorous, and only a portion of the enormous genus *Pheidole* comprises such species.   The
small genus *Pheidologeton* is also granivorous.   Among the Tetramorii,
Tetramorium cespitum is only rarely and sporadically granivorous,
and this is perhaps true of a certain number of species of *Meranoplus*.
Among the Myrmicii, *Messor* and *Ischnomyrmex* comprise harvesting
species, whereas the species of the allied *Stenamma* and *Aphænogaster*
are predaceous.   *Holcomyrmex,* now regarded as a subgenus of *Monomorium, Pogonomyrmex, Oxyopomyrmex* (with its subgenus *Goniomma*), which are closely related to Messor, and probably also *Ocymyrmex,* are highly granivorous.

The earliest of all recorded myrmecological observations undoubtedly relate to two harvesting ants, *Messor barbarus* and *structor*.   The
former occurs throughout the Mediterranean littoral of Europe, Asia

and Africa and presents in the warmer portions of its range, which is now known to extend southward to the Cape of Good Hope, a bewildering complex of subspecies and varieties. *M. structor* seems to be absent in Africa, but ranges through southern Europe and Asia as far as Java. The ancient peoples were undoubtedly familiar with the granivorous habits of these ants and probably also with those of a third species, *M. arenarius*, inhabiting the deserts of North Africa. To them refer the many allusions in the writings of Solomon and the Mischna, and of the classic writers Hesiod, Æsop, Ælian, Plutarch, Orus Apollo, Plautus, Horace, Virgil, Ovid and Pliny. Mediæval authors, like Aldrovandus and Bacon, merely repeated the accounts of the ancients. The entomologists of the early portion of the last century, however, failing to find any harvesters among the ants of temperate Europe, began to doubt, or even to deny their existence. This skepticism is much in evidence in the works of Gould (1747), Latreille (1802), Huber (1810), Gené (1845), Kirby and Spence (1846), and Blanchard (1871). The subject was taken up, however, by Sykes (1829) and Jerdon (1851) in India, by Moggridge (1873) in southern France and by Buckley (1861*a*), Lincecum (1862), McCook (1877*a*, 1879*c*), Morris (1880) and Mrs. Treat (1878) in the United States. These authors succeeded in showing that the ancient accounts were correct. For a detailed history of the subject and for extracts from the various authors of antiquity, the reader is referred to Bochart's " Hierozoicon " and to the works of Moggridge and McCook. Here I shall confine myself to the recent observations, considering first, in all brevity, the Old World harvesters and concluding with a somewhat fuller account of our American species.

Fig. 151. Diagram of nest of *Oxyopomyrmex santschii*. (Santschi.) Explanation in text.

Sykes was the first of modern observers to describe the storing of seeds by ants. He saw *Pheidole providens* at Poona, India, bringing grass seeds, which had been moistened by the rains, out of the nests and exposing them to the sun to dry. Jerdon confirmed these observations on *Ph. providens*, *Ph. diffusa* and *Solenopsis rufa*, a subspecies of the tropicopolitan *S. geminata*. He saw the ants not only drying their piles of seeds but also collecting them from different plants and storing them in the nests, although he was unable to ascertain the purpose of these activities. All doubt was removed, however, by Moggridge's excellent work, which was carried out at Mentone in 1871 and 1872 on *Messor barbarus* and *structor,* the very species that had been observed by the ancients. He opened the nests of these ants and studied their granaries, which are flat chambers connected by galleries and irregularly scattered over an area sometimes nearly 2 m. in diameter and to a depth of about 35 cm. in the soil. He saw the workers collect the seeds from the ground or even pluck them from the plants, remove

Fig. 152. Nest of *Messor pergandei* in Arizona desert, in a spot where the alkali prevents the growth of nearly all plants except *Suæda.* The dark material at the border of the crater is seeds and chaff rejected by the ants. In more favorable spots in the desert the seeds produce the ring of plants seen in Fig. 154. (Original.)

their envelopes and cast the chaff and empty capsules on the kitchen middens outside the nest. During the winter a nest of the average size may contain as much as a quarter of a liter of seeds. Among the stores in the granaries he was able to recognize seeds belonging to at least eighteen different families of plants. In confirmation of Pliny and Plutarch he maintains that the ants bite off the radicle to prevent the seeds from germinating, a process which is also arrested by bringing them when damp with the rain to the surface, spreading them in the sun and then carrying them back to the granaries. Some of the seeds sprout, nevertheless, either in the nests or on the kitchen middens. " As the ants often travel some distance from their nest in search of food, they may certainly be said to be, in a limited sense, agents in the

FIG. 153. Nest of *Messor pergandei* in the Arizona desert, showing circle of chaff. (Original.)

dispersal of seeds, for they not unfrequently drop seeds by the way, which they fail to find again, and also among the refuse matter which forms the kitchen midden in front of their entrances, a few sound seeds are often present, and these in many instances grow up and form a little colony of strange plants. This presence of seedlings foreign to the wild grounds in which the nest is usually placed, is quite a feature where there are old established colonies of *Atta barbara,* where young plants of fumitory, chickweed, cranesbill, *Arabis Thaleana,* etc., may be seen on or near the rubbish heap. . . . One can imagine cases in which the ants during the lapse of long periods of time might pass the seeds of plants from colony to colony, until after a journey of many stages, the descendants of the ant-borne seedlings might find themselves transported to places far removed from the original home of their immediate ancestors." Moggridge also observed that not only *Pheidole pallidula* but also *Ph. megacephala,* an Old World ant which now over-runs the warm portions of both hemispheres, are harvesting ants.

The more recent investigations of Forel (1894*a*), Ern. André (1881*e*), Emery (1899*a*), Lameere (1902), Escherich (1906), and others have confirmed Moggridge's observations. Forel and Lameere have studied the habits of *M. barbarus* and *arenarius* in the deserts of North Africa. According to Forel, the latter species, which is the most powerful insect of that region, excavates enormous nests over an area 7–10 m. in diameter and to a depth of 2 m., with several openings,

Fig. 154. Crater of *Messor pergandei* in the Arizona desert, showing ring of herbaceous plants that have sprung up from discarded seeds in the chaff circle. (See Figs. 152 and 153.) (Original.)

each surmounted by a crescentic crater sometimes 50 cm. broad and made of coarse sand pellets. The granaries are flat chambers about 15 cm. in diameter and 1.5 cm. high, connected by galleries with one another and with the surface. Lameere believes that the area occupied by single colonies of this ant is even greater than that given by Forel. He also describes the harvesting habits of another *Messor* (*M. caviceps*) and of two species of *Holcomyrmex* (*H. lameerei* and *chobauti*) peculiar to the sandy and extremely barren portions of the desert. *H. chobauti* resembles *M. caviceps* in having a pronounced cavity on the under side of the head. Of the former species he says: "I saw the long files of workers carrying seeds of the 'drin' (*Aristida pungens*) to their nests. The seed of this plant has the form of a slender spindle surmounted by a long, trifid and plumose spine. The ant rides this grain as a witch rides her broom; she carries it beneath her, holding it firmly by the small end in her mandibles with the end of the grain fitting into the notch under her head. This interesting character, which this ant shares with *M. caviceps,* may be regarded as an adapta-

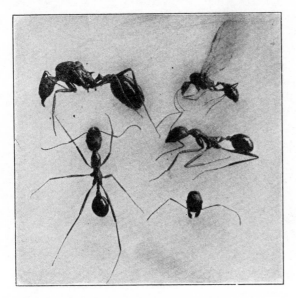

Fig. 155. Deälated female, male, and workers of *Ischnomyrmex cockerelli*, × 2. (Original.)

tion to the method of carrying the drin seed. It should be noted that I found *M. caviceps* in a region of the Eolian desert where the drin is almost the only plant that can subsist. On the other hand there is no drin in the region of Hamada where I first found *H. lameerei,* which has the under side of the head but little excavated."

Still another interesting ant of the North African desert has been recently discovered in Tunis by Santschi. This is a small black species, *Oxyopomyrmex santschii.* Its habits are described as follows by its discoverer in a letter published by Forel (1904*a*): The nests are " so characteristic that when one has once seen one of them, nothing is easier than to find others. I am surprised to learn that they have not attracted the attention of other observers. Especially remarkable is the tiny crater, which has the form of a cone [Fig. 151] hardly more than 4–5 cm. in diameter and 2.5–3 cm. high. The circumference of its funnel-shaped top is 3–4 cm. across and its margin is always perfectly circular and entire, except in nests in process of construction,

FIG. 156. Crater of *Ischnomyrmex cockerelli* in Arizona desert, showing the large rough entrance. (Original.)

when it is at first semilunar like the very small nests of *Messor arenarius*. At the bottom of the funnel the small entrance is found at a depth of 2–3 cm. It is horizontal, attaining a length of 5 cm., a breadth of 1 cm. and a height of 5 cm. In this first chamber the pupæ are kept for the purpose of enjoying the warmth, and here I have found a number of workers and winged females. Thence the gallery continues to descend to a depth of 15–20 cm. and finally opens into two or three chambers of the same dimensions as the first. These contain pupæ and an ample provision of very small seeds. This ant is therefore granivorous. I surprised a few of the workers entering the nest with seeds in their mandibles, but they go out foraging singly and not in files like *Messor* and other genera. They are very slow in their movements and are very apt to stop motionless at the least alarm. Day or night one or two of the workers may be seen on the outer surface of the crater, scarcely moving unless molested, but when disturbed they hurriedly retreat into the nest to spread the alarm. Their habits are rather nocturnal. If a light is brought near the nest when a worker is on the point of leaving it with a grain of sand, she hurriedly backs into the entrance and there stops, closing it perfectly with her burden. If the observer remains very quiet, she eventually comes forth and deposits her load on the slope of the crater. There are scarcely more than thirty individuals in a nest. I have found this species only in a very circumscribed area, south of Kairouan, on compact, sandy soil in

Fig. 157. Male, virgin female, and worker of the Texan harvester, *Pogonomyrmex molefaciens,* nearly twice natural size. (Original.)

which the chambers are easily excavated." I quote this description at length and reproduce Santschi's figure on account of the remarkable resemblance of the *Oxyopomyrmex* nest to those of the fungus-growing *Trachymyrmex* to be described in the next chapter. The genus *Oxyopomyrmex* is represented by several species, some of which have been placed in a subgenus, *Goniomma.* One of these, *G. hispanica* of southwestern Europe, is also a harvesting ant, according to Ern. André (1881e).

To the old observations of Sykes and Jerdon on harvesting ants in India, Wroughton (1892) has added accounts of the habits of *Holcomyrmex scabriceps* (Fig. 150) and *Pheidologeton ocellifer.* Of the former he says: " In a community of this genus there are workers of all sizes. *Holcomyrmex* is, as a rule, a most industrious harvester, and sets about her work in a most methodical way. The workers never forage individually for grain, but all take the same road and all return by the same road; the result being that every nest is the starting point of one, or often of several, well-beaten tracks, cleared of vegetation and obstacles, and extending sometimes 100 feet and more in length. How these tracks are engineered I have never discovered, but am pretty certain that they are made gradually; a commencement at hazard is made, and then, as the country immediately adjoining the road is exploited, the road itself is carried forward. Where one of these roads crosses a sheet of bare rock, it is there marked in white; I can only presume that this is the result of some chemical action, set up by the formic acid exuding from the ants; this acid, though too small in quantity in a single ant to cause any appreciable effect, might easily become sufficient when thousands of ants are continually passing, backwards and forwards, all day long. *Holcomyrmex* brings home the grain unthreshed, and, in this form, it is taken into the nest, from whence the chaff is brought out and deposited around the entrance, or, where the force of a prevalent wind is felt, on a heap to leeward." Wroughton does not believe that *H. scabriceps,* which Rothney regards as the harvester *par excellence* of India, compares with *Pheidole* as a harvester.

The following note on *Pheidologeton ocellifer,* an ant with highly polymorphic workers, was communicated to Wroughton by Aitken: " The entrance (of the nest) which is strewn with chaff, is large, but the passage soon splits up, and I failed to follow it. I turned up a lot of pupæ, however, close to the surface. The community is enormous and industrious, collecting large seeds of trees or plants, which it takes a dozen to carry; these are taken in and the husks are thrown out afterwards. If *P. ocellifer* meets a white ant or any other insect, she collects it in the same way. The smaller soldiers often laid a jaw to a burden, but the giants appear to do nothing." Wroughton confirms this observation on the carnivorous tastes of *Pheidologeton.* He found also that the huge soldiers neither dig nor defend the nest and that they are less pugnacious than the smaller workers. It is probable that they function as seed crushers like the soldiers of the allied genus *Pheidole.*

Armit (1878), Roth (1885) and Tryon (1900) have published a few observations on harvesting ants in another arid or semiarid region, Australia. These are *Pheidole longiceps, Meranoplus dimidiatus* and *M. diversus.* Tryon calls attention to the seed-distributing habits of the *Pheidole* in the following passages: " That this Brisbane harvesting ant, also, is an important agent in the local dispersion of plants—especially weeds—and is connected with their sudden appearance on heaps of soil excavated from a depth, is sufficiently demonstrated in the following observations: The ants of one nest were noticed to be harvesting the seeds of *Portulacca oleracea* Linn. and of *Amaranthus viridis* Linn.—both common weeds—and growing at a comparative distance from the nest. These seeds had remained stored up in their nest for some time, when rain suddenly came on, and under its influence the seeds—especially those of the latter plant—commenced to germinate. Of those which had already thrown out a radical, this was bitten off and brought to the surface; some of these seeds were also gnawn into, and the ruptured black perisperm—containing more or less food substance—in like manner rejected. Other seeds, which had swollen in response to moisture, were carried up for the purpose of being dried and re-stored. In the midst of these operations, however, rain came on again, and the ants retired, leaving seeds on the surface. These immediately germinated, and a small patch of *Amaranthus* grew up, making the site of what was before a nest of harvesting ants, quite isolated among plants of different character. On a second occasion

Fig. 158. Large mound nest (modified crater) of *Pogonomyrmex molefaciens* with entrance in depression at summit. (Original.)

a nest, in which much seed of *Eleusine indica* was known to have been harvested some months since, was dug up. Some of the grass seed selected·from the nest was afterwards sown; also some of the earth from the nest which was known to contain both seeds of this plant and of another species of *Amaranthus*. In both cases the sowings were made in situations remote from such places in which any of these plants were already growing, and, as a result, in the course of time, numerous plants of both *Eleusine indica* and this second *Amaranthus* sprang up in these new localities, where they continued to flourish."

The genus *Meranoplus,* to which some of the observations of the Australian naturalists mentioned above refer, is related to *Tetramorium,* the type of which is the pavement ant, *T. cespitum,* of Europe and of our Atlantic States. It is, therefore, interesting to note that this ant occasionally stores seeds in the chambers of its nests. This has been observed by Janet in Europe, and I have also seen the chambers of a colony of this ant near Mamaroneck, N. Y., filled with grass seeds. In this case we have apparently either an evanescent or an incipient habit.

Turning to America we find a goodly array of harvesting ants, nearly all members of genera we have already considered and nearly all inhabitants, like the Old World harvesters, of warm and exceptionally arid regions. Our species are the following:

1. Solenopsidii: *Solenopsis geminata,* represented by the typical form of the species and several varieties; and probably no less than twenty species of *Pheidole.*

2. Myrmicii: Five species of *Messor,* two of *Ischomyrmex* and some thirty species of *Pogonomyrmex,* which are about equally divided between North and South America. This last genus may be regarded, perhaps, as the New World representative of the African *Ocymyrmex.*

Solenopsis geminata, the "fire-ant," is armed, as its popular name indicates, with a formidable sting which it uses on the slightest provocation. Its colonies are populous and so numerous that it may be said to be in possession of a large portion of the soil of the American tropics. The nests are made under stones or consist of numerous untidy craters, fused and scattered about irregularly. It is difficult to say whether this ant is more granivorous than entomophagous, for it attacks and eats almost everything that comes in its way. It will even attend coccids on the roots of grasses and occasionally do some damage to soft fruits, like strawberries or germinating garden seeds. During the summer and autumn months its shallow nest-chambers contain quantities of carefully husked seeds, which usually belong to species of *Euphorbia, Croton, Plantago* and other herbaceous plants. It seems to be less fond of grass seeds. I have already called attention to the preference of this ant for nesting in loamy soil along streams and to its remarkable habit of floating about in balls when its nests are inundated (p. 146).

Of the numerous harvesting species of *Pheidole,* only one, *Ph. pilifera,* is common in the Northern States. It has been studied by Morris, McCook and Mrs. Treat. *Ph. vinelandica* and *tysoni,* which range as far north as New Jersey and New York, have similar habits. I have found a considerable number of harvesters among the species of the dry deserts of Colorado, Texas, New Mexico, Arizona and Mexico (*Ph. coloradensis, instabilis, ceres, sitarches, soritis, vaslitti, carbonaria,* etc.). Though far more peaceable, these ants often resemble *S. geminata* in their nesting habits. Some of them at least (*Ph. instabilis, sitarches*) are certainly unable to prevent the germination of seeds in their granaries during the wet weather. I infer, therefore, that they do not bite off the radicle as has been claimed for the European *Messor* and the Australian *Pheidole*. The large-headed soldiers of the numer-

FIG. 159. Disk of *Pogonomyrmex rugosus* in the Arizona desert. (Original.)

ous carnivorous species of *Pheidole* function as trenchers and carve the tough insects brought into the nest by the small, feeble workers, and thus make the soft tissues accessible to the community. Among the seed-storing species, however, the soldiers have become the official nut-crackers of the colony. I have seen the workers of some of the species (*instabilis* and *sitarches*) feeding the larvæ directly with pieces of crushed seeds.

More striking are the habits of our largest harvesters belonging to the genera *Messor, Ischnomyrmex* and *Pogonomyrmex*. With the single exception of the Florida harvester (*P. badius*), all of these ants are confined to the dry plains and deserts of the Western and Southwestern States, where, just as in the deserts of the Old World, insect food is scarce, at least during many months of the year.

Of the five species of Messor, *M. pergandei, carbonarius, andrei, julianus* and *stoddardi,* which are confined to the extreme southwestern portion of the United States and northwestern Mexico, I have been able to study only the first in a living condition. It is a shining, jet-black ant of moderate size, very common in the deserts of southern Arizona and the Mojave Desert of California. The workers, which form populous colonies, vary much in the size of the body and the head, like the Mediterranean *M. barbarus.* The nests (Figs. 152–154) are single or more rarely multiple craters, much flattened, with rounded slopes, 50 cm. or more in diameter, and with one to three large and very irregular central openings. Sometimes these are slit-shaped and as much as 5 or 6 cm. long. The rough galleries and granaries are excavated to a depth of at least 60 cm. in the hardest and most sunbaked portions of the desert soil. Late in the afternoon long files of workers may be seen in the full activity of harvesting. Sometimes these files may be followed for a distance of 20 or 30 m. from the nest before the ants disperse among the scant vegetation in search of seeds. They seem to have no preferences, but eagerly seize all the mature seeds they find and carry them to the nest, where they carefully remove the husks and store the edible kernels in the granaries. The chaff and seed-pods are then carried out and dumped on the kitchen midden which forms a crescentric or circular zone at the periphery of the crater. Sound seeds are often thrown out with the chaff and eventually germinate, so that old nests are often marked by a circlet of growing plants, just as Moggridge has described for the European species. There can be little doubt that the other North American species of *Messor* have very similar habits. A number of alcoholic specimens of one of these, *M. andrei,* sent me by Professor H. Heath from California, still bear grass-seeds in their clenched mandibles.

One of our two species of *Ischnomyrmex, I. cockerelli* (Fig. 155) is widely distributed over the deserts of western Texas, southern New Mexico and Arizona and northern Mexico from an altitude of 2,500 feet in the northern portion of its range (at Monahans, Texas) to 7,000 feet on the Mexican plateau. The other species, *I. albisetosus,* seems to be a rarer ant of more circumscribed distribution. At Fort Davis, Texas, both species were found nesting side by side, so that I was able to compare their habits. *I. cockerelli* is a large, very slender, long-legged ant of a deep cherry-red color, with jet black gaster adorned with a large yellow spot at its base. It stalks about very slowly and is quite unable to sting, but instead endeavors to defend itself with the milk-white, faintly odorous secretion of its anal glands. Though the colonies are rather populous, the workers forage singly. They carry one another like the species of *Leptothorax,* the deported ant being held by the mandibles while curling her body up over the head of her carrier. The nests (Fig. 156) are so large and made of such rough materials that one can hardly believe that they can be the work of such frail insects.

Fig. 160. Disk of *Pogonomyrmex rugosus,* showing one of the paths extending off towards the upper right-hand corner of the figure. A partial ring of chaff and rejected seeds is seen to the left of the entrance. (Original.)

They are huge craters from 60 cm. to 2 m. in diameter and from .20–.50 cm. in height, built of coarse desert soil intermingled with large pebbles sometimes 2 cm. in diameter. The center of the crater is funnel-shaped, with a great entrance of irregular outline frequently as much as 5–8 cm. across. The galleries and chambers are proportionally large and excavated in such hard soil and to such a depth that I have never been able to explore them satisfactorily. Although these nests bear a certain resemblance, on a large scale, to those of *Messor pergandei,* they seem even more like the work of some desert rodent or reptile. *I. albisetosus* is a smaller and more opaque species, covered with abundant, very coarse, white, hairs. Its nests resemble those of *cockerelli,* but are usually smaller and more often situated under large stones. Both species are omnivorous, with an evident preference for fruits and seeds. At Monahans, I found the craters of *cockerelli* covered with the disjointed pods of the mesquite (*Prosopis juliflora*) which had been carried into the nest, deprived of the sweet pulp enclosing the hard seeds and then rejected. On the kitchen middens I also recognized the legs and elytra of three species of *Eleodes* and of several other beetles. At Fort Davis, the workers of *albisetosus* were seen carrying in the dried seeds of umbelliferous plants, grasses and cottonwood (*Populus fremonti*), and occasionally stopping to collect pieces of insects (shards of *Podophylla* and *Coccinella*) and bits of cow-dung, or even bird-droppings. None of these substances, however, is stored in the nests, but merely carried in and then rejected. These ants are not, therefore, highly developed harvesters like those of the allied subgenus *Messor,* but resemble more closely the northern species of *Aphænogaster.* In Connecticut I have often seen *A. picea* collecting and temporarily storing in its nests small flowers, green seeds or the pulp-covered akenes of raspberries, and Emery long ago made a similar observation on an Italian variety of *A. testaceopilosa.* Of this ant he says: " It is not predaceous but collects soft vegetable substances, such as petals of flowers and green seeds, which it carries into the nest and then rejects, after having extracted from them any utilizable substances," and he adds in a foot-note: " In a courtyard of the University of Palermo I saw this ant daily collecting the petals of roses that were somewhat dried but still of the natural tint, and later rejecting them, soiled and crumpled, and of a yellow color, as if they had been triturated. The typical *A. testaceopilosa,* which I have observed in Sardinia, has intermediate habits and lives partly on prey, partly on vegetable substances." During the summer of 1907 I was able to confirm Emery's observations on several colonies of *A. testaceopilosa* in the Alameda at Gibraltar. These observations are of considerable interest in connection with the habits of the fungus-growing ants to be considered in the next chapter.

The most characteristic American harvesters are the large or medium-sized, black or red ants of the genus *Pogonomyrmex,* which is closely related to *Myrmica* of the temperate and boreal portions of the Northern hemisphere. In most of the species of *Pogonomyrmex* the head of the workers and females bears on its under side a conspicuous beard of long, curved hairs (ammochætæ), a character to which the generic name ("bearded ant") refers and one which occurs also in many species of *Messor,* in *Holcomyrmex* and in other desert ants (see p. 16). The genus ranges from British America to Patagonia, but the species are almost exclusively confined to the dry mountainous deserts and plains, where some of them ascend to an altitude of 5,000–8,000 feet. Most of them are aggregated in two groups, one of which inhabits Argentina and Chile; the other the Southwestern States and northern Mexico, and few are known to occur in the long intermediate region. The subgenus *Ephebomyrmex,* which comprises small, beardless species, with coarse, reticulate sculpture is represented by a single form (*E. schmitti*) in Hayti, another (*E. nægelii*) in Brazil, and a few in Mexico, Texas and Arizona (*E. imberbiculus, pima* and *townsendi*). Another subgenus, *Janetia,* is represented by a single species (*J. mayri*) in Colombia. Only one of the species of *Pogonomyrmex s. str.,* the Florida harvester (*P. badius*), is known to occur east of the Mississippi River. According to Forel (1901*m*), *P. occidentalis* has been taken in Hawaii.

Little is known of the habits of the South American *Pogonomyrmex.* Berg (1890) has published a few notes on *P. cunicularis* and five other species occurring in Argentina, Chile and Uruguay, but no mention is made of their harvesting habits. Their nests seem to be insignificant, with the exception of those of *cunicularis,* which are described as surmounted by craters 50 cm. in diameter erected in sandy soil. *Janetia,* according to Forel, does not harvest seeds, but this

Fig. 161. Incipient nest of *Pogonomyrmex molefaciens,* a small pile of pebbles hiding the nest entrance; natural size. (Original.)

statement is open to doubt. All of the North American *Pogonomyrmex* (including those of the subgenus *Ephebomyrmex*) are unquestionably harvesting ants, although none of them disdains insect food whenever it can be procured. They all excavate their nests in soil fully exposed to the rays of the sun and are able to endure prolonged droughts. According to my observations our species may be divided into four groups, as follows:

1. *P. subdentatus, apache, sancti-hyacinthi* and *desertorum,* and *Ephebomyrmex imberbiculus, townsendi* and *pima.* These are small species confined to the deserts of Texas, New Mexico, Arizona, California and northern Mexico. Their colonies are always insignificant and widely scattered, comprising only a few dozen individuals. The nests are small, obscure craters, 10–20 cm. in diameter and a few centimeters high. The workers make no attempt to cut down the surrounding vegetation, which often grows on the crater immediately around the entrance.

2. *P. californicus, comanche* and *badius.* Larger than the preceding and living in colonies of one to a few hundred individuals. They nest exclusively or by preference in sand, and construct flat, single or multiple craters from 30–60 cm. in diameter and 3–5 cm. high with rounded slopes and oblique, central entrances. The workers make no attempt to clear away the vegetation around the nest.

3. *P. barbatus* and its numerous subspecies and varieties: *molefaciens, rugosus, fuscatus, marfensis, nigrescens,* etc. This is the largest and most powerful of our species, the celebrated "Texan harvester" or "agricultural ant." It forms extensive colonies of several hundred individuals and shows great variability in the construction of its nests. In their simplest form, *e. g.,* in *rugosus,* these present a bare, circular disk, or area 1–2 m. in diameter, produced by cutting down and removing all the vegetation around the central opening (Figs. 159 and 160). In other cases, *e. g.,* in *molefaciens,* the opening is at the summit of a conical crater of pebbles, partly or wholly covering the disk and sometimes as much as 50 cm. high (Fig. 158). This crater, as well as the underlying soil, to a considerable depth (5 m. according to one account!) is perforated with flat chambers connected by galleries.

4. *P. occidentalis,* which, like *barbatus,* forms large colonies and clears away the vegetation from great circular areas, which vary from 2–5 m. in diameter. In the center of the area it always constructs an elegant gravel cone (modified crater) 60 cm. to 1 m. in diameter and 20–30 cm. high, with an oblique, excentric opening near the base and nearly always on the eastern or southern slope. The cone and underlying soil, sometimes to a depth of 3 m., are riddled with flat chambers, which, as in *barbatus,* are denser and more numerous in the cone and more scattered and connected by longer galleries in the soil (Fig. 164).

Some years ago I published a few observations on *E. imberbiculus* and *P. subdentatus* (1902b). These and the other species of the first of the above groups, like all ants that form small colonies, are very timid and inoffensive. Workers of *imberbiculus* kept in an artificial nest were seen to feed their larvæ on pieces of house-flies and crushed seeds.

Of the species of the second group, only one, the Florida harvester (*P. badius*) has come under the observation of previous authors. Mrs. Mary Treat (1878) studied this ant in Florida, and McCook (1879c) made a few observations on workers kept in confinement. It harvests the seeds of many plants (*Euphorbia, Croton, Aristida,* etc.), and stores them in the flat granaries of its nests. It not only collects seeds that have fallen to the ground but plucks them directly from the plants, husks them and deposits the chaff on the kitchen middens at the periphery of its low, rounded craters. My own observations, made in the sandy grounds about Jacksonville, Florida, confirm those of Mrs. Treat, who failed to find any tendency on the part of this ant to cut down the vegetation or to clear areas around its nests. *P. badius* differs from all the other known species of the genus in having highly polymorphic workers. The huge-headed soldiers are not abundant in the colonies and seem to be no more aggressive or pugnacious than the intermediate and small workers. *P. comanche,* which is common in the sandy post-oak woods about Austin and Milano, Texas, and in the

Fig. 162. Incipient crater of *Pogonomyrmex rugosus* in patch of *Astragalus* which the ants are beginning to cut down and clear away. ⅛ natural size. (Original.)

alluvial bottoms of the Colorado River in the same region, and *P. californicus,* which is abundant in sandy portions of the deserts of Texas, New Mexico, Arizona and California, have very similar habits. The latter is represented by several local varieties and subspecies. Both species carefully close their nest entrances at night. The incipient nests are crescentic or semilunar with the very oblique entrance on one side, but as the crater grows, it becomes circular and eventually surrounds the entrance. The marriage flight of *californicus* and its method of establishing colonies are described in a former chapter (p. 189 *et seq.*).

P. *molefaciens* (Fig. 157), the common Texan variety of the Mexican *barbatus,* was first studied by Buckley (1861, 1866, 1867) and Lincecum (1862, 1866, 1874) and later by McCook (1879c) and myself (1902). The papers of Buckley and Lincecum contain some of the earliest modern observations on harvesting ants. P. *molefaciens* ranges from the seashore at Galveston and Corpus Christi to an altitude of 5,000 ft. in western Texas and over 8,000 ft. in Mexico, where it often inhabits the same stations as the typical *barbatus*. The latter is readily distinguished by its black head and thorax and red gaster, whereas *molefaciens* is ferruginous red throughout.

The Texan harvester has attracted no little attention on account of Lincecum's statement that it actually sows the seeds of the " ant-rice " (*Aristida stricta* and *oligantha*) around the periphery of its disks or mounds, and cultivates the crop in addition to harvesting and storing it in its granaries. This notion, which even the Texan schoolboy has come to regard as a joke, has been widely cited, largely because Darwin stood sponsor for its publication in the Journal of the Linnean Society. McCook, after spending a few weeks in Texas observing *P. molefaciens* and recording his observations in a book of 310 pages (1879c), failed to obtain any evidence either for or against the Lincecum myth. He merely succeeded in extending its vogue by admitting its plausibility. Four years of nearly continuous observations of *molefaciens* and its nests enable me to suggest the probable source of Lincecum's misconception. If the nests of this ant can be studied during the cool winter months—and this is the only time to study them leisurely, as the cold subdues the fiery stings of their inhabitants—the seeds, which the ants have garnered in many of their chambers will often be found to have sprouted. Sometimes, in fact, the chambers, are literally stuffed with dense wads of seedling grasses and other plants. On sunny days the ants may often be seen removing these seeds when they have sprouted too far to be fit for food and carrying them to the refuse heap, which is always at the periphery of the crater or cleared earthen disk. Here the seeds, thus rejected as inedible, often take root and in the spring form an arc or a complete circle of growing plants around the nest. Since the *Pogonomyrmex* feeds largely, though by no means exclusively, on grass seeds, and since, moreover, the seeds of *Aristida* are a very common and favorite article of food, it is easy to see why this grass should predominate in the circle. In reality, however, only a small percentage of the nests, and only those situated in grassy localities, present such circles. Now to state that the *molefaciens,* like a provident farmer, sows this cereal and guards and weeds it for the sake of garnering its grain, is as absurd as to say that the family cook is planting and maintaining an orchard when some of the peach stones, which she has carelessly thrown into the backyard with the other kitchen refuse, chance to grow into peach trees.

There are several other facts that go to show that the circle of grass about the *molefaciens* nests is an unintentional and inconstant by-product of the activities of the ant-colony. First, the *Aristida* often grows in flourishing patches far from the nests of *molefaciens.* Second,

FIG. 163. Mound of *Pogonomyrmex occidentalis* at Las Vegas, New Mexico, showing large cleared area around cone. (Original.)

one often finds very flourishing ant colonies that have existed for years in the midst of much travelled roads or in stone side-walks thirty meters or more from any vegetation whatsoever. In these cases the ants simply resort for their supply of seeds to the nearest field or lawn, or pilfer the oat-bin of the nearest stable. Third, it is evident that even a complete circle of grass like that described by Lincecum and McCook would be entirely inadequate to supply more than a very small fraction of the grain necessary for the support of a flourishing colony of these ants. Hence they are always obliged to make long trips into the surrounding vegetation, and thereby wear out regular paths which radiate from the cleared disk in different directions, often to a distance of 10–20 m. from the nest. These paths, in the case of the typical Mexican *barbatus,* remind one of human footpaths, as they may be as much as 10–15 cm. wide. The existence of these well-beaten paths, which are often found in connection with grass-encircled nests, is alone sufficient to disprove Lincecum's statements.

The reader may be referred to McCook's work (1879c) for an account of many interesting details in the habits of *molefaciens.* I shall stop to record only a few observations on the marriage flight, the method of establishing formicaries, the development of the nests, etc., matters which have been either overlooked or inadequately described by previous authors. During three successive years (1901–1903) at Austin, Texas, the nuptial flight of *molefaciens* took place on one of the last days of June (28 and 29) or the first in July. On one of these occasions (July 4, 1903) the flight was of exceptional magnitude and beauty. A few days previous the country had been deluged with heavy rains, but Independence Day was clear and sunny, the mesquite trees were in full bloom and the air resounded with the hum of insects. For several days I had seen a few males and winged females stealthily creep out of the nest entrances as if for an airing, but hurry back at the slightest alarm. From 1.30 to 3 o'clock, however, on the afternoon of July 4, all the numerous colonies which I could visit during a long walk through the fields and woods west of the town, gave forth their males and females as if by a common impulse. The number issuing from a single large nest was often sufficient to have filled a half liter measure. Soon every mound and disk was covered with the bright red females and darker males, intermingled with workers, many of whom kept on bringing seeds and dead insects into the nest as unconcernedly as if nothing unusual were happening. The males and females, quivering with excitement, mounted the stones or pebbles of the nest or hurriedly climbed onto the surrounding leaves and grass and rocked to and fro in the breeze. Then, raising themselves on their feet and spreading their opalescent wings, they mounted obliquely one by one into the air. I could follow them only for a distance of 10 or 20 m. when their rapidly diminishing bodies melted away against the brilliant, cloudless sky. Many pairs, hesitating to take flight, chased one another about on the surface of the nest. The amorous males seized many of the females before they could leave the ground. Lizards crept forth in great numbers and gulped down quantities of the fat females, while others were borne off into the air by large robber flies (Asilidæ). By a little after three o'clock the males and females had left the nest and only the workers were seen pursuing the quiet routine business of bringing in seeds. Later in the afternoon innumerable fertilized and deälated females which had descended from their flight, were running hither and thither over the ground in search of suitable places in which to establish their formicaries. At nightfall a terrific shower, amounting almost to a cloud-burst, descended on the country. When I arose the following morning the weather was clear

Fig. 164. Section of nest of *Pogonomyrmex occidentalis,* showing arrangement of chambers and of some of the connecting galleries. (Photograph by G. A. Dean.)

again, but I was unable to find a single female on the rain-scoured soil. One and all had been swept into the streams that were booming through the gullies and cañons on their way to the Colorado River. At 12 M. I saw about the entrance of a nest a few males and virgin females and on digging into it detected several others. An examination of other colonies, which had celebrated their nuptial flight the day before, revealed the same conditions. It is certain, therefore, that the *molefaciens* colonies do not throw off all their males and females during the nuptial flight, and are thus able to avoid a complete destruction of the annual sexual generation. This conclusion is also borne out by the observations of Mr. W. H. Long, Miss A. Rucker and Miss M. Holliday, who witnessed several minor nuptial flights during the latter part of the summer (August 6–10). I have also seen mature males and winged females in the nests in March and April, so that there are probably small flights also during the spring months. But unlike many other ants, *molefaciens* does not deälate and permanently detain in the nest a number of females in addition to the mother-queen that originally established the formicary. At any rate, I have never been able to find more than one deälated queen in a colony, which, therefore, occupies only a single nest. This is also true of the other species of *Pogonomyrmex* that have come under my observation.

The formicaries of *molefaciens* are founded in the same manner as those of *P. californicus* described in a former chapter. As Lincecum was the first to observe, the recently fertilized female digs down into the soil to a depth of about 15 cm., closes the opening after her and gradually brings to maturity a brood of about a dozen very small and timid workers. During the following spring the workers open the nest to the surface, but are always careful to keep the entrance hidden under a few sticks or pebbles, which have the appearance, as Lincecum says, of having been drifted together by the wind (Fig. 161). It is not till the second year, when a number of large workers have been produced, that the ants begin to cut down the vegetation around the nest entrance, now left fully exposed, and to establish their circular disk, which is continually enlarged as the number of workers increases. On the deserts east of Alberquerque, New Mexico, I saw a number of incipient colonies of *P. rugosus* in the act of cutting down young *Astragalus* plants and clearing disks about 30 cm. in diameter (Fig. 162). The further development of the nest differs with the character of the soil. Where this is an even adobe or sandy loam, no crater is constructed, but the disk is merely enlarged. In localities where there are many pebbles scattered over the soil, these are assiduously collected and built into a crater (Fig. 158). The cleared disk is obviously an adaptation for securing the maximum amount of dryness for the granaries in the soil, and although seeds are often stored in the crater chambers, the latter seem to be of even greater utility in incubating the brood. The larvæ, as in *E. imberbiculus,* are fed with pieces of crushed or broken seeds. In my artificial nests these pieces were coated with saliva by the workers before being administered to the brood, a precaution which may insure the conversion of the starch into sugar and facilitate its assimilation by the larvæ.

The occident harvester (*P. occidentalis*) which ranges over the Great Plains from Montana to northern Texas, New Mexico and Arizona, rarely descending below 5,000 feet and thriving best at an altitude of 6,000 to 8,000 feet, has been studied by Leidy (1877) and McCook (1882) and more recently by Headlee and Dean (1908) and myself.

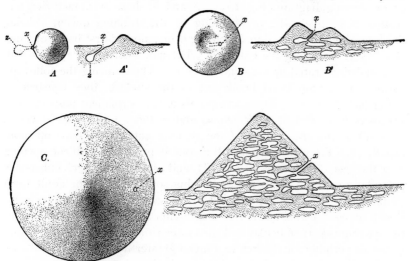

Fig. 165. Diagrams of three stages in the development of the modified masonry dome of *Pogonomyrmex occidentalis*. (Original.) *A*, Small mound of earth thrown up by queen when starting her formicary; *x*, entrance, *z*, first chamber; *A'*, same nest in section; *B*, crater nest (second year) formed by incipient colony; *B'* section of same; *C*, mound, or dome of adult colony; *C'* section of same showing galleries and chambers.

It is a smaller ant than *P. barbatus* and much more precise and uniform in its nesting habits. Its constructions are, in fact, the most elegant and extensive of any of the known species of the genus. As in the case of *barbatus*, the edge of the carefully cleared disk on which the fine gravel cone rests is sometimes surrounded by a circle of grass or other plants which grow from the refuse heap (Fig. 163). *P. occidentalis* is not in the habit of foraging in files, so that no paths radiate from the cleared disk. This absence of paths is attributed by McCook to the sparse and tufted character of the vegetation of the Great Plains, which makes beaten roads unnecessary.

During July, 1903, I witnessed the nuptial flight of this insect near

Colorado Springs.   It took place on a clear afternoon and resembled in nearly all respects the nuptial flight of *molefaciens* described above. During the summer months of 1906 I saw deälated females founding their colonies in the rocky plains about Buena Vista, Colorado.   The female enters the soil obliquely, throwing the earth backward with her legs or carrying it out with her mandibles till it accumulates in the form of a small fan-shaped mound as in *molefaciens* and *californicus*.   I have inferred the manner of growth of the crater from examination of many nests of different sizes and ages, and represent the process in the accompanying diagram (Fig. 165).   *A* and *A'* show in surface view and section respectively the nest as dug by the deälated queen, *x* being the opening and *z* the cell in which she brings up her first brood of small workers after closing the entrance.   The moundlet of excavated earth is soon disintegrated by the wind or rain.   When, during the following spring, the young brood break out to the surface, they construct a crater like *B* and *B'*.   This corresponds to the permanent nests of such forms as *P. comanche, californicus* and *badius*.   Gradually, however, the wall of the crater back of the slanting entrance is built up more rapidly than the wall in front, till a cone is produced with the opening near the base on one side (*C* and *C'*), and as it grows the chambers are extended up into it from the underlying soil.   This is the adult form of the nest and is not represented in the sand-inhabiting species mentioned above.   *P. molefaciens* also presents a stage like *B* and *B'*, but the opening is perpendicular and the crater rim grows uniformly around its whole periphery and often to a much greater height.   *B* and *B'* may also be taken to represent on a large scale the permanent nest-form of the small species of the genus, *P. desertorum, Ephebomyrmex imberbiculus,* etc.

A good account of the distribution and nesting habits of *P. occidentalis* in the higher, western portion of Kansas has been published by Headlee and Dean.   These authors give measurements of the nests and interesting figures of their architecture.   One of these figures is here reproduced with Mr. Dean's permission (Fig. 164).

In conclusion, attention may be called to the stinging habits of *Pogonomyrmex*.   In this respect the smaller and more timid species are no more formidable than other Myrmicine ants of the same size dwelling in small colonies.   But this is not the case with *P. occidentalis, P. barbatus* and the allied varieties and subspecies.   The sting of these ants is remarkably severe, and the fiery, numbing pain which it produces may last for hours.   On several occasions when my hands and legs had been stung by several of these insects while I was excavating their nests, I grew faint and almost unable to stand.   The pain appears to extend along the limbs for some distance and to settle in the lymphatics of the groin and axillæ. If it be true, as has been reported, that the ancient Mexicans tortured or even killed their enemies by binding them to ant-nests, *P. barbatus* was certainly the species employed in this atrocious practice. It is commonly supposed that the poison responsible for the pain inflicted by these and other ants is formic acid, but chemical analysis of *P. molefaciens* by Melander and Brues (1906) failed to reveal any traces of this substance. Hence the poison of this insect must be some unknown substance, possibly a nucleoalbumin. This confirms the opinion of other authors, who, like Fürth (1903), deny that the general physiological effects of the sting, even in the European ants, are due to formic acid.

CHAPTER XVII

THE RELATIONS OF ANTS TO VASCULAR PLANTS

"Plantas itaque norunt formicæ."—Michael Gehlerus, 1610.

"Die Ergründung der interessanten Gemeinschaft zwischen Pflanzen und Ameisen wurde bisher als ein rein botanisches Problem aufgefasst. Aber gerade hierin liegt—wenn mir ein Urteil in dieser Frage zugestanden werden sollte—die Ursache der geringen Erfolge, um nicht zu sagen der Misserfolge. Man war stets allzusehr geneigt, die Anpassungsfähigkeit der Pflanzen an plötzlich eintretende, sie berührende Verhältnisse, als erheblich hinzustellen, umgekehrt aber glaubte man diejenige von lebenden Wesen mit so achtungsgebietender Begabung, wie solche den Ameisen eigen ist, übergehen zu müssen; der Instinkt dieser findigen Tiere täuschte eben über den nur höchst schwerfällig arbeitenden Anpassungsmechanismus der Pflanze hinweg." — Rettig, "Ameisenpflanzen und Pflanzenameisen," 1904.

The hypothesis of intimate mutualistic relations between ants and the higher plants is one of those fascinating constructions in which certain gifted and imaginative botanists have rivalled the inventors of the mimicry hypothesis in the zoölogical field. Both of these constructions have been treated as facts of the utmost value in supporting a still more general hypothesis—that of natural selection, and both, after having been carried to extremes by their respective adherents, are now facing the reaction that is overtaking Neodarwinism. Authors like Fritz Müller, Schimper, Huth, Delpino, Beccari and Heim have marshalled a formidable array of observations in favor of the view that many plants develop elaborate structures to be used as lodgings by certain pugnacious ants or even furnish these insects with exquisite food substances, and in return for these services are protected by their tenants from the leaf-cutting ants or from other leaf-destroying animals. These observations are now being subjected to critical revision by authors like Rettig and H. von Ihering, whose attitude towards the whole subject is avowedly skeptical and reactionary. It behooves us therefore to examine both sides of the argument and, if possible, to adopt a position which will favor and not forestall further investigations.

We may divide our subject into two parts and consider, first, the plant adaptations that are said to indicate symbiosis, and second, the ants that are associated with plants. The supposed adaptations may be considered under two heads: the dwelling places and the food provided for the ants. The former consist either of preformed cavities or of structures from which the pith or loose tissue can be easily removed and thus converted into habitable tenements.   In both cases the cavity is entered through a small orifice which either preëxists or is made by the ants.   This orifice then constitutes the nest opening, or entrance. These simple requirements are fulfilled by a great many plant structures which therefore make admirable domiciles for small ants that live permanently in small colonies or for incipient colonies of larger ants that later form populous communities.   The rigid vegetable tissues are an excellent protection against enemies, and the cavities are moist, dark and free from moulds, so that they make perfect nurseries for the larvæ and pupæ.   Cavities of this description are especially utilized by ants in the tropics, probably because there these insects are more abundant and the struggle for existence is keener.   The following paragraphs will show how numerous and variable are the plant organs that may be tenanted by ants:

1. **Cavities in Stems.**—Almost any hollow or pithy stem, with resistant walls sufficiently thin to be pierced by ants, may be entered and occupied by these insects.   Some plants, however, are especially well-suited to these purposes, for example, those of the Old World genera *Randia, Myristica, Clerodendron, Kibara* and *Bambusa,* with preformed cavities, and *Endospermum* and *Juglans* with pithy stems; among the New World genera: *Cecropia, Triplaris, Tachigalea, Humboldtia, Tachia, Ficus, Cordia, Duroia, Coussapoa, Pterocladon, Pterocarpon, Bombax, Cladium,* etc., with preformed cavities, and *Coccoloba uvifera, Sapium, Schwartzia, Platymyschium*

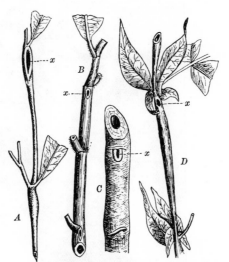

FIG. 166. Stems of " myrmecophilous " plants. (Escherich, after Schimper.)   *A, Ficus inæqualis; B, Triplaris americanus; C,* same, older stem; *D, Humboldtia laurifolia; x,* entrance to cavity of stem.

and *Sambucus* with pithy stems.   The entrances to the cavities are actually foreshadowed as pits in the internodes in *Cecropia* and *Clerodendron.*

2. **Tubers, Bulbs, Pseudobulbs, Rootstocks, etc.**—Many examples could be cited under this head.   The most celebrated are the Malayan Rubiaceous epiphytes of the genera *Myrmecodia* and *Hydnophytum,*

which have large pseudobulbs full of preformed cavities, nearly always tenanted by ants. Certain ferns of the genus *Lecanopteris* from the same region, and certain orchids of the genera *Grammatophyllum* and

FIG. 167. The "Palo Santo" (*Triplaris boliviana*) in fruit, from a specimen in the herbarium of the New York Botanical Garden. (Original.)

Schomburgckia are also cited as providing accommodations for ants in their pseudobulbs.

3. **Ascidiæ or Bursæ of Leaves and Petioles.**—The straight or convoluted leaf-petioles of certain pitcher plants (*Nepenthes bicalcarata*)

are often hollowed out and inhabited by ants (Heim), and the curious ascidia of *Dischidia rafflesiana* are similarly utilized.   In North America various species of ants inhabit the old, dry pitchers of *Sarracenia*.   In

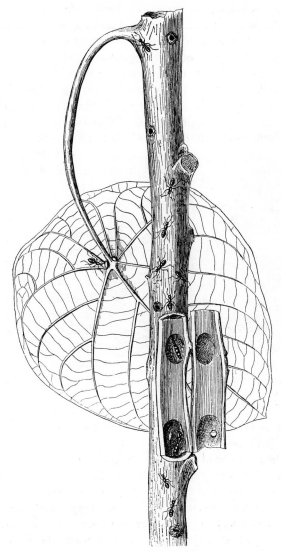

FIG. 168. Stem and leaf of *Endospermum formicarum*, the former inhabited by colonies of *Camponotus quadriceps*. (Dahl.) Two nest openings are seen in upper part of stem. Where the petiole joins the leaf there are two nectaries.

South America several genera of plants (*Tococa, Majeta, Microphyscia, Calophyscia, Myrmedone, Hirtella*) have bladder-like dilatations of the petiole or base of the leaf which are regularly inhabited by colonies of small ants.

4. **Spaces Between or Under Leaves.**—In four species of East Indian palms belonging to the genus *Korthalsia* the spiny ochrea, or leaf-sheath, is enlarged and boat-shaped and applied to the stem in such a way as to enclose a cavity, which, according to Heim, is often tenanted by ants. Many plants with equitant or clasping leaves furnish similar lodgings (*Calamus amplectens,* the banana, etc.). In tropical America certain epiphytic Tillandsias are very generally inhabited by ants, as I have repeatedly observed in Mexico, Florida and the West Indies. Sometimes a single bud-like *Tillandsia* will contain colonies of three or four species in the spaces between its overlapping leaves.

FIG. 169. Rootstock of fern (*Lecanopteris carnosa*) inhabited by ants, from Central Luzon. From a specimen in the New York Botanical Garden. (Original.)

5. **Thorns.**—Several species of *Acacia,* both in Africa (*A. fistulosa*) and tropical America (*A. spadicigera, sphærocephala, hindsii*), bear pairs of thorns which are enormously enlarged or inflated and filled with loose tissue. The ants gnaw round holes near the pointed tips of the thorns, remove the tissue and take possession of them as nests.

6. **Seed-pods.**—Dried seed-pods of plants, after the seeds have escaped or decayed, are sometimes converted into ant lodgings. Professor C. H. Eigenmann sent me from Cuba several colonies of *Camponotus inæqualis* which he found nesting in the pods of a leguminous vine.

7. **Galls.**—These may also be cited in this connection, though they have been considered in a previous chapter (p. 208).

A survey of these various cases shows very clearly that ants may take possession of any vegetable cavity which suits their convenience, and that in the great majority of cases at least, the plants show no adaptations to the insects. But the plants are not limited to this letting of apartments rent-free; they are said to offer the more alluring inducement of a free supply of food, both solid and liquid.

1. **Floral Nectaries.**—Like other Hymenoptera and insects in general, ants are fond of visiting flowers and imbibing their nectar. The

floral nectaries are regarded as alluring organs and volumes have been written on the insects and birds that visit them. In these works, however, the ants are not seriously considered, probably because they treat the flowers very cavalierly, for, unlike the bees, they do not concentrate their attention on particular plants and make cross-fertilization one of their main avocations.

2. **Extrafloral, or Extranuptial Nectaries.**—These organs which, like the floral nectaries, secrete a saccharine liquid, are situated on the most diverse portions of the plant body, and occur in hundreds of species, both among ferns and flowering plants.[1] While there can be no doubt that in many of these plants the extrafloral nectaries are assiduously visited by ants, it by no means follows that these organs have been developed for the purpose of attracting these insects. Indeed, it must be admitted that the significance of the nectaries of this type is far from clear. Some botanists, like Bonnier, Johow, and Lloyd, believe that they may be excretory organs and that the excretion is carried off in small quantities dissolved in the liquid nectar. It has been noticed that the organs in question are sometimes developed only on young leaves, as in the poplar and brake fern, and that the formation of sugar is in all probability the result of more active metabolism in the surrounding tissues or due to other unusual physiological conditions of rapid growth. The excretion thus formed is then utilized by ants and many other insects (wasps, flies, beetles, etc.). This sober physiological explanation is rejected by Schimper (1888) and others on the ground that the excretory function of these nectaries has never been proved. They are therefore interpreted as alluring organs devised especially for ants and scattered over the surface of the plant for the purpose of extending the surveillance of these insects. Their development on the young leaves is said to be only what we should expect, for such parts would be in greatest need of protection from injury or defoliation. Even Schimper, however, is compelled to admit that this view of the extrafloral nectaries can be accepted only if it can be proved, "first, that the visitations of the ants confer protection on the plants with extranuptial nectaries and that in the absence of the insects a much greater number would perish or fail to produce flowers or set seeds, than when the insects are present, and second, that

[1] The following is a list of some of the genera that comprise species with extrafloral nectaries: *Pteris, Polypodium, Acrostichum, Populus, Quercus, Pæonia, Rhipsalis, Sarracenia, Darlingtonia, Gossypium, Psidium, Balsamina, Vicia, Phaseolus, Dolichos, Lablab, Cassia, Acacia, Erythrina, Canavalia, Ailanthus, Rosa, Cratægus, Prunus, Syringa, Passiflora, Sambucus, Viburnum, Luffa, Impatiens, Melampyrum, Turnera, Crozophora, Marcgravia, Stillingia, Alchorea, Ricinus, Centaurea, Helianthus.*

the nectaries have no other function in the life of the plant and cannot be regarded as having arisen for some other function." Neither of these propositions has been established, although there is a little evidence to show that the ants actually protect certain plants whose nectaries they are in the habit of visiting. But Schimper, who studied this subject in Brazil, admits that plants with extrafloral nectaries differ greatly in the extent to which they are visited by ants, and I have reached a similar conclusion from observing species of *Cassia, Stillingia, Ricinus, Ailanthus* and *Populus.* Schimper endeavored to ascertain whether the extrafloral nectaries had any such function as that attributed to them by Johow and Bonnier. He extirpated all the nectaries of *Cassia,* and finding no visible changes in the well-being of the plant, concluded that the organs have little importance in metabolism and that their main function is to attract ants. This does not follow from the experiment, however, for it is quite possible that with extirpation of the organs under discussion their function might be transferred to other parts of the plant.

3. **Food-bodies.**—These structures are known to occur in only a few plants peculiar to the American tropics. In *Cecropia* and *Porouma* they are called " Müllerian bodies," and are yellow or red, elliptical corpuscles about the size of a millet seed. They are found embedded in a dense mat of hairs forming a large cushion, or " trichilium " at the base of the leaf-petiole. In *Cecropia* these bodies, which Schimper found to contain oily and albuminous substances, are easily detached and are carried away and eaten by the ants. Whether this is also the case in *Porouma* has not been ascertained. *Acacia sphærocephala* possesses similar corpuscles, known as " Beltian bodies," but these are borne singly on the tips of the leaflets (Fig. 178, *C*).

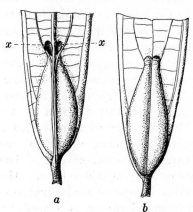

FIG. 170. Base of leaf with ascidia, of *Tococa lancifolia.* (Escherich, after Schumann.) *a,* Lower; *b,* upper surface of leaf; *xx,* openings of ascidia.

4. **Bead-glands (" Perldrüsen ").**—These are modified trichomes or elevations, which sometimes appear as transparent bead-like bodies, scattered in great numbers over the surfaces of green plants. According to Rettig (1904), they are characteristic of certain Vitaceæ, Piperaceæ, Melastomaceæ and Urticaceæ, rarer in Moraceæ, Bigoniaceæ

and Sterculiaceæ. This author has detected them on the leaves of *Cecropia*, where they had been overlooked by previous observers. Like the Müllerian and Beltian corpuscles, the bead-glands are rich in fatty oils, proteins and sugar. In *Bunchosia gaudichaudiana* they are visited by ants (*Cremastogaster* and *Cryptocerus*), according to Fritz Müller. Other species, however, belonging to the genera *Gnetum,*

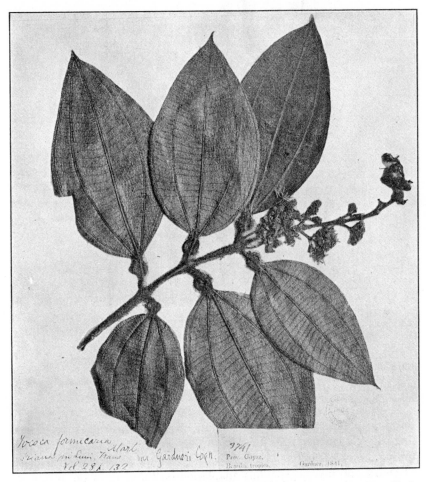

FIG. 171. *Tococa formicaria,* from a specimen in the herbarium of the New York Botanical Garden. (Original.)

Leea and *Pterospermum,* which possess these glands, are described as "free from ants." Both the food bodies and the "Perldrüsen" are obviously modified glands, and differ from the nectaries much as certain animal structures, like the milk glands, in which the cells themselves break down to form the secretion, differ from the salivary glands which secrete a liquid without undergoing disintegration.

5. **Pith and Other Vegetable Tissues.**—Dahl (1901) describes certain ants of the Bismarck archipelago and their larvæ as feeding on

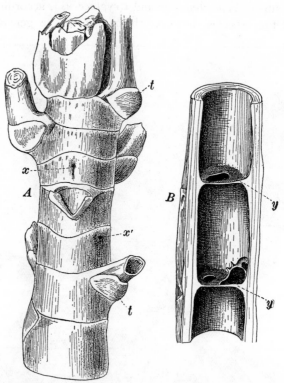

FIG. 172.   *Cecropia adenopus* (Schimper.)   *A*, Tip of branch with leaves cut off; *t*, trichilia at base of leaf petioles; *x*, prostoma or depression in internode; *x′*, stoma or opening to hollow internode made by *Azteca muelleri* at the prostoma.   *B*, Longitudinal section of stem showing the hollow internodes and at (*y*) the septa perforated by the ants.

the pith in the twigs of *Clerodendron,* and von Ihering (1907) finds that *Azteca muelleri* eats the tissue that grows over the perforation through which it enters the hollow twigs of the *Cecropia.*   There is, of course, no myrmecophilous adaptation on the part of the plants in these cases.

Turning now to the ants which are supposed to take advantage of the inducements offered by the plants, we find in both hemispheres many species that are very fond of wandering over the vegetation and visiting the nectaries, food-bodies, etc.   In the tropics whole genera have become largely or exclusively arboreal, but this does not mean that the food of the insects is obtained exclusively or even in great part directly from the plants, for, as will be shown in a future chapter, many ants visit plants mainly for the purpose of feeding on the excrement of the aphids, coccids, etc. In the Old World the exclusively, or at any rate, very largely arboreal genera are *Œcophylla, Cataulacus, Sima* and *Polyrhachis,* in the New World *Azteca, Pseudomyrma, Cryptocerus, Myrmelachista* and *Allomerus,* and in both hemispheres *Dolichoderus, Camponotus, Cremastogaster* and *Iridomyrmex.* The only forms, however, which are so exclusively arboreal as to show unquestionable structural adaptations to this habit, belong to the genera *Azteca, Pseudomyrma, Sima* and to *Colobopsis,* a subgenus of *Camponotus.* Concerning the habits of *Azteca* and *Pseudomyrma* Forel (1904) says: " The species of *Azteca* show very disparate conditions in the castes of the same species. Sometimes the head of the female is elongated, sometimes greatly broadened; and in like manner vary the proportions of the large and small workers. Emery was the first to call attention to this fact in his excellent monograph of the genus *Azteca* [1894k]. I believe that these differences are correlated with differences in habit. Just as the species of *Eciton* are the robbers of the soil in the primeval forest and the *Atta* species are the destroyers of the foliage of the neotropical woods, so the species of *Azteca* and *Pseudomyrma* are the true monarchs of the trees. To my knowledge, none of the species of *Azteca* and only one *Pseudomyrma* (*P. elegans*) nest in the ground. But what a varied arboreal existence is led by these little monkeys among the ants as they climb and scurry about everywhere on the trees! Some of them build carton nests on the trunks and branches, others nest in great cavities in the trunks; others (*A. hypophylla*) nest under the leaves of certain vines with these organs closely applied to the trunks, and close up any openings at the edges of the leaves with carton. Others, again, make use of the cavities of dead branches, while still others nest in the natural medullary cavities of living *Cecropia* trees or any hollow swellings or spaces in all kinds of plants. Finally Mr. Ule has discovered and described antgardens in which grow certain epiphytes that are sown by species of *Azteca.* Now I believe that the long, narrow head of the female and of the large workers of many members of this genus, as well as that

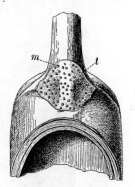

FIG. 173 Base of leaf petiole of *Cecropia adenopus.* (Schimper.) *t,* Trichilium, or hairy cushion in which the Müllerian bodies (*m*) are formed.

of many species of *Pseudomyrma* point to a life in very narrow, tubular branches and twigs. The small *Azteca* worker is small enough to enter and leave such openings without the great elongation of the head, which in the much larger queen is necessary for the accommodation of the powerful mandibular muscles. The nearly brainless and jawless male

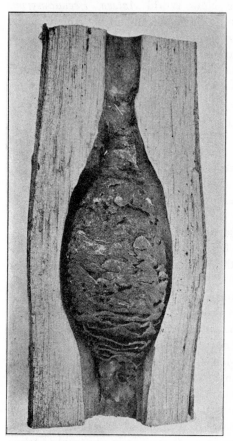

does not require this adaptation. A broad, depressed head points to a life in much flattened cavities (*A. hypophylla*), etc. There are, to be sure, other differences in the form of the head (*trigona* and *aurita*, both carton-builders) that cannot be accounted for in this way." At least one species of *Azteca* (*A. viridis*) is green, a very unusual color in ants and evidently an adaptation to life among living leaves. In *Pseudomyrma* species the whole body is greatly elongated. These are, in fact, the most slender of ants and anyone who has seen colonies of them filling narrow twigs and stems like so many sardines packed in a box, will be sure to regard the lengthening of the body as an adaptation to life in small tubular cavities. The species of the Old World genus *Sima* resemble the species of *Pseudomyrma* very closely in structure and habits. The soldiers of *Colobopsis*, as I have shown in a former

FIG. 174. Carton nest of *Azteca muelleri* in the main trunk of *Cecropia adenopus;* Santa Catharina, Brazil. From a specimen in the American Museum of Natural History. (Original.)

chapter (p. 211) have singularly truncated heads, adapted to fitting into and closing the perfectly circular entrances to the galleries of the nests which are always in wood or in the hollow culms of sedges. Perhaps the soldiers of many species of *Cryptocerus* and *Cataulacus* use their wonderful heads for the same or similar purposes.

The foregoing facts, it must be confessed, do not furnish a very solid foundation for the myrmecophily hypothesis that has been built upon them. At most they disclose considerable adaptability on the part of the ants, and a rather dubious or clumsy counter adaptation on the part of the plants. But the authors who would convince us that there is a definite symbiosis between such very different organisms, advance as their *chevaux de bataille* a few cases in which certain exquisitely arboreal ants live in a definite association with certain plants that present unusual structural characters. Such are the association of the Brazilian *Azteca muelleri* with *Cecropia adenopus,* that of the Malayan *Iridomyrmex myrmecodiæ* with *Myrmecodia* and *Hydnophytum* and that of *Pseudomyrma* with *Acacia* in Central and with *Triplaris* in South America. We must therefore consider these cases in somewhat greater detail.

The relations of *Azteca muelleri* to *Cecropia adenopus* have been studied by Fritz Müller (1876, 1880), Schimper (1888), and von Ihering (1891, 1907). The tree known as the "imbauba" or "imbauva" belongs to the Urticacæ and is very slender and candelabrashaped, growing to a height of 12–15 m. It is most abundant along the Brazilian littoral. The trunk and branches are hollow except at the nodes, where there are thin transverse septa (Fig. 172). The sap is colorless, not milky nor rubber-containing, as stated by some authors. The crown of foliage is meagre and consists of large, palmately lobed leaves. At some time of its life each node bears a leaf, the long petiole of which has at its base a hairy cushion, known as the trichilium (Figs. 172*t*, 173*t*), in which the yellow Müllerian bodies

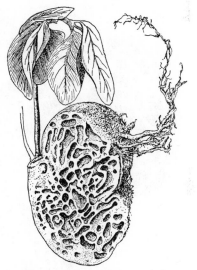

FIG. 175. *Hydnophytum montanum* of Siam, showing pseudobulb in section. (Forel.)

(*m*) are imbedded. The cavities of older and larger trees are almost without exception tenanted by *Azteca muelleri,* which perforates the septa and thus causes all the internodal cavities to communicate with one another, both in the trunk and branches. The ants do not, however, live in the smallest, still actively growing twigs. The just-fecundated queen enters the branches while the tree

Fig. 176. *Myrmecodia pentasperma* of Bismarck Archipelago, with pseudobulb opened to show ants (*Iridomyrmex cordatus*) inhabiting the cavities. (Dahl.)

is still young (50 cm. to 2 m. high) at a particular point, a small depression at the upper end of a furrow at the top of the internode, where, as Schimper has shown, the wall lacks the fibro-vascular bundles and is most easily perforated. Von Ihering calls the depression the "prostoma," the perforation which is formed in it the "stoma." The queen thus enters an internode by making a stoma and feeds on the tissue ("stomatome") which, according to von Ihering, soon proliferates over and closes the opening from the inside. In the small internodal cavity the first workers, six to eight in number, are reared, and these restore communication with the outside world by again open-

FIG. 177. Hollow thorns of *Acacia sp.* inhabited by *Pseudomyrmax fulvescens;* Jalapa, Mexico. (Original.) The entrances are near the tips of the thorns.

ing the stoma. Von Ihering says that as many as five to ten queens may each start a colony in one of the internodes of the same tree, that these colonies forsake the internodes in which they were reared and migrate to more distal internodes and that they eventually engage with one another in conflicts that terminate in the death of all except one of the queens and a fusion of the worker personnel of the different colonies to form one larger community. Such a fusion of hostile colonies is so contrary to what is known to occur in other ants that it may well be doubted. It is more probable that only one of the original colonies together with its queen survives and that all the others are either massacred, or driven away from the tree.

After this single colony has grown and perforated the septa it starts a spindle-shaped carton nest in the bole, a little distance above the ground. This so-called "metropolitan" nest (Fig. 174), which was discovered by von Ihering, resembles the carton nests built by other species of the genus on the branches of *Cecropia* and other trees. Where the nest occurs the bole of the *Cecropia* presents a spindle-shaped enlargement, which von Ihering regards as a gall—"the largest known gall," but his figures and several of these nests recently acquired by the American Museum of Natural History prove conclusively that such an interpretation is erroneous. The wall of the hollow trunk, where it encloses the nest, shows no structural modification except a bending outward of the woody fibers. About half the thickness of this wall is gnawed away by the ants from the inside, leaving a thin zone encircling the trunk, which naturally bulges out under the weight of the superposed trunk and crown of foliage. As there is no hypertrophy of the tissues in the spindle-shaped deformation, the term gall, as applied to a structure of such simple mechanical origin, is a misnomer. When the metropolitan nest is established the ants make a large entrance in the adjacent wall of the trunk and through this and the other openings in the branches pass to and from the foliage. They collect the Müllerian bodies and store them in the nest where they can be eaten at leisure. So dependent is the *Azteca* colony on the *Cecropia* for this food that it perishes when the tree dies or is cut down.

Those who have seen the living imbauba and its occupants are unanimous in describing the insects as rushing out and fiercely attacking any one who ventures to touch the foliage. Alien ants, especially, are vigorously assailed and either killed or driven from the tree. Von Ihering, however, calls attention to the fact that various Chrysomelid larvæ, caterpillars and the sloth (*Bradypus tridactylus*) are permitted to feed on the leaves unmolested. Fritz Müller and Schimper believed that the *Azteca* protects the tree from defoliation by the large leaf-cutting ants of the genus *Atta,* but von Ihering has shown that the plant, even when entirely free from its so-called protectors, is rarely or never visited by *Atta.* It thus appears that the *Cecropia* is not known to have any enemies against which the *Azteca* could avail. The animosity of these ants is probably greatest against alien colonies of their own species, and is directed to retaining possession of the feeding grounds and neighborhood of their nest. This is, of course, a well-known trait of ant-colonies in general. Although von Ihering says that " in order to thrive the imbauba no more requires the *Azteca* than a dog does fleas," he nevertheless believes that the Müllerian bodies and the prostome are myrmecophilous adaptations. In this, he seems to me, to concede too much, for if the ants are of no use to the *Cecropia,* why should the latter develop structures for the purpose of attracting and retaining this superfluous bodyguard? And of the three Cecropian structures, which might be regarded as indicating myrmecophily, namely, the cavities of the trunk and branches, the prostomes and the Müllerian bodies, the first can hardly be an adaptation to harboring ants, the second are produced, or at any rate, started, as Schimper admits, by the pressure of the axillary buds against the surface of the internodes, while the Müllerian bodies, though continually formed anew as they drop off or are carried away by the ants, may have an excretory or some other nonmyrmecophilous function, for aught that is known to the contrary. The adaptation, therefore, has every appearance of being on the side of the ant rather than on that of the tree. This is also indicated by two other considerations: first, by the habits

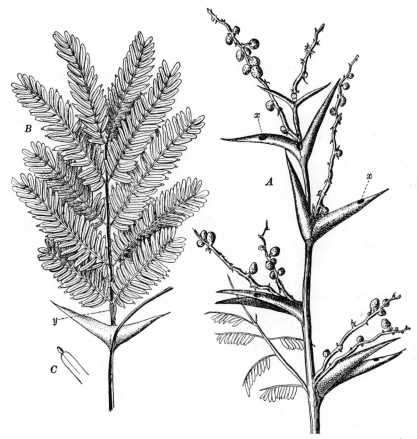

Fig. 178. *Acacia sphaerocephala.* (Schimper.) *A,* End of branch showing pairs of hollow thorns which are inhabited by ants (*Pseudomyrma*); *x,* openings of nests; *B,* leaf of same plant; *y,* nectary on upper surface of petiole; *C,* tip of leaflet enlarged showing Beltian body.

of the *Azteca,* which seems to have taken up its abode in the *Cecropia* within comparatively recent times, since it has not abandoned the construction of large fusiform carton nests like those produced on the branches of trees by many other species, although the cavities of the *Cecropia* seem to be better adapted to long cylindrical nests or would seem to render the construction of carton nests altogether superfluous. In the second place, certain species of *Cecropia,* having essentially the same structure as *C. adenopus,* are nevertheless free from ants. This is true, for example, of *C. peltata,* as I have observed in Porto Rico (1907d). Here no species of *Azteca* occurs and the tree is almost never tenanted by ants of any description, although it has well-developed prostomes and distinct Müllerian bodies. It thrives on the mountains of the island, even when its foliage is much eroded and perforated by insects. Of the Brazilian species, *C. lyratiloba,* according to von Ihering, resembles *adenopus* in having Müllerian bodies and in being regularly inhabited by *Azteca.* The same is true of *C. sciadophylla,* which is peopled with *A. emeryi* according to Forel. Both Schimper and von Ihering, however, found *C. hololeuca* without trichilia and without ants. The former author also describes and figures this tree as lacking the prostomes. The allied genus *Porouma* is imperfectly known. Rettig says that it has Müllerian bodies like *Cecropia,* and Forel (1904i) mentions *Azteca duroiæ* as occurring in its twigs.[1]

The "myrmecophilous" Rubiaceæ, embracing the genera *Myrmecodia* (Fig. 176), *Hydnophytum* (Fig. 175) and *Myrmephytum,* with about sixty species, confined to the Austromalayan region, have been studied by Rumphius (1750), Gaudichaud (1826), Caruel (1872), H. O. Forbes (1880, 1886), Beccari (1884, 1885), Treub (1883, 1888), Burck (1892), Haberlandt (1893), Karsten (1895), Dahl (1901) and Rettig (1904). These plants are epiphytes on trees or rocks in hot, sunny places and grow from large, bulbous stems full of cavities that communicate with the outside by means of small holes. These bulb-like structures are nearly always occupied by ants. Treub found that the cavities arise in the very young plant and are not started, though they may be subsequently enlarged, by the insects. *Iridomyrmex myrmecodiæ,* a subspecies of *I. cordatus,* is the ant most frequently found nesting in these plants, but species of the same or other genera have also been recorded (*Camponotus maculatus, Cremastogaster difformis* and *Pheidole javana*). In some species of *Myrmecodia* the bulb bristles with spines, as if for protection, but notwithstanding the presence of these structures and the ants, no one has been able to detect the existence of any enemy that might injure or devour the plants. Treub observed that specimens grown in localities inac-

---

[1] In a very recent study ("Cecropia peltata und ihr Verhältnis zu Azteca Alfari, zu Atta sexdens und anderen Insekten," etc., *Biol. Centralbl.,* 29, 1909, pp. 1–16, 33–55, 65–77, pls. 1–5), Fiebrig is even less inclined than von Ihering to accept the theory of myrmecophily among plants. He shows that *Cecropia peltata* of Paraguay (apparently not the *C. peltata* of the Antilles!) is not protected from its great number of insect and other enemies by the *Azteca alfari,* though this ant constantly occupies its cavities and feeds on its Müllerian bodies.

cessible to the ants throve as well as those filled with the insects. And he, Karsten, Rettig and others, after a careful study, found that the walls of the cavities are provided with lenticelli and that the cavities themselves probably have a twofold function: to contain air and thus prevent the tissues of the plant from becoming overheated during hot, dry spells, and to take up and to store water for purposes of growth at other seasons of the year. It would seem, therefore, that the ants merely take advantage of the cavities without either benefiting or injuring the plant.

This case of *Myrmecodia* and the allied Rubiaceæ is very interesting as epitomizing the change of opinion which will eventually extend to other instances of so-called symbiosis between ants and plants. Rumphius in 1750 declared *Myrmecodia* to be a zoophyte, believing that the ants brought together twigs and built a nest out of which the *Myrmecodia* germinated. He therefore called the plant "*nidus germinans formicarum rubrarum et nigrarum.*" Now we have a physiological explanation, which some may regard as a sordid anticlimax to this and other fanciful views concerning the relations of the *Myrmecodia* to its tenants. But to the thinking naturalist Rumphius's explanation is

FIG. 179. Ant gardens of the Amazon. (Ule.) *A*, Large spherical ant garden covered with seedling plants; *B*, small garden on *Cordia.*

merely a childish absurdity, while that of the recent botanists is infinitely more stimulating to the scientific imagination, disclosing as it does, on the one hand, the age-long struggles of a plant to live on the atmosphere and its moisture while exposed on hot cliffs and tree-trunks, and, on the other hand, the no less persistent endeavors of the plastic ant to find new domiciles for its pullulating commonwealths.

The classical account of the relations of *Acacia sphærocephala* (Fig.

177 and 178) and a species allied to *Pseudomyrma bicolor* is given by
Belt in " The Naturalist in Nicaragua " (1874). He describes the large
paired thorns tenanted by the ants, the extranuptial nectaries on the leaf-
petioles and the yellow food-bodies at the tips of the leaflets, and puts
these various structures down as so many symbiotic adaptations. He
says that " hundreds of ants are to be seen running about, especially
over the young leaves. If one of these be touched, or a branch shaken,
the little ants (*Pseudomyrma bicolor* Guér.) swarm out from the hollow
thorns and attack the aggressor with jaws and sting. . . . These ants
form a most efficient standing army for the plant, which prevents not
only the mammalia from browsing on the leaves, but delivers it from
the attacks of a much more dangerous enemy, the leaf-cutting ants."
Belt sowed the seeds of *Acacia* in his garden and reared some of the
young plants. "Ants of many kinds were numerous; but none of
them took to the thorns for shelter, nor the glands and fruit-like bodies
for food. . . . The leaf-cutting ants attacked the young plants and
defoliated them, but I have never seen any of the trees out on the
savannahs that are guarded by the *Pseudomyrma* touched by them, and
have no doubt the *Acacia* is protected from them by its little warriors."
There are several other thorn-inhabiting *Pseudomyrmæ* (*belti, fulvescens, spinicola*) that nest in this and other species of *Acacia* in Central
America and Mexico, and a *Cremastogaster* is also mentioned by Belt
in this connection. Concerning the development of the thorns he says:
" The thorns, when they are first developed, are soft, and filled with a
sweetish pulpy substance; so that the ant, when it makes an entrance
into them, finds its new house full of food. It hollows this out, leaving
only the hardened shell of the thorn. Strange to say this treatment
seems to favor the development of the thorn, as it increases its size,
bulging out towards the base; whilst in my plants that were not touched
by the ants, the thorns turned yellow and dried up into dead but persistent prickles. I am not sure, however, that this may not have been
due to the habitat of the plant not suiting it." According to Rettig
(1904) this latter statement is based on insufficient observation, for the
enlargement of the thorns is not produced by the ants, although it does
not make its appearance till the plant has grown considerably.

It has been known for some time that the Old World also has its
acacias with enlarged thorns tenanted by ants. Gerstaecker (1871),
Schweinfurth (1867–'68) and more recently Keller (1892) have called
attention to the East African " uwadi " acacia (*A. fistulosa*), the greatly
inflated thorns of which are white at first but when old become brown
or black. According to Keller these thorns are nearly always inhabited
by species of *Cremastogaster* (*chiarinii, ruspolii* or *acaciæ*). He main-

tains that *A. fistulosa,* which furnishes a gum of commercial value, is never eaten by cattle and he attributes this immunity to the protecting ants. Concerning the growth of the thorns he says: "Of the manner in which the young inflations arise I am unable to form any satisfactory conception. They are produced in great numbers at the beginning of the rainy season, when the vegetation awakens, and are then green and soft. I never saw a hole in one of them. *They are completely closed on all sides,* and it is not till later that they are opened by the ants. I have seen no injuries, wounds, nor anything that could indicate that the deformation is due to insects, and I cannot therefore regard the inflations of the thorns as gall-formations. With this conclusion also harmonizes the fact communicated to me by Schweinfurth, that acacias grown from seed in Cairo also developed the inflations. The only explanation I can suggest is that in this plant an originally abnormal growth has become perfectly normal, under the influence of natural selection, through adaptation to symbiosis with ants." Keller calls attention to the singular fact that only a small number of the thorns on a plant become inflated. This suggests that bacteria or other pathogenic organisms may be responsible for the deformation, which is then put to good use by the ants.

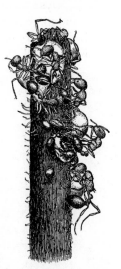

Fig. 180. Broken twig of sunflower (*Helianthus annuus*) showing ants (*Myrmica brevinodis*) caught and killed by the exuding sap. (Original.)

A few words may be added on certain South American plants of the genera *Cordia, Humboldtia, Ficus* (*e. g., inæqualis*), *Tococa* (Figs. 170 and 171) and *Triplaris* (Figs. 166, *B* and 167) and the East Indian *Clerodendron fistulosum.* All of these have preformed cavities either in the stems or in bursæ on the leaves and petioles. *Clerodendron* is said to have in the internodes preformed thin spots, or prostomata, which are selected as entrances by the ants (*Colobopsis clerodendri*). The leaves of this plant are furnished with innumerable nectaries along the midrib on the lower surface. In *Cordia nodosa* the flower-bearing stem is dilated above and contains a short, conical cavity which, according to Schimper, is not homologous with the medullary cavity of other plants, as its walls are formed by a fusion of a number of stems. The chamber, which is furnished with a small preformed opening above, is commonly tenanted by ants. Schumann (1888) and Metz (1890) have noted the remarkable fact that

this plant, when growing in the Antilles, fails to develop the hollow
swellings in the stems. The hollow twigs of the Polygonaceous *Triplaris,* or " palo santo," of which some twenty species are known, are
said to be invariably occupied by *Pseudomyrma.* Of these ants Forel
(1904*i*) says: " Through the investigations of Mr. Ule the fact becomes
more and more firmly established that a definite group of *Pseudomyrma*
species (*arboris-sanctæ, dendroica* and *triplaridis*) lives symbiotically
in the natural medullary cavities of *Triplaris.* In 1896 I myself

Fig. 181. Mound of *Formica exsectoides* .70 meters high and 2.46 meters in
diameter, almost completely covered with a moss (*Polytrichum commune*) which
eventually envelops the summit of the nest and extinguishes the colony. (Original.)

observed in Colombia how *P. arboris-sanctæ* var. *symbiotica* fiercely
attacked anyone who touched the tree. Their brood filled the whole
living tree from the trunk to the smallest green branches. They seemed
to have entered this secure and ramifying domicile through a small
dead and broken branch on the lower part of the trunk."

No doubt the various cases cited in the preceding pages are of great
interest, both to the botanist and myrmecologist, but it is equally certain
that none of them has been studied with sufficient care to warrant the
conclusions advocated by Belt, Schimper and others. The relationships under discussion are all compatible with the view that the ants
have adapted themselves to the plants—*plantas itaque norunt formicæ*
—but the converse of this proposition is in most, if not in all instances,
open to doubt. Travelers and naturalists who observe for a short

time in the tropics, where all of these wonderful cases occur, are very apt to jump to conclusions, and carefully devised experiments, which alone can throw the necessary light on the subject, are still wanting.

The opinion here maintained is indirectly supported by what is known concerning some of the other relations that may obtain between plants and ants. These relations may be considered under the following heads:

1. **Ants as Seed Distributors.**—In the preceding chapter Moggridge's observations on the distribution of seeds by *Messor barbarus* were mentioned, together with other facts which indicate that ants are important agents in scattering seeds. This habit is not confined to granivorous species. Lubbock (1894) saw *Lasius niger* carrying violet seeds into its nest. More recently Sernander (1903) and some other botanists have come to believe that the ants eat the caruncles and that these structures are developed as lures, like the extrafloral nectaries and food-bodies, to induce the ants to carry the seeds to a distance and thus increase the chances of their survival. Dr. E. B. Southwick tells me that he has seen the ants in Central Park, N. Y., carry away the seeds of the blood-root (*Sanguinaria canadensis*) and feed on their caruncles.

2. **Ant-gardens.**—This name is given by Ule (1902) to certain sponge-like ant-nests (Fig. 179) which he found built on the branches of trees in the forests of the Amazon. These nests consist of soil carried up by the ants (*Azteca olithrix, ulei* and *traili* and *Camponotus femoratus*) and held together by the roots of numerous epiphytes, which grow out of it on all sides, making it resemble the head of a Medusa. The ants not only perforate the soil with their galleries but, according to Ule, actually plant the epiphytes. This he infers from seeing the insects in the act of carrying the seeds. Perhaps these are brought into the nest for the sake of their caruncles and then germinate in the rich soil, but it is quite as probable that they are sown by the wind.

3. **Plants Injurious to Ants.**—If it be true that some plants deserve to be called "myrmecophilous," because they are helpful to ants in the struggle for existence, it is equally true that there are other plants that might with even greater justice be called "myrmecophobic," or "myrmecechthric," because they are injurious or even deadly to these insects. Such are, for example, certain moulds and bacteria. Queen ants while founding their colonies in damp cavities in soil or decaying wood often succumb to the incursions of these organisms, which under certain conditions may even exterminate the brood of larger colonies. Miss Fielde (1901b) says: "*Penicillium crustaceum* grows to ripeness, in

either darkness or light, upon eggs, larvæ or pupæ, if left for a few days unattended in the humid atmosphere required by the ants, and its sprouting spores may be seen on their surfaces under a magnification of about five hundred diameters. If the spores are left undisturbed they cover the young with a delicate dense white coat that becomes sage-green with the ripening of the new spores. . . . This delicate mould does not grow upon the bodies of dead ants, but is there replaced by *Rhyzopus nigricans,* with long and spreading hyphæ, and in this

FIG. 182. Old mound of *Formica exsectoides* covered with vegetation and with only a few lingering remnants of the colony in its summit. (Original.)

may lie the cause for the carrying off and casting away of all ants that die or are killed in the nest."

Botanists have described several peculiar arrangements in higher plants, such as excessive hairness, slipperiness or stickiness of the stems, or special palisades of hairs about the floral nectaries (nectarostegia) as means of preventing ants and other desultory arthropods from plundering the secretions intended for bees and other cross-fertilizing agents. But these arrangements, if really developed for this purpose, are often inefficacious. Vosseler (1906) has recently described an African ant which manages to get around the woolly hairs protecting the nectaries in *Cobæa scandens* and gains access to these organs by biting a hole through the base of the petal, a habit which has also been observed in bees that are confronted with flowers whose nectaries they are unable to reach in any other way. But there are graver maladjustments between plants and ants, maladjustments that may lead to the death of the insects in great numbers or even to the extinction of their colonies. I have described a number of such cases in a recent paper (1906*l*). The abundant and sticky juices of *Silene, Lactuca* and *Helianthus* exuding onto the stems or petioles often entrap and kill numbers of ants (Fig. 180). We owe to a similar property of the resiniferous conifers of the Tertiary the preservation of the ants in the Baltic and Sicilian ambers. Our North American pitcher plants (*Sarracenia*) also entrap, kill and digest enormous numbers of ants in the liquid at the bottoms of their ascidia. The ants most frequently found in these modified leaves are *Cremastogaster pilosa,* a species which will sometimes even nest in the dead pitchers of a plant whose active green leaves are busy killing them off in great numbers—a singular commentary on the "intelligence" of these insects, especially when we stop to consider that *C. pilosa* is one of the ants that constructs such beautiful sheds over aphids and coccids.

Another hostile relationship between plants and ants has been described in detail by Holmgren (1904). He observed that the mound nests of *Formica exsecta* in the bogs of Lapland are gradually invaded and eventually so completely covered with a dense carpet of moss (*Polytrichum strictum*) that the ants are either driven away or destroyed. This moss is in turn replaced by a carpet of *Sphagnum,* in which many plants eventually take root, so that the ants are instrumental in forming the hummocks of moss and hence facilitate the growth of peat-forming vegetation. In the bogs of Prussia, according to Kuhlgatz (1902), the *Myrmica* nests are invaded in a similar manner by *P. strictum,* and I have been able to observe various stages in the extinction of colonies of our North American *F. exsectoides* by an allied moss, *P. commune* (1906*l*). This moss starts in the form of a narrow zone around the base of the huge mound nests (Fig. 181) and gradually grows upward till it completely envelopes their summits with a dense mat and either smothers the colony outright or compels it to emigrate (Fig. 182).

CHAPTER XVIII

THE FUNGUS–GROWING ANTS

"Quoique dans l'immense série des êtres, la fourmi ne soit qu'un point qui sans sa mobilité échapperoit presque à nos regards, il n'en est pas moins vrai que cet atome animé est digne d'être l'objet de nos méditations. C'est ici qu'il convient de dire que l'Auteur de la nature n'est jamais plus lui-meme que dans ce qu'il y a de plus petit."—Latreille, "Histoire Naturelle des Fourmis," 1802.

Although our examination, in the last chapter, of the relations between ants and vascular plants has led us to doubt the existence of a true symbiosis between these organisms and to interpret their relations as the result of a direct adaptation on the part of the ants, we are compelled to admit that there is what may be called a true symbiosis

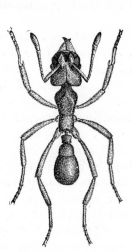 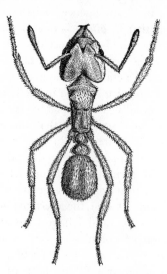

FIG. 183. Worker of *Myrmicocrypta brittoni* of Porto Rico. (Original.)

FIG. 184. Worker of *Sericomyrmex opacus* of South America. (Original.)

between ants and some of the lower plants. These ants all belong to the Myrmicine tribe Attii, which is peculiar to tropical and subtropical America, and the plants with which they are so intimately associated are fungi. The association is symbiotic, because the fungi are provided with their substratum, or nutriment by the ants, and in turn supply these insects with their only food.

The Attii, of which about one hundred species, subspecies and varieties have been described, are all fungus-growers and -eaters. The tribe ranges from about 40° S. to 40° N. of the equator, but is best represented in the tropics. The species have been assigned to five genera, which, beginning with the most primitive, are *Myrmicocrypta, Cyphomyrmex, Apterostigma, Sericomyrmex* and *Atta*. The last of these is divided into six subgenera: *Mycocepurus, Mycetosoritis, Trachymyrmex, Mœllerius, Acromyrmex* and *Atta s. str.* The subgenus *Atta*

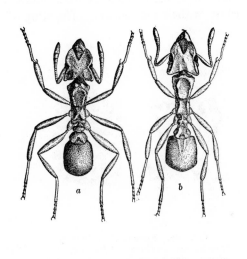

FIG. 185. Worker of *Apterostigma pilosum* of Brazil. (Original.)

FIG. 186. Two species of *Cyphomyrmex* occurring in the United States. (Original.) *a, C. rimosus; b, C. wheeleri.*

comprises the leaf-cutting, or parasol ants, the largest and most powerful species of the tribe, living in great colonies and inhabiting the territory between 30° north and 30° south of the equator. The workers are highly polymorphic and much smaller than the males and females. The colonies of the species of *Mœllerius* and *Acromyrmex* are much less populous, and the workers, though variable in size, do not exhibit such marked polymorphism as those of *Atta s. str.* In *Trachymyrmex* and the remaining subgenera the workers are monomorphic and but little smaller than the males and females, and the colonies are even feebler than those of *Acromyrmex. Mycetosoritis* and *Mycocepurus* are in certain respects transitional to the genera *Cyphomyrmex* and *Myrmicocrypta* (Fig. 183), and species of the last show affinities with *Sericomyrmex* (Fig. 184). *Apterostigma* (Fig. 185) is very aberrant, resembling in form certain Myrmicines of the subgenera *Aphæno-gaster* and *Ischnomyrmex*. The workers of *Atta* are covered with stiff, erect or suberect, hooked or curved hairs, and the surface of the body is tuberculate or spinose. In *Cyphomyrmex* the body is smoother and covered with short, appressed, scale-like hairs. In *Sericomyrmex* and *Apterostigma* the hairs are soft, flexuous and very abundant. With few exceptions all the Attii have the surface of the body opaque and of a ferruginous, brown or blackish color. All the species, moreover, though very powerful and able to make surprisingly extensive excavations in the soil, are very slow and sedate in their movements. The sting of the workers is vestigial, but

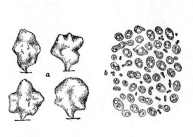

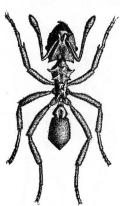

FIG. 187. Fungus (*Tyridiomyces formicarum*) cultivated by *Cypho-myrmex rimosus* on insect excrement. (Original.) *a,* Bromatia, or food bodies; *b,* yeast-like cells of which these consist.

FIG. 188. Worker of *Mycocepurus smithi* of the American tropics. (Original.)

in the larger species the sharp jaws may be used as most efficient organs of defence. The smaller species are extremely timid and when roughly handled " feign death " like many beetles. In all the species the hard, rough or spinose integument must afford efficient protection from alien ants and other enemies.

The Attii are such conspicuous, abundant and destructive insects in tropical America that we are not surprised to find an extensive literature on their taxonomy and habits. The latter have been described by Buckley (1860), Bates (1863), Lincecum (1867), Norton (1868), B. R. Townsend (1870), Belt (1874), McCook (1879*a*, 1879*b*), Morris

(1880), Brent (1886), Tanner (1892), Moeller (1893), von Ihering (1894, 1898), Urich (1895*a*, 1895*b*), Swingle (1896), Forel (1896*a–c*, 1897, 1899–1900, 1901), Sampaio (1894), Goeldi (1905*a* and *b*, Forel 1905) and J. Huber (1905). I have recently reviewed these authors in a paper on the North American Attii (1907*c*), to which the reader is referred for many details that cannot be given in this chapter.

The first important observations on these insects were published by Belt in his interesting volume, " The Naturalist in Nicaragua." He

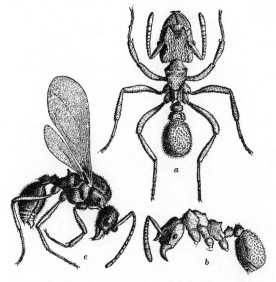

Fig. 189. *Mycetosoritis hartmani* of Texas. (Original.) *a,* Worker, dorsal view; *b,* same in profile; *c,* male.

was the first to surmise the use to which the leaves, etc., are put by *Atta cephalotes,* concerning which he writes: " Notwithstanding that these ants are so common throughout tropical America, and have excited the attention of nearly every traveller, there still remains much doubt as to the use to which the leaves are put. Some naturalists have supposed that they used them directly as food; others, that they roof their underground nests with them. I believe the real use they make of them is as a manure, on which grows a minute species of fungus, on which they feed;—that they are, in reality, mushroom growers and eaters. This explanation is so extraordinary and unexpected, that I may be permitted to enter somewhat at length on the facts that led me to adopt it. When I first began my warfare against the ants that attacked my garden, I dug down deeply into some of their nests. In our mining operations we also, on two occasions, carried our excavations from below up through very large formicariums so that all their underground workings were exposed to observation. I found their nests below to consist of numerous rounded chambers, about as large as a man's head, connected together by tunnelled passages leading from one chamber to another. Notwithstanding that many columns of the

Fig. 190. Section of *Mycetosoritis hartmani* nest in pure sand; about ⅙ natural size. Two of the chambers contain pendent fungus gardens. (Photograph by C. G. Hartman.)

ants were continually carrying in the cut leaves, I could never find any quantity of these in the burrows, and it was evident that they were used up in some way immediately they were brought in. The chambers were always about three parts filled with a speckled, brown, flocculent, spongy-looking mass of a light and loosely connected substance.

Throughout these masses were numerous ants belonging to the smallest division of the workers, which do not engage in leaf-cutting. Along with them were pupæ and larvæ, not gathered together, but dispersed, apparently irregularly, throughout the flocculent mass. This mass, which I have called the ant-food, proved, on examination to be composed of minutely subdivided pieces of leaves, withered to a brown color, and overgrown and lightly connected together by a minute white fungus that ramified in every direction throughout it. I not only found this fungus in every chamber I opened, but also in the chambers

FIG. 191. Fungus garden of the *Mycetosoritis* nest shown in Fig. 190 enlarged about ¼. (Photograph by C. G. Hartman.)

of the nest of a distinct species that generally comes out only in the night-time, often entering houses and carrying off various farinaceous substances, and does not make mounds above its nests, but long winding passages, terminating in chambers similar to the common species and always, like them, three parts filled with flocculent masses of fungus-covered vegetable matter, amongst which are the ant-nurses and immature ants. When a nest is disturbed, and the masses of ant-food spread about, the ants are in great concern to carry away every morsel of it under shelter again; and sometimes, when I dug into the nest, I found the next day all the earth thrown out filled with little

pits that the ants had dug into it to get out the covered up food.
When they migrate from one part to another, they also carry with them
all the ant-food from their old habitations. That they do not eat the
leaves themselves I convinced myself, for I found near the tenanted
chambers, deserted ones filled with the refuse particles of leaves that
had been exhausted as manure for the fungus, and were now left, and
served as food for larvæ of *Staphylinidæ* and other beetles.

" These ants do not confine themselves to leaves, but also carry off

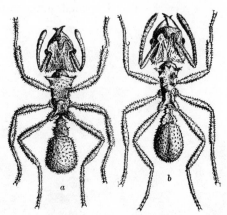

Fig. 192. Two North American species of *Trachymyrmex*. (Original.) *a, T.
turrifex; b, T. septentrionalis.*

any vegetable substance that they find suitable for growing fungus on.
They are very partial to the inside white rind of oranges, and I have
also seen them cutting up and carrying off the flowers of certain shrubs,
the leaves of which they have neglected. They are very particular
about the ventilation of their underground chambers, and have numerous holes leading up to the surface from them. These they open out
or close up, apparently to keep up a regular degree of temperature
below."

Observations on *A. cephalotes* were resumed in 1892 in Trinidad
by Tanner, who was the first to study these insects in artificial nests
and to prove that not only the adult *Attæ* but also the larvæ feed on
the fungus described by Belt. A year later, Alfred Moeller published
the most important of existing works on these ants and their relations
to the fungi which they cultivate. He studied several Brazilian species
of *Atta* belonging to the subgenus *Acromyrmex* (*discigera, coronata,
octospinosa, mœlleri*) and to the genera *Apterostigma* (*pilosum, mœlleri,
wasmanni,* and an undetermined species) and *Cyphomyrmex* (*auritus,
strigatus*). *A. octospinosa* and *discigera,* which nest in the woods,

form truncated cones of dead leaves and twigs, beneath which they excavate a single chamber containing a large fungus garden sometimes 1.5 meters long. *A. mœlleri* has similar habits, but *coronata* resembles the species of the subgenus *Atta s. str.* in forming several chambers, each with its own fungus garden. In all of these species the garden is built up on the floor of the chamber in the form of a loose sponge-work of triturated leaf-fragments, permeated with fungus hyphæ which he

FIG. 193. Tower-shaped nest crater of *Trachymyrmex turrifex* in Texan cedar brake; natural size. (Photograph by A. L. Melander.)

describes as follows: " Over all portions of the surface of the garden are seen round, white corpuscles about .25 mm. in diameter on an average, although some of them are fully .5 mm., and sometimes adjacent corpuscles fuse to form masses 1 mm. across and of irregular form. After a little experience one learns to detect these corpuscles with the naked eye as pale, white points which are everywhere abundant in all nests. Under the lens they sometimes have a glistening appearance like drops of water. They are absent from the youngest, most recently established portions of the garden, but elsewhere uniformly distributed, so that it is impossible to remove with the fingers a particle too small to contain some of the white bodies. I call these the ' kohlrabi clusters ' of the ants' nests. They constitute the principal, if not the only food of the species of *Atta.*" These clusters are made up of the "heads of kohlrabi which are small terminal dilatations of the hyphæ of a spherical or oval form." Moeller confirmed Belt's observations on the solicitude of the ants for their gardens, and showed that these insects in artificial nests will completely rebuild these structures within twelve hours after they have been disintegrated or scattered. He saw the ants eating the fungus and was able to satisfy himself that the different species of *Atta* will eat the kohlrabi from one another's colonies, but not that of *Apterostigma* or *Cyphomyrmex.* Belt supposed that the smallest workers, or minims comminute the leaves and build up the fungus gardens. According to Moeller, however, this is the

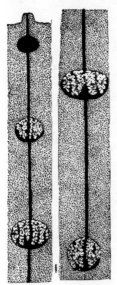

office of the mediæ, as the leaves are too thick to be manipulated by the smallest workers. The latter have another function, namely, that of weeding the garden and keeping down the growth of spores belonging to alien fungi. Moeller emphasizes the remarkable fact that the gardens are pure cultures although the hairy, rough-bodied workers must be continually bringing into the nests all sorts of spores and bacteria. It is probable, also, that the minims are instrumental in producing the "kohlrabi heads," as these are not developed when the mycelium is grown in artificial culture media apart from the influence of the ants. He summarizes the results of this portion of his studies in the following words: "All the fungus-gardens of the *Atta* species I have investigated, are pervaded with the same kind of mycelium, which produces the 'kohlrabi clusters' as long as the ants are cultivating the gardens. Under the influence of the ants neither free aërial hyphæ nor any form of fruit are ever developed. The mycelium proliferates through the garden to the complete exclusion of any alien fungus, and the fungus garden of a

Fig. 194. Diagram of nest of *Trachymyrmex turrifex* with five chambers. The right half of the figure is a continuation of the lower portion of the left half. (Original.)

nest represents in its entirety a pure culture of a single fungus. The fungus has two different forms of conidia which arise in the garden when it is removed from the influence of the ants. The hyphæ have a very pronounced tendency to produce swellings or diverticula, which show several more or less peculiar and clearly differentiated variations. One of these, which has presumably reached its present form through the influence of cultivation and selection on the part of the ants, is represented by the 'kohlrabi heads.'"

Moeller undertook to determine the systematic position of the fungus. He naturally supposed that the discovery of the fruiting form would show it to be an Asco- or Basidiomycete. Although he failed to raise either of these forms from his mycelial cultures, he succeeded on four occasions in finding an undescribed Agaricine mushroom with wine-red stem and pileus growing in extinct or abandoned *Acromyrmex* nests. From the basidiospores of this plant, which he called *Rhozites gongylophora,* he succeeded in raising a mycelium resembling in all respects that of the ant gardens. Three of the species of *Acromyrmex* did not hesitate to eat portions of this mycelium and of the pileus and

FIG. 195. Vestigial nest crater of *Trachymyrmex septentrionalis.* (Original.) The nest entrance is at *x,* the pile of sand pellets shown in the lower right-hand corner represents the crater of *Atta texana* and *Mœllerius versicolor.*

stem of the *Rhozites.* He believed, therefore, that he had definitely established the specific identity of the fungus cultivated by the ants. A careful perusal of Moeller's observations shows an important lacuna at this point. That his *Attæ* ate portions of the pileus and stem of the *Rhozites* does not prove that it is the fruiting form belonging to the fungus they habitually cultivate and eat. Nor is Moeller on much surer ground when he assumes that the mycelia cultivated by different

genera of Attii belong to different species of fungi, for it is very prob
able that the ants of one species would avoid fungus taken from the
nest of another on account of the alien nest-aura. Certainly, to the
human olfactories, the fungus gardens of *Atta texana* have a very

striking odor which is altogether lacking in the gardens of *Trachymyrmex,*
and it would be strange if
these differences did not
affect the appetites of such
sensitive insects as the
ants. In my opinion, it is
not improbable that the
fungi cultivated by the ants
may be more closely re-
lated to the moulds (As-
comycetes) than to the
mushrooms (Basidiomy-
cetes). Moeller does, in
fact, call attention to certain Ascomycete peculiarities in the mycelium cultivated by *Acromyrmex
discigera.* This is a matter, however, to be settled
by the mycologist, and I
merely call attention to it
in this connection, be-
cause Moeller's somewhat
guarded statements have

FIG. 196. Diagram of a large nest of a
southern variety of *Trachymyrmex septentrionalis,* showing near the surface the small original
chamber of the queen, five chambers with pendent fungus gardens, and a newly excavated
chamber in which the garden has not yet been
started. (Original.)

assumed an unduly positive form in subsequent reviews of his work.

The species of *Apterostigma* investigated by Moeller usually nest in
cavities in rotten wood which is often also inhabited by other insects.
The fine wood castings and excrement of these insects are used by the
ants as material with which to construct their fungus-gardens. *A.
wasmanni* constructs the largest nests, and it is only in the gardens of
this species that the mycelium produces structures analogous to the
"kohlrabi heads" and "clusters" of *Acromyrmex.* The "heads,"
however, are club-shaped instead of spherical dilations of the hyphæ.

The gardens of *pilosum, mœlleri* and of another undetermined
Apterostigma, which live in feeble colonies of only twelve to twenty
individuals, are suspended from the roofs of the small cavities, 3 to 4

cm. in diameter, in the rotten wood and exhibit a peculiar structure not seen in other Attii. " The garden is often completely, or at least nearly always in great part, enclosed in a white cobweb-like membrane. It was often possible to obtain a view of uninjured nests of *A. pilosum* that had been excavated in clefts of the rotten wood. In such cases the envelope enclosed the whole fungus gar-den like a bag, with only a single orifice or entrance. The envelope is attached in a pendent position to the surrounding wood, roots or particles of earth by means of radiating fibers, and this explains why the gardens are so easily torn asunder while the nest is being uncovered." Even in cap-tivity these ants persisted in hanging their gardens to the sides of the glass dishes in which they were kept.

FIG. 197. Worker of *Mœllerius versicolor* of Mexico, Texas and Arizona. (Original.)

The two species of *Cyphomyrmex* ob-served by Moeller were found nesting under bark or in rotten wood like *Apterostigma*. The largest gardens of *C. strigatus* are only 8 cm. long, whereas those of *C. auritus* may attain a length of 15 cm. and a breadth and height of 5 cm. These gardens are never pendent and never enclosed in a mycelial envelope. In other respects they resemble those of *Apterostigma* and are grown on the same substrata.

Moeller's studies were confined to the adult colonies of the Attii. The question as to how these ants came by their fungi in the first place, was subsequently answered by the researches of Sampaio (1894), von Ihering (1898), Goeldi (1905*a* and *b*) and Huber (1905, 1907, 1908). Sampaio found fungus gardens in very young formicaries of the Brazilian *Atta sexdens*, and von Ihering showed that the virgin female of this species, on leaving the nest for her marriage flight, carries in her infrabuccal pocket a pellet of hyphæ taken from the fungus garden of the maternal formicary. This pellet is the unex-pelled refuse of her last meal. After fecundation she digs a cavity in the soil, closes its opening to the outside world and sets to work to found a colony. She spits out the pellet of hyphæ and cultivates it, while she is at the same time laying eggs and rearing the larvæ. Von Ihering and Goeldi maintain that she crushes some of her eggs and uses them as a substratum for the incipient fungus garden. J. Huber

describes the behavior of the young queen in greater detail and is able
to trace the development of the colony up to the hatching of the first
brood of workers. He finds that the female expels the pellet from her
buccal pocket the day following the nuptial flight. It is a little mass
.5 mm. in diameter, white, yellowish or even black in color, and consists of fungus hyphæ imbedded in the substances collected from the
ant's body by means of the strigils on her fore feet and thence deposited in her mouth. By the third day six to ten eggs are laid. At this
time also the pellet begins to send out hyphæ in all directions. The
female separates the pellet into two masses on this or the following
day. For the next ten to twelve days she lays about ten eggs daily,
while the fungus flocculi grow larger and more numerous. At first

Fig. 198. Nest craters of *Mœllerius versicolor* in a sandy "draw" in the deserts of
Arizona. (Original.)

the eggs and flocculi are kept separate, but they are soon brought
together and at least a part of the eggs are placed on or among the
flocculi. Eight or ten days later the flocculi have become so numerous
that they form when brought together a round or elliptical disk about
1 cm. in diameter. This disk is converted into a dish-shaped mass with
central depression in which the eggs and larvæ are thenceforth kept.
The first larvæ appear about fourteen to sixteen days after the *Atta*

female has completed her burrow, and the first pupæ appear about a
month after the inception of the colony. At this time the fungus
garden has a diameter of only 2 cm. There are no "kohlrabi" corpuscles in the earlier stages, and when first seen they are at the periphery
of the disk. A week later the pupæ begin to turn brown and in a few
days the first workers hatch. Hence the time required for the establishment of a colony under the most favorable conditions is about forty
days. After this rapid survey of the matter, Huber asks the important question: How does the *Atta* female manage to keep the fungus
alive and growing? Obviously the small amount of substance in the
original pellet must soon be exhausted and the growing hyphæ must

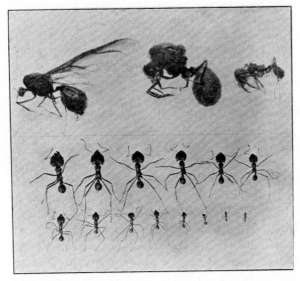

Fig. 199.   Male, deälated female, soldier and series of workers of *Atta texana;*
natural size. (Photograph by A. L. Melander and C. T. Brues.)

be supplied with nutriment from some other source. His interesting
answer to this question may be given in his own words: "After carefully watching the ant for hours she will be seen suddenly to tear a
little piece of the fungus from the garden with her mandibles and hold
it against the tip of her gaster, which is bent forward for this purpose.
At the same time she emits from her vent a clear yellowish or brownish
droplet which is at once absorbed by the tuft of hyphæ. Hereupon the
tuft is again inserted, amid much feeling about with the antennæ, in
the garden, but usually not in the same spot from which it was taken,
and is then patted in place by means of the fore feet. The fungus
then sucks up the droplet more or less quickly. Often several of these

drops may be clearly seen scattered over the young fungus garden. According to my observations, this performance is repeated usually once or twice an hour, and sometimes, to be sure, even more frequently. It can almost always be observed a number of times in succession when a mother ant that has no fungus, as sometimes happens in the cultures, is given a piece of fungus belonging to another *Atta* female or from an older colony. The mother ant is visibly excited while she explores the gift with her antennæ, and usually in a few minutes begins to divide it up and rebuild it. At such times she first applies each piece to her vent in the manner above described and drenches it with a fecal droplet." From these observations Huber concludes that the droplet must be liquid excrement and that the fungus owes its growth to this method of manuring. A direct use of malaxated eggs for this purpose was never observed and could not be detected by microscopical examination, although a number of observations showed that the same result may be accomplished indirectly, namely, by the female eating her own eggs. This habit is so common and apparently so normal that Huber estimates that nine out of every ten eggs are devoured by the mother, often as soon as they are laid. The life of the *Atta* female in her little cell during all this time is very rhythmical. At regular intervals she conscientiously examines the walls of the cavity, flattens out the earth, etc. She devotes more time to licking and manuring the fungus garden and, of course, lavishes most care on the brood. As soon as the larvæ appear they are fed directly with eggs thrust into their mouths by their mother. Huber concludes that this is their normal diet till the first workers hatch. He never saw the female either eating the fungus mycelium herself or feeding it to the young. As proof of this contention he cites the case of one of his *Atta* queens who brought up a brood without a fungus garden. With the appearance of the firstling workers, which are minims, that is, workers of the smallest worker caste, a change comes over the colony. They begin to usurp the functions of the mother ant. They manure the garden, which at the time of their appearance measures hardly more than 2.5 cm. in diameter, and feed the larvæ with their mother's eggs. The workers themselves, however, feed on the "kohlrabi" which has been developing on the hyphæ in the meantime. After about a week some of the workers begin to dig in the earth, and ten days after the appearance of the first worker and seven weeks after the inception of the colony, they break through to the surface of the soil and surround the entrance of the nest with a tiny crater of earthen pellets. They now begin to bring pieces of leaves, cut and knead them up into minute wads, and insert them in the fungus garden. The method of manuring the garden with

fecal droplets seems now to be abandoned.   The mother *Atta* henceforth pays no attention to the development of the garden or to the
brood, but degenerates into a sluggish egg-laying machine, while the
multifarious labors of the colony devolve on the workers.   In the meantime the " kohlrabi " has become so abundant that it can be fed to the
larvæ.   In concluding his paper Huber makes the important observation that fertile females of *Atta sexdens* are readily adopted by strange

workers of their own species.   Such
adoptions may be frequently re-
sorted to in a state of nature and
would perhaps account for the
enormous size and great age of some
of the formicaries of the larger species of *Atta*, which in this respect
resemble the colonies of *Formica
rufa* and *F. exsectoides* in the north
temperate zone.

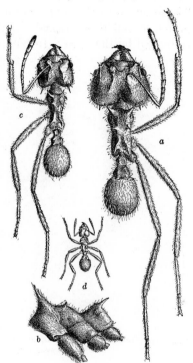

Only a few of the Attiine ants
have spread from their original
tropical home into the southern, subtropical portions of the United
States.   These are *Cyphomyrmex
rimosus* var. *comalensis* and subsp.
minutus, *C. wheeleri*, *Mycetosoritis
hartmani*, *Trachymyrmex septentrionalis* with the var. *obscurior*, *T.
turrifex* and *arizonensis*, *Mœllerius
versicolor* and its subsp. *chisosensis*
and *Atta texana*.   I have been able
to observe all of these except *T.
arizonensis* in a living condition, and
as they exhibit nearly the whole
range of Attiine habits they may be

FIG. 200.   *Atta texana.*   (Original.) *a*, Soldier ; *b*, thorax of same in
profile ; *c*, worker media ; *d*, worker
minima ; all drawn to same scale.

very briefly described.   For many additional details the reader is referred to my paper mentioned above.

1. *Cyphomyrmex.*—Our two species of this genus, the most primitive in the series, have very different habits. *C. rimosus* (Fig. 186, *a*),
which is widely distributed through the tropics, enters the tip of Florida
and southwestern Texas.   It makes small, concealed nests under stones
or logs in rather damp, shady places and collects caterpillar excrement
as a substratum on which to grow its fungi (Fig. 187).   These are
very unlike the fungi raised by any other Attiine ants except *Myco-*

cepurus (Fig. 188), being yellowish, compact, irregularly polygonal or pyriform bodies, .25–.55 mm. in diameter, and consisting of elliptical cells much like those of the yeast plant (*Saccharomyces*). To this fungus I have given the name *Tyridiomyces formicarum*. *C. wheeleri* (Fig. 186, *b*) is a nocturnal species which nests under stones on the dry hills of western Texas. It collects small plant slivers and culti-vates on them a flocculent, snow-white mycelium with well-developed "kohlrabi clusters" and "heads," or bromatia and gongylidia, as I prefer to call these hyphal modifications in this and the other fungi cultivated by the Attii. In both of our species of *Cyphomyrmex* the

Fig. 201.   One of the craters of an *Atta texana* nest; about ⅙ natural size.   (Photo-graph by C. G. Hartman.)

gardens are small (only a few cm. in diameter) and of irregular shape. They are never suspended but lie on the floors of small dilations in the rough earthen galleries of the nest.

2. *Mycetosoritis*.—Our single species, *M. hartmani* (Fig. 189), is a small brown ant, which lives in the sand of the Texan post-oak woods. Here it builds small craters, the openings of which run down vertically into the sand to a depth of 24–79 cm., suddenly dilating at long intervals into two to four subspherical chambers, which vary from 1.3–3.4 cm. in diameter (Figs. 190 and 191). As a rule, these chambers, which are thus strung along the gallery like beads on a thread, increase in size with the depth. While excavating their chambers the ants leave the rootlets of plants dangling into them as suspensoria for their fungus gardens. These consist of flower anthers

collected from the surface of the sand, built up into a flocculent mass
and held together and to the pendent rootlets by means of a snow-
white mycelium studded with the usual bromatia.

3. *Trachymyrmex.*—*T. turrifex* (Fig. 192, *a*) and *arizonensis* are
confined to the dry regions of the southwest. The nest of the former
resembles that of *Mycetosoritis,* but is larger and, as a rule, in more

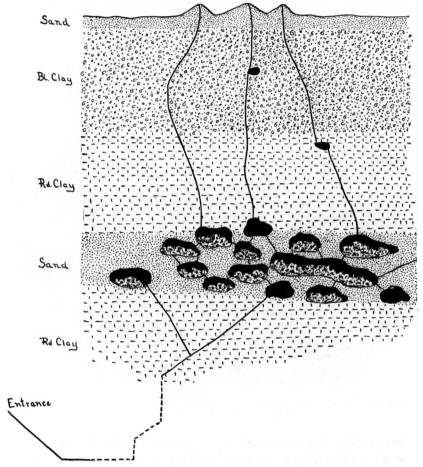

FIG. 202. Diagram of a large *Atta texana* nest in strata of sand, blue and red clay.
(From a sketch by A. L. Melander and C. T. Brues.)

compact soil. The vertical gallery, which opens on a turret-shaped
crater made of bits of sticks and leaves (Fig. 193), descends to a
depth of 38–110 cm. and has at intervals four to five subspherical
chambers 2–5 cm. in diameter and increasing in size with the depth

(Fig. 194). The gardens are suspended like those of *Mycetosoritis* and consist of triturated vegetable substances (leaves, oak-catkins, etc.) covered with a white mycelium. *T. septentrionalis* (Fig. 192, *b*), our most widely distributed Attiine ant, ranges from Texas through the Southern and Atlantic States as far north as the Raritan River in New Jersey. Its nests, which are always excavated in sand, consist of two to seven subspherical chambers (Fig. 196). When there are only

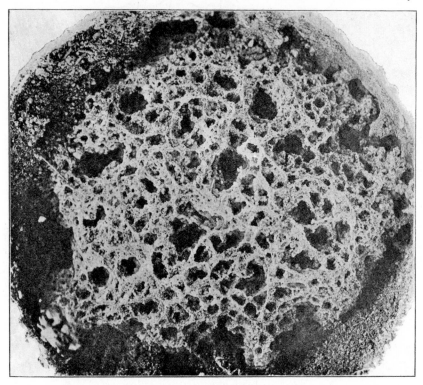

Fig. 203. Entire fungus garden of *Atta texana;* about ¼ natural size. (Photograph by A. L. Melander and C. T. Brues.)

two of these, the nest usually resembles that of *Mycetosoritis* and *T. turrifex,* although the entrance is oblique and the excavated sand is thrown out to one side of the opening and not built up in the form of a regular crater (Fig. 195). When several chambers are present, there are two or three galleries each with one or two chambers, branching off from the main or entrance gallery below the first chamber. The total depth of the nest is usually much less than in *turrifex* (about 35 cm.). The gardens resemble those of *turrifex,* but the fungus has a more bluish tint and the substratum is coarser and less flocculent and often consists of caterpillar droppings.

4. *Mœllerius.*—Our only species is *M. versicolor* (Fig. 197), a Mexican ant which enters the extreme southern portion of Texas and Arizona. It constructs elegant craters 10–30 cm. in diameter in sandy depressions in the deserts (Fig. 198). The subterranean portion of the nest has not been satisfactorily explored, but probably consists of a single large chamber with a single fungus garden on its floor, as in the South American species of *Mœllerius* and the closely allied *Acromyrmex*. *M. versicolor,* unlike the ants of the preceding groups, is a true leaf-cutter, *i. e.,* it defoliates shrubs and trees like the species of *Atta s. str.* and does not collect the substances for the substratum of its gardens from the surface of the ground about the nest.

5. *Atta s. str.*—*A. texana* (Figs. 199 and 200), the leaf-cutting ant, our only species of this subgenus, occurs in loamy or sandy soil in central Texas. It is the largest and most formidable of our species and often does considerable injury to cultivated plants along the Brazos and Guadeloupe Rivers. Its habits are similar to those of the South and Central American *A. cephalotes* and *sexdens.* Externally the nest appears as a large, flat mound, often covering an area of more than 100 sq. m., and made up of a number of more or less fused craters, 10–100 cm. in diameter, with large openings (3–6 cm.) leading into galleries of the same diameter. These galleries often extend to a depth of 2–5 m., where they enter chambers sometimes 50–100 cm. long and 30 cm. broad and high, with flattened floors and arched ceilings (Fig. 202). On the floor of each chamber lies a large garden, made of triturated leaves, built up in the form of an irregular comb or flattened sponge, covered with a white mycelium and studded with the usual bromatia, or food-bodies (Fig. 203). *A. texana* is the only one of our species which has highly polymorphic workers. The minimæ always remain in the gardens where they carefully weed the hyphæ and prevent the growth of any alien fungi that may be introduced by the foraging workers; the mediæ cut, carry in and triturate the leaves and build up the garden; while the maximæ, or soldiers, guard the nest.

The foregoing series of forms together with others occurring only in tropical America, show a perceptible advance in the fungus-growing habit within the Attiine tribe. The lower genera *Cyphomyrmex,* and probably also *Myrmicocrypta,* make small, crude nests, with irregular, sessile gardens of insect excrement. *Apterostigma, Sericomyrmex, Mycetosoritis* and *Trachymyrmex* all excavate more regular nests and construct pendent gardens of insect excrement and vegetable débris.

The gardens of *Apterostigma* are provided with a special mycelial envelope, but they are naked in all the other Attiine genera and subgenera. *Mœllerius* and *Acromyrmex* make a single large garden on the floor of the single nest-chamber. Finally, in *Atta s. str.*, the nest attains huge dimensions and comprises a number of large chambers, each with its sessile fungus-garden resembling the single garden of *Acromyrmex* and *Mœllerius*.

While this series of forms shows an interesting and significant advance in the methods of raising fungi, it throws little light on the origin of this complicated and extraordinary habit. Forel is inclined to believe that the ancestral Attii lived, like the existing *Apterostigma*, in rotten wood and gradually acquired the habit of cultivating on insect excrement the fungi which they chanced to find in the moist galleries of their nests. Von Ihering surmises that the Attii are descended from harvesting ants which transferred their appetite from the hard seeds in their chambers to the delicate fungi that accidentally grew on these stores. In this connection Santschi's observations on the seed-storing *Oxyopomyrmex,* cited on p. *273*, are very suggestive. Besides the Attii there are also two other groups of fungus-growing insects, the ambrosia beetles (Scolytidæ), which cultivate fungus on their excrement or on the walls of their burrows in the trunks of trees, and a long series of paleotropical termites which raise fungi on sponge-like masses of their excrement in large chambers like those of *Atta s. str.* A study of these cases and of the female *Atta* while she is establishing her colony, would seem to indicate that all fungus-growing insects originally used their own excrement as a substratum for their gardens and only later took to adding other substances (excrement of other insects and pieces of leaves in the Attii, wood-shavings in the ambrosia beetles). But how these various insects first came into possession of the fungi which they now so assiduously cultivate and transmit from generation to generation, we are unable to state, especially as our knowledge of these plants is still so rudimentary that we cannot even say whether they are Ascomycetes or Basidiomycetes, independent species or merely permanently or temporarily modified phases of certain well-known moulds or mushrooms. The study of the Attii and other fungus-growing insects has only just begun, and further advance in this fascinating subject will be more difficult for the mycologist than for the entomologist. The latter, however, will have to build on the investigations of the former.

CHAPTER XIX

THE RELATIONS OF ANTS TO PLANT-LICE, SCALE-INSECTS, TREE-HOPPERS AND CATERPILLARS

" Hæ formicarum vaccæ."—Linné, " Systema Naturæ," Ed. 12, I, 1766.

" Viennent enfin ces peuplades qui couvrent la surface de la terre, et dont les républiques sont si nombreuses que le globe ne leur suffiroit pas si la nature n'eût mis de justes bornes à leur multiplication. Une foule d'insectes deviennent leur proie; la petitesse des individus est compensée chez elles par le nombre, mais la force n'est pas leur principale ressource. Ce ne sont pas non plus les fleurs et les fruits qui leur fournissent leur pâture ordinaire; elle est l'objet d'une industrie plus recherchée. Les peuplades dont nous parlons, vont la recueillir auprès de certains êtres pacifiques qui vivent en troupes, et leur prodiguent sans contrainte les sucs qu'ils savent extraire des plantes. Elles ont l'art de s'en faire entendre, de les réunir dans leur habitation, et de les défendre contre leurs ennemis."—P. Huber, " Recherches sur les Mœurs des Fourmis Indigènes," 1810.

In gaining their wide and intimate acquaintance with the vegetable world the ants have also become acquainted with a large number of insects that obtain their nutriment directly from plants, either by sucking up their juices or by feeding on their foliage. To the former group belong the phytophthorous Homoptera, the plant-lice (Aphididæ), scale insects or mealy bugs (Coccidæ), tree-hoppers (Membracidæ), lantern-flies (Fulgoridæ) and jumping plant-lice (Psyllidæ); to the latter belong the caterpillars of the Lycænid butterflies, the " blues," or " azures " as they are popularly called. All of these creatures excrete liquids which are eagerly sought by the ants and constitute the whole, or at any rate, an important part of the food of certain species. In return the Homoptera and caterpillars receive certain services from the ants, so that the relations thus established between these widely different insects may be regarded as a kind of symbiosis. These relations are most apparent in the case of the aphids, and as these insects have been more often and more closely studied in Europe and America, they may be considered first and at somewhat greater length.

The consociation of the ants with the aphids is greatly facilitated by the gregarious and rather sedentary habits of the latter, especially in their younger, wingless stages, for the ants are thus enabled to obtain a large amount of food without losing time and energy in ranging far afield from their nests. Then, too, the ants may establish their nests in the immediate vicinity of the aphid droves or actually keep them in their nests or in " sheds " carefully constructed for the purpose.

Nearly all plants, except the cryptogams, may be infested by aphids, and no part of the plant is free from their attacks. Certain species prefer the leaves, others the twigs, and still others the roots and subterranean stems. Most species live on the surfaces of the plants but a number also make and inhabit galls. Only the former, of course, are accessible to the ants. The sedentary and gregarious habits of the aphids also expose them to a host of enemies, among which the Coccinellid beetles and their larvæ, the larvæ of certain Diptera (Syrphidæ) and Neuroptera (*Chrysopa, Hemerobius*) and a host of small parasitic Hymenoptera (Pteromalidæ, Braconidæ, Crabronidæ) are the most formidable.

The aphids pierce the integument of the plant with their slender, pointed mouth-parts and imbibe the juices which consist of water con-

F ɪ ɢ. 204.   Portion of tap-root of wormwood (*Artemisia vulgaris*) with *Lasius umbratus* workers attending young and adult plant-lice (*Trama radicis*). (Mordwilko.) *a*, Sucking adult *Trama* with hind legs raised; *b*, ant palpating *Trama* with her feelers; *c*, ant receiving droplet of honey-dew from anus of *Trama; d* and *e*, ants carrying away plant-lice in their jaws; *f*, *Trama* with droplet of honey-dew suspended from perianal hairs.

taining in solution cane sugar, invert sugar, dextrin and a small amount of albuminous substance. In the alimentary tract of the insects much of the cane sugar is split up to form invert sugar, and a relatively small amount of all the substances is assimilated, so that the excrement is not only abundant but contains more invert and less cane sugar than the juices of the plant. This excrement is voided in colorless drops, and when it falls on the leaves of the plants and dries in the air is known as " honey-dew," the *ros melleus, mel aërium, roscida mella, melligo,* ὅου μέλι of the ancient writers. Réaumur (1737) and Leche (1765) seem to have been the first to ascertain that the honey-dew, which the ancients supposed to come from the plants, from the sky or from some other mysterious source, is voided by the droves of plant-lice. Within more recent years this subject has been exhaustively studied by Büsgen (1891). The quantity of honey-dew excreted by the aphids, when we consider the small size of these insects, is most surprising. Büsgen found that a single linden aphis excretes nineteen drops in twenty-four hours, while the maple aphis excretes as many as forty-eight drops during the same period. A source of nutriment at once so rich and so inexhaustible, could hardly remain unnoticed and unexploited by the ants in their interminable search for liquid food.

Some ants (*Leptothorax* sp.) obtain the honey-dew merely by licking the surface of the leaves and stems on which it has fallen, but many species have learned to stroke the aphids and induce them to void the liquid gradually so that it can be imbibed directly. A drove of plant-lice, especially when it is stationed on young and succulent leaves or twigs, may produce enough honey-dew to feed a whole colony of ants for a considerable period. But the aphidicolous habit has not been acquired by all ants. The highly carnivorous Dorylinæ and Ponerinæ never attend these insects and care nothing for their excretions, and the same is true of the exquisitely carnivorous, granivorous and fungus-eating genera of Myrmicinæ (*Pseudomyrma, Pogonomyrmex, Atta,* etc.). Other Myrmicine genera, such as *Myrmica, Cremastogaster, Tetramorium* and *Monomorium* contain many aphidicolous species. The two highest subfamilies, however, the Dolichoderinæ and Campono-

FIG. 205. Carton aphid-tent built by *Cremastogaster lineolata* on twig of swamp huckleberry. (Original.)

tinæ, represent the most perfect development of the habit, especially the genera *Iridomyrmex, Dolichoderus, Azteca* and *Liometopum* of the former, and *Lasius, Brachymyrmex, Prenolepis, Plagiolepis, Œcophylla, Formica, Myrmecocystus* and *Lasius* of the latter subfamily. In our north temperate region the species of *Lasius*

excell those of all other genera in this respect; in fact, the yellow, subterranean ants of the subgenus *Acanthomyops,* which is peculiar to
North America, live exclusively on the excrement of root-aphids and
coccids.

The behavior of ants in the presence of aphids has been observed
by P. Huber (1810), Forel (1874), Witlaczil (1882), Lubbock
(1888a), Büsgen (1891), Lichtenstein (1877–'80), Forbes (1894,
1905, 1906), Del Guercio, Kolbe (1888), Shouteden (1902), Mordwilko (1896, 1901, 1907), and others too numerous to cite. One of
the best of the early accounts of this behavior is that of Huber (p. 181
et seq.) : "A thistle branch was covered with brown ants [*Lasius niger*]
and aphids. I observed the latter for some time, in order, if possible,
to ascertain the precise moment when they emitted this secretion from
their bodies; but I remarked that it exuded very rarely of itself, and
that the aphids, when separated from the ants, discharged it to a distance, by making a movement like a sudden jerk.

"Why did nearly all the ants that were climbing about on the
stems, have their abdomens distended as if with some liquid? This
question I was able to answer by watching a single ant, whose exact
method of procedure I will endeavor to describe. I saw her first crawl
over some aphids without pausing and without disturbing them; but
she soon halted near one of the smallest and seemed to caress its
abdomen, stroking it alternately first with one and then with the other
antenna. I was surprised to see the liquid escape from the aphid's
body, and the ant seize and imbibe the droplet at once. Her antennæ
were thereupon applied to another much larger aphid, which, on being
caressed in the same manner, voided a larger drop of the nutrient
liquid. The ant advanced to seize it, and then moved on to a third
which she caressed in the same manner. The liquid was voided immediately and received by the ant. She moved on; a fourth, probably
already exhausted, refused to respond to her solicitations and the ant,
probably divining that she had nothing to expect, quitted this aphid for
a fifth from which I saw her obtain a further supply of food.

"A few such repasts are quite sufficient, and the satiated ant returns
to the nest. Thereupon I watched the other ants that had remained
behind on the thistle, and they were seen to present the same scene. I
always noticed that the arrival of the ants and the stroking of their
antennæ preceded the evacuation of the liquid, and that the attitude
of the plant-lice, with their heads directed downward, seemed to be
assumed for this very purpose. I witnessed this remarkable procedure
thousands and thousands of times; it was always employed by the ants
with the same success whenever they wished to obtain food from the

aphids. If the latter are too long neglected, they discharge the honey-dew on the leaves, where the returning ants find and collect it, before they approach the insects by which it was voided. But if the ants visit the aphids assiduously, the latter seem to comply with their desires by hastening the moment of evacuation. This is indicated by the diameter of the exuded droplet; and at such times they do not eject the ant-manna to a distance, but, so to speak, retain and hand it over to their attendants.

" It sometimes happens that the ants are so numerous on a particular plant that they exhaust the aphids with which it is covered. Under such circumstances they stroke the bodies of their nurses in vain and are compelled to wait till these have pumped up a fresh supply of sap from the stems. The aphids are by no means parsimonious, and if they have anything to give, never fail to respond to the ants' solicitations. I have repeatedly seen the same aphid yield several drops in succession to different ants that seemed very eager for the syrup."

FIG. 206. Earthen aphid-tent built by *Cremastogaster lineolata* on dog-wood. (Original.) The round entrance is in the lower right-hand corner.

Many aphids bear on the sides of the sixth abdominal segment a pair of tubules with terminal orifices, known as cornicules, siphons or nectaries. Réaumur and other earlier authors saw drops of liquid exuding from these as well as from the anal opening, and from such observations has come the erroneous statement that the honey-dew is a secretion of the siphons instead of being merely the excrement of the plant-lice. Linné, for example, says of these insects: " Pleræque duo cornua, postica abdominis gerunt, quibus excernent rorem melleum hæ formicarum vaccæ! " And although this error, which was also promulgated by Buckton in his well-known " Monograph of the British Aphids " (1881–1883), has been disproved by Witlaczil, Büsgen, Kolbe, Forel, Mordwilko and others, we still find it tenaciously retained in many popular works on ants, not to mention text-books of entomology. So careful an author as Comstock, in a book intended for students (" The Study of Insects," p. 157), says: " On the back of the sixth abdominal segment there is, in many species, a pair of tubes, through which a sweet, transparent fluid is excreted. . . . The fluid which is excreted through the abdominal tubercles is the substance known as honey-dew." McCook also perpetuates this old error by publishing figures representing ants taking drops from the siphons of aphids. The discharge of the drops of honey-dew from the anus and not from the siphons, is so easily observed with a pocket lens or even with the naked eye wherever aphids abound, that there is little excuse for

Fig. 207. Carton coccid-tent built by *Cremastogaster pilosa* around a twig of pitch pine. (Original.)

repeating the blunders of Linné and his successors. The actual conditions are shown in the figure (Fig. 204) which, for lack of a better one, I reproduce from the recent papers of Mordwilko (1896, 1907).

What, then, is the function of the siphons? The early writers replied to this question with a variety of more or less fantastic suppositions, although in general they believed these organs to have a secretory function. Réaumur was the first to remark that the siphons secrete a liquid of a more yellowish color than that expelled from the anus, and subsequent authors have shown that the siphonal secretion has a sticky and wax-like consistency. Büsgen finally pointed out the usefulness of this liquid. "I was able," he says, "to ascertain the function of the tubules by observing the operations of a lace-wing larva [*Chrysopa*], the so-called aphis-lion, among a drove of plant-lice. This pale yellow animal, with a dark dorsal stripe and a length of only a few millimeters, hatches from a small egg, which is found during the summer attached by means of a long stalk to the most various plants. The larvæ are usually found on the lower surface of the leaves, and are easily captured, notwithstanding their agility. Their food consists in great part of plant-lice which they seize with their sucking mandibles and hold fast till reduced to mere shrivelled bits of chitin. When these larvæ are to be used for experiment, they are best left to starve for a night and then placed among a drove of aphids suitable for observation. When attacking they strike their jaws from below into the body of the plant-louse with a sudden blow and at once begin to suck out its juices. When the attack happens to be rather awkward, the aphid has time to smear the secretion, which is at once discharged from the tubules, over the face and forceps of the larva, which is thus, at least temporarily, disconcerted and frightened. To be sure, I never saw a larva free an aphid which it had once succeeded in seizing. The secretion hardens on the larva immediately and thus forms a most uncomfortable coating, causing the creature to desist from the chase, while it cleanses its forceps and forehead. This consumes time and can only be accomplished by the aphis-lion's seizing some slender object, like the tooth of a leaf, for the purpose of rubbing off the secretion. While in such a helpless condition, it may itself fall a prey to enemies which it need not fear at other times. Its agility and sucking jaws, capable of being opened to an extraordinary width, make it a formidable enemy even to the ants, which it may actually overcome in the dark. On two occasions after confining a brown garden ant [*Lasius niger*], the most frequent guest of our aphid droves, in a small box with an aphis-lion, I found the ant sucked dry in the course of a few hours. In the day-time, however, I have seen the ants drive the larvæ off their preserves. Still the above observations show that notwithstanding the protecting guard of ants, the aphids require a special weapon, which may annoy, though it cannot kill, their enemy.

" Even more striking is the use of the tubercles in the case of the lady-bird beetles (Coccinellidæ), those well-known enemies of the aphids.

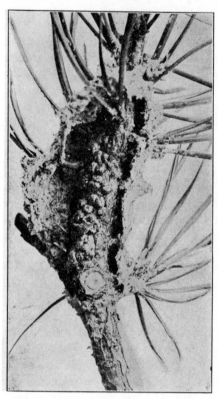

On the approach of one of these beetles, the rose-aphis at first seeks safety in her long legs, which, when touched, apprise her of danger before the enemy can reach her body. Sometimes she merely turns to one side without drawing her proboscis out of the plant tissues, at other times she lets herself drop bodily to the ground. If change of place does not put her out of reach of danger she begins operations with her tubules and smears the whole forepart of the beetle with their secretion. Usually the volley does not fall so much on the beetle's face as on its prothorax under which the head may be so far withdrawn as to suggest that this retractility may be merely a means of protection in just such emergencies."

Mordwilko has shown that the siphons are best developed in certain species of Aphididæ that live singly and not in droves or colonies and are not attended by ants, whereas these repugnatorial

Fig. 208. Carton tent like the one shown in Fig. 207, but opened to show the coccids and the walls of the edifice. (Original.)

glands may be vestigial or completely lacking in the species habitually thus attended. This is certainly suggestive of their great importance as organs of defense. Many aphids, too, secrete a thick covering of white wax, which may protect their thin-skinned bodies from the attacks of some of their enemies. In this connection, Mordwilko has called attention to the long, projecting anal spine of certain aphids. This he interprets as a mean of defense against the ants themselves, since it must hinder them in directly imbibing the drops of honey-dew. In the same way the Russian author interprets also the waxy secretion which may fall on and pollute the limpid drops of excrement, but this is certainly not true of all wax secreting aphids. The common alder blight (*Pemphigus tessellatus*) secretes wax in abundance, but is, nevertheless, eagerly attended by several species of ants. It is difficult to understand why some aphids should repel the advances of the ants when other species apparently derive so much advantage from their companionship, for, although no complete list has as yet been published of the species of aphids and the ants with which they are always or only temporarily associated, we know, nevertheless, that a few species of the former are definitely symbiotic with ants, and that there are others with more or less pronounced proclivities of the same kind. Wasmann (1894) cites *Forda formicaria* as regularly myrmecophilous and Shouteden (1902) mentions *Paracletus cimiciformis* as living only in the nests of ants. Both of these species are radicicolous, that is, they occur on the roots and not on the aërial portions of the plants. But there is also, at least in North America and Europe, a long series of radicicolous aphids that occur with more or less frequency in ant nests. Shouteden records no less than seventeen species, representing nine genera (*Geoica, Forda, Tetraneura, Schizoneura, Pemphigus, Trama, Chaitophorus, Aphis* and *Microsiphum*) as occurring in the nests of *Lasius niger* alone. In North America varieties of this ant, and especially *L. nearcticus, brevicornis* and the various members of the subgenus *Acanthomyops,* harbor in their subterranean galleries a great many aphids. Mrs. W. P. Cockerell (1903) has shown that these include species of *Tychea* and *Forda* (*F. kingi, interjecti, lasii* and *pallidula*). Mordwilko cites *Lasius brunneus* as living exclusively at the expense of species of *Stomachis,* which are found on the stems and leaves of plants. Further studies of ants and aphids by investigators familiar with the species of both of these groups will unquestionably bring to light many additional instances of such intimate symbiosis.

Much of what has above been said of the aphids will apply also to the scale-insects and mealy-bugs (Coccidæ). These are even more sedentary than the aphids, and may also occur on both the roots and aërial surfaces of the plants. They are, however, more largely confined to warm countries, whereas aphids are more abundant in temperate regions. Abdominal tubules are absent in coccids, but they protect their bodies by secreting a covering of powdery white wax or a hard or tough scale. Like the aphids, they excrete honey-dew, often in considerable quantities, from the anal orifice. The manna of Biblical tradition is now known to be the honey-dew of one of these insects (*Gossyparia mannifera*) which lives on the tamarisk. This excretion

is still called " man " by the Arabs who use it as food.   But long ages
before the Israelites and Arabs had learned to eat the sweet ejecta of
this single species, the ants had learned to value the honey-dew of a
great many different scale-insects.   Imbedded in the Prussian and

Fig. 209.   Carton tent built by *Cremastogaster pilosa* over the alder-blight (*Pemphigus tessellatus*).   The structure probably originally enclosed the whole colony of
aphids, but the latter in growing and spreading further up the alder branch, broke
through the walls of the tent.   Natural size.   (Original.)

Sicilian amber are many ants, in most part so closely related to existing
aphidicolous and coccidicolous species that we must ascribe to them a
like similarity in habits.   In fact, a few large blocks of amber sent me
by Prof. Tornquist, and containing numerous workers of *Bothrio-*

myrmex gœpperti mingled with aphids, show that these ancient Dolicho-
derines must have had essentially the same habits as their modern
cousins.

One of the earliest accounts of the relations of ants to coccids
is that of Forel (1875) who found *Brachymyrmex heeri,* that had been
imported from tropical America into the hot-houses of Europe, attending *Lecanium hemisphæricum* and *Dactylopius adonidum.* Our North
American *B. heeri* subsp. *depilis* attends root coccids and aphids like
the species of *Lasius.* From the nests of our ants of this genus, Cockerell (1891, 1903, 1905) and King (1897*a,* 1898–'99, 1902*b*) have described a number of species of *Ripersia, Dactylopius, Lecanopsis,
Phenacoccus* and *Orthezia,* and whoever, early in the spring, examines
the formicaries of our yellow species of *Lasius* in the open woods of
the Eastern States will be sure to find their galleries white with these
small, elliptical, snow-white insects. Many of our other ants also
exhibit a great fondness for coccids of the above mentioned and other
genera. In Texas I frequently found *Cremastogaster punctulata* attending dense herds of *Eriococcus texanus* on roots, and even so large
an ant as *Camponotus sansabeanus* nearly always keeps a number of
individuals of *Dactylopius wheeleri* in its nests. On the exposed twigs
of oaks the curious pea-like coccids of the genus *Kermes,* which often
drip with honey-dew, are great favorites with our species of *Cremastogaster, Prenolepis, Lasius* and *Dolichoderus,* and in Arizona the honey
ant, *Myrmecocystus testaceus,* exhibits a similar fondness for the singular, wax-covered species of *Orthezia* on the dry shrubs of the desert.
Guilding (1829–33) and Trimen (1886) have found ants associated
with the curious subterranean coccids known as "earth pearls" (*Margarodes*) in St. Vincent and South Africa, and the association of the
arboreal ants of the genus *Azteca* with various coccids (*Palæococcus
rosæ, Coccus nanus, Akermes colimæ, Pseudococcus cuatalensis* and
Lachnodiella cecropiæ) in Trinidad, Mexico, Nicauragua and Brazil,
has been mentioned by Fritz Müller (1880–'81), Emery, Cockerell
(1903) and von Ihering (1907). Even in remote New Zealand, according to W. W. Smith (1892*a,* 1892*b*), *Ripersia* and other coccids
abound in the nests of the species of *Monomorium* and *Huberia* so
characteristic of that region.

The Psyllidæ, or jumping plant-lice, appear to be related to the
aphids, but void solid excrement in addition to the liquid honey-dew.
The latter is very abundant, however, and in some of the numerous
Australian species hardens to form scales of manna, or " sugar-lerp."
These scales are so abundant that they are collected and eaten by the
aborigines and the children of the white settlers. According to Frog-

gatt (1900), who has given us an excellent account of these insects, a single person may collect as much as two to three pounds of this manna in a day. Two closely related species, *Spondyliaspis eucalypti* and *S. mannifera,* which, like many of the Australian Psyllids, feed on various *Eucalypti,* are the most active producers of lerp. Of course, such a substance could hardly fail to attract ants. Nevertheless, the recorded observations on the relations of these insects to Psyllids appear to be rather meager. Froggatt describes the larvæ of *Cometopsylla rufa,* which excretes a very crystalline and brittle lerp, as smothered with numbers of *Iridomyrmex purpureus,* which feed upon the excretions and protect the Psyllids "to some extent." Concerning *Thea formicosa* he says: " The larvæ form no lerp but hide under loose bits of bark on the trunks of several white-stemmed gums [*Eucalypti*], thickly enveloped in white flocculent matter, thickest round the abdomen, which exudes from beneath their shelter and reveals their hiding place, and when abundant dots the trunks all over with white blotches. Other colonies are found congregated on the stems of small trees, where they are frequently covered by ants with a thick felted sheath of woody débris, sometimes extending for four or five feet from the ground and completely sheltering them. The ants, *Iridomyrmex nitidus* Mayr, swarm over them in this covered gallery, and evidently protect them for the sake of the honey-dew that is secreted." The "sheath of woody débris" here described is, of course, a "tent" or "cow-shed," like those built by our northern ants over aphids and coccids. *Thea opaca,* though less abundant than *Th. formicosa,* is found in similar localities, and is always "covered with ants." Our northern Psyllidæ, especially the pear-tree *Psylla* (*Ps. pyricola*), which excretes great quantities of honey-dew, are in all probability occasionally attended by ants.

FIG. 210. Lycænid caterpillar. (Original.) *a,* Mouth-shaped orifice of median honey-gland on antepenultimate segment; *b,* one of the pairs of extensile organs on the penultimate segment.

The relations of the ants to the tree-hoppers (Membracidæ, Cercopidæ) are but little known, as these insects are abundant only in warm countries. Lund long ago found that the Cercopidæ and Membracidæ take the place of aphids in the lives of many Brazilian ants, and Belt (1874) described the relations of the Membracids of Nicaragua to species of *Pheidole* and *Dolichoderus.* More recently additional observations have been made by Baer (1903) in Argentina and Green (1900) in Ceylon. Baer saw *Camponotus punctulatus* attending *Enchenopa ferruginea.* Green's observations relate to species of *Centrotus,* some of which have a long, brightly colored anal tube. He says that he has " watched the larvæ of various species of *Centrotus* being assiduously attended by ants. The larvæ are gregarious, frequenting the succulent shoots of plants, and have an extensile organ at the extremity of the body, from which the coveted fluid is emitted. This organ is distinctly 3-segmented. In the species from which the accompanying drawings were made [Fig. 212], the small terminal segment was of a crimson color; the penultimate segment black, with a broad white median band; and the basal segment (of the extensile part) white. When the insect is undisturbed, the organ is withdrawn into the long conical segment which apparently terminates the body, but is extended immediately upon application by the attendant ants." I have repeatedly seen whole colonies of *Formica obscuripes, ciliata* and *oreas* attending droves of young Membracids in Colorado. The Homoptera responded to the antennal caresses of the ants in precisely the same manner as plant-lice and scale-insects. In Maine and Massachusetts *F. glacialis* and *subsericea* are often found attending *Publilia concava* on the stems and petioles of golden rod. I have described and figured (1906*b*) the sheds constructed by our eastern *Formica integra* over small colonies of *Vanduzea arcuata* about the trunks of young birch trees.

As the relations between ants and the various Homoptera above mentioned have been regarded as mutualistic, it may be well, before proceeding further, to marshall the facts which seem to warrant this interpretation. The term " mutualism " as applied to these cases, means, of course, that the aphids, coccids and membracids are of service to the ants and in turn profit by the companionship of these more active and aggressive insects. Among the modifications in structure and behavior which may be regarded as indicating on the part of aphids unmistakable evidence of adaptation to living with ants, the following may be cited:

1. The aphids do not attempt to escape from the ants or to defend themselves with their siphons, but accept the presence of these attendants as a matter of course. The same patient attitude is exhibited by coccids and membracids.

2. The aphids respond to the solicitations of the ants by extruding the droplets of honey-dew gradually and not by throwing them off to a distance with a sudden jerk as they do in the absence of ants. Even at such times, or when artificially stroked with some delicate object in

imitation of an ant's caressing antennæ, according to Mordwilko, some species of *Trama, Stomachis, Pemphigus, Pentaphis* and *Aphis* extrude the drops very gradually, indicating that the habit has become fixed through association with ants.

3. Many species of Aphididæ that live habitually with ants have developed a perianal circlet of stiff hairs which support the drop of honey-dew till it can be imbibed by the ants. This circlet is lacking in aphids that are rarely or never visited by ants (Mordwilko).

4. Certain observations go to show that aphids, when visited by ants, extract more of the plant juices than when unattended. According to Bos (1888) this is the case with *Aphis papaveris* when feeding on bean plants. These are more seriously injured when *Lasius niger* is soliciting food from the aphids.

5. Although the siphons are lacking in some aphids which are not visited by ants, and either live solitary lives or are concealed in galls, the absence or reduction of these repugnatorial glands is usually most

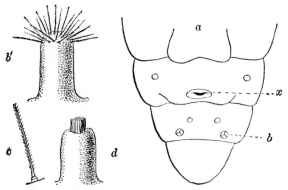

Fɪɢ. 211. Caterpillars of *Lycæna pseudargiolus.* (Edwards.) *a.* Posterior segments seen from above; *x*, opening of honey gland; *b*, extensile organ; *b'*, same fully exserted; *c*, one of the plumose hairs with which its tip is furnished; *d*, organ with hairs withdrawn.

marked in species that live with ants, which presumably protect them from many of their enemies. On the other hand, the siphons reach their greatest development in some of the solitary and rather agile species that are not attended by ants (*Siphonophora* and *Rhopalosiphum*).

The adaptations on the part of the ants are, with a single doubtful exception, all modifications in behavior and not in structure.

1. Ants do not seize and kill aphids as they do when they encounter other sedentary and defenceless insects. This was noticed by Linné in the case of *Formica rufa*, of which he says: " Adscendit arborem, ut aphides illius vaccas mulgeat nec occidit."

2. The ants stroke the aphids in a particular manner in order to

make them excrete the honey-dew and know exactly where to expect the evacuated liquid.

3. The ants protect the aphids. Several observers have seen the ants driving away predatory insects. Büsgen's observations on *Chrysopa* larvæ are cited above (p. 345). Ferton (1890), speaking of *Tapinoma erraticum* and its aphids, says: " While observing the aphid-hunting Hymenoptera in their attacks on their prey, I was impressed with the jealous surveillance of the ants, and the protracted manœuvres of the hunters in deceiving these guardians. *Cemonus unicolor* Fabr. and *Pemphredon insigne* V. d. L., which I was especially able to follow, showed by their detours and subterfuges that their real enemy is not the aphid, but the ant which protects it." Indeed, the fierce watchfulness of *Formica sanguinea* or *F. rufa* must be apparent to any observer who disturbs these ants while they are attending their aphids. The former at once open their mandibles and rush at the intruder and the latter throw back their heads, sit up with the tips of their gasters directed forward and discharge volleys of formic acid in the direction whence they are threatened. Belt has observed the workers of *Pheidole* protecting their membracids in a similar manner.

4. Many aphidicolous ants, when disturbed, at once seize and carry their charges in their mandibles to a place of safety, showing very plainly their sense of ownership and interest in these helpless creatures.

5. This is also exhibited by all ants that harbor root-aphids and root-coccids in their nests. Not only are these insects kept in confinement by the ants, but they are placed by them on the roots. In order to do this the ants remove the earth from the surfaces of the roots and construct galleries and chambers around them so that the Homoptera may have easy access to their food and even move about at will.

6. Many aphidicolous and coccidicolous ants, as was shown in a former chapter (pp. 223, 224) construct, often at some distance from their nests, little closed pavilions or sheds of earth, carton or silk, as a protection for their cattle and for themselves (Figs. 205–209). This singular habit may be merely a more recent development from the older and more general habit of excavating tunnels and chambers about roots and subterranean stems.

7. The solicitude of the ants not only envelops the adult aphids and coccids, but extends also to their eggs and young. Numerous observers (Huber (1810), Lubbock (1896), Lichtenstein (1870, 1877–'80), Del Guercio, Forbes (1894), Weed (1891), Shouteden (1902), Mordwilko (1907), Webster (1907), and others) have observed ants (species of *Lasius*) in the autumn collecting and storing aphid eggs in the chambers of their nests, caring for them through the winter and in the spring

placing the recently hatched plant-lice on the stems and roots of the
plants.   Forbes, Weed and Webster have shown that our common *L.
americanus* is thus instrumental in rearing and disseminating throughout the fields a root aphid (*Aphis maidiradicis*) which is very injurious
to Indian corn.   Webster gives the following account of his extended
observations on the relations of these insects to each other: " Now,
taking up the life history of the root-aphis, we find eggs in the fall, it
is true, but only in the burrow of and attended by these ants.   If there
are eggs, egg-laying females, or males elsewhere they have yet to be
discovered.   The ants care for these eggs throughout the winter, shifting them about, according to Forbes, as they do their own young, to
accommodate them to changes of weather and moisture.   In spring,
the young, as soon as they hatch from these eggs, are transferred by
the ants to the roots of young fox-tail grass, smart-weed, and even rag-
weed.   The young are carried out to pasture, as it were, during fair
weather, but in bad weather, or on cold nights, they are taken back
to the burrows of the ants.   The plants just mentioned are the ones
that push up early in spring in last year's corn lands, and especially in
fields that have been plowed and allowed to stand untouched for a
week or so.   Usually the farmer plows his ground in spring and pays
little attention to this early growth of weeds and grass, as he can generally dispose of it as soon as he begins to cultivate the corn, although
this is not until the rows of young plants can be followed by the eye
across an ordinary field.   As soon, however, as the corn plants begin
to show above ground the ants not only transfer the young root-aphids
from the burrows to the roots of corn, but they will also remove them
from the roots of grass and weeds and recolonize them on the roots
of young corn.   Now these young aphids are all females and within
a few days they begin to give birth to young, also all females ; these,
too, are cared for by the ants, which place them on the freshest and
most tender rootlets.   This procedure goes on about the roots of corn
throughout the spring and summer.   Forbes has found that under the
most favorable artificial conditions there may be as many as sixteen
generations between April and October, ten of which may coexist
at the same time.   It is hardly probable, however, that so many generations can exist under ordinary field conditions ; nevertheless, it may be
rightly inferred from this that the multiplication of the species is enormous.   These ants not only transfer the root-aphids from one root to
another of the same plant, but will carry them from one plant to another
a considerable distance away.   In the spring of 1887 the writer placed
a number of flower pots containing young growing uninfested corn
plants between rows of infested hills of corn in the field.   The corn

in the infested hills was then pulled up, exposing the roots on which the aphids were clustered. The little brown ants at once began to carry the aphids to new quarters, and the next day the latter, some of them full grown, were abundant on the roots of the corn in the pots, although there were none on them when the pots were put in place. Ants were observed over a yard away from the plants that had been uprooted, with root-aphids in their mouths, to all appearances searching for a suitable place in which to establish their charges on the roots of corn. Thus it is that from the laying of the eggs in fall to the last or egg-laying generation of the following year this aphis is wholly dependent on the little brown ant for its existence in the cultivated fields, and the farmer can justly charge up his losses through the attacks of the root-aphis to the influences of this ant. But the matter does not terminate here, as will be seen by what follows.

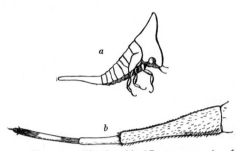

Fig. 212. Membracid (*Centrotus* sp.) of Ceylon. (Green.) *a*, Larva from the right side; *b*, protruded anal segments of same.

"So long as the roots upon which the root-aphids are colonized afford an abundance of nourishment for them, all will be wingless, but as soon as the roots become tough and woody or dry out there will be a generation of both winged and wingless individuals, the former escaping from the burrows about the roots to fly to other plants, and in all probability to other fields, where they may be found on the leaves. The ants usually transfer the wingless females to more succulent roots, but seem to pay little or no attention to the winged individuals, letting these make their way out and away. But in May, 1887, the writer was able to watch some of these winged nomadic individuals in a corn field to which they had migrated and to note the results of their wanderings. A field of corn had been planted on May 18. Five days later there came a heavy rain storm that flattened the surface of the ground, which was soon encrusted by the action of the wind and sun. Four days afterwards there were freshly thrown up mounds of earth about some of the corn plants, and ants were busily engaged in and about these and running up and down over the young corn. On examining these mounds and burrows the writer was surprised to find winged root-aphids giving birth to young on the roots attended by ants. All of these young were very small, at most but a few days old. Other winged individuals were found on the leaves and even on the stems of corn, and when any one of these was placed where the ants could find it, it was promptly captured by an ant and transported to the roots of the corn.   Observation showed that as soon as the ants running about over the young corn plants found a winged aphis they made a burrow about the base of a plant, and soon domiciled the wanderer on the root under their guardianship.   Then when the aphis began to give birth to young these were promptly removed to another part of the same root, or to another root close by, and there watched over by the patient and industrious ants.   The same thing was observed going on about a young plant of fox-tail grass in this same corn-field."

8. Some writers have described the ants as facilitating the exit of the winged sexual generation of aphids from their nests by opening up galleries for this very purpose to the surface of the soil.

9. Others (Lichtenstein, Mordwilko) have seen ants (*Lasius niger, flavus* and *umbratus*) in the act of clipping off the wings of female aphids.   Whether this is done because these organs hinder the ants from imbibing the honey-dew, or in order to prevent the escape of the aphids from the nest, or for some other reason, has not been determined.

10. The single structural adaptation which may, perhaps, have been developed through association with aphids, coccids and membracids is the greatly distensible crop of the Camponotinæ.   It is quite as probable, however, that the peculiar properties of this organ may be due to the habit of collecting and retaining large quantities of nectar or other plant-secretions.

Certain Fulgoridæ, at least in Europe and North Africa, have intimate relations with ants, according to the observations on species of *Issus,* and especially of *Tettigometra,* contributed by Rouget (1866), Puton (1869), Lichtenstein (1870, 1880), Delpino (1872, 1875), Forel (1890, 1894), Schneider (1893), Silvestri (1903), Lesne (1905) and Torka (1905).   Silvestri has studied *T. impressifrons* and *T. costatus,* which live in the nests of *Tapinoma nigerrimum.*   The young fulgorids which, like the radicicolous aphids and coccids, obtain their food from roots and underground stems, furnish the ants with a sweet liquid.   This is not excrement, however, as in the case of the other Homoptera above described, but, according to Silvestri, "a secretion from cellular glands, distributed in areas on the following segments of the body: dorsally two (*i. e.,* one on each side of the median sagittal plane) on the submedian portion of the prothorax, two on the submedian region of the second abdominal segment and two on the sublateral portions of each abdominal segment from the third to the seventh inclusive; and ventrally, two on the lateral portions of the prothorax, two on the median portion of the third abdominal segment and two sublaterally on each abdominal segment from the fourth to the seventh inclusive." This author believes that the larvæ of a Coccinellid beetle, *Hyperaspis reppensis,* which live in the *Tapinoma* nests and are treated by the ants as true myrmecophiles, feed on the *Tettigometra.* The adult beetles, however, seem to be less indulgently regarded by the ants. Torka finds that the larvæ of *T. obliqua,* found in great numbers about the roots of oats and rye, are assiduously attended by *Formica cinerea* and *Lasius niger.*

Perhaps further investigations will bring to light a number of cases in which Heteropterous Hemiptera are attended by ants. One such case, in fact, has been recorded, namely, a Ceylonese species of *Coptosoma* which according to Green (1900) is attended by *Cremastogaster* in the same manner as the above described Homoptera. Wasmann (1901) mentions the larvæ of *Neoblissus parasitaster* as living in the nests of *Solenopsis geminata* in Brazil, but this may be a case of true myrmecophily.

The relations of ants to the caterpillars of the Lycænid butterflies have been repeatedly described by a number of observers: Freyer (1836), Ploetz (1865), McCook (1877), W. H. Edwards (1878a, 1878b, 1884), Saunders (1878), Thwaits (1881), Miskin (1883), Aurivillius (1884, 1887), Doherty (1886), Scudder (1888), de Nicéville (1888, 1889, 1890, 1900), von Aigner-Abafi (1898, 1899), Wroughton (1892), Thomann (1901), Dodd (1902a, 1902b), Green (1902), Frohawk (1904, 1906) and Viehmeyer (1907). The most comprehensive accounts have been furnished by Edwards, de Nicéville, Thomann and Viehmeyer. No less than sixty-five species, representing twenty-nine genera of Lycænidæ, are mentioned as having caterpillars that are attended by ants. According to Viehmeyer the list embraces twenty-three species of *Lycæna* alone. The larvæ of this and the allied genera are somewhat depressed with rounded anterior and posterior ends and with the tense and highly sensitive skin covered with short, sparse hairs (Figs. 210 and 211). As Guenée long ago (1867) showed for *Lycæna bætica,* these caterpillars possess three peculiar organs, one an unpaired gland (*a, x*) in the middorsal line of the antepenultimate, or eleventh segment, and a pair of short protrusible tentacles on the dorsolateral portions of the penultimate, or twelfth segment (*b*). The median gland has the form of a sac or papilla which can be protruded through a transverse, mouth-shaped slit, and each of the tentacles is fringed at its tip with a dense circlet of stiff, finely plumose hairs (Fig. 211, *d, b'*). The ants caress the posterior, somewhat flattened extremity of the caterpillar with their antennæ as they do that of the plant-louse, and the caterpillar responds by emitting from the

median gland a glistening droplet of a colorless and presumably saccharine liquid which is eagerly imbibed by the attendants. The
function of the tentacles is unknown. De Nicéville believes that they
may represent vestiges of a pair of organs which are very long and
tufted in an Indian Lycænid (*Curetis thetys*) and are very rapidly
whirled around when the caterpillar is touched, as if for the purpose of frightening away its enemies. From the fact, however,
that the tentacles of the European and North American species are
most frequently protruded when the caterpillars are being caressed
by the ants, Thomann concludes that these peculiar organs act as signals
and diffuse some odor which serves to attract and fascinate the ants.

Not only are many of the Lycænid larvæ attended while feeding on
the leaves or flowers of plants, but they are often found in the ants'
nests. Some of the species pupate and even hatch as butterflies in the
galleries of the nests. Only in a few instances have the names of the
attendant ants of our northern Lycænids been recorded. As would be
expected, these are members of the genera *Lasius, Formica, Camponotus, Prenolepis* and *Myrmica.* In India, according to Dodd (1902*a*),
Thwaites (1881) and de Nicéville (1900), species of *Pheidole* and
Cremastogaster, and especially *Œcophylla smaragdina,* are the principal
attendants. *Œ. smaragdina,* in that country and in Australia, is, in
fact, constantly found with many species of the caterpillars and often
keeps them in the silken nests and " cow-sheds " described in a previous
chapter (pp. 223, 224). De Nicéville says that the butterflies will often
oviposit only on trees inhabited by ants: " If the right plant has no
ants, or the ants on that plant are not the right species, the butterfly
will lay no eggs on that plant. Some larvæ will certainly not live
without the ants, and many larvæ are extremely uncomfortable when
brought up away from their hosts or masters. In many cases it is just
as important for breeding purposes to know the right species of ants
as to know the right food-plant. In Kanara this is particularly noticeable in the cases of *Castalius ananda,* de Nicéville, *Zesius chrysomallus,*
Hübner, *Aphnæus lohita,* Horsfield, and *Catapœcilma elegans,* Druce.
On one occasion Mr. Bell was collecting larvæ at Katgal, and the ants
were principally on *Zizyphus rugosa,* Lamk. (Natural Order Rham-
neæ), but were also swarming all over six or seven species of different
trees all round, and on all of these trees there were larvæ of *C. ananda*
covered with ants and eating the leaves of the trees in all cases. Since
then Mr. Bell has noticed the larva of *C. ananda* eating the leaves of
many different plants and always in company with the same species
of ants. With regard to the *Zesius, Aphnæus* and *Catapœcilma* mentioned above, the female butterflies first look for the right species of

ants, and the species of food-plant seems to be quite a secondary consideration, at any rate, to a considerable extent.   The larvæ of *Zezius* may be found on very nearly any plant that harbors the large red ant, *Œcophylla smaragdina* Fabricius, so much so that Mr. Bell has often had a strong suspicion that the butterfly larvæ will occasionally eat the ant larvæ, although he has not actually seen them do so.   The larva of this butterfly feeds on many species of plants not recorded on the lists, as Mr. Bell made no particular note of them, all these plants being affected by the large red ants.   The larvæ of *Aphnæus* and *Catapœcilma* are only found on plants affected by ants of the genus *Cremastogaster*.   As regards the four species of butterflies named above, the larvæ are often found in the ants' nests, and their pupæ also, but not invariably."

These observations show that the relations between ants and Lycænid larvæ may be very intimate, and certainly suggest a kind of mutualism, or symbiosis like that obtaining between the ants and the phytophthorous Homoptera.   As in this latter case, it is maintained that the ants protect the caterpillars from their enemies in return for their sweet secretion, but our knowledge of this matter is not sufficient to permit of far-reaching inferences.   It is very probable, nevertheless, that further study of the Lycænidæ, especially in the tropics where this family is enormously developed, has many surprises in store for us. This may be inferred from what is known of the habits of some of the aberrant species that are not amicably attended by ants.   Thus the caterpillar of our curious North American *Feniseca tarquinius* has become carnivorous and feeds on wax-secreting aphids, the so-called alder blight (*Pemphigus tessellatus*), and an Indian species (*Spalgis epius*) is known to feed on Coccidæ.   The singular *Liphyra brassolis* of India and Australia is said by Dodd (1902) to live in the nests and to feed on the larvæ of *Œcophylla smaragdina*.   The caterpillar is covered with a tough shell, as if to protect it from the mandibles of its host, and it actually pupates within its larval skin like a cyclorrhaph Dipteron (Chapman, 1902) !   The butterfly on hatching in the ants' nest is enveloped with a peculiar coating of white, gray and brown, fugitive scales, which protect it from its hosts, for, as Dodd says, " it is highly probable that the ants have no friendly feeling for the perfect insect and would most likely attack and kill it during its long rest after emergence, if it were not especially and wonderfully protected.   So it will be seen that the loose scales act as a perfect protection, for directly the ants encounter these they are in trouble, they fasten on to their feet and impede their movements, or, if their antennæ or mandibles come in contact with any part of the butterfly, the scales adhere thereto, so that the ant is soon in a bad way and has quite enough to do in attempting to free himself of his encumbrances without taking any further interest in the butterfly, from which he retreats as well as possible. It is exceedingly ludicrous to observe the ants endeavoring to free themselves, their legs move awkwardly and their mandibles are opened and closed in evident annoyance and perplexity, and they are also much concerned about the state of their antennæ for the obnoxious scales will not be shaken off, and they seem to become very low-spirited."

Another Indian Lycænid (*Allotinus horsfieldi*) attends aphids in the butterfly stage, stroking them with its long fore-legs and sucking up the excreted honey-dew with its proboscis (Bingham, 1907)! These observations suggest the existence of complicated "three-cornered" relations between ants, Lycænids and aphids. It would be interesting to know whether the *Allotinus* larva is attended by ants in the same manner as the aphid is attended by the butterfly. In the case of *Feniseca tarquinius* I find a triple relationship of a different kind, for I have observed the alder blight, on which the larvæ of this Lycænid feeds, being attended by at least six different species of ants of the genera *Prenolepis, Camponotus, Formica, Cremastogaster* and *Dolichoderus,* so that here we have a condition very similar to that described by Silvestri (*vide supra,* p. 357) for *Tapinoma, Tettigometra* and *Hyperaspis.*

It will be seen that the intimate relations described in this chapter as existing between ants on the one hand and the various Homoptera and Lycænid caterpillars on the other, excepting, of course, such forms as *Spalgis* and *Feniseca,* have a common peculiarity. In all of these cases the ants are supplied with food in the form of an excretion or secretion elaborated from the juices of plants. Wasmann has therefore designated these relationships as *trophobiosis* to distinguish them from the cases of myrmecophily proper, which will be the subject of Chapters XXI and XXII.

CHAPTER XX

HONEY ANTS

"In general all these animals live from hand to mouth, and if there are some which know how to economize, there are likewise those which do not ignore the advantages of a savings bank."—J. P. Van Beneden, *Amer. Natur.*, 1874.

A singular adaptation which has grown out of the relations of ants to plants and to the plant-destroying Homoptera, is that of the honey-ants. It has been shown that many ants are in the habit of collecting nectar and honey-dew, storing it in their distensible crops till they reach their nests and then distributing it by regurgitation to their larvæ and sister ants. This habit, as a rule, is most highly developed in the Camponotinæ and Dolichoderinæ, which have a thin and pliable integument that permits a considerable expansion of the gastric walls. In these ants the crop is often so distended with the saccharine liquids above mentioned that the sclerites are forced apart and appear as dark spots or islands on the tense intersegmental membranes. Through these the limpid ingluvial contents may be distinctly seen while the other organs of the gaster are forced up against its walls. This condition is often noticed in foraging workers of our common species of *Campo-notus, Lasius, Brachymyr-mex, Prenolepis* and *Ny-anderia.* In *P. imparis,*

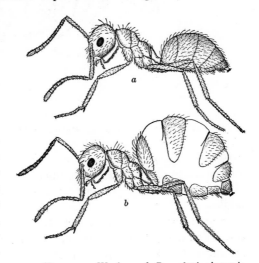

Fig. 213. Worker of *Prenolepis imparis.* (Original.) *a,* Worker in ordinary condition; *b,* replete.

for example, a small black or brown ant, which is very widely distributed over temperate North America, the crop may be so greatly distended with nectar or honey-dew (Fig. 213) that the insect, which ordinarily has a quick and graceful gait, can only waddle along with some difficulty. All of the workers of the *Prenolepis* colony seem to be able to assume this replete condition, but they retain it only temporarily, that is, till the contents of the crop, or ingluvies, have been distributed.

The conditions seen in *Prenolepis* may be said to represent one of the incipient stages in the development of the true honey ants. This development is characterized first, by an exaggeration of the tendency to repletion, second, by a restriction of this tendency to certain workers, and third, by repletion becoming a permanent morphological modification. But as repletion does not set in until after the worker hatches, we must regard it as an acquired physiological state depending on the environment, that is, on the amount of nectar or honey-dew obtainable in a given locality. Although all workers are able to distend their crops considerably while foraging, true, or perfect repletes are devel-

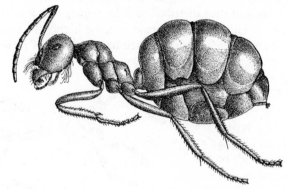

Fig. 214.   Replete worker of *Melophorus bagoti* of Australia.   (Original.)

oped only within the nest, where they remain and store the sweets brought in by the foragers, and thus function as living bottles or casks to which the hungry workers can resort during seasons of scarcity or famine.

Honey ants have been described from North America, South Africa and Australia. The various species show considerable differences in the degree of gastric distension which they are able to attain. In some cases this is no greater than that of *Prenolepis*, in others the gaster may be swollen out till it forms a perfect sphere, so large and with walls so tense and easily ruptured that the insect cannot walk about and is compelled to lead a quiescent life, hanging by its claws from the roofs of the nest chambers. This extreme degree of distension is reached in certain subspecies and varieties of our American species of *Myrmecocystus*. The various known honey ants may be described in the order of increasing development, although this will make it necessary to begin with forms that are but little known and reserve till the last the *Myrmecocysti,* whose habits have been more thoroughly studied. In conclusion, I will describe a few aberrant Myrmicine ants that have been regarded as honey ants, and close with a few general remarks on the significance of the replete habit among the Camponotinæ and Dolichoderinæ.

1. *Melophorus bagoti* and *cowlei.*—The genus *Melophorus* was based by Lubbock in 1884 on worker specimens of *M. bagoti* from cen-

Fig. 215. Garden of the Gods near Manitou, Colorado; looking north; showing in the foreground the rocky ridges on which *Myrmecocystus horti-deorum* nests. (Original.)

tral or western Australia (" 21° S. Lat."). He transposed the generic and specific diagnoses that had been written out for him by Forel, but the latter rectified the blunder a few years later (1886*d*). *M. bagoti* is of a rich ferruginous red color and has polymorphic workers. The length of the smaller ones has not been recorded, but the larger measure 13–16 mm. In the latter the gaster is distended somewhat as in the *Prenolepis* repletes, and is, as Forel has stated, far from attaining the amplitude of *Myrmecocystus.* The insect is undoubtedly able to walk about and in all probability does not hang from the roof of its galleries. During the summer of 1907 Professor Forel kindly gave me a replete of *M. bagoti,* from which the accompanying figure is drawn (Fig. 214). In this specimen the gastric sclerites are greatly enlarged. Apparently they were originally much smaller, but along their borders the intersegmental membranes seem to have hardened and turned brown secondarily. The lines representing the original lateral borders of the sclerites are shown in the figure.

Froggatt (1896) described *M. cowlei* as a *Camponotus,* but his figures and description show very clearly that it is a typical *Melophorus,* closely related to *bagoti.* The replete, which measures 17 mm., has the gaster distended to much the same extent as that of *bagoti,* but the sclerites seem to be shorter and the intersegmental membranes larger. Froggatt described all three phases of *M. cowlei* from specimens taken at Illamurta in the James Range and Spencer Gorge in the McDonnell Range, in the very heart of Australia. He says that this ant is known to the natives as the " Ittootoonee " and gives the following notes sent him by Baldwin Spencer: " I came across a single nest of the golden yellow species, which was a small one, consisting of branching passages close to the surface, under a little block of quartzite in one of the gorges amongst the McDonnell Ranges. In this nest the honey ants, though considerably swollen out, seemed to be able to move about slowly. Perhaps it was a young colony and they were not fully developed."

2. *Leptomyrmex rufipes.*—This is the only honey ant known to occur among the Dolichoderinæ. The genus *Leptomyrmex,* which is confined to Australia and New Guinea, is characterized by its very slender and emaciated body, extremely long legs and singular head (Fig. 3, *F*). In 1886 Forel published the following note on *L. rufipes:* " In the excavated nests of this variety Mr. Turner found workers with the gaster considerably dilated by the crop full of transparent honey. The gaster resembled that of *Myrmecocystus,* without, however, attaining such dimensions." In an alcoholic specimen of this ant, which I saw in Professor Forel's collection, the gaster appeared to be much more distended than in the repletes of *Prenolepis* and *Melophorus.*

3. *Plagiolepis trimeni.*—This species was discovered by Mutschinson at Natal and described by Forel in 1895(*c*). The types were all repletes, 6.5 mm. in length, of which the head and thorax together measured only 2 mm. They are described as being of a " sordid brownish yellow color, more reddish on the head and thorax; the sides of the gastric segments brownish; feet and antennæ yellowish." The gaster " is distended with honey, like a round cyst, transparent, as large as a hemp seed, on which the chitinous laminæ of the segments appear as islands. The anterior portion of the first segment has a

hollow depression in which fits the petiolar scale. With the aid of a lens it is possible to distinguish below and behind the stomach and gizzard with its reflected calyx, both of them displaced and flattened against the gastric wall." Forel further states that the gaster is "nearly as fully distended as that of *Myrmecocystus melliger.* . . . Locomotion must be almost impossible in this insect. Its appearance

Fig. 216. Nest crater of *Myrmecocystus horti-deorum.* About ⅙ natural size. (Original.)

is that of a *Myrmecocystus* nurse *en miniature."* *P. trimeni* must therefore represent a stage of repletion intermediate between *Preno-lepis* and *Melophorus* on the one hand and *Myrmecocystus* on the other.[1]

4. *Camponotus inflatus.*—Lubbock described the worker of this ant in 1880 from specimens taken at Adelaide, Australia. His diagnosis was, however, so imperfect that the insect had to be redescribed by Forel (1886*d*). McCook (1882*b*) has also studied and figured this species (1882, Figs. 71 and 74). According to Forel, it "has nothing

[1] During the summer of 1909, Professor Forel showed me in his collection two other African honey ants, which he had recently acquired, namely, *Plagiolepis jouberti,* in which the replete has a gynæcoid thorax, and *Acantholepis abdominalis.*

to distinguish it particularly from other *Camponoti,* except the purely physiological gastric distension which is evidently due to the enormous plentitude of the crop, as in *Myrmecocystus melliger.* This distension, however, is smaller than that of *melliger."*

More recently (1896) Froggatt has described the male and female of *C. inflatus* from specimens collected at Ayers Rock, Illamurta, in the James Range of central Australia. All three phases of this ant are black with paler legs and antennæ. The repletes measure 17 mm. Froggatt records the following notes sent him by Baldwin Spencer: " The black honey ant (*Camponotus inflatus* Lub.) is called ' Yarumpa' by the natives, by whom it is esteemed a great luxury; it is, *par excellence,* the honey ant of the central country, and ranges across to the Murchison in western Australia. We found them plentiful in certain districts on the hard, sandy plains, and also often very abundant in patches among the Mulga scrub. The ground all round Ayers Rock, to the south of Lake Amadeus, was strewn with heaps of sand where the natives had been digging them out. They construct no mounds over their nests; the entrance, which is an inch in length by a quarter of an inch in width, leads down into a vertical shaft or burrow from five to six feet in depth. About a foot below the surface horizontal passages about a foot in length lead off from the main shaft, at the end of which were three or four of the honey ants, while the bottom of the main shaft, which is excavated into a larger cavity, contained a considerable number. The ' honey ants' are quite incapable of movement and must be fed by the workers. Unlike all the other ants noticed in this country, they did not appear to collect twigs, leaves or grass to carry into their burrows."

5. *Myrmecocystus melliger, mexicanus* and *horti-deorum.* — The genus *Myrmecocystus s. str.* is confined to North America, ranging over the deserts and dry plains from the City of Mexico to Denver, Colo. Two species have been recognized, *melliger* and *mexicanus,* with some eight subspecies and varieties (Wheeler, 1908*d*). Most of these are highly insectivorous and show no tendency to form repletes, but the var. *horti-deorum* (Figs. 217–219), of New Mexico and Colorado, is known to have repletes like those of the species *mexicanus* to which it belongs.

The repletes of *Myrmecocystus,* which have long been esteemed as an article of food by the Indians of Mexico and the Southwestern States, were first described by Llave (1832) in an obscure Mexican periodical from Mexican specimens, but it is impossible to determine the species to which he referred. Wesmael (1838) also based *M. mexicanus* on Mexican specimens. Both of these authors described the nests of the ants merely from hearsay. Later various, more or less erroneous, observations on the var. *horti-deorum* were made at Santa Fe, N. M., by Captain W. B. Fleeson (Edwards, 1873), Saunders (1875) and Loew (1874). The first to publish a trustworthy account of this, or in fact of any of our *Myrmecocysti,* was McCook (1882*b*). He discovered *horti-deorum* in the Garden of the Gods, near Manitou, Colo. (Fig. 215). The nests, which were found on the tops of stony ridges, are described in great detail. The large circular entrance, 2–2.5 cm. in diameter, is in the center of a cone-shaped crater of small pebbles 8–25 cm. in diameter at the base and 5–8 cm. high (Fig. 216). The entrance opens into a vertical or oblique gallery which at a depth of 9–15 cm. breaks up into several smaller galleries. These usually

Fig. 217. Male, female, minima and maxima workers of *Myrmecocystus horti-deorum,* slightly enlarged. (Original.)

run to one side of the entrance gallery. At a depth of 20–35 cm. the smaller galleries lead into chambers with smooth, flattened floors and rough, vaulted ceilings. These chambers vary from 12–15 cm. in length and 7–10 cm. in width, and may be 4 cm. high in the middle. McCook has described some very large formicaries, the galleries of one of which extended over an area of more than 2 m. and reached a depth in the soil of more than a meter. From the ceilings of the chambers the repletes hang, side by side, by means of their claws, and the vaulting is evidently left rough as an adaptation to this peculiar habit (Fig. 220). The repletes are capable of more movement than has usually been supposed, but if they fall from the ceiling they are unable to regain their pendent position without assistance. Large nests may contain as many as three hundred repletes distributed over several chambers.

McCook effectively dispelled the notion that the repletes manufacture the honey which they contain, a notion started by Wesmael and held by several writers, by showing how they obtain and store the liquid. *M. horti-deorum* is decidedly nocturnal, unlike the different subspecies and varieties of *melliger,* which are diurnal. Indeed, the etiolated appearance and pale yellow color of the northern forms of *mexicanus* at once suggest a fondness for darkness, just as the deeper tints of the typical form of the species suggest diurnal or crepuscular habits. During the day, therefore, the workers of *M. horti-deorum* are never seen outside of the nest, but frequently a guard of workers is stationed just within the large opening, apparently for the purpose of preventing other ants, spiders, etc., from entering. McCook found that during July the workers leave the nest in a file at about 7.30 P. M. and visit the shin oaks (*Quercus undulata*) which grow abundantly along the rocky ridges in the Garden of the Gods and the surrounding country. The twigs of these oaks are often covered with small woody galls about the size of a pea and of a more or less conical or spheroidal shape, the work of the Cynipid *Holcaspis perniciosus.* At night these galls exude minute droplets of a sweet, watery secretion which is eagerly imbibed by the ordinary workers, carried to the nest in their crops and fed to the repletes (Fig. 222).

Forel, in 1880, showed that the gaster of the replete *horti-deorum* owes its size and rotundity exclusively to an enormous distension of the crop, or ingluvies and not of the stomach as Leidy (1852) and Blake (1873) had supposed, and that all the other structures found in the gaster of the ordinary worker are present in the replete, though they are necessarily flattened against the gastric wall. These observations were confirmed by McCook's careful dissections and figures of the gaster of ordinary workers, semirepletes ("semirotunds") and repletes. He inferred that "the process by which the rotundity of the honey-bearers has probably been produced, has its exact counterpart in the ordinary distension of the crop in overfed ants; that, at least the condition of the alimentary canal, in all the castes, is the same, differing only in degree, and therefore, the probability is very great that *the honey-bearer is simply a worker with an overgrown abdomen.*" He found, moreover, that "a comparison of the workers with the honey-bearer shows that there is absolutely no difference between them except in the distended condition of the abdomen" and he therefore inferred "that the worker majors, for the most part, and sometimes the minors, are transformed by the gradual distension of the crop, and expansion of the abdomen, in the honey-bearers, and that the latter do not compose a distinct caste. It is probable, however, that some of the majors have a special tendency to this change by reason of some peculiar structure or form of the intestine and abdominal walls." Although McCook gave these excellent reasons for believing that the replete must develop from a worker of the ordinary type, he did not actually witness the transformation. His account covers a great many other details in the behavior of *M. horti-deorum,* but as many of these are common to most other Camponotine ants, they need not be discussed in this connection.

My own observations on *M. horti-deorum* were made during July and August, 1903, and 1906. At first I worked in the Garden of the Gods and located several nests on the ridges where McCook made his classical observations many years ago. But the region is now so over-

run by tourists that it is no longer a favorable spot for the quiet study of ant colonies. I therefore sought new localities and was soon able to locate several fine nests south of the Fontaine-qui-Bouille along Bear Creek and Red Rock Cañons. A few nests were also found west of Manitou and south of the Ute Pass at a much greater distance from the Garden of the Gods. In all of these localities there are thickets of shin oaks (*Quercus undulata* and *gambeli*), and the nests are situated only on the summits of dry, stony ridges, just as they are in McCook's locality.

FIG. 218. Repletes of *Myrmecocystus horti-deorum,* slightly enlarged. (Original.)

During the two summers I excavated fully a dozen fine colonies of *horti-deorum* and was able to confirm in nearly every detail McCook's interesting account of the nest architecture and the habits of the ordinary and replete workers. I was unable to make observations at night, but have no doubt that McCook's account of the foraging habits is perfectly trustworthy. I am inclined to believe, however, that the exudations of the *Holcaspis* galls may furnish only a portion of the food of the ants and that these insects obtain much, if not most, of their honey from the coccids and aphids on the oaks and other plants in the neighborhood. It would be strange, indeed, if these ants did not take advantage of a food supply so much more copious than that furnished by the galls.

I have been able to prove, what has been surmised by McCook and his predecessors, namely, that workers of the ordinary size and form develop into repletes. In the nests which I excavated during July there were many callow workers, males and females. While keeping several colonies in artificial nests it occurred to me that the change from the ordinary to the replete worker must begin during the callow stage, while the integument of the gaster is still very soft and distensible. I accordingly isolated a number of young callows in two of my nests and fed them with maple syrup and cane sugar water. They partook of these substances greedily, and a few of the workers in each nest gradually began to assume the replete condition. During the course of four to six weeks several of them became what I have called semirepletes (McCook's semirotunds), and four, three in one nest and one in the other, actually attained the dimensions of the perfect replete. Most of the workers, however, showed no inclination to assume this form. In most cases, as McCook has shown, it is the major workers which most readily become repletes, but this is not an invariable rule. In the honey chambers of opulent colonies I have usually found also a few replete mediæ and minimæ hanging among their larger but no more turgid sisters. Thoroughly hardened workers of the ordinary form, according to my observations, are no longer able to become repletes. It is probable that McCook's failure to secure these from isolated major workers was due to his using old individuals in his experiment.

Why certain callows should aspire to become animated pots or tuns, while others prefer to be active foragers and providers, is an enigma. I do not believe, however, that this is due to differences in the " structure or form of the intestine and abdominal walls," as McCook suggests. It is more probably an unusual example of the division of labor, which is shown by careful study to exist in various forms and degrees among all ants with monomorphic workers. The individual worker performs different duties at different stages in its life, beginning in its callow stage as a mere nurse, then becoming a forager, warrior or guard, and in its old age sometimes encroaching on the function of the queen and becoming a parthenogenetic mother, or gynæcoid. It is not improbable that many worker ants acquire habits—using this word, for the moment, in its restricted and technical sense as employed in human psychology—and tend to perform throughout life the particular function which they happen to assume while in the callow stage. This may account for the development of the passive replete, not only in *M. hortideorum,* but also in all other honey ants. Those who, in anthropomorphic mood, are wont to extoll the fervid industry and extraordinary feats of muscular endurance in ants, should not overlook the beatific patience and self-sacrifice displayed by the replete *Myrmecocystus* as it hangs from the rafters of its nest, month in, month out—for years, perhaps—a reservoir of temperamental as well as liquid sweetness.

6. *Cremastogaster inflata* and *difformis*.—Frederick Smith (1857, 1858c) published an account of two Myrmicine ants, which has led to

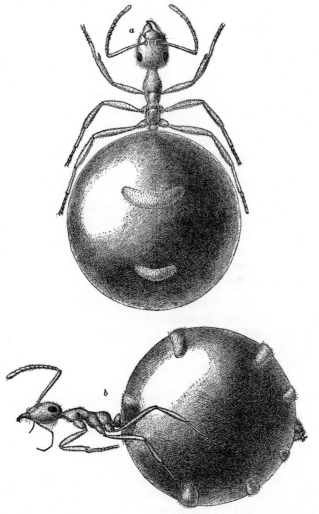

Fig. 219. Repletes of *Myrmecocystus horti-deorum*. *a,* Dorsal, *b,* lateral view. (Original.)

their being regarded as honey ants. Both species range from Tenasserim to Borneo through Burma, Java and Sumatra. *C. inflata* occurs also in the Philippines and *difformis* in Celebes. Of the latter species

Emery has described a subspecies, *physothorax,* and a variety, *mucronata.* In these ants the gaster remains unmodified but the epinotum, or posterior portion of the thorax, is greatly enlarged in *difformis* and even inflated in *inflata* (Fig. 223). In this species it is also of a honey-yellow color, unlike the remainder of the body, which is dark brown or black. Emery (1900*b*) has also described another species, *C. tumidula* from Sumatra which shows an incipient stage in the enlargement of the epinotum.

Smith described *C. inflata* as " one of those singular and anomalous species which, without any particle of information, derived from observation, puzzle and perplex the naturalist; what can possibly be the use of the bladder-like excrescence on the thorax of this insect, it is difficult to imagine; to the touch it is elastic, and apparently forms a receptacle for saccharine fluids. With the aid of a microscope, a small, circular orifice can be seen at each of the posterior lateral angles of the swollen part, and small, crystallized particles are apparent, not only within the orifice, but scattered over the surface of the inflation; we may, therefore, reasonably suppose that this singular apparatus is for the purpose of elaborating a suitable and necessary aliment for the larvæ of this singular insect." Of *C. difformis* he says: " This species resembles the *C. inflata* in form; but the swollen portion of the thorax is of a solid consistency; it forms, however, a similar laboratory of saccharine matter; the orifice from which it exudes is not exactly at the posterior angles, but a little way beneath; in some specimens masses of crystallized particles can be seen beneath the orifice; of this species, both large and small workers have been examined, and the same apparatus is found on them both."

More recently Bingham (1903) has made a few observations on these ants, which he describes as follows: " *C. difformis, physothorax* and *inflata* have the metathorax remarkably large and swollen, with a hollow in each side interiorly, communicating exteriorly by a tiny aperture. In live specimens there seems to be a continual flow from this aperture of a sweet fluid, and I have watched the workers of *C. physothorax* licking one another's thoraces vigorously."

These brief but interesting notes leave the reader in some perplexity. Janet (1898*e*) surmised that the epinotal enlargement in *C. inflata* might be due to hypertrophy of the peculiar glands which he, Meinert and Lubbock had found in this portion of the thorax of our northern ants (see p. 38). In a number of specimens of *C. inflata* in my collection, from Zamboangan, Philippines, two broadly elliptical or nearly circular openings are seen on each side of the epinotum (Fig. 223). The upper, which is somewhat smaller, is the tracheal orifice, or stigma, the lower is undoubtedly the opening of the epinotal chamber and leads directly into one of the large inflated cavities. As all of my specimens are dry and carded, I am unable to ascertain the histological structure of these organs. I am convinced, however, that they represent, as Janet supposed, an enormous development of the organs found in the coresponding portion of the epinotum of our common ants. This is also indicated by an examination of specimens of *C. difformis* from Perak and of *mucronata* from Sumatra. In these the openings of the

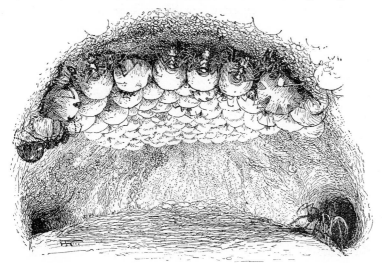

FIG. 220. Repletes of *Myrmecocystus horti-deorum* hanging from roof of **honey** chamber. (McCook.)

epinotal chambers are more ventral and more slit-shaped than in *inflata,* and may therefore be described as intermediate between those of *inflata* and our northern species of *Cremastogaster.*

As the function of the epinotal glands, even in our common ants, is still unknown, we can hardly expect to form a satisfactory conception of the hypertrophied homologues of these organs in a few Indomalayan ants that have hardly been studied in a living condition. That these organs should secrete a sweet liquid to be fed to the ants or their young is surprising at first thought and suggests the nursing habits of the Mammalia, but when we stop to consider that ants are in the habit of feeding their young and one another with a secretion of the labial, or salivary glands, we can see no reason why, in certain species, the thoracic glands might not be developed for a similar purpose. It will be very interesting, nevertheless, if future investigation proves that certain species of *Cremastogaster,* a genus whose members are so conspicuously fond of feeding on the saccharine excrement of aphids and coccids, have themselves developed a capacity for distilling a substance resembling honey-dew.

In the foregoing pages the habit of developing repletes has been shown to recur sporadically in at least six different genera of ants, namely, *Prenolepis, Melophorus, Plagiolepis, Leptomyrmex, Campo-notus* and *Myrmecocystus*. We are therefore dealing with a case of convergent development and as in other cases of this kind, we are led to determine the external conditions that act as the common

Fig. 221.   Replete *Myrmecocystus horti-deorum* in the act of regurgitating food to workers of the ordinary form.   (McCook.)

stimulus in calling forth this peculiar adaptation.   The geographical distribution of the various honey ants seems to point to drought as one of the most important of these conditions, for nearly all of these insects are confined to the dry plains and deserts of North America, South Africa and Australia.   Forel seems to be the only author who has noticed this peculiarity in the distribution of the honey ants.   He says (1902c): "The extraordinary distension of the crop seems to be frequent in the Australian species of the genera *Melo-phorus, Camponotus* and *Leptomyrmex*.   I suppose that this is due to the extremely dry climate of the country, which must compel the ants to remain, often for long periods, in their subterranean abodes.   At such times a store of provisions in living bags must be very useful to them."

There can be little doubt of the truth of this statement, but I believe that it should be expressed in a different manner.   The impulse to develop repletes is probably due to the brief and temporary abundance of liquid food (honey-dew, gall secretions, etc.) in arid regions and the long periods during which not only these substances, but also insect food are unobtainable. The honey is stored in the living reservoirs for the purpose of tiding over such periods of scarcity, and the ants remain in their nests because they do not need to forage. Hence the confinement mentioned by Forel is not the immediate but one of the ulterior effects of drought. I am convinced from my observations on desert ants that no amount of drought will keep these insects in their nest when they are in need of food.

While excavating the nests of *M. horti-deorum* I was impressed with certain peculiarities in their structure and situation, which seem to be explainable only as adaptations to the development of repletes. One of these peculiarities is the great hardness of the soil that is preferred by the ants. This is the more astonishing because the workers are very slender and delicate organisms. It is evident that such soil is well adapted to the construction of vaulted chambers like those in which the repletes hang, whereas soft or friable soil would be most unsuitable. The development of repletes also makes it necessary for the ants to seek very dry situations for their nests. Hence we always find them, in the environs of Manitou at least, on the summits of ridges which shed the rain very rapidly. The honey chambers must be kept very dry, both to prevent the disastrous re-

Fig. 222. Galls of *Holcaspis perniciosus* on twigs of *Quercus undulata*, showing the exuding droplets which are collected by the workers of *Myrmecocystus horti-deorum*. (Original.)

sults of crumbling and slipping walls and to obviate the growth of moulds on the repletes, which are, of course, imprisoned for life in dark cavities and filled with substances that are favorable to the development of fungi. I believe also that the size of the nest openings and galleries, which are so much larger than would seem to be required by such small, slender ants, may be an adaptation to securing plenty of fresh air in the honey chambers. If these suppositions are correct. there is obviously a reciprocal relation between the replete habit and an arid environment: the ants store honey because they are living in an arid region where moisture and food are precious, and the storing of honey in replete workers, in turn, is possible only in very dry soil.

Prenolepis imparis would seem to be an exception to the general rule of distribution in the honey ants, since the typical form of this

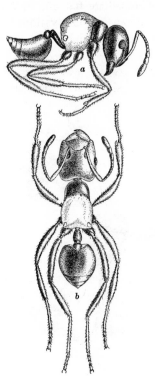

species occurs in rather shady places and in clayey soil which holds moisture rather tenaciously. It is not improbable, however, that what is known as var. *testacea* Emery is really the primitive form of this species. This ant nests in sandy soil and is one of the most abundant insects in the pine barrens of New Jersey and in similar localities in the Eastern States. These are xerophytic regions, as shown by the pines, scrub oaks and many other plants. The sand in which this vegetation grows does not retain water readily and therefore presents conditions not unlike those of the deserts and Great Plains. The dark colored typical *imparis* is much less abundant and probably represents a secondary adaptation to moist woods and firmer soil. This would explain the existence of repletes in an ant inhabiting rather humid, shady localities.

Fig. 223. Worker of *Cremastogaster inflata*. *a*, Lateral; *b*, dorsal view, × 8. (Original.)

Most ants of temperate, mesophytic regions have a mixed diet, consisting of insects, honey-dew and plant secretions. When such species come to live in deserts, or rather arid regions, where the long droughts of summer and the cold of winter restrict plant and insect life to a brief season, they usually take on one of the four following adaptations:

1. They may exaggerate the insectivorous habits which they already possess and become ravenous and highly predatory hunters. They thus manage to secure a sufficient amount of food even under unfavorable conditions. This adaptation is beautifully shown in the Old World *Myrmecocysti* (*Cataglyphis*), which are represented by the greatest number of species, subspecies and varieties in the deserts of North Africa. The same tendency, however, is apparent in certain races of the American *M. melliger* (*orbiceps* and *mendax*).

2. Many species have taken to eating and harvesting seeds—a very obvious adaptation to arid regions covered with a short-lived herbaceous flora, as is shown by the species of *Pogonomyrmex* in the New World, *Messor, Solenopsis* and *Pheidole* in both hemispheres, and *Holcomyrmex, Oxyopomyrmex, Goniomma, Meranoplus* and *Pheidologeton* in the Old World (Chapter XVI). These ants still feed upon insects when these are obtainable, but seeds furnish such an inexhaustible and nutritious food supply that the habit of collecting and storing them in the nests has become highly developed.

3. A number of species, which have been described in detail in the foregoing pages, have taken to storing nectar and honey-dew in the crops of a physiological caste, the repletes.

4. Some ants (Attii) manage to live and thrive in very arid regions because they cultivate and eat fungi. Although this habit, which has been described in Chapter XVIII, probably originated in the luxuriant rain-forests of the tropics, several fungus growing species have emigrated into the deserts of northern Mexico, western Texas and southern Arizona. In these regions they can always obtain the vegetable débris for the substratum on which to grow their fungi, and these delicate plants can, of course, be successfully cultivated some distance below the surface of the soil. These Attiine ants thus no longer depend on the precarious food-supply of the desert, for in raising their crops they are at a greater advantage than the farmer who makes his home in the arid lands of the Southwest.

CHAPTER XXI

PERSECUTED AND TOLERATED GUESTS

"Les Sociétés de Fourmis sont rendues puissantes par le nombre des individus qui les composent, par la ténacité, le courage et les instincts compliqués, par les organes très perfectionnés, les moyens d'attaque et de défense que possèdent ces individus; par le milieu favorable et la protection que leur fournissent leurs retraites bien abritées; par une division du travail qui peut être poussée très loin. De toutes ces conditions particulièrement avantageuses, il résulte que les Sociétés de Fourmis ont, en général, une existence extrêmement longue et vivent dans une véritable opulence. Il n'en faut pas plus pour expliquer qu'un nombre aussi extraordinairement considérable d'espèces animales aient été attirées près d'elles, aient cherché à profiter des avantages dont elles jouissent, aient tenté de vivre dans leurs nids, aient pu s'y installer à la suite d'une accoutumance des Fourmis à leur présence et, dans certains cas où ces dernières ont trouvé un avantage à cette présence, aient fini par être soignées et protégées par leur hôtes."—Janet, "Rapports des Animaux Myrmécophiles avec les Fourmis," 1897.

The relations of the ants to the aphids and caterpillars described in Chapter XIX represent only one of the many phases of symbiosis. These relations, like those of the ants to the vascular plants, are of the ants' own seeking and outside of their nests; that is, they are extranidal. The ants may even be said to be mildly parasitic on the aphids and caterpillars. The symbiotic relations to be described in this and the following chapter, on the contrary, obtain within the confines of the nest and are therefore intranidal. In these relations, which are extremely diversified, the ants are, as a rule, passive or indifferent, and the other insects foist themselves upon the ants and assume the rôle of satellites, parasites or commensals. Such insects, when they regularly inhabit ant-nests, either throughout life or during one or more of their developmental stages, are known as myrmecophiles, or ant-guests, in a broad sense. The ants have such a plastic organization that they are not only able to assume an active rôle towards the aphids and a passive rôle towards the myrmecophiles, but, as will be shown in Chapters XXIII to XXVII, they may even enter into manifold active and passive symbiotic relations to other species of ants (social symbiosis).

Our knowledge of the myrmecophiles is less than a century old. It grew slowly at first through the occasional contributions of J. P. W. Müller (1818), Savi (1819), Maerkel (1841, 1844), von Hagens (1863, 1865), Lespès (1868a, 1868b), Forel (1874) and Lubbock (1894), but recently the interest and importance of the subject have been more fully appreciated, owing to the investigations of Wasmann, Janet, Escherich, Reitter, Hamilton, Schwarz, Viehmeyer and others. Wasmann alone, in a series of more than a hundred and fifty papers, may be said to have contributed as much as all other authors to our knowledge of these remarkable insects.

The number and diversity of myrmecophilous arthropods are almost incredible. In 1894 Wasmann enumerated 1,246 species. This list comprises 1,177 insects, 60 Arachnida and 9 Crustacea. Of the insects 993 are Coleoptera (283 Staphylinidæ, 117 Pselaphidæ, 90 Clavigeridæ,

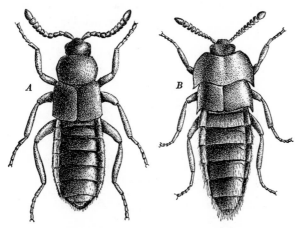

Fig. 224. Synechthran and synœkete Staphylinids. (Original.) *A, Myrmedonia funesta; B, Dinarda dentata.*

169 Paussidæ, 43 Thorictidæ, 128 Histeridæ, etc.). Since 1894 many additional species have been brought to light, so that the total number now known is at least 1,500, including fully 1,000 beetles. These, however, represent only a portion of the existing myrmecophilous fauna of the world. Wasmann's and Escherich's estimate of 3,000 species is probably below rather than above the total number that will be recorded when the ant-nests of the tropics and many other regions have been as carefully searched for these insects as those of Europe.

The existence of this great number of myrmecophiles can be accounted for only on the supposition that ant-nests have a strong attraction for terrestrial arthropods. It is not difficult to understand how this can be the case since, in the first place, the nests are usually permanent abodes inhabited for months or years by successive broods of ants. Second, these nests have at all seasons a slightly higher temperature than the surrounding soil. Third, there is usually more or less refuse food or offal, pupal exuviæ and dead ants, at least in the superficial

chambers. Fourth, the living larvæ and pupæ represent an abundant
and highly nutritious food supply for any insects that can elude the
watchfulness of the ants. Fifth, the ants, in protecting themselves
from larger animals, necessarily protect any small organisms living
in their nests. Sixth, the philoprogenitive instincts of the ants
are capable of being deceived and exploited, for these insects are so
fond of nursing that they are always ready to lavish their affections
on any organisms that resemble ant larvæ. Since the dwellings of
termites, social wasps and bees offer many of the attractions here
enumerated, it is not surprising to find that these insects, too, have their
nest-mates and parasites. These, however, are far less numerous than
the myrmecophiles.

More extraordinary than the number of myrmecophiles is the diversity of their relations to the ants. It is by no means easy to frame an

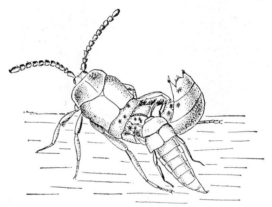

Fig. 225. *Dinarda dentata* eating mites from the surface of *Lomechusa strumosa.*
(Wasmann.)

ethological classification of this perplexing assemblage of assassins,
scavengers, satellites, guests, commensals and parasites, for the same
species may assume different relations towards the ants in its different
developmental stages, or it may be sufficiently versatile to combine the
habits of different groups. Nevertheless, Wasmann has succeeded in
working out a very good classification, which is sufficiently elastic for
most purposes. He divides all myrmecophiles into the following four
groups:

1. **Inimically Persecuted Intruders, or Synechthrans.**—These insects live in the nests as scavenegers or cowardly assassins of isolated
ants, and are treated with marked hostility. They have to elude the
ants in order to get at their food, which usually consists of dead or
diseased ants, the brood or the refuse of the nest.

2. Indifferently Tolerated Guests, or Synœketes.—These live in the nests without being noticed by the ants or without arousing any great animosity, because they are either too small or too slow of movement to be perceived, or have no specific odor that differentiates them from their environment, or because the ants are unable to seize and hold them and therefore soon learn to let them alone.

3. True Guests, Symphiles, or Myrmecoxenes.—Species which are amicably treated, *i. e.,* licked, fondled, fed and even reared by the ants. These guests represent the most extreme and remarkable development of myrmecophily.

4. Ecto- and Entoparasites.—Species that live either on or in the ants and present adaptive peculiarities similar to those of the ecto- and entoparasites of other animals.

The symphiles represent the élite, as Wasmann calls them, of the myrmecophiles, and number hardly more than 300 to 400 species, whereas the synœketes are much more numerous. With the increasing intimacy of the symbiotic relation as we pass from the first to the fourth of the groups above mentioned, there goes a concomitant increase in the number and magnitude of adaptive characters. The object of the myrmecophiles is to live their own sweet lives unmolested in the midst of the warmth and plenty of the nest. We see, therefore, a general tendency in many of these creatures to mimic the ants in color, form or pilosity (mimetic type), in others to assume a limuloid shape, with broad shoulders and rapidly tapering abdomen, combined with a hard or very slippery surface, which prevents their being held fast by the ants (loricate type), and in others to develop tufts of yellow, scent-diffusing hairs, which appeal to the gustatory and olfactory senses of the ants (symphiloid type). The mimetic and loricate types are most perfectly realized among certain synechthrans and

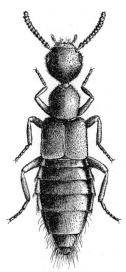

FIG. 226. *Megastilicus formicarius,* a synechthran from the nests of *Formica exsectoides.* (Original.)

synœketes, whereas the symphiloid characters, though foreshadowed in some of these insects, reach their full development only in the true guests. The parasites of ants, finally, like those of other animals, have acquired the most exquisite and specialized apparatus for exploiting the individual host. I shall here consider a number of typical synechthrans and synœketes and continue with an account of the symphiles and parasites in the next chapter.

The Synechthrans.—This group, which is not a very large one, comprises a number of agile, carnivorous Staphylinid beetles belonging to the genera *Myrmedonia, Myrmœcia, Lamprinus, Quedius, Xantholinus, Megastilicus,* etc., which lurk in the less frequented galleries of the nests and avoid encounters with the ants. One of the most interesting of these genera is *Myrmedonia,* which is represented by numerous species on all the continents and is of generalized and primitive structure, so that it is regarded by Wasmann as related to the ancestral form from which some of the more specialized Staphylinid synœketes and symphiles have sprung. The European species have been carefully studied by Wasmann (1886). The sooty *M. funesta* (Fig. 224, *A*) resembles its host, *Lasius fuliginosus,* in color, and the same is true of the black and red *M. humeralis* which lives with *Formica rufa.* The beetles lurk about the burrows and feed on dead or disabled ants, but they also lie in wait near the entrance and destroy solitary ants that are returning to the nest. Wasmann has seen five or six *Myrmedoniæ* fall upon a single ant, tear her limb from limb and then quarrel with one another over the fragments like a pack of hungry hounds. The ants detest these jackals and rush at them with open jaws, but the latter merely turn up their flexible tails and emit a disagreeable secretion. This causes the ants to start back, and the beetles escape. Our American species of *Myrmedonia, M. cremastogastris, planifer* and *schwarzi,* which have been taken in the nests of *Cremastogaster lineolata,* probably have very similar habits. The South American forms have been found in the nests of *Eciton* and *Pogonomyrmex,* the African forms with *Dorylus.* According to Wasmann (1892) *Myrmœcia fussi,* which lives with *Tapinoma erraticum,* resembles *Myrmedonia* in its behavior. In this case, too, the synechthran resembles its host, being shining black in color and intermediate in stature between the worker and queen *Tapinoma.* It lurks in the unfrequented galleries of the nest and kills the ants at night when they lie huddled together and overcome with the cold. The *Tapinoma* worker, on meeting the *Myrmœcia,* turns the tip of her gaster forward and emits her strong-smelling venom. In the United States *Megastilicus formicarius* (Fig. 226), which is not uncommon in the large mound nests of *Formica exsectoides,* is, according to my observations, a typical synechthran. It resembles its host in its black and red coloration and ant-like appearance. When confined with the ants in a small artificial nest, it is invariably killed in the course of a few hours, but in the natural nests it adroitly eludes its host in the same manner as *Myrmedonia,* for, when an ant tries to seize it, it raises the tip of its flexible abdomen and seems to emit a whitish fluid which causes the ant to start back, as if a flask of ammonia had been suddenly uncorked in its face, thus giving the beetle time to run away. *Megastilicus* is certainly too feeble to kill living *F. exsectoides* workers. It probably feeds on the remains of insects brought into the nest or on the larvæ of the ants.

The Synœketes.—For convenience in handling this large and heterogeneous group I shall divide it into four sections: the neutral synœketes; the mimetic, loricate and symphiloid forms; the myrmecocleptics, and the strigilators.

(*a*) *Neutral Synœketes.*—To this section may be assigned a number of insects which pay no attention to the ants or their brood, but live on the refuse or nest materials and spend their time seeking these on the walls of the galleries and chambers. They do not mimic the ants, although they are sometimes protected either by small size, tough integument or by specially constructed cases. They seem to pass unnoticed by the ants, or, if perceived, probably appear as a part of the lifeless environment. Typical examples of these neutral synœketes are the tiny white Podurans of the genus *Cyphodeira* [*Beckia*], so abundant in the nests of many different ants, both in Europe and America. They flit about the dark galleries like diminutive ghosts and are probably invisible to the ants. The slow-moving, snow-white slater, *Platyarthrus hoffmannseggi* of Europe, is similarly panmyrmecophilous and elicits no more attention than the much smaller *Cyphodeira*. A whole fauna of Trichopterygid beetles (*Ptenidium, Ptilium,* etc.), mites (*Lælaps*), *Ceratopogon* larvæ, microlepidopteran caterpillars (*Myrmecocœla ochroceella* in Europe and *Epizeuxis americalis* in the United States) and Phoridæ may often be found in the superficial chambers of ant-nests and undoubtedly obtain most of their food as scavengers on the kitchen middens. Some of these creatures, like the Phoridæ with subapterous females (*Commoptera solenopsidis, Xanionotum hystrix, Ecitomyia wheeleri*) described by Brues (1901, 1902*b*) from the nests of various Texan ants, are of unusual interest on account of their aberrant structure and relationship to the remarkable *Termitoxenia* and *Termitomyia* of termite nests.

FIG. 227. Larva of *Microdon tristis.* (Original.)

Besides these insects, nearly all of which are of small size, one occasionally finds certain larger larval and pupal forms which, one would suppose, could hardly be overlooked by the ants. Such are, *e. g.*, the larvæ of the Clythrinæ, a group of Chrysomelid beetles, represented in Europe by the genus *Clythra,* in the United States by *Coscinoptera.* The adult beetles are found on plants, but the larvæ are sometimes common in the superficial chambers of ant-nests. They inhabit cylindrical or pear-shaped earthen cases of their own construction. These are open only at one end which can be closed by the hard head of the larva. Occasionally the ants gnaw holes in the earthen case and devour the enclosed larva or pupa, but as a rule these synœketes are completely ignored. Escherich (1897, 1906) claims to have detected a tendency towards brood parasitism in a *Clythra* which inhabits the nests of *Tetramorium cespitum* in Asia Minor. The larva often withdraws into its case so as to leave an empty cavity in front of its head. The ants, seeking for cozy little depressions in which to hide their egg-packets, often place them in this cavity. The *Clythra* larva then moves its head forward and devours the eggs. But these insects are never sufficiently abundant in the nests to destroy many of the eggs, and they probably feed very largely on the refuse of the kitchen middens among which they are most frequently found.

Another insect that belongs among the neutral synœketes and bears a slight resemblance to *Clythra,* is the singular wine-red Microlepidopteron, *Pachypodistes goeldii,* recently observed by Hagmann (1907). The larva of this moth lives in the paper nests of the arboreal *Dolichoderus gibboso-analis* of Brazil. It feeds on the carton of the nest and with this substance builds a mussel-shaped case from which it can protrude its head and in which it pupates after completing its growth. When the moth emerges it is covered throughout with a dense coating of erect, golden-yellow, fugitive hairs, 3 mm. long, which protect it from the ants till its wings have expanded and it is able to escape from the nest. This recalls the singular Lycænid *Liphyra* described by Dodd and Chapman (see p. 359). This insect is also a synœkete like *Pachypodistes,* though I referred to it in connection with the trophobiotic Lycænidæ. Both *Liphyra* and *Pachypodistes* are protected by a hard case in their larval and pupal stages, the former by an induration of its own integument, the latter by a case constructed from the materials of the nest, and the hatching imagines of both insects baffle the ants with an envelope of fugitive scales.

Several Scarabæid beetles are also to be included among the synœketes. The European *Cetonia floricola, e. g.,* passes its larval and pupal stages in the depths of *Formica rufa* nests, and in the United States the allied *Euphoria inda* and *hirtipes* bear a similar relation to *F. integra, obscuripes* and *exsectoides.* I have seen *E. inda* fly from a distance straight to a *F. exsectoides* mound and at once bury itself in the earth and débris. According to Wasmann the larvæ of the Cetoniine beetles are tolerated by the ants "partly with indifference and partly with hostility."

Among the most singular synœketes are the larvæ of the Syrphid flies belonging to the genus *Microdon*. These larvæ (Fig. 227), which have been repeatedly described as mollusks (under the generic names *Scutelligera, Parmula* and *Ceratoconcha*) or as Coccidæ, are tough-skinned, elliptical creatures, with a flat creeping-sole and a convex, often prettily reticulated dorsal surface. They move about very slowly in the superficial chambers of the nest. When ready to pupate, they simply remain stationary and attached to the walls of the galleries by means of their creeping-soles, assume a deep brown color, while the integument becomes indurated and more brittle and forms the puparium enclosing the pupa proper. The fly emerges by breaking off the anterior dorsal third of the puparium. Verhoeff (1892) has observed the fly in the act of ovipositing in the nest. It was repeatedly driven away by the ants (*Formica sanguinea*), but kept returning until the eggs were deposited. Three species of *Microdon* flies have been bred from ant-nests in Europe (*M. mutabilis, devius* and *api-formis*).

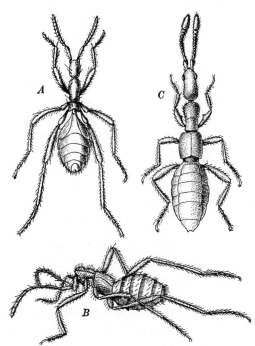

Fig. 228. Mimetic Staphylinids that live with Doryline ants. (Wasmann.) *A, Mimeciton pulex; B, Ecitomorpha simulans; C, Dorylostethus wasmanni.*

Though the larvæ of our American forms are not infrequent, none had been bred until very recently, when Mr. William T. Davis and myself (1908*d*) succeeded in raising specimens of *M. tristis* from a number of larvæ found in *Formica schaufussi* nests in New Jersey and New York. Another species is represented in my collection by some larvæ and pupæ which I found in nests of *F. obscuripes, ciliata,* etc., in Colorado. Brues (1903*b*) has described an extraordinary, lemon-yellow and very convex *Microdon* larva taken by Professor H. Heath from a nest of *Monomorium minimum* in California, and I have described a very flat larva from the nest of *Pseudomyrma mexicana* (1901*b*), so that the larvæ of at least four North American species are known. As Lea (1893) has described a species (*M. variegatus*) from Australia, the genus is probably cosmopolitan. The ants, as a rule, do not seem to notice the *Microdon* larvæ and pupæ and these are left behind when the ants move to a new nest. The young larvæ seem to shrivel and die when removed from the ants, but I have been unable to ascertain what they find to eat in the nests. In one of my artificial formicaries the ants killed a young larva that had failed to get hold of a surface with its vulnerable creeping-sole. They turned the helpless creature over on its back and for two days kept licking and biting it till it was reduced to a mere granule. According to Wasmann the fly, which is more or less tomentose, is sometimes licked by the ants, but it seems to spend little time in the nest. In my artificial nests the imaginal *M. tristis* on emerging from their puparia were attacked and killed by their host, *F. schaufussi* (Wheeler, 1908*d*).

(*b*) *Mimetic, Loricate and Symphiloid Synœketes.*—These are the most numerous and typical of the tolerated guests and appear to attain their highest development among the Doryline ants. This is surprising because these ants have no fixed abode and their synœketes have to lead the life of camp-followers, moving from place to place in the caravans of their restless hosts. This life has its compensations, however, for the Dorylines are powerful marauders and there is always an abundance of fresh food to be had in their temporary quarters. For nearly all that is known of these Doryline guests we are indebted to Wasmann, who has shown in a long series of papers (1890–1904) that they are mostly Staphylinid beetles and that among these the mimetic, loricate and symphiloid types have been remarkably developed and independently of one another in each hemisphere. Thus among the guests of *Dorylus* and *Ænictus* of the Ethiopian region we have the mimetic genera *Dorylostethus* (Fig. 228, *C*), *Dorylobius*, *Dorylophila*, *Dorylopora*, *Dorylocerus*, *Dorylomimus*, *Dorylogaster* and *Stilicus;* the loricate genera *Pygostenus*, *Doryloxenus*, *Anommatophilus*, *Anommatoxenus*, *Discoxenus*, *Mimocete* and *Trilobitidius* (the last a Silphid); and the symphiloid genus *Sympolemon.* Roughly corresponding to these we have as guests among the Ecitons of tropical America the mimetic genera *Mimeciton* (Fig. 228, *A*), *Ecitophya*, *Ecitophila*, *Ecitomorpha* (Fig. 228, *B*), *Ecitonilla*, *Ecitoxenia*, *Ecitochara*, *Ecitopora*, *Ecitotonia*, *Ecitonusa;* the loricate genera *Xenocephalus*, *Cephalo-*

plectus and *Ecitoxenus,* and the symphiloid genera *Ecitogaster* and
Ecitodulus. These correspondences between the guests of the Old
World driver ants and those of the New World legionary ants represent
a very interesting case of convergent development, for none of the
genera is common to both hemispheres and all of them have the appearance of having developed independently in adaptation to their respective
hosts. The most remarkable mimetic form is *Mimeciton pulex,* which
lives with the Brazilian *Eciton prædator.* But the smaller Ecitons of
the Southern States also have their mimetic guests (*Ecitonidia wheeleri*
and *Ecitoxenia brevipes* with *Eciton schmitti,* and *Ecitonusa schmitti*
and *foreli* with *E. carolinense*). As the
Doryline ants are blind, but endowed
with a very keen contact-odor sense,
Wasmann assumes that the guest's mimicry in form and pilosity is for the purpose of deceiving its hosts, whereas its
color mimicry may enable it to remain
unseen by birds and other enemies while
it is moving along in the procession of
the ants. While Wasmann is probably
right in regarding the peculiar resemblance between guest and host as due to
a tactile mimicry, further speculation had
best be postponed till the insects can be
carefully observed in their natural
environment.

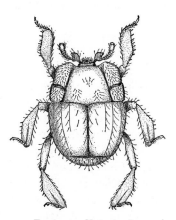

FIG. 229. *Hetærius brunneipennis.* (Original.)

The tendency to develop mimetic, loricate and symphiloid characters is not confined to the guests of the driver and legionary ants, but
is discernible also among the guests of many of our northern species.
Two of the common Staphylinids living with *Liometopum occidentale*
in Colorado, namely, *Dinardilla liometopi* and *Apteronina schmitti,* are
clearly mimetic, the former in color and pilosity, the latter in form.
In the species of *Dinarda* of Europe, we have guests which resemble
the loricate dorylophiles and ecitophiles in form and also mimic their
hosts in color. The genus has been carefully studied by Wasmann
(1901*e,* 1904*d,* etc.), who regards it as representing a series of forms
actually in process of speciation. The various *Dinardæ* have definite
hosts: *D. dentata* living with *Formica sanguinea, mærkeli* with *F. rufa,*
hagensi with *F. exsecta, pygmæa* with *F. fusco-rufibarbis, nigritoides*
with *F. fusca,* and *nigrita* with *Aphænogaster testaceopilosa.* *D. dentata, mærkeli* and *hagensi* are red and black like their hosts, *pygmæa*
is dark and nearly unicolorous like *F. fusco-rufibarbis, nigritoides* and

nigrita black like the ants with which they live.   These synœketes are also graduated in size according to their hosts, the largest and most primitive form being *dentata* (Fig. 224, *B*), whereas the others are hardly more than smaller subspecies or varieties, which Wasmann conceives to have been produced by a kind of unconscious selection on the part of their respective host ants.   *D. dentata* is not uncommon in *sanguinea* nests, where it is usually tolerated with indifference.   It mingles freely with the ants, but when attacked, as sometimes happens, it behaves like *Myrmedonia* and *Megastilicus,* raising the tip of its abdomen and startling its pursuer.   It feeds on dead ants and other insects and is also fond of eating the ectoparasitic mites from the bodies of the living ants and their other guests (Fig. 225).   In this capacity it is very useful to its hosts.   When *sanguinea* moves to a new nest, it is accompanied by the *Dinarda*.   This has been observed by several writers, and during the summer of 1907 I myself saw near Würzburg two of these beetles running along like ecitophiles in a procession of *sanguinea* workers that were carrying their slaves and pupæ to a new nest.

To the symphiloid type may be assigned several of the guests of our northern ants, but I shall here consider only the Histerid beetles of the genera *Triballus* and *Hetærius* and the Cetoniine beetles of the genus *Cremastocheilus.*   The numerous Histeridæ that live with ants have retained unmodified the hard, shining integument and seed-like form of the free-living species, which constitute the greater bulk of this family.   Professor T. Kincaid has sent me a few specimens of *Triballus californicus* which he took from nests of *Myrmica mutica* in Washington.   Though deep red, like many symphiles, this beetle has no yellow trichomes and is therefore in all probability an indifferently tolerated guest.   The same is true of many species of other Histerid genera (*Myrmetes, Dendrophilus, Sternocœlis, Eretmotes, Hister,* etc.).   The genus *Hetærius,* however, which is represented both in Europe and North America, has the thorax and legs peculiarly modified and the former sometimes furnished with trichomes.   Forel (1874) and Wasmann (1886) at first regarded the European *H. ferrugineus,* when living with *Polyergus rufescens,* as an indifferently tolerated guest which feeds on the cadavers of the ants, but Escherich (1897), who observed it in nests of *Lasius alienus,* is inclined to regard it as a true symphile.   The ants lick the beetle and carry it about, but have great difficulty in seizing it with their mandibles on account of its hard, smooth and rounded surfaces.   Escherich describes one of their attempts as follows: "On uncovering the nest I saw an ant trying to seize a *Hetærius.* She persisted for a long time but her jaws kept slipping from the smooth chitinous exoskeleton. Finally she succeeded in getting hold of one of the legs and carried the guest a short distance in this manner, till it suddenly slipped out of her mandibles. Then the ant made no further attempts to seize the beetle, but with her fore-feet rolled it along for some distance, like a barrel, while it held its legs completely withdrawn." Of our North American species *H. blanchardi* is recorded by Schwarz (1890) as occurring in the nests of *Aphænogaster fulva,* and *H. brunneipennis* as living in those of *Formica subsericea* and *exsectoides.* *H. horni* occurs in the nests of *F. schaufussi,* according to Wickham (1892). I have taken *brunnei-pennis* also in the nests of *F. neocinerea* in Illinois. Brues (1903) records the occurrence of a new species in the nests of *F. subpolita* in California.

I have recently published some notes on *H. brunneipennis* (1908c). April 12 seven of these beetles were placed in an artificial nest with a number of *F. subsericea* workers and larvæ and kept under observation till June 30. Although the golden-yellow trichomes are scattered over the elytra and thorax of *H. brunneipennis* (Fig. 229) and not collected in masses on the sides and front of the thorax, as in some of the species from the Western States (*e. g., H. tristriatus*), these structures nevertheless powerfully attract the ants. The beetles run about the nest with surprising agility, considering the awkward shape of their body and legs, or stand motionless with the anterior part of the body elevated and the fore pair of legs raised from the floor, turned forward and strongly flexed at their femorotibial joints. When a beetle in this position happens to be touched by the antennæ of a passing ant, it begins to wave its fore legs as if to attract attention. The ant stops, begins to lick the beetle or seizes it with her jaws. The body of the latter, being very hard and smooth, slips from her grasp but the ant redoubles her efforts. She either seizes it by one of its legs, since the beetle does not feign death nor withdraw its appendages, but allows itself to be carried about the nest, or she stops, seizes it with her fore feet and, holding it in a vertical position, proceeds to lick its head in a very quick and effusive manner. For some time the beetle keeps its head withdrawn into its thorax, after the Histerid fashion, till the ant stops abruptly, protrudes her tongue and regurgitates a drop of food on its face. Then the beetle protrudes its head, opens its mouth, works its jaws and rapidly absorbs the liquid, which sometimes floods the whole cavity in the fore part of the thorax. Thereupon the ant again falls to licking the beetle as if to wipe its face free from the moisture, and either leaves the creature to its own devices or regurgitates another drop. Again and again the licking and feeding may alternate, as if the ant were fascinated with her pet and could not feed and fondle it enough. This performance is, in fact, so frequently repeated that I could nearly always observe it whenever I uncovered the nest. I have rarely witnessed a more comical sight than the behavior of these slender, black ants while they are holding the chunky, little red urchins in their paws and pouring liquid into them as if they were so many casks. Comical, too, is the behavior of the beetle while it is waiting to be noticed, with its head and fore legs elevated. At such times is assumes a ridiculous, cocky air. Often, instead of receiving the caress and food which it is expecting, it is inadvertently knocked over onto its flat back by some scurrying ant intent on more important business. Then the beetle lies for a few moments with sprawling legs, but soon succeeds in righting itself and either scampers away or at once strikes its favorite attitude again. It seems to be greatly aided in the righting movements by the peculiar position of its tarsi, which are strongly flexed backward on the tibiæ, so that when it is lying on its back, the claws are brought into the most advantageous position for taking hold of the floor of the nest. Like the European *ferrugineus, H. brunneipennis* also feeds on solid substances. It eagerly seeks out any dead or wounded ants on the refuse heap of the nest, and may be seen gnawing at their joints or mouth-parts or eating its way into the soft parts of the gaster, after having made a large hole in the chitinous integument. It will also spend hours gnawing away with its sharp little mandibles at the bodies of caterpillars and other insects that have been partially eaten

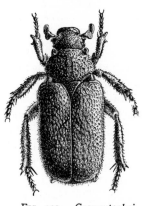

Fig. 230. *Cremastochei-lus castaneæ.* (Original.)

by the ants. Occasionally the body of a single small caterpillar or dead ant will be covered with the beetles, all busily feeding. At such times the ants often come up, tear them away and feed them with regurgitated food. The beetles straighten up and patiently submit to the fondling, licking and feeding, but as soon as the ants move away, return to their ghoulish repast.

The singular genus *Cremastocheilus* (Fig. 230), which comprises more than twenty species, seems to be peculiar to North America. All of the species have very hard bodies and many of them are furnished with tufts of golden trichomes at the anterior and posterior corners of the thorax. The very peculiar mentum is cup-shaped and fits closely over the small mouth parts. A few of the species are deep red, but most of them are opaque or shining black, with coarsely punctate or pitted surfaces. Their movements are very slow and awkward. The larvæ live in the débris of the nests, like the larvæ of *Cetonia,* and pupate in fragile earthen cocoons (Wheeler, 1908*e*). I have taken one of the smaller red species (*C. spinifer*) in a nest of *Pheidole desertorum* in western Texas. *C. canaliculatus, castaneæ* and *harrisi* are not uncommon in the nests of various species of *Formica* (*schaufussi, exsectoides, subsericea,* etc.) in the Eastern States. More rarely these same species occur in nests of *Componotus* and *Aphænogaster.* Schwarz records *C. knochi* from the nests of *F. subænescens* in Colorado, and in the same state I have taken many specimens of *C. wheeleri* from the nests of various forms of *F. rufa. C. crinitus* occurs in the nests of *F. gnava* in Texas, *C. mexicanus* in the nests of the same ant in Arizona. There is little doubt that the true hosts of *Cremastocheilus* are species of *Formica* and that the occurrence of these beetles with other ants is either secondary or accidental. In my artificial nests the beetles were almost continually being dragged about by their legs, but were neither fed nor licked by the ants. These insects, however, persistently gnawed at the anterior and posterior thoracic angles of the beetles as if much attracted by the trichomes (Fig. 231). I am inclined, therefore, to regard the *Cremastocheili* as degenerate symphiles, which are now able to live as indifferently tolerated or even as persecuted synœketes, because their hard armor shields them perfectly from the mandibles of the ants. Even the mouth parts and antennæ are protected by the peculiar mentum, and the legs are so tough that they cannot be disarticulated by the ants. I was quite unable to ascertain the nature of the food of these beetles, some of which lived several weeks in my nests without eating. According to Brauns (Wasmann, 1900*a*) the Cetoniine beetles of the genera *Plagiocheilus* and *Myrmecocheilus,* which are allied to *Cremastocheilus,* live in the nests of *Plagiolepis* in South Africa.

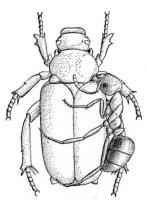

Fig. 231. *Formica integra* worker gnawing at the hind thoracic angle of *Cremastocheilus castaneæ.* (Original.)

(*c*) *Myrmecocleptics.*—Janet (1896*b*) gave the name of myrmecoclepty to the peculiar behavior of the Lepismid *Atelura* [*Lepismina*] *formicaria,* which is common in the nests of various European ants. This insect is decidedly of the loricate type, with broad thorax, rapidly tapering abdomen and very smooth surface, so that it cannot be readily seized by its host. Janet says that " these guests keep circulating and gliding about among the ants [*Lasius mixtus*], but never remain standing in their neighborhood. I have sometimes seen the ants threaten the *Lepismina* and even spring upon them, but the latter are so agile that they always escape. Nevertheless, in my artificial nests, where they have greater difficulty in concealing themselves than in the natural nests, they are eventually captured. Two days after installing them in the nest, I found five cadavers which the ants were holding in their mandibles and carrying about the nest." The *Atelura* will eat honey from the manger of the nest, but they seem, as a rule, to obtain their food by running up and imbibing some of the liquid regurgitated by one ant to another. After furnishing the nest with honey Janet made the following observations: " From the instant that the first foragers

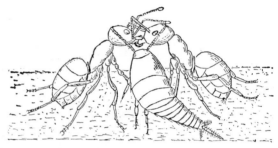

Fig. 232. *Atelura* coming up to snatch the droplet of food that is being regurgitated by one *Lasius mixtus* worker to another. (Janet.)

returned to the inhabited chamber of the nest, the *Lepismina* showed by their excitement, that they perceived the odor of honey. Soon a considerable number of ants were grouped in couples for the purpose of regurgitating. They elevated their bodies slightly and often raised their fore legs, thus leaving a vacant space under their heads. As soon as a *Lepismina* came near such a couple, it thrust itself into the space, raised its head, suddenly snapped up the droplet that was passing in front of it and made off at once as if to escape merited pursuit [Fig. 232]. But the ants standing face to face are not free enough in their movements even to threaten the audacious thief, who forthwith proceeds to take toll from another couple, and continues these tactics until his appetite is appeased." The habits of the golden yellow *Atelura wheeleri,* which occurs in the nest of many ants in Texas and northern Mexico, are probably very similar to those of *formicaria.* Escherich (1903*a,* 1905), who has recently monographed the Lepismidæ, records a number of species of *Lepisma, Braunsina, Lepismina* and *Atelura* as living with ants or termites. Like many other synœketes these insects are panmyrmecophilous and not restricted to particular hosts.

(*d*) *The Strigilators.*—I propose this name for a group of synœketes that lick the surfaces of ants and seem to feed very largely, if not exclusively, on the cutaneous secretions and the thin coating of saliva with which the ants cover one another. To this group belong the little wingless crickets of the genus *Myrmecophila*, the equally diminutive cockroaches of the genus *Attaphila* and the Staphylinid beetle *Oxysoma*. The symbiotic ants *Leptothorax emersoni* and *glacialis* also have similar habits, but these are more conveniently described in another connection (Chapter XXIII).

Like many other synœkete genera, *Myrmecophila* has a world-wide distribution. Two species (*M. acervorum* and *ochracea*) have been described from Europe, one from North Africa (*M. salomonis*), one from India (*flavocincta*), one from the Bintang Islands (*dubia*), one from Australia (*australis*), five from the United States (*pergandei, formicarum, oregonensis, nebrascensis* and *nehawkee*) and two from South America (*americana* and *prenolepidis*). Most, if not all, the species tend to become panmyrmecophilous. *M. acervorum* lives with ants of the genera *Formica, Lasius, Myrmica, Aphænogaster* and *Tetramorium*. *M. flavocincta* occurs with *Plagiolepis longipes* and *Prenolepis longicornis* and has been introduced into Brazil with the latter ant. *M. ochracea* inhabits the nests of *Messor barbarus, Pheidole pallidula* and *Liometopum microcephalum*. I have received *M. australis* with specimens of *Camponotus nigriceps*. According to Pergande (Scudder, 1899), *M. pergandei*, the largest species of the genus, lives with *Camponotus pennsylvanicus, melleus, fallax* var., *Formica subsericea, pallide-fulva, integra, Aphænogaster tennesseensis* and *Cremastogaster lineolata*. *M. formicarum* lives with *Camponotus levigatus* and *M. oregonensis* with *F. neorufibarbis*. Cockerell found *M. nebrascensis* in the nests of a *Formica* at Santa Fe, N. M.; in Texas I have taken it with *Formica gnava, Pogonomyrmex molefaciens, Camponotus sansabeanus* and *Pachycondyla harpax*. *M. nehawkee* is recorded only from the nests of *Cremastogaster lineolata*. The males of the European *Myrmecophila acervorum* seem to be extremely rare, if not altogether unknown; they have been seen in all the American species except *pergandei*. All the species are peculiar in having a wide but discontinuous distribution; that is, they are very common in certain localities and completely absent from others, for no apparent reason. The habits of only a few of the species have been studied. I here give some observations which I made during the spring of 1900 on *M. nebrascensis*, taken from colonies of *Formica gnava* and placed in artificial nests of

the Texan harvester (*Pogonomyrmex molefaciens*).   April 3, twenty
Myrmecophila, eight or ten of which had been squeezed or had lost one
or both saltatory legs during capture, were placed in a *Pogonomyrmex
molefaciens* nest.   All the disabled individuals were at once seized and
dispatched in so vindictive a manner that I could not doubt that the
ants were irritated by the pungent *gnava* nest-odor still clinging to the
crickets.   In an instant all the ants in the compartment of the nest had
gathered in little groups, each devouring a *Myrmecophila.*   The uninjured crickets made not the slightest attempt to escape, but felt themselves perfectly at home as soon as they set foot on the floor of the
nest.   Their adaptation to a new nest and to an ant of larger size and
belonging to an entirely different subfamily from their former host,
was immediate and complete.   With constantly vibrating antennæ they
began to dodge in and out among the little groups of ants.   From time
to time one of them would be seen cautiously approaching an ant, that
was busy with its dinner of *Myrmecophila,* and fall to nibbling at its legs
or the tip of its abdomen (Fig. 233).   There could be no doubt that the

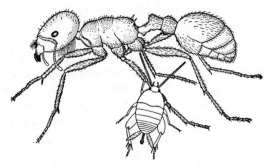

FIG. 233.   *Myrmecophila   nebrascensis*   gnawing at the tibia of *Pogonomyrmex
molefaciens.*   (Original.)

cricket derived some benefit from the oily secretions covering the ant's
body.   At first the ant disregarded this nibbling, which probably resembles the attentions of the toilet habitually received from sister ants, but
the cricket's scraping mandibles and maxillæ soon grew to be annoying
and the ant either moved away or turned her head, opened her mandibles and made a lunge at the *Myrmecophila,* like a large dog annoyed
by a puppy.   But before the huge mandibles had closed, the cricket was
far away, nibbling at the gaster of some other ant.   The cricket can
get at only the legs and gaster of its host, since the spreading legs
prevent its reaching the thorax.   It often stands on its hind legs, as
represented in the figure, and places its fore legs on the ant's leg, in
order to reach the femur or tibia.   For very obvious reasons it avoids

nibbling at or even approaching the ant's head. It is always alert, as if perpetually aware of danger and ready to dodge at the slightest movement of the ant. Occasionally, in the narrow confines of an artificial nest, the ants do succeed in capturing and devouring one of their vigilant little nest-mates, but the fact that of the eleven sound crickets remaining after these observations were made, eight were still alive June 22, when I had to discontinue my observations for the summer, shows that the crickets are extremely expert in keeping out of danger. During all this time the attitude of the ants towards the *Myrmecophila* remained unchanged, so far as I could observe. The ants are compelled to tolerate the little crickets for a very simple reason. The former, with their long bodies, incapable of much lateral flexure, always walk or run in long straight or sinuous paths, and are quite unable to turn around abruptly, whereas the stout-bodied crickets move in a complicated zigzag path made up of very short lines and abrupt angles. This seems to be the key to the symbiosis of the two insects: they manage to get on together in the limited space of an ants' nest

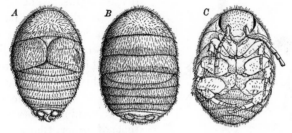

FIG. 234. Myrmecophilous cockroach (*Attaphila fungicola*) from fungus garden of *Atta texana*. (Original.) *A*, Male, dorsal view; *B*, female, dorsal view; *C*, same, ventral view.

because they have very different and, as it were, interdigitating modes of progression. Since the ants are quite able to clean themselves and one another and even take delight and spend much time in this employment, they probably derive little or no advantage from the crickets. The latter, while deriving much of their sustenance from the surfaces of the ants, are often seen haunting even the galleries abandoned by their hosts, scrutinizing the walls and nibbling at them from time to time. There can be no doubt that they find here the same substances which cover the ants, for the walls of the galleries of a populous nest soon become greasy from the attrition of the constantly passing ants. Sometimes the crickets may be seen nibbling at dead ants that have been temporarily abandoned in the galleries or placed on the kitchen midden.

In 1901 Wasmann published some observations on the European *M. acervorum* and also called attention to the all but forgotten work of Savi (1819) on this same insect. From these observations its habits appear to be very similar to those of *nebrascensis*. This cannot be said, however, of the south European *ochracea*. Both Emery (Wasmann, 1901) and Silvestri (1903) believe that this insect feeds on the larvæ of its host. It is probable, therefore, that the species of *Myrmecophila* are more versatile in their relations to the ants than has been supposed, and further observations should be made in regions where these crickets abound.[1]

The little cockroaches of the genus *Attaphila* (Fig. 234) inhabit the nests of the fungus-growing Atti and are the only insects known to live on intimate terms with these ants. The type of the genus (*A. fungicola*) which I described in 1900, from the fungus gardens of *Atta texana*, measures only 3–3.5 mm. in length, is of a yellowish brown color and has very small, apparently vestigial eyes, one-jointed cerci and peculiar

antennæ, consisting of a few cylindrical joints. The females are wingless, the males have vestigial tegmina and hind wings. The antennæ are always mutilated, their terminal joints being bitten off, in all probability while the ants are clipping their fungi. The structure of the remaining joints is so unlike that of other Blattidæ that *Atta-*

FIG. 235. *Oxysoma oberthueri* on *Myrmecocystus viaticus.* (Escherich.)

phila has been regarded as the type of a distinct subfamily, the Attaphilinæ. Since publishing my first account of this singular insect, I have had an opportunity to observe its behavior in an artificial nest. It does not feed on the fungus as I at first supposed, but mounts the backs of the large *Atta* soldiers and licks their surfaces after the manner of *Myrme-*

---

[1] Since the manuscript of this book went to the printer, Schimmer has published a fine account of the genus *Myrmecophila,* containing many valuable observations on *M. acervorum* (Beitrag zu einer Monographie der Gryllodeengattung Myrmecophila Latr., *Zeitschr. f. wiss. Zool.,* 93, 1909, pp. 409–534, pls. 22–24). He finds that this versatile insect not only feeds, like *M. nebrascensis,* on the surface secretions of its hosts, but also on liquid food solicited from them directly, or stolen, after the manner of *Atelura,* while it is being disgorged by the ants to one another, or just after it has been placed on the mouths of the larvæ. The cricket also eats dead ant larvæ and the insect food brought into the nest. No males of *M. acervorum* could be found, and Schimmer gives very good reasons for regarding the females as permanently parthenogenetic and thelytocous. The eggs, which are very large (1.1 mm. long and .56 mm. broad) are laid among the ant's eggs and hatch in about six weeks from the time of oviposition.

cophila.   Attaphila, however, is tolerated by the ants without the slightest signs of hostility.   The mutilation of the antennæ is probably accidental or unintentional.

In 1901 Bolivar described a second species of *Attaphila* (*A. bergi*), taken many years ago in the nests of *Acromyrmex lundi,* in Argentina and Uruguay.   This species is very similar to the Texan form and it, too, seems always to have the antennæ mutilated.   According to Bolivar, " it is found in the nests of the ants, sitting on the back, neck or even on the head of the sexual individuals (never on the neuters), and when these swarm forth during the spring and summer, it is also carried out of the nests, still attached to its host."   Sheldon has recently described from the nest of a South American wasp (*Polybia pygmæa*) a peculiar Blattid (*Sphecophila polybiarum*) which superficially resembles *Attaphila* in many particulars.

Another strigilating synœkete is *Oxysoma oberthueri,* a Staphylinid beetle which lives with *Myrmecocystus viaticus* in the deserts of Algiers where it has been observed by Escherich (1902b).   Like *Attaphila* this beetle mounts the bodies of its host and licks or shampoos them with great eagerness, evidently feeding on the surface secretions (Fig. 235). Escherich is inclined to regard this beetle as a kind of degenerate symphile, because it has a very short tongue and sparse yellow trichomes, but as it is treated with indifference by its hosts, its proper place is among the synœketes.

CHAPTER XXII

TRUE GUESTS, ECTO- AND ENTOPARASITES

"Es gibt wohl wenige Gebiete der Zoologie, wo Morphologie und Biologie sich so nahe berühren, so innig durchdringen und sich gegenseitig so ergänzen wie hier: die Biologie erschliesst erst das volle Verständniss der betreffenden morphologischen Charaktere, und andererseits lassen die morphologischen Charaktere uns oft bereits die Biologie jener Wesen vorauserkennen und geben uns die wichtigsten Winke für die Erforschung derselben."—Wasmann, " Die Myrmekophilen und Termitophilen," 1896.

The persecuted and tolerated guests described in the last chapter are merely the plebeian precursors of the aristocracy among the myrmecophiles, the 300 or 400 true guests, which are no longer content to be treated with animosity or indifference, but have acquired more intimate and even friendly relations with the ants. These true guests are not, therefore, to be found skulking in the unfrequented galleries of the nest, or suspiciously dodging about among the ants, but live in their very midst with an air of calm assurance, if not of proprietorship. As a rule, they have abandoned such indefinite or panmyrmecophilous attachments as those of the synœketes and have settled down to associations with particular host species or genera. The ants, however, still remain the passively exploited partners of the alliance; they become, in fact, only the more easily mulcted and despoiled as the symbiotic intimacy increases, till, in some cases, they seem to be suffering from a social obsession or disease like the alcoholism of human communities. It is but a step from these true guests, or symphiles, to the parasites in the restricted sense. Some have regarded the symphiles, like the synechthrans and the synœketes, as parasites on the ant colony, in contradistinction to the ecto- and entoparasites, which exploit the individual ant or ant larva, but this, as we shall see, is a somewhat artificial distinction.

The Symphiles.—These are very largely beetles, and though they belong to many different families, they show a remarkable adaptive convergence, for in order to solicit food from the ants and ingratiate themselves by means of peculiar exudations, they have developed the following peculiarities in coloration, in the structure of glands, mouthparts and antennæ:

1. *Symphilic Coloration.*—Wasmann has called attention to the peculiar red color and oily surface characteristic of many true guests.

This is best seen in the Lomechusini, Clavigeridæ and Paussidæ, but is also apparent in many other species (certain *Cremastocheilus,* Silphidæ, Thorictidæ, etc.) which are, perhaps, degenerate symphiles. The exact signification of this symphilic coloration is not known.

2. *Trichomes.*—Several of the earlier students of myrmecophily (Erichson, Lacordaire, W. P. J. Müller) observed that the true guests, as a rule, bear tufts of red or golden yellow hairs (trichomes, or

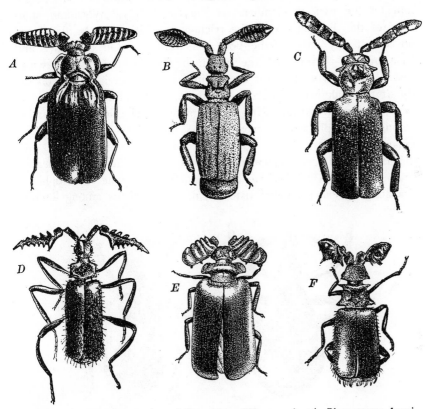

Fig. 236. Various species of Paussidæ. (Wasmann.) *A, Pleuropterus brevicornis; B, Paussus hova; C, Pentaplatarthrus natalensis; D, Paussus dama; E, Lebioderus goryi; F, Paussus spiniceps.*

trichodes) which are assiduously licked by the ants, and much has been made of these structures by Wasmann, who regards them as the most characteristic organs of symphiles. He has shown that they are borne by the chitinous integument at points or depressions where clusters of unicellular glands open, and that they have the important function of rapidly diffusing some aromatic secretion. Glands of a similar type, from which the trichomes may have developed, are present in many

nonmyrmecophilous insects, *e. g.*, the epinotal glands of the ants themselves, the dorsal glands of the Blattidæ, the scent glands of Lepidoptera, etc. Wasmann states that the secretion is not liquid, but " volatile
or etherial, perhaps a fatty ether." The ants are so inordinately fond
of it that he believes that it must affect them very much as a good
cigar affects a smoker. Perhaps it would be nearer the truth to say
that its fascination is more like that exercised by catnip or oil of berga-
mot on the various members of the cat family. Wasmann summarizes the distribution of the trichomes, which may be developed
on almost any part of the body, as follows: "On the sides and
base of the portions of the abdomen not covered by the wing-
cases (*Lomechusa* group of Staphylinids, many Clavigerids) ; on the
tip of the abdomen (*Lomechusa* group), or pygidium (many *Paussus*) ; at the tips of the wing-cases (many Clavigerids, *Chætopisthes*
among termitophilous Scarabæids) ; on the sides of the wing-cases
(many *Paussus*) ; at the posterior corners or edges of the prothorax (*Pleuropterus* and many *Paussus* among Paussids, *Lomechon*
among Silphids, *Corythoderus* and *Chætopisthes* among termitophilous
Scarabæids, *Tylois* among Histerids, many *Thorictus* among Thoric-

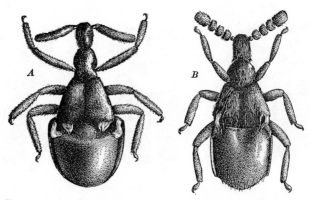

Fig. 237. Two highly myrmecophilous Pselaphidæ. (Original.) *A, Adranes lecontei*
of North America; *B, Claviger testaceus* of Europe.

tids) ; on the anterior corners of the prothorax (*Napochus termitophilus*) ; on the much elevated sides of the prothorax (*Teratosoma*
among Histerids, *Gnostus* among Gnostids) ; in a median transverse
groove on the prothorax (many *Paussus*) ; on the neck, between the
head and prothorax (the myrmecophilous *Napochus* among the Scydmænidæ, *Tetramopria* among Proctotrupids) ; on a perforated horn on
the vertex (several *Paussus*) ; on the front (*Pogonoxenus* among Tene-

brionids); on the antennal club (many *Paussus*); and even on the coxæ and tips of the femora (*Lomechusa*)."

3. *Mouthparts.*—The symphiles are not only licked, but also fed by the ants. This has led to a peculiar shortening and broadening of the tongue, its fusion with the paraglossæ and a reduction in the number and size of the joints of the labial palpi, in many symphiles. These modifications make the tongue a more spoon-like organ, adapted to receiving the liquid regurgitated by the ants.

4. *Antennæ.*—In the symphiles these organs have, in many cases, undergone peculiar modifications, depending upon whether they are used primarily as organs of communication, of transportation, or of protection. In communication they may have a two-fold function, since they may be employed either in making supplicatory movements in order to induce the ants to regurgitate, or the movements may be of

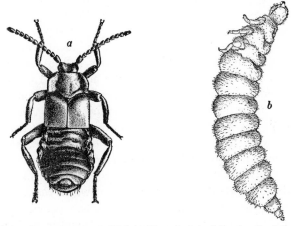

FIG. 238. *Lomechusa strumosa.* (Original.) *a*, imaginal beetle; *b*, full-grown larva.

such a character as to deceive the ants into mistaking the beetles for other members of the colony. Space forbids an adequate account of the wonderful variety of structures in the antennæ of the symphiles. Suffice it to say that the antennæ adapted for stroking the ants approach those of the Formicidæ in structure and movement; others have the joints fused and dilated (*Paussus*) and are used as handles, by means of which the ants can carry or drag their guests about the nest. Such antennæ are obviously protective, but there are also protective antennæ of another type which are short, compact and spindle-shaped, so that they slip through the jaws of the ants. Such antennæ are best developed in certain synœketes and synechthrans and may be said to have a function the very opposite of communication.

The symphiles, as already stated, are nearly all Coleoptera. They belong to the families Paussidæ, Clavigeridæ, Pselaphidæ, Thorictidæ, Cossyphodidæ, Silphidæ, Nitidulidæ, Ectrephidæ, Gnostidæ, Scydmænidæ, Staphylinidæ, Brenthidæ and Tenebrionidæ. As it will be impossible here to describe or even to enumerate the various species, I shall confine myself to some of the more striking and interesting types.

Of all myrmecophilous insects the Paussidæ (Fig. 236) are the most extraordinary. They are an aberrant offshoot of the Carabidæ, and, with the exception of two species of *Homopterus,* that have been taken in equatorial South America, are all paleotropical. Although nearly 300 species are known, the behavior of very few has been carefully observed, and the accounts are so different as to indicate a wide range of myrmecophilous habits within the family. The group, on account of the variety and bizarre structure of its species, is a favorite one with coleopterists. It has been studied by Boyes (1843), Westwood (1843–'45), Dohrn (1851), Gueinzius (1858–'59), Peringuey (1883, 1886), Raffray (1885–'87, 1892), Wasmann (1888, 1890*g,* 1894*g,* 1896*h,* 1897*q,* 1904*c,* etc.) and Escherich (1898, 1907). The salient characters of the family are found in the antennæ which vary in the number of their joints from 11 to 2. In the latter case the distal joint is formed by a fusion of several. Wasmann divides the family into four groups of genera according to the number of joints: first, *Protopaussus* with 11 joints; second, *Arthropterus, Homopterus, Orthopterus, Cerapterus* and *Pleuropterus* with 10 joints; third, *Ceratoderus, Merismoderus* and *Pentaplatarthrus* with 6, and *Paussoides* with 5 joints; and fourth, *Lebioderus, Platyrhopalus, Paussomorphus, Paussus* and *Hylotorus* with two joints. Several of these groups, of which *Paussoides* is one, were already represented in the Prussian amber (Lower Oligocene). These beetles are not only anomalous in the number of joints in the antennæ, but also in the form of these organs, which in some species are broad and elliptical, in others shaped like ribbons, antlers, scimitars, drumsticks, boats, etc. Westwood described *Paussus sphærocerus* as having phosphorescent antennæ "like two lanthorns spreading a dim phosphoric light," and Wasmann believes that this observation is correct, as the two spherical antennal clubs in a cabinet specimen examined by him had a peculiar yellow color like the phosphorescing spots on the thorax of *Pyrophorus.* The remarkable development of trichomes in some of the species and their absence in many others indicate that these beetles are not all symphiles, though they are probably all myrmecophiles. In some forms, like *Paussus cucullatus,* the tufts of golden hairs may be present on the pygidium, in the median thoracic groove, in the double frontal pits and in the clefts of the antennal clubs. In

general these tufts are the better developed the greater the reduction in the number of the antennal joints, but *Protopaussus* is an exception to this rule. The Paussidæ are also peculiar in possessing crepitating repugnatorial glands like the bombardier beetles (*Brachynus*), but distinct from the alimentary tract though opening at the tip of the abdomen. The secretion of these glands in *Cerapterus 4-maculatus*, according to Loman (1887), contains pure iodine! The Paussidæ usually live in nests of *Pheidole,* more rarely in those of *Acantholepis, Cremastogaster, Aphænogaster* and *Tetramorium.* All these ants are much smaller than the beetles. According to Escherich (1907a), who is one of the few who have observed these insects in a living condition, some of the species are treated by the ants as synechthrans, some as syncœketes and some as symphiles. He says: " *Paussus turcicus,* which I met with in Asia Minor, is extravagantly loved by its hosts (*Pheidole pallidula*), is continually licked, caressed with the antennæ and not infrequently carried about in the nest. Much less affection is lavished by its hosts on the decidedly smaller *Paussus favieri,* which I studied in North Africa (Oran). In this case it is hardly possible to speak of a friendly relationship, for the ants usually ignore their guest completely, and only occasionally lick it in a per-
functory manner. Cooler still, or rather inimical, is the behavior of ants towards *Paussus arabicus* Raff. which I had an opportunity to study in northern Abyssinia (Erythrea)." Peringuey (1906) has made similar observations on the south African *P. lineatus* and *linnæi,* the former of which is treated with indifference, the latter with hostility. Both Peringuey and Escherich saw the beetles devouring the ant brood. Since even *P. turcicus* is not fed by the ants, the species of *Paussus* cannot be said to have reached the highest stage of symphily. Escherich believes that in this genus syncœky and synechthry have been secondarily derived from symphily by a kind of degeneration, but it seems more probable that

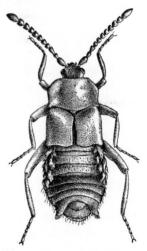

FIG. 239. *Atemeles pubicollis.* (Original.)

these conditions are primitive, especially as they prevail, in all probability, among many of the less specialized genera of the family. The repugnatorial glands, whose very existence suggests the primitively synechthran or syncœketic character of the group, are said to function less frequently in the symphilic than in the other species. At any rate,

Escherich found this to be the case in the species which he studied. The larvæ of the Paussidæ are still unknown.

The families Gnostidæ, Ectrephidæ and Cossyphodidæ are very small and aberrant, the first being allied to the Paussidæ and containing only two species, *Gnostus formicola* and *meinerti*, taken from *Cremastogaster* nests in South America; the second allied to the Scydmænidæ and containing the genera *Ectrephes, Polyplocotes* and *Diplocotes*, with some seven species peculiar to Australia; and the third, of very uncertain affinities and containing the genera *Cossyphodes, Cossyphodites* and *Cossyphodinus*, represented by a few species in South Africa. Brauns (1901), who has studied the family last mentioned, finds that

Fig. 240.   *Atemeles* soliciting food from a worker *Myrmica*.   (Wasmann.)

Cossyphodites woodroofei, which is abundant in the nests of *Plagiolepis custodiens*, has trichomes in a cavity at the tips of its peculiar, ribbed wing-cases.

Vastly richer in species are the families Clavigeridæ and Pselaphidæ, sometimes regarded as a single family and comprising hundreds of species of small red or yellow beetles with short wing-cases and ant-like bodies.   Many, if not all, the Clavigeridæ and several genera of Pselaphidæ are myrmecophilous, but the true guests seem to be confined to the former family.   Some Pselaphids, like our American *Decarthron stigmosum*, which is sometimes common in the nests of *Aphænogaster fulva* and *treatæ*, and the species of *Batrisus* and *Chennium*, seem to represent transitions between the synœketes and the symphile types. The Clavigeridæ are more interesting because they often show decidedly symphilic characters, such as antennal modifications and trichomes at the posterolateral corners of the wing-cases.   Indeed, the antennæ of the former sometimes rival those of the Paussidæ.   They are usually cylindrical, but their joints may fuse and become drum-stick-shaped (*Rhynchoclaviger, Adranes*), flattened and twisted (*Neocerus*), or even antler-like, as in *Microclaviger cervicornis* of Madagascar.   Among

our American Clavigerids *Adranes cœcus* and *lecontei* (Fig. 237, *A*)
are worthy of mention, but nothing is known of their habits except
that they live with species of *Lasius*. The only form that has been
at all carefully studied is the common European *Claviger testaceus*
(Fig. 237, *B*). This beetle, which is totally blind, figures promi-
nently in the works of W. J. P. Müller, Maerkel, Wasmann, Hetchko,
Janet and others. It lives only with species of *Lasius,* being most
often seen in the nests of *L. flavus,* an ant which it closely resembles
in color. It is provided with golden trichomes which are licked
by its host, and is fed with regurgitated food, although it often eats
the ant larvæ. Hetchko (1896)
found that it also eats other insect
food and can be kept alive apart from
the ants for a period of 57 days.
Janet has kept individuals alive in
company with ants for more than four
years. The beetles are often carried
about by the ants in their jaws and
permitted to ride for hours at a time
on their backs.

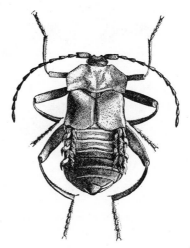

Symphily reaches its most perfect
expression in the Lomechusini, a
sharply circumscribed group of beetles
which has been diligently studied for
the past twenty years by Wasmann.
He has recorded his observations in
more than thirty special papers (see

FIG. 241. *Xenodusa cava.* (Original.)

literature in Appendix E) and never tires of referring to these insects
in his more general works. The following paragraphs, taken from
one of his papers (1897*a*), give a summary of the life-history of
these beetles:

"The Lomechusa group, embracing the palearctic genera *Lomechusa* and *Atemeles* and the nearctic genus *Xenodusa,* contains, from
an ethological point of view, the most interesting and at the same time
the largest of the true ant-guests (symphiles) of the north temperate
region. These Staphylinids, which belong to the subfamily Aleocharinæ, are treated by the ants like their own kith and kin, live in
antennary communication with them, are cleaned and licked and occasionally carried about, and are fed from the mouths of their hosts,
although they are also able to feed independently and frequently devour
the ant brood. The ants are especially attracted to these beetles on
account of the prominent tufts of yellow hairs on the sides of their

abdomen which are licked by the host with evident satisfaction. Not only do these beetles themselves live as guests among the ants, but the same is also true of their larvæ. The larvæ of *Lomechusa* and *Atemeles* are reared by the ants like their own brood; they are licked, fed with regurgitated food and before pupation covered or embedded in

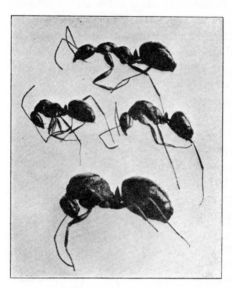

cells like their own larvæ. When the nest is disturbed they are carried by the ants in preference to their own larvæ and pupæ to a place of safety. The predilection of the ants for these adopted larvæ is all the more remarkable because they are the worst enemies of the ant-brood and devour enormous numbers of the eggs and larvæ of their hosts. This brood parasitism, in fact, causes the development of abortive individuals intermediate between the female and worker castes, and these intermediates, which I have called pseudogynes, gradually bring about a degeneration of the parasitized colonies.

FIG. 242. Worker, pseudogynes and deälated queen of *Formica incerta*. (Original.)

" Within the *Lomechusa* group an important ethological difference obtains between *Lomechusa* and *Atemeles,* inasmuch as the former is homœcious, *i. e.,* the species of this genus have each but a single host (a species of *Formica*), in whose company they complete their whole life-cycle; whereas the *Atemeles* are heterœcious, since as adult beetles they live with *Myrmica rubra* and a species of *Formica,* but have their larvæ reared only by the latter. The fact that *Lomechusa* has only a single host explains the more highly developed *passive* character of its symphily. This is shown by the fact that the beetle is more affectionately treated by its normal hosts and is fed, not like an ant, but like an ant-larva. The heterœcious character of the *Atemeles,* which are compelled twice during their life to change their normal hosts, once in the spring when they migrate for reproductive purposes from *Myrmica* to *Formica,* to have their larvæ reared by the latter, and once in the summer when they migrate from *Formica* to *Myrmica* for the purpose of hibernating, enables us to explain the greater *active* perfection of their symphily, their greater initiative towards the ants, and the close imitation of their behavior. The last peculiarity is especially apparent in that they do not, like *Lomechusa, Claviger* and *Amphotis,* beg the ants for food merely by stroking them with their antennæ, but also raise their fore feet after the manner of ants, and stroke the cheeks of the regurgitating hosts [Fig. 240]. On this account they are treated by their normal hosts like ants and not like ant-larvæ."

Five species of *Lomechusa* and a greater number of species and varieties of *Atemeles* have been described. Of these *L. strumosa* (Fig. 238) is the best known. It is exceedingly rare in England, but common in many places on the Continent (Holland, Luxemburg, Saxony, Switzerland). Its normal host is the blood-red slave-maker, *Formica sanguinea,* though very rarely it may be found in the nests of *F. rufa* and *pratensis.* Of the species of *Atemeles, pubicollis* (Fig. 239) breeds in the nests of *F. rufa, paradoxus* in those of *F. rufibarbis* and *emarginatus* in those of *F. fusca.* The American *Xenodusa* is also represented by several species, the best known of which is *X. cava* (Fig. 241). Like *Atemeles,* this beetle has two hosts, but both of these are Camponotine ants. It passes the winter in the nests of *Camponotus pennsylvanicus* or *noveboracensis* and breeds in the early summer in the nests of *Formica* species. I have seen its larvæ in the nest of *F. incerta.* They have longer appendages than *Lomechusa* larvæ and can walk about and beg the ants for food by raising and stroking their cheeks with the anterior pair of feet. Like the larvæ of *Atemeles* and *Lomechusa,* they devour the ant brood.

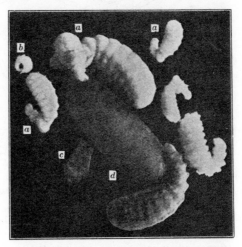

FIG. 243. Larvæ and pupæ of *Pachycondyla harpax* and its commensal *Metopina pachycondylæ.* (Original.) The *Pachycondyla* larvæ marked *a,* have each a *Metopina* larva around the neck; *b,* isolated *Metopina* larva; *c, Metopina* puparium; *d,* cocoon of *Pachycondyla.*

There is evidence that colonies of *incerta* infested with *Xenodusa* tend, like those of *sanguinea* infested with *Lomechusa,* to produce pseudogynes. These queer, mongrel forms (Figs. 57, *b*; 242; 267, *b*) are an abortive combination of the female thorax with the stature, gaster and head of the worker. They are usually paler in color than the normal

workers and very lazy, cowardly and incompetent—" frustrate exist-
ences," as Wasmann appropriately calls them.   Usually they make
up 5–7 per cent., more rarely as much as 20 per cent., of the personnel
of *sanguinea* colonies infested with *Lomechusa*.   In one colony of
incerta, which I found in Connecticut, nearly 80 per cent. of the individuals were pseudogynes.   Wasmann accounts for the development
of these singular beings on the assumption that the ants of colonies,
whose larval broods are being devoured by the *Lomechusa* larvæ,
try to transmute into workers some of the larvæ which have already
developed somewhat along the path terminating in the queen phase.
These efforts result in the production of forms that belong to
neither caste, that is, " outcasts " or pariahs.   Wasmann has also

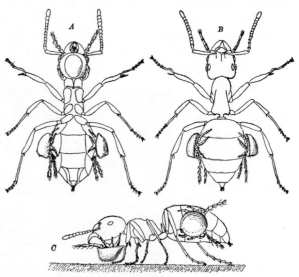

Fig. 244. *Lasius mixtus* worker carrying three *Antennophorus pubescens* in their
        normal positions.   (Janet.)   *A,* Ventral, *B,* dorsal, *C* lateral view.

suggested what seems to me the more probable explanation that
the pseudogynes may arise without any effort at transmutation but
from female larvæ that have been merely neglected and left unfed
after they have passed the stage at which such treatment would
lead to the formation of workers.   Of the two hypotheses the latter
is simpler and accords better with the other known peculiarities of
ant development.   That the pseudogynes are not the result of pathogenic conditions in the egg or mother queen has been proved experimentally by Viehmeyer (1904), who removed an aged *sanguinea* queen
from a colony that for years had been producing pseudogynes, owing

to the presence of *Lomechusa* larvæ, and caused her to be adopted by a new set of unusually healthy workers from an uninfested colony. Under the changed conditions her eggs developed into larvæ that gave rise to perfectly normal workers.

As a rule the pseudogynes make their appearance in *sanguinea* colonies only after these have been infested with *Lomechusa* for several consecutive years and are therefore in an exhausted or moribund condition.   I was impressed with this fact during the summer of 1907, while examining a large number of mostly slaveless *sanguinea* colonies in two separate localities in the Upper Engadin. Nearly all of these colonies contained abundant *Lomechusa* larvæ, but many were, nevertheless, very populous and flourishing and contained no pseudogynes.   These were found only in a few very weak colonies which in some cases contained almost no normal workers. Such colonies, which were nearly all situated in lower and damper ground, represented, in all probability, the wrecks

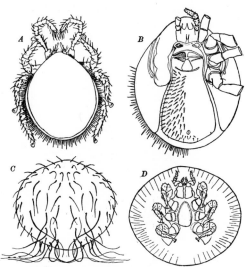

FIG. 245.   Parasitic mites.   (Berlese.)   *A. Echinomegistus wheeleri* (dorsal view), from *Lasius aphidicola; B,* same, ventral view; *C, Cillibano hirticoma* (dorsal view) from *Eciton schmitti; D,* ventral view.

of once opulent communities that had succumbed to the inevitable annual scourge of *Lomechusa.*

This being the effect on the colonies that harbor the *Lomechusa,* one naturally inquires, why the habit of rearing these parasites has not long since led to the extinction of *sanguinea?*   This question has been at least partially answered by Wasmann.   He finds that the ants treat the beetle larvæ like their own, even when the former are ready to pupate, and therefore embed them in the soil.   And this is what the *Lomechusa* require, but they must not be unearthed again after pupation, like the ant brood, or they perish.   The ants, however, are utterly ignorant of these different developmental requirements and therefore unearth as many of the *Lomechusa* pupæ as they can find.   Thus death, in the guise of what might be called a regulatory nemesis, overtakes all except the few pupæ that have been forgotten or overlooked by the ants, but these few are sufficient to insure the survival of *Lomechusa strumosa* in its struggle for existence.

The singular life-histories of the Lomechusinæ and other symphiles have been made the basis of a number of speculations by Wasmann. The fact that the ants actually rear and feed insects that destroy their brood is supposed by him to militate against natural selection, on the ground that this principle can be invoked only to account for the development of characters beneficial to the species. He therefore

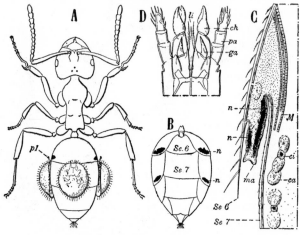

FIG. 246. *Cillibano comata*, parasitic on *Lasius mixtus*. (Janet.) *A, Lasius* worker with three *Cillibano* in their normal position; *p*, antenniform foot of *Cillibano*; *B*, Gaster of *Lasius* slightly compressed to show the black scars, (*n*) left by the mouthparts of the *Cillibano*; *C*, Cross-section of integument around one of the scars; *ma*, articular membrane; *M*, muscle fibres; *ca*, adipocytes; *ci*, intercalary cells; *D*, rostrum of *Cillibano*; *li*, ligula; *ch*, cheliceræ; *pa*, palps; *ga*, acute galea.

believes that the ants themselves act as the selecting agency, not only rearing and feeding the guests, but actually producing, by a kind of unconscious cultivation, such symphilic characters as the trichomes and the peculiar antennal modifications. This he calls "amical selection" and compares it with man's treatment of his domesticated animals and plants. The ants are induced to undertake this selection through the strong appeal which the true guests make to their powerful and obsessional philoprogenitive instincts. The treatment of the *Lomechusa* larvæ shows very clearly that the ants must regard them as their own progeny, whereas the adult beetles make an additional appeal with their trichomes. All this may be granted, but Wasmann goes further and maintains that there is "at least a special modification of the philoprogenitive instincts, a modification which during the course of phylogeny has become differentiated from the more general instincts of this type." He believes that we are justified, therefore, in speaking of " special symphilic instincts," which, from the nature of the definition, would be hereditary. It will be noticed that Wasmann fails to distinguish between the " instinct stimulus," the " instinct action" or objective aspect of instinct and its subjective aspect, the " instinct disposition." Escherich (1898*b et al.*) has repeatedly attacked Wasmann's amical selection hypothesis, on the ground that there is nothing to show that the ants exercise any selective choice among their guests or that there is anything corresponding to " special symphilic instincts." The philoprogenitive instincts are quite sufficient to account for the phenomenon, which is merely a parasitic disease, or instinct aberration, comparable to the rearing of the young cuckoo by its foster parents, or the rearing of puppies by cats, of kittens by hens, etc. In these cases we do not postulate a special hereditary instinct modification, but a simulation of the normal stimulus by an abnormal object. The instinct action is normal, but adapts itself to the changed conditions and there is nothing to indicate that the instinct disposition has undergone any phylogenetic change. Wasmann's contention is disproved, as Escherich has pointed out, by the way in which the ants unearth the *Lomechusa* püpæ.

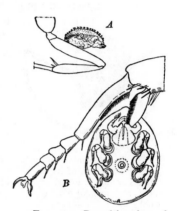

FIG. 247. Parasitic mites of *Lasius mixtus.* (Janet.) *A, Uropoda ovalis* fixed in its normal position by an adhesive uropod to the extensor surface of the middle femora of the *Lasius* worker; *B, Urodiscella philoctena* in its normal position, attached by one of its forelegs to the pectinated spur of the fore tibia of the *Lasius* worker.

In his attempt to substitute amical for natural selection Wasmann also overlooks the fact that ants live in opulence, to use Janet's expression, compared with solitary animals, and are therefore able to support a host of parasites on what may be called their large margin of vitality, without serious danger to the existence of the species. In fact, there is no essential difference between the behavior of *F. sanguinea* towards *Lomechusa* and that of other hosts towards their respective parasites of no matter how extreme a type, for all organisms nourish with their juices the parasites that manage to implant themselves in their tissues, just as the ants feed the *Lomechusa* with regurgitated food. Wasmann's objection would apply not only to all parasites but to all predaceous animals, for in both cases the victimized species exists at the present time only because it has great reproductive powers or a margin of redundant vitality which can be exploited by its enemies and parasites; and the survival of these enemies and parasites themselves in turn depends on their refraining from overstepping this margin. In the case of *sanguinea* the enormous reproductive powers of the species must more than compensate for the destruction of colonies by the *Lomechusa*.

Ectoparasites.—With the Lomechusini we may close our account of the true guests, although these include also several other interesting

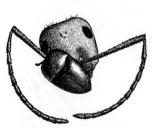

forms, like *Lomechon* among the Silphidæ, *Amorphocephalus* among the Brenthidæ and *Pogonoxenus* among the Tenebrionidæ. Turning to the parasites proper, we find it impossible to draw a hard and fast line between symphiles and ectoparasites, owing to the existence of such intermediate forms as *Thorictus, Antennophorus* and *Orasema*. The group of ectoparasites as a whole is a heterogeneous assemblage of mites, Hymenoptera, Diptera and Coleoptera. The Coleoptera, however, are represented only by certain species of *Thorictus*.

Fig. 248. *Thorictus fo-reli* in its normal position, attached by means of its jaws to the antennal scape of *Myrmecocystus megalocola.* (Original.)

Some of the ectoparasites, of which the Phorid flies of the genus *Metopina* and the Gamasid mites of the genus *Antennophorus* may be taken as interesting examples, are hardly more than commensals. In two papers (1901*e*, 1907*a*) I have described the singular habits of *Metopina pachycondylæ*, which lives in *Pachycondyla harpax* colonies in Texas. Its small larva clings to the necks of the ant-larva by means of a sucker-like posterior end and encircles its host like a collar (Fig. 243). Whenever the ant-larva is fed by the workers with pieces of insect placed on its trough-like ventral surface, within reach of its mouthparts, the larval *Metopina* uncoils its body and partakes of the feast; and when the ant-larva spins its cocoon it also encloses the *Metopina* larva within the silken web. The commensal, however, moves to the caudal end of its host and forms a small, flattened puparium which is applied to the wall of the cocoon. This is obviously an adaptation for preventing injury from the jaws of the worker ants when the cocoon is being opened and the callow extracted from its anterior end. The ant hatches before the *Metopina* and the empty cocoon with the puparium concealed in its posterior pole is carried to the refuse heap. There the fly emerges and escapes from the cocoon by the opening through which its host emerged. The *Metopina* larva consumes so little food and is so considerate of its host, that it can hardly be said to produce any injurious effect on the colony; at any rate, the larvæ which have borne commensals develop into perfectly normal workers. The ants

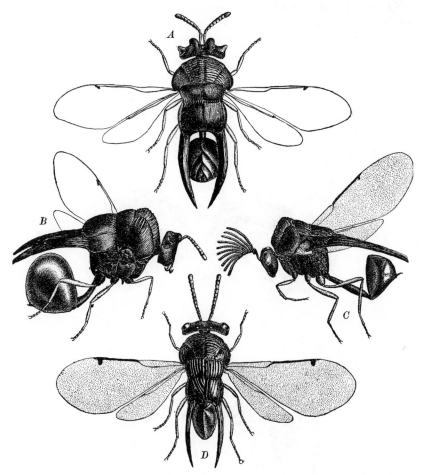

Fig. 249. Chalcidid ant parasites. (Original.) *A, Isomeralia coronata,* female; *B,* lateral view of same; *C, Kapala floridana,* male; *D,* female of same.

clean the commensals while they are cleaning their own progeny and show no signs of even being aware of their presence in the nest.

Another case of commensalism is that of the European *Antennophorus* species (*A. uhlmanni, pubescens, foreli* and *grandis*), studied by Janet (1897*b*), Wasmann (1902*j*) and Karawaiew (1905*c*, 1906*a*). These mites occur only in the nests of *Lasius* and cling to the workers

by means of their three posterior pairs of legs while the large fore pair
is stretched out and moved about like antennæ.   Janet found that these
creatures, whether present in odd or even numbers, are always oriented
in a symmetrical position with respect to their host (Fig. 244).   When
only one *Antennophorus* is present, it clings to the gula, or ventral
surface of the ant's head, with its fore legs directed towards the ant's
mouthparts.   When two are present, there is one on each side of the

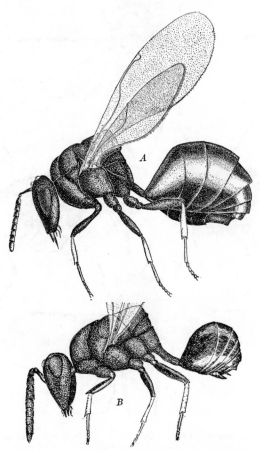

FIG. 250.   *Orasema viridis*.   (Original.)   *A,* Female; *B,* male.

head or one on each side of the gaster; in the former case the antenniform appendages are directed towards the anterior, in the latter towards
the posterior end of the ant's body.   When there are three mites, one
attaches itself to the gula and the two others to the sides of the gaster.
Four place themselves in pairs on the sides of the head and gaster.   If

six are present, which rarely happens, four are arranged in pairs on the sides of the head and gaster, while of the two remaining individuals, one attaches itself to the gula, the other to the mid-dorsal surface of the gaster. Janet believes that these symmetrical arrangements are for the purpose of balancing the burden and thus making it easier for the ants to carry. When attached to the head the mite obtains its food by drinking from the regurgitated droplet as it is being passed to or from

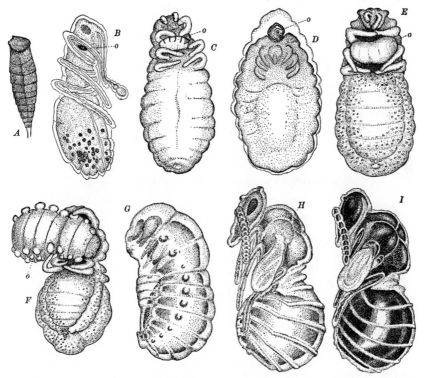

FIG. 251. Development of *Orasema viridis*. (Original.) *A*, First larval stage of *Orasema*. *B*, pupal worker of *Pheidole instabilis* with *Orasema* larva (*o*) attached to side of neck; *C*, female *Pheidole* pupa with somewhat older *Orasema* larva (*o*) attached in sternal region; *D*, female *Pheidole* pupa with *Orasema* larva (*o*) in same stage as in preceding figure, attached behind head; *E*, female *Pheidole* pupa (phthisogyne) with older *Orasema* larva (*o*) in sternal region; *F*, *Orasema* larva (*o*) beginning to pupate, with vesiculate knobs on its surface; *G*, *Orasema* pupa fallen from its host and developing within the vesiculate skin; *H*, fully formed pupa; *I*, pupa pigmented and ready to hatch.

the mouthparts of the host, or it titillates the ant with its antenniform legs and induces her to regurgitate for its special benefit. The mites attached to the gaster obtain their food by stroking other ants in the vicinity or by reaching out and partaking of the droplets as they pass

from one ant to another. The ants try to rid themselves of the parasites when these first attach themselves, but after they have taken up
their definitive, symmetrical positions, they seem to be tolerated with
indifference. There is nothing to indicate that the ants, while cleaning
one another, are even aware of the existence of the parasites. The
relations of the allied American ectoparasitic mites to their host ants
have not yet been studied. *Echinomegistus wheeleri* (Fig. 245, *A* and
B), which occurs on *Lasius aphidicola,* is probably very similar to
Antennophorus in its habits.[1]

The number of mites living in the nests or on the surfaces of ants
seems to be very great. Berlese, in a recent work (1904) has described
more than sixty species of myrmecophilous Gamasidæ alone. The
habits of a few of these have been studied by Janet and Wasmann and
may be very briefly described. *Cillibano* [*Discopoma*] *comata* is a
peculiar tortoise-shaped mite which attaches itself to the workers of
Lasius mixtus and its larvæ (Fig. 246). On the ants it always assumes
a definite position. According to Janet, when only one is present, it
places itself on the side of the second gastric segment. If there are
two, they place themselves symmetrically, one on each side. If there is

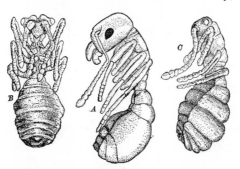

a third, it is attached in the
mid-dorsal line of the same
segment. Rarely as many
as six may be present; in
which case there are three
also on the third gastric
segment in positions cor-
responding to those on the
second. The ants dislike
the *Cillibano* and tear them
to pieces whenever they
can seize them. The mites,
however, usually slip out
of their mandibles or apply

FIG. 252. *A,* Normal pupa of *Pheidole instabilis* worker; *B,* and *C,* phthisergates, produced by parasitism of *Orasema viridis* larvæ on
the larvæ of the same ant. (Original.)

the edges of their bodies so closely to the surfaces of the ants that they
cannot be picked off. From scars (Fig. 246, *B, C, n*) left on the intersegmental membranes of the ant's gaster Janet infers that the *Cillibano*
sucks the blood of its host. The types of another *Cillibano* (*C. hirticoma*), with long, flexuous dorsal hairs, were found by me in Texas on
an *Eciton schmitti* queen (Figs. 147, *c*; 245, *C, D*). This mite attaches
itself not only to the body, but also to the antennæ and legs of its host.

[1] I have recently found an undescribed species of *Antennophorus* on our
North American *Acanthomyops interjectus.*

Janet calls attention to two other Gamasids, *Uropoda ovalis* (Fig. 247, *A*) and *Urodiscella philoctena* (Fig. 247, *B*). The former attaches itself by means of a glue-like secretion to the legs of ants, the latter clings to the comb of the strigil by means of one of its fore legs. This species evidently feeds on the dirt which is scraped by the ant from its body and appendages. A similar mite is sometimes found attached to the spurs on the legs of our American carpenter ant (*Camponotus pennsylvanicus*). Still another Gamasid, *Oölælaps oöphilus,* has been described by Wasmann. It is found on the eggs and packets of very young larvæ of *Formica sanguinea* and *rufibarbis* and lives on the salivary secretion with which the ants coat their young progeny. Many of the mites found attached to adult ants probably feed on the same substance.

Wasmann (1897e) has also published some observations on a Sarcoptid mite (*Tyroglyphus wasmanni*) which lives in the nests of *F. sanguinea* and, in the adult, nymphal and larval forms, feeds on dead ants. At times, however, its hypopi become exceedingly numerous and cover the bodies of the living ants in masses. These hypopi always orient themselves with their heads towards the distal end of the appendage or part of the body on which they are resting. They seem to take no nourishment, but their great numbers impede the ants' movements and eventually kill them.

Some of the beetles of the family Thorictidæ, comprising the single genus *Thorictus* of the Mediterranean region, must also be included among the ectoparasites, if we accept Wasmann's account of their habits (1898a, 1898b). These are small, subtriangular, reddish brown creatures, with tufts of golden trichomes at the posterolateral corners of the prothorax. Several of the species, like the myrmecophilous Histeridæ, seem to live on dead ants, but others (*T. foreli* and *pauciseta*) are regularly found, as Forel (1894a) first observed, attached by means of their bidentate mandibles to the antennal scapes of *Myrmecocystus* workers. The host of *T. foreli* is *M. megalocola,* that of *pauciseta, M. desertorum.* The prothorax of the beetle is provided with a groove or depression to fit the scape, towards the distal end of which the beetle's head is always directed (Fig. 248). In this position the insect may remain for weeks in spite of all the efforts of the ant to dislodge it. Escherich (1898c) found that the beetle is frequently licked and that it sometimes attaches itself to the legs as well as to the antennæ. Wasmann maintains that it punctures the scape and sucks the blood of the ant and that *Thorictus* is therefore both an ectoparasite and a symphile. Other species of the genus seem not to have this habit of clinging to the ants. Mr. Walter Granger brought me from the Fayum several specimens of *Thorictus castaneus* which he found free in the chambers of a *Myrmecocystus bombycinus* nest. These have much larger trichomes than either *foreli* or *pauciseta* and lack the peculiar prothoracic depression.

It has been found that certain groups of Chalcidid Hymenoptera, notably the Eucharinæ, contain a number of very interesting ant-parasites, which are often brilliantly metallic and have bizarre forms. The first of these (*Eucharis myrmeciæ*) was discovered in the cocoon of a bull-dog ant (*Myrmecia forficata*) by Forel (1890a), who believed it to be an entoparasite. Cameron (1891) described another species (*Chalcura bedeli*) from the nests of the Algerian *Myrmecocystus viaticus,* and more recently (1907a) I have shown that species of several other Eucharine genera (*Orasema, Pseudochalcura, Kapala, Isomeralia, Pseudometagia*) are ant-parasites (Figs. 249 and 250). The life history of only one of the species, *Orasema viridis*, is at all adequately known (Fig. 251). This is a brilliant metallic blue and green fly which lives in the nests of several Texan and Mexican *Pheidole,* especially *Ph. instabilis.* The young larva is somewhat thysanuriform and attaches itself to the neck of the ant-larva, sucking out its juices and in the course of a few days undergoing several ecdyses, pupating and hatching, without necessarily withdrawing sufficient substance from the ant-larva to prevent its pupating in turn. But such larvæ have nevertheless lost much of the material which in uninfested individuals goes to form the head, thorax and eyes of the adult, so that these parts are very poorly developed in the pupæ. These pupæ, which I have called phthisergates (Fig. 252, *B* and *C*), phthisogynes and phthisaners, according as they arise from depleted worker, female or male larvæ, never hatch. Both the larval and adult *Orasema* are effusively licked and fondled, and the latter are even fed by the *Pheidole* workers. The Chalcidids, however, have no affection for the ants, but endeavor to leave the nest at the earliest possible moment in order to mate in the open fields. Another *Orasema* (*O. coloradensis*) leads a similar life in the nests of *Solenopsis validiuscula* and *Ph. vinelandica* in Colorado, and a third species (*O. wheeleri*) was found in the nests of *Ph. ceres* in western Texas. I have also found the pupæ of *Pseudochalcura gibbosa* in the cocoons of *Camponotus noveboracensis,* together with remains of the ant-pupæ, showing that the eggs and young larval Chalcidids must attach themselves to mature *Camponotus* larvæ ready and able to spin their cocoons. Two to four of the *Pseudochalcura* pupæ sometimes occur in a single cocoon. For further details concerning the parasitic Chalcidids, the Lomechusini and several other myrmecophiles the reader is referred to my paper on the " Polymorphism of Ants " (1907*a*).

The Entoparasites.—These constitute an even more diversified assemblage of forms than the ectoparasites. The only entoparasitic Coleopteron, however, is the Stylopid *Myrmecolax nietneri,* described by Westwood (1861) from the gaster of a Ceylonese ant. The habits of this beetle probably resemble those of the species of *Stylops* and *Xenos* which develop in the abdomens of bees and wasps. Among the remaining entoparasites may be mentioned certain Diptera, Hymenoptera and Nemathelminthes.

The Diptera are represented by several Phoridæ and the Conopid genus *Stylogaster.* The Phorid *Apocephalus pergandei,* according to Fox (1887) and Pergande (1900), lays its eggs on the heads of *Camponotus pennsylvanicus* workers. The larvæ hatching from these eggs enter the cranial capsule through the occipital foramen and feed on the tissues, causing the ant to become very lethargic. Later the creature literally loses its head, and the larvæ pupate and hatch. Pergande has described the frantic efforts of the ants to rid themselves of these terrible executioners. Coquillet (1907) has recently described another Phorid, *Plastophora crawfordi,* which was taken in the act of ovipositing on the head of a *Solenopsis geminata* in Texas. I have already alluded to the various peculiar Phorids with wingless females (p. 383). They, too, may be entoparasitic in their larval stages, but as there is no evidence of such habits, I have placed them among the synœketes.

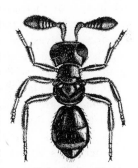

Fig. 253. *Pheidoloxenus wheeleri* from the nests of *Pheidole instabilis.* (Original.)

As the Conopidæ are known to be parasitic in the bodies of adult bees and wasps, it is not surprising to find that some of these flies also attack ants. Bates (1893) observed species of the genus *Stylogaster* hovering over *Eciton* armies in Brazil, and Townsend (1897) captured numbers of three species of the same genus in Mexico, while they were following an army of *Eciton foreli.* There can be little doubt that they lay their eggs on the bodies of the ants and that the larvæ are entoparasitic.

Among the entoparasites is also to be included a number of minute Hymenoptera of the families Braconidæ, Chalcididæ and Proctotrupidæ. The best known of these is the Braconid *Elasmosoma berolinense,* which has been seen by Giraud (1871), Forel (1874), Pierre (1893), Olivier (1893), and Wasmann (1894*g*) ovipositing on the bodies of *Formica, Camponotus* and *Lasius*. The larva of the parasite develops in the ant's gaster.[1] Wasmann (1899) has described and figured two interesting European Proctotrupids, *Solenopsia imitatrix*, from the nests of *Solenopsis fugax*, and *Tetramopria aurocincta*, from those of *Tetramorium cespitum*. *Solenopsia* seems to mimic the *Solenopsis workers* and *Tetramopria* is provided with golden trichomes and for this reason is regarded by Wasmann as a true guest. Ashmead (1893) enumerates among American Bethylids four species of *Pseudisobrachium* (*mandibulare, montanum, myrmecophilum* and *rufiventre*) as living in the nests of *Formica* and *Camponotus*. An exquisite, subapterous, purple, green and gold Asaphine Chalcidid, *Pheidoloxenus wheeleri* (Fig. 253), which lives in the nests of *Pheidole instabilis*, is probably also entoparasitic on the ants or their progeny during its larval stages.

Finally, we come to a number of extraordinary round worms which live in ants or their larvæ. Janet (1893e, 1897e) and de Man (1894) have described several Nematodes from the bodies of worker ants. The former investigator saw some of these worms, several centimeters long, issue from the orifice of the labial glands of *Formica fusca,* and he and de Man described another form, *Pelodera janeti,* which lives in the pharyngeal glands of *Lasius* and *Formica*. "Within these glands the *Pelodera* are bathed in a yellow liquid on which they feed. They complete a larval stage in the glands and then escape from them to live a free life on the detritus of the nest. There they give rise to a series of generations whose larvæ are distinctly different from those living in the heads of the ants and develop without entering the insects." Other Nematodes belonging to the family Anguillulidæ have been seen in ants' nests, but nothing is known concerning their habits and development. The Gordiids are represented by *Gordius formicarum,* which von Siebold took from the gaster of an ant, and by *Mermis,* the larvæ of which live in the crops of the larval, pupal and adult workers of several different neotropical Formicidæ and produce a great distension of the gaster in the imaginal instar. I first observed these parasites in the Texan *Pheidole commutata* (1901d, 1907a). They enter the larva and apparently by unduly stimulating its appetite cause it to be fed excessively, so that it becomes unusually large at the time of pupation and produces a gigantic worker form, with ocelli (Fig. 254, *B* and *C*). This form, which I have called the mermithergate, was first seen by Emery (1890d) in the Costa Rican *Pheidole absurda,* but he supposed

---

[1] Cockerell ("A New Braconid of the Genus Elasmosoma," *Proc. Ent. Soc. Washington,* 10, 1908, pp. 168, 169) has recently described a species of *Elasmosoma* (*E. vigilans*) parasitic on *Formica subpolita* in Colorado.

it to be an egg-laying "parthenogenetic female." Since the publication
of my paper (1901*d*) he has reëxamined this specimen and several other
worker ants with larger gasters and traces of ocelli in his collection and
has found them to contain *Mermis*. Besides the two species already
mentioned, he has recorded the occurrence of mermithergates in *Odontomachus hæmatodes* and *chelifer, Neoponera inversa, Ectatomma
tuberculatum, Pachycondyla fuscoatra* and *Paraponera clavata*. These
pathological forms therefore occur rather generally, at least in the
neotropical Myrmicinæ and Ponerinæ.

It is interesting to compare the modifications induced in their
respective hosts by the parasites *Orasema, Mermis* and *Lomechusa*.

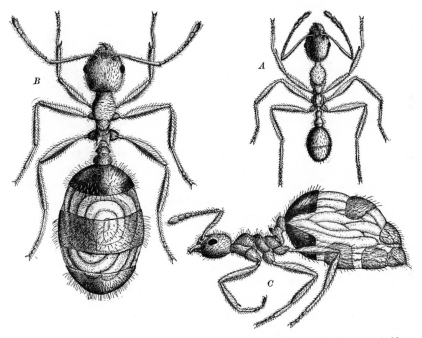

Fɪɢ. 254. Parasitism of *Mermis* in *Pheidole commutata*. (Original.) *A;* Normal worker of *Pheidole commutata; B,* mermithergate, or worker containing *Mermis*
parasite which it possessed as a larva; *C,* same, lateral view.

While the effects in all three cases are wrought through a withdrawal
of nourishment from the developing larvæ, each of the parasites adopts
a different method. Thus the ectoparasitic *Orasema* larva extracts
important juices from the body of the *Pheidole* larva directly and with
great rapidity, thereby reducing its host to a mere skin, which, though
still able to pass on to the pupal stage, no longer possesses sufficient
substance or vitality to reach the imaginal stage. The *Mermis* larva

develops much more slowly within the alimentary tract of the ant larva and appropriates a portion of the food before it has been assimilated. Finally, the *Lomechusa* within the *Formica* nest leads to a withholding of the necessary food from the larvæ, or, if Wasmann's view be adopted, at least to a withholding of the proper kind of food. And the results of these different methods of direct and indirect vampirism are the phthisergate, the mermithergate and the pseudogyne, respectively.

In concluding this chapter brief mention must be made of two other categories of animals which have ethological relations to the ants, namely, the myrmecophags and myrmecoids. The myrmecophags merely prey on the ants without showing any desire to live in their nests. To this group belong several spiders (*Theridion*), the ant-lions (*Myrmeleon*), the peculiar larvæ of the Dipteron *Lampromyia miki,* which in the north African deserts entraps ants in pits like those of the ant-lions, certain solitary wasps (Crabronidæ), some amphibians (toads), reptiles (lizards, amphisbænians), birds (woodpeckers, ant-thrushes) and mammals (ant-eaters). The Doryline and slave-making ants regularly eat the larvæ and pupæ of other ants, and even man himself in some parts of the world is myrmecophagous.

The myrmecoids are the ant-mimics and are therefore hard to distinguish from the myrmecophiles. They comprise a great many arthropods, especially jumping spiders (*Synemosyna, Synageles,* etc.), Heteroptera (*Alydus calcaratus, Nabis lativentris,* etc.), wasps and tiger beetles. Some of these insects may be at the same time myrmecophags or myrmecophiles, and their striking resemblance to ants may aid them in approaching their prey. Among the celebrated cases of myrmecoidy may be mentioned the Sudanese cricket *Myrmecophana fallax,* which is extremely ant-like, and the Indian wasp *Rhinopsis ruficornis,* which closely mimics *Sima rufonigra.* The striking resemblance of some of our longicorn beetles of the genera *Clytanthus, Euderces, Cyrtophorus* and *Tillomorpha* to ants must have been noticed by every collector. Mr. Wm. Beutenmüller informs me that a black longicorn, *Michthysoma heterodoxum* of North Carolina, mimics the workers of *Camponotus pennsylvanicus* to an extraordinary degree. Forel and Emery have pointed out certain cases of mimicry among the ants themselves, for example, *Dolichoderus 4-notatus, Colobopsis truncata* and *Camponotus lateralis,* the workers of which are all very similar in color and behavior and are often found running on the same tree. Whether these and many other cases of myrmecoidy are anything more than accidental resemblances remains to be seen.

CHAPTER XXIII

THE COMPOUND NESTS

"Le but unique de tous les actes comme de toutes les représentations des insectes sociaux, c'est l' élevage des jeunes; mais si le but est unique, les moyens sont nombreux."—Espinas, "Des Sociétés Animales," 1877.

In several of the foregoing chapters I have discussed the ethological relations of ants to a variety of other organisms—flowering plants, fungi, Homoptera, caterpillars and a host of other arthropods belonging to the most diverse natural orders. These chapters, however, did not include an account of some of the most interesting symbiotic relations, namely, those of the ants to other species of their own taxonomic group and to termites. This living together of colonies of different species may be properly designated as social symbiosis to distinguish it from the simple symbiosis that obtains between individual organisms of different species and the intermediate form of symbiosis exhibited by individual organisms, like the myrmecophiles and termitophiles that live in ant or termite colonies.

The researches of the past forty years have brought to light a remarkable array of instances of social symbiosis, varying so much in intimacy and complexity that it is possible to construct a series ranging from mere simultaneous occupancy of a very narrow ethological station, or mere contiguity of domicile, to an actual fusion, involving the vital dependence or parasitism of a colony of one species on that of another. Such a series is, of course, purely conceptual and does not represent the actual course of development in nature, where, as in the animal and vegetable kingdoms in general, development has not followed a simple linear course, but has branched out repeatedly and terminated in the varied types existing at the present time.

It is convenient to follow the European writers, von Hagens, Forel, Wasmann and others, in grouping all the cases of social symbiosis under two heads, the compound nests and the mixed colonies. Different species of ants or of ants and termites are said to form compound nests when their galleries are merely contiguous or actually interpenetrate and open into one another, although the colonies which inhabit them bring up their respective offspring in different apartments. In mixed colonies, on the other hand, which, in a state of nature, can be formed only by species of ants of close taxonomic affinities, the insects live together in a single nest and bring up their young in common. Although each of these categories comprises a number of dissimilar types of social symbiosis, and although it is possible, under certain circumstances, as will be shown in the sequel, to convert a compound nest into a mixed colony, the distinction is nevertheless fundamental. It must be admitted, however, that both types depend in last analysis on the dependent, adoption-seeking instincts of the queen ant and on the remarkable plasticity which enables allied species and genera to live in very close proximity to one another. By a strange paradox these peculiarities have been produced in the struggle for existence, although this struggle is severer among different species of ants than between ants and other organisms. As Forel says: " The greatest enemies of ants are other ants, just as the greatest enemies of men are other men." And just as the *homo homini lupus* may wear many a pleasing disguise, so the *formica formicæ lupa* may secure the aid or protection of another species of ant by exhibiting an engaging demeanor. This will be more apparent when we come to the cases of the mixed colonies. In the present chapter my remarks will be confined to the compound nests, with a brief consideration of the various known cases.

A. Plesiobiosis.—I have given this name (1901c) to the cases in which two or more colonies of different species of ants or of ants and termites establish their nests in contiguity or very close proximity, as often happens under the same stone. These are the double, triple, etc., nests of Forel (1874) and represent the most rudimental form of social symbiosis. The species nesting in this manner are either indifferent or hostile to one another, as may be readily observed by their behavior when the stone is removed and the walls between the nests broken asunder so that the insects can meet face to face, or one of the species is timid or hypogæic in its habits. Two or more aggressive species can hardly live under the same stone, as their nest entrances would be necessarily so close together that the insects would be apt to encounter one another continually while entering or leaving the nest. I have never found two well-developed colonies of the same species under the same stone. Indeed, such a condition could hardly be maintained for any length of time, since the colonies would in all probability either become friendly and fuse into one, or would fight till one was compelled to seek quarters elsewhere. The fact that different species are able to live in plesiobiosis is probably due to differences of habit of sufficient magnitude to diminish or temper somewhat the struggle for existence.

B. Parabiosis.—This term was introduced by Forel (1898b) to designate a peculiar type of compound nest with inosculating galleries in which two different Colombian ants (*Cremastogaster parabiotica* and *Dolichoderus debilis*) were living together amicably, though keeping their broods separate. The workers were seen leaving the nest in a common file, which, however, eventually bifurcated, each species proceeding to its own feeding ground. This case, as Forel remarks, bears some resemblance to the joint flocks of certain birds, like those of the European *Corvus cornix* and *C. corone*. Under the term parabiosis may also be included the friendly or indifferent relations existing between certain species of ants which I found inhabiting the epiphytic

Fig. 255. Mound of *Pogonomyrmex occidentalis* showing at (*a*) a crater of *Dorymyrmex pyramicus*. (Original.)

Tillandsias (especially *T. benthamiana*) on trees in Mexico, Florida and the West Indies. These plants often contain whole colonies of ants, with their larvæ and pupæ snugly packed away like so many anchovies in the spaces between the moist, overlapping leaves. The ants gnaw little holes through the leaves to serve as entrances to the interfoliar chambers, and these holes often perforate several leaves and extend to the very core of the bud-like plant. Sometimes a single colony is divided up into companies, each occupying the space under a leaf, but not infrequently two or even three flourishing colonies of as many species may live in a single *Tillandsia,* the whole habitable por-

tion of which is rarely more than 5–8 cm. long and 4 cm. in diameter.
Sometimes these colonies are curiously intermingled in such a manner
that though there is no actual blending and the space under a single
leaf is always occupied by ants of the same species, nevertheless the
whole colony or portions of a single colony may be completely surrounded by leaf spaces occupied by another colony.   The *Tillandsia*
ants, of which I have observed more than a dozen species (*Pseudomyrma elongata* and *flavidula, Monomorium floricola, Xenomyrmex
lucayanus, Cremastogaster minutior* and *steinheili, Leptothorax petio-
latus, Cryptocerus aztecus, varians* and *wheeleri, Tapinoma littorale,
Camponotus planatus, rubroniger* and *inæqualis*) are mostly small and
of a conciliatory or timid disposition.   These various species, however,
like *Dolichoderus debilis* and *Cremastogaster parabiotica,* frequently live
in independent nests in twigs, under bark, etc.

C. Cleptobiosis.—Forel (1901*b*) suggests that this term be restricted
to those cases in which small ants establish their nests near or on the

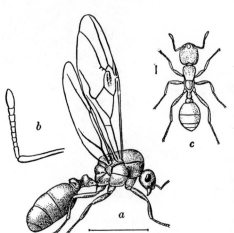

nests of larger species and
either feed on the refuse food
or waylay the workers when
they return to their home and
compel them to give up their
booty.   Certain Dolichoderine
ants, like *Tapinoma erraticum, Iridomyrmex analis,
Forelius maccooki* and *Dorymyrmex pyramicus,* appear
to have developed habits of
this kind. Wroughton (1891)
has seen an Indian ant (*Cremastogaster*) " lie in wait for
Holcomyrmex, returning
home, laden with grain, and

FIG. 256. *Carebara lignata* of the Indomalayan Region. (Bingham.) *a,* Female; *b,*
antenna of same; *c,* worker.

by threats, rob her of her
load, on her own private road
and this manœuvre was executed, not by stray individuals, but by
a considerable portion of the whole community."   In the West
and Southwest *Dorymyrmex,* as McCook (1879*c*) and I have observed, often builds its little craters within the bare clearings or
even on the nest cones of *Pogonomyrmex molefaciens* and *occidentalis* and is not molested by these harvesters (Fig. 255).   *Dorymyrmex* is a very agile and pugnacious little ant with a rank *Tapinoma*
odor.   It probably feeds on the remains of insects brought in by the

Pogonomyrmex. It is possible, however, as I have suggested (1901*c*), that both *Dorymyrmex* and *Forelius* merely nest in the *Pogonomyrmex* clearings because they prefer barren, sunny spots.

D. Lestobiosis.—Forel (1901*b*) has given this name to an extensive group of forms, the "thief ants," which I formerly included under cleptobiosis. At least the workers of these ants are of very small size and nest in the earthen walls separating the roomy galleries and chambers of termites and other larger ants. The lestobiotic species, most of which belong to the Myrmicine tribe Solenopsidii, comprise the following:

1. *Pheidole calens,* a small granivorous ant which nests on the mounds of *Pogonomyrmex barbatus* in Mexico, and probably helps itself to the seeds stored up by this ant in the flat, superficial chambers of its nest.

2. *Solenopsis fugax* of Europe, the African *S. orbula* and *latro,* the North American *S. molesta* and *texana,* and probably also many of the South American members of the genus. The workers of these ants are all very small and yellow, with vestigial eyes and are decidedly hypogæic in their habits. They often, but by no means always, live in the gallery walls of other and much larger ants. When this is the case, the passages occupied by the *Solenopsis* communicate with the apartments of the other species and are too tenuous to admit the workers of the latter. These do not appear to notice the little thieves which move about freely in the galleries and chambers and kill and eat their helpless larvæ and pupæ, as Forel (1869, 1874), Wasmann (1891*h*), and especially Janet (1897*e*), have observed in *S. fugax.* Our American *molesta* has very similar habits, but is often found leading an independent existence. It is also sometimes a pest in kitchens and is known to eat dead insects and the sprouting kernels of maize (Forbes).

3. *Diplomorium longipenne.*—Workers of this ant, which are small and yellow like those of *Solenopsis,* were sent me by Dr. Hans Brauns, who took them in Cape Colony in nests of a pale variety of *Messor barbarus.* These specimens were labelled "thief ants," and probably lived with the *Messor* in the same manner as *Solenopsis* lives with species of *Formica* and other genera.

4. *Carebara vidua, lignata,* etc.—These ants, which occur only in the African and Oriental regions, have minute, yellow, small-eyed workers like *Solenopsis,* but their males and females are gigantic and dark-colored, and have well-developed eyes and ocelli (Fig. 256). *Carebara vidua* was found by Haviland (Forel, 1901) nesting in the hills of *Termes natalensis.* There can be little doubt that the workers feed on the termites or their young and on account of their diminutive

size or neutral odor can move about unnoticed among their soft-bodied hosts.

5. The following species are closely allied to *Solenopsis* and *Carebara* and in all probability enter into similar ethological relations to various species of termites: *Erebomyrma longi* (Fig. 257) of Texas and *peruviana* of Peru; *Carebarella bicolor* and the species of *Trano-*

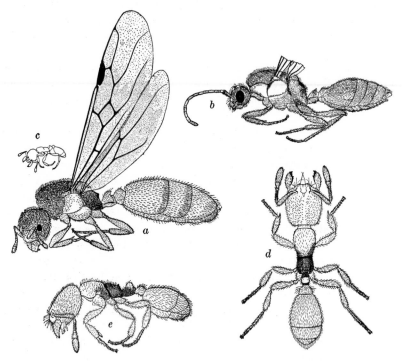

FIG. 257. *Erebomyrma longi.* (Original.) *a*, Female; *b*, male; *c*, worker drawn to same scale as male and female; *d*, worker enlarged, dorsal view; *e*, same, lateral view.

pelta of South America; the species of *Oligomyrmex* of India and Australia, and *Aëromyrma nossindambo* of Madagascar. The following, mainly Brazilian species, have also been recorded as living in termite nests: *Monomorium termitobium, heyeri* and *decamerum, Cremastogaster alegrensis* and *quadriformis, Pheidole termitobia, Tapinoma heyeri* and *Brachymyrmex termitophilus.* In the United States *Pheidole lamia* (Fig. 258) and the various species of *Strumigenys* often live, apparently as thief-ants, in the nests of other Formicidæ.

The tribe Solenopsidii, to which belong the above mentioned species of *Diplomorium, Carebara, Erebomyrma, Carebarella, Tranopelta, Oli-*

gomyrmex, Aëromyrma and *Solenopsis,* have two peculiarities which have been interpreted by Forel as the result of lestobiosis, namely, the diminutive size and hypogæic habits of the workers and the huge size of the males, and especially of the females. The remarkable dimorphism of the female sex, which reaches its extremest development in *Carebara,* the fertile female of which is more than a thousand times as large as the sterile female, or worker, is easily accounted for by the peculiar habits. The workers are compelled to remain dwarfs in order to move about unperceived among their hosts and pass through the

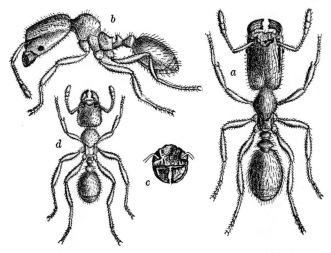

Fig. 258. *Pheidole lamia.* (Original.) *a,* Soldier; *b,* same in profile; *c,* head of same from front; *d,* worker.

slender galleries to and from their own nests. This subterranean habit is also responsible for their pale color and the vestigial condition of their eyes. At the same time these anæmic pygmies are able to rear such gigantic males and females because the larvæ and pupæ of their hosts furnish an abundant supply of highly nutritious food. The sexual forms retain their deep pigmentation and large eyes because they mate in the sunlight like the corresponding phases of most other ants.

E. **Phylacobiosis.**—This term is applied by Wasmann (1901–'02) to the relations supposed to exist between the Brazilian *Camponotus termitarius* and *Eutermes fulviceps, Anoplotermes ater* and *morio.* The *Camponotus* is said to nest only in the hills of these termites and as it seems to be on friendly terms with them, Wasmann is of the opinion that it acts as a guard or protection ("eine Art Schutztruppe "). This case, however, like many of the other compound nests, is in need of further investigation.   It is quite probable that *C. termitarius* may be carnivorous and represent merely an additional case of lestobiosis.

F. Xenobiosis.—I have given this name to certain types of compound nests in which the relations between ants of two different species are of a very definite and intimate character.   In these cases one of the species, known as the inquiline, or " guest ant," can live only in association with a host, and unlike several of the species included under the preceding captions, is never found living alone.   Although the guest ants live with their hosts on terms of mutual toleration or even friendship, each species rears its brood in chambers of its own excavation. In midsummer, however, when these broods mature, individuals of all three phases of both species are found intermingled, moving about in the chambers of the host and freely consorting with one another.   This condition is rarely seen in any other forms of social symbiosis, for in the mixed colonies, to be considered in the following chapters, the sexual phases of the host species are, in nearly all cases, suppressed.

1. *Formicoxenus nitidulus* (Fig. 259).—The habits of this small,

FIG. 259. *Formicoxenus nitidulus.* (Original.)   *a*, Worker; *b*, ergatomorphic male.

slender, shining, yellowish-red ant, which much resembles certain species of *Leptothorax,* have been described by Adlerz (1884), Forel (1874, 1886*d*), Wasmann (1891*h*) and Janet (1897*e*).   It is a sub-boreal species and nests only in the interior of the great débris mounds of *Formica rufa* and *F. pratensis.*   Here it excavates small chambers which communicate by means of slender passages with the galleries and chambers of its much larger hosts.   Wasmann found a colony of *Formicoxenus* inhabiting the cavity of an old cocoon of *Cetonia floricola,* a chafer which passes its larval and pupal stages at the bottom of *rufa* nests. The guest-ant moves about freely among its host who treats it with indifference. Some observers have occasionally noticed slight indications of hostility between the two species. When the *rufa* moves to a new nest the *Formicoxeni* follow in the files of the host, carrying one another and their brood. None of the authors above mentioned, notwithstanding the closest observations, has been able to detect any other relations between the inquiline and its host. The *rufa* are never seen to feed the inquilines, and the latter have never been seen to eat the progeny of their host or the dead insects brought into the nest, so that the nature of their food remains an enigma.

Formicoxenus nitidulus is, moreover, an interesting species, because the male, discovered by Adlerz in 1884, is wingless and highly ergatomorphic. It can be distinguished from the worker only by the more curved antennal funiculi and their additional joint, the presence of stemmata (which, however, occur also in some workers), the additional gastric segment and the genital appendages; the eyes, head, thorax and legs are remarkably like those of the worker. The wingless condition of this male makes a nuptial flight impossible, of course, so that mating has to take place on the surface of the *Formica* nest or on the ground and stones in the neighborhood. The mating has been seen by several European observers, and during July, 1907, I had an opportunity to witness it near Samaden, on the slopes of Piz Ot, at an altitude of about 2,000 m. in the Upper Engadin. After a cold night, the sun remained behind a mass of clouds at about 9 A. M. when I saw dozens of *Formicoxeni* of all three phases, but mostly males, running hither and thither over the small twigs and other débris forming the outer covering of an old *rufa* nest which I had stopped to examine. The males moved very quickly, with feverishly vibrating antennæ, and were so amorous that they often seized workers and attempted to mate with them. The few winged females were soon supplied with partners and the supernumerary males continued to hurry about over and among the little sticks of the nest. Then the sun suddenly emerged from the clouds and, as if by magic, all the *Formicoxeni* disappeared into the nest. I waited for some time and during the remainder of the morning returned repeatedly to the spot, but none of the tiny inquilines reappeared.

2. *Formicoxenus ravouxi and corsicus.*—These two species are known only from female specimens. The former was taken in France by Ern. André (1893*a*) in a nest of *Leptothorax unifasciatus*. The host of the latter species is unknown.

3. *Xenomyrmex stolli.*—Forel (1884*b*) described this small, shining, dark-brown ant, which is allied to *Monomorium,* from some specimens found in Guatemala, living in a huge oak-gall in company with a much

larger ant, *Camponotus abscisus.* More recently Emery (1893–'94) has
described a subspecies of *stolli* as *floridanus,* from specimens taken by
Pergande in Florida from a hollow twig of *Sideroxylon,* and I have
described (1905*b*) a variety, *lucayanus,* taken in a *Tillandsia* in the
Bahamas. As both of these forms were living in independent formicaries, it is not improbable that the typical *stolli* was merely living in
plesio- or parabiosis with the *Camponotus.*

4. *Phacota sicheli* and *noualhieri.*—The former species was described by Roger (1862*b*) from a single worker taken in Andalusia,
the latter by Emery (1895*j*) from a single worker taken in a nest of the
Algerian *Monomorium subnitidum.* Nothing is known of the habits
of these two species of *Phacota,* so that their position here is purely
conjectural.

5. *Myrmoxenus gordiagini* is a small ant recently discovered by
Ruzsky (1902, 1905) living in the Kirghis steppes in nests of *Leptothorax serviculus.* This is probably a case of xenobiosis, but nothing
definite seems to be known concerning the relations of the two species.

6. *Sifolinia lauræ.*—This ant, recently described by Emery (1907)
from a female specimen taken in Italy, is structurally related to *Formicoxenus, Myrmoxenus* and *Harpagoxenus,* and is, therefore, in all
probability, a parasitic or xenobiotic insect. Its host is unknown.

7. *Myrmica myrmoxena.*—Many years ago (1874) Forel described
a singular diminutive male and female as aberrant forms of *Myrmica
levinodis,* since they were taken in a nest of this species by Bugnion at
an altitude of about 2,000 m. in Switzerland. Although no one has
since found these small forms, Forel now regards them as types of a
distinct species (*M. myrmoxena*), probably living in xenobiosis with
the closely allied *levinodis.*

8. *Symmyrmica chamberlini* (Fig. 260).—This interesting little ant
is allied to *Formicoxenus* in all three phases, especially in the male, which
is ergatoid (Wheeler, 1904*b*). This sex, however, is much less worker-
like in the structure of the head and thorax than the male of the European inquiline. The workers often have stemmata. The only specimens I have seen were sent me by Mr. F. V. Chamberlin, who found
them in Utah living in nests of *Myrmica mutica.* The following note,
which accompanied the specimens, leaves little doubt that the relations
of the *Symmyrmica* to its host are similar to those of *Formicoxenus*
to *Formica rufa:* "Nests of *Myrmica mutica* are common in some
localities near Salt Lake City over the flood-plains of the Jordan River.
The soil where they occur oftenest is prevailingly argillaceous and
sometimes contains much 'alkali.' I have not found them in stony or
gravelly ground. All the nests observed opened free from any cover,

and not a few were seen in the middle of foot-paths, although they prefer loose soil.   In several parts of a ten-acre field where the soil is of the usual character, I found nests of this *Myrmica* containing the symbiotic species.   Three of these compound colonies were present, two now being in a collection stored at my home in Utah, the other being the one you have examined.   I never succeeded in finding one of the compound nests elsewhere than in this particular field.   My

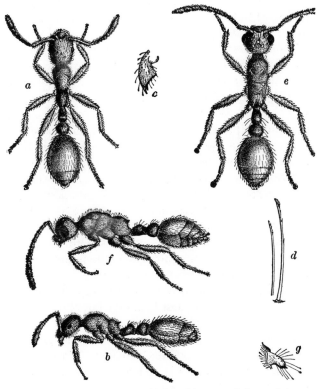

FIG. 260. *Symmyrmica chamberlini.* (Original.) *a* and *b*, worker; *c*, mandible, *d*, hairs of same; *e* and *f*, ergatomorphic male; *g*, mandible of same.

attention was drawn to the first compound nest by seeing two individuals of *Symmyrmica* disappear into a burrow immediately following a *Myrmica* worker.   Upon excavating I found others of the symbiotic form, mostly collected in a chamber about eight inches below the surface of the ground.   The nest seemed to be above the average in size." *Myrmica mutica,* which closely resembles in structure and habits the European *M. rubida,* is very common in the mountains of Colorado, but although I examined many nests in that state during two different summers, I failed to find any traces of the *Symmyrmica.* We must conclude, therefore, that this ant is either very rare or very local. As it may be said to represent an archaic form of *Formicoxenus,* it is possible that this European ant was once a guest of *M. rubida,* which is closely related to *M. mutica,* and only later became associated with *F. rufa.* This is suggested by the fact that the present host belongs to a different subfamily and by the extreme ergatomorphism of the males. This specialization is, at any rate, an interesting example of the more advanced state of development of European as compared with North American species belonging to the same or allied genera.

9. *Leptothorax emersoni* (Fig. 261).—This boreal ant is known only from the mountains of New England, but there can be little doubt that it occurs also in eastern British America. I found it first in the Litchfield and Berkshire Hills. Mrs. A. T. Slosson has since taken it on the summit of Mt. Washington and I have found it also at South Harpswell, Maine. It lives only in xenobiosis with another boreal ant, *Myrmica canadensis,* a variety of *M. brevinodis.* I have described the habits of these ants at length in two papers (1901*c,* 1903*f*), to which the reader is referred; here only the more essential particulars need be mentioned. *M. canadensis* builds its nest in the soil of bogs, in clumps of moss (*Polytrichum*) or under logs and stones, and the *Leptothorax* excavates small cavities near the surface and communicating by means of short, tenuous galleries with those of its host. The broods of both species are brought up separately. The *Leptothorax,* though consorting freely with the *Myrmica* workers in their galleries, resents any intrusion of these ants into its own chambers. The inquilines do not leave the nest to forage but obtain all their food, in a very interesting manner, from their hosts. Both in the natural and artificial nests the *Leptothorax* are seen to mount the backs of the Myrmicas and to lick or shampoo their surfaces in a kind of feverish excitement. This shampooing has a two-fold object: to obtain the oleaginous salivary secretion with which the Myrmicas cover their bodies when they clean one another, and to induce these ants to regurgitate the liquid food stored in their crops. The *Leptothorax* devote most of their time to licking the heads and clypei of their nest mates, stopping from time to time to imbibe the liquid food from their lips. Whenever the *Myrmica* workers return to the nest after visiting the aphids on the neighboring plants, they are intercepted by the *Leptothorax* and compelled to pay toll in this comical manner. The *Myrmica* always treat their little guests with the greatest consideration and affection. In Lubbock nests they are often seen to break into the *Leptothorax* chambers, as if seeking an opportunity to be shampooed. On such occa-

sions the inquilines seize them by their mandibles, antennæ or legs and try to force them to withdraw. Then the broken walls are rebuilt by the inquilines and new entrances are made into the *Myrmica* galleries at other points. When colonies of both species, together with their brood, are placed in nests containing no earth, the *Leptothorax* collect all their young in a pile and act towards any *Myrmica* that approaches them as they do when their earthen cells are invaded. For days the little ants struggle to maintain the integrity of their exposed nursery and even build around it ramparts of sugar or other substances which they may find in the nest, but the intrusions of the *Myrmica* become so frequent and insistent that they finally give up and allow their larvæ and pupæ to become mingled with those of their host. As soon as this occurs the ants no longer form a compound nest, but a mixed colony. While the two species are living together the *Leptothorax* never approach the food dish or feed independently, but if a colony of this species is isolated the workers begin to visit the food and feed, rather awkwardly at first, but eventually quite like ordinary ants. This indicates that the symbiosis between the two species must be of comparatively recent development. In natural colonies the feeding of the inquilines does not seem to constitute a serious drain on the hosts, as the latter, even when supporting a few hundred of the little

FIG. 261. *Leptothorax emersoni* and *Myrmica canadensis.* (Original.) The two largest ants are workers of *M. canadensis;* in the lower middle portion of the figure a worker *L. emersoni;* in the vertical row to the right, a male, deälated female, ergatoid female and worker of this species.

satellites, are nevertheless able to bring up a great number of workers, males and females of their own species. Although the *Leptothorax* may be said to be truly parasitic, they have lost none of their essential instincts, such as those of excavating the nest and rearing their young. Only their feeding habits have become peculiarly modified, without, however, completely supplanting the ability to eat independently. Nevertheless the opulent trophic conditions among which the inquilines live have begun to tell on the structure of the workers, for these have a pronounced tendency to assume the characters of the queen. Miss Holiday (1904) and I have shown that a large percentage of the workers possess ocelli and even resemble the female in size, in the structure of the thorax, and in possessing a well-developed receptaculum seminis and ovaries. Hence we may say that the abundant food supply has a tendency to increase the fertility of the workers and to reduce the dimorphism of the female sex. If this tendency, which is the reverse of that observed under similar circumstances among lestobiotic ants like *Carebara,* should continue, it would probably give rise to one of two conditions in the course of further evolution: either the worker caste would disappear completely, leaving the species to be represented by males and winged females, or the winged female would be suppressed, leaving only males and ergatoid females. As winged females seem to be produced by *Leptothorax emersoni* in rather small numbers, I am inclined to believe that evolution will take the latter course. In the ants to be considered under the head of permanent social parasitism evolution has moved along the other path and led to a complete extinction of the worker caste.

10. *Leptothorax glacialis.*—This ant, which I have described (1907*h*) as a subspecies of *L. emersoni,* occurs in the Rocky Mountains of Colorado at elevations of over 2,500 m. It lives with *Myrmica alpina,* a western variety of *M. brevinodis,* in relations very similar to those described above for the two eastern forms, except that *glacialis* seems to feed less on the surface secretions and more on the regurgitated food of its host. Observations on a colony in an artificial nest also seemed to show that the instinct to feed independently is more blunted or vestigial in *glacialis* than it is in *emersoni.*

The relations of *L. emersoni* and *glacialis* to their respective hosts represent the nearest approach to the formation of mixed colonies that has been observed among xenobiotic ants. Indeed, so cordial and intimate are the relations between these species and their hosts that even the instinct to rear their broods in separate apartments can be suppressed experimentally and the insects induced to form a true mixed colony. If in a state of nature *L. emersoni* and *glacialis* should develop a habit of mingling their eggs, larvæ and pupæ with those of the *Myrmica,* these inquilines would probably soon cease to excavate nests of their own and become permanent social parasites.

CHAPTER XXIV

THE TEMPORARY SOCIAL PARASITES

" Est-on bien sûr que les mœurs parasitaires soient dérivées de l'amour de l'inaction? Le parasite est-il devenu ce qu'il est parce qu'il a trouvé excellent de ne rien faire? Le repos est-il pour lui avantage si grand que, pour l'obtenir, il ait renié ses antiques usages? Eh bien, depuis que je fréquente l'hyménoptère dotant sa famille de l'avoir des autres, je n'ai encore rien vu qui, chez lui, dénotât le fainéant. Le parasite, tout au contraire, mène vie pénible, plus rude que celle des travailleurs. Suivons-le sur un talus calciné par le soleil. Comme il est affairé, soucieux; comme il arpente d'un pas brusque la nappe ensoleillée; comme il se dépense en recherches interminables, en visites le plus souvent infructueuses! Avant d'avoir fait rencontre d'un nid qui lui convienne, il a plongé cent fois dans des cavités sans valeur, dans des galeries non encore approvisionnées. Et puis, si bénévole que soit l'hôte, le parasite n'est pas toujours des mieux reçus dans l'hôtellerie. Non, tout n'est pas roses dans son métier."—Fabre, " Souvenirs Entomologiques," III, 1890.

Mixed colonies of ants were first discovered by P. Huber nearly a century ago (1810) and have since been studied in Europe by Darwin, Forel, Lubbock, Adlerz, Wasmann, Janet, Reichenbach, Escherich, Viehmeyer and many others; in America by McCook, Mrs. Treat, Forel and myself. These colonies present a great number of singular problems, on many of which light has been shed only within the past decade. In the study of this, as in that of so many other subjects, the startling and complex phenomena were the first to be seen and to call for an explanation. Various inadequate explanations were then advanced, till, in seeking support for these, the investigator happened on some obscure and hitherto disregarded or misinterpreted phenomenon which suddenly changed the aspect of the whole subject. Thus the highly specialized slave-making behavior of *Polyergus* and *Formica sanguinea* was the first to be observed by Huber and this was so extraordinary that it engrossed the attention of observers for nearly a century. As the slave-making forays are executed by worker ants, it was natural to seek for their origin and signification in the activities of this caste. In the meantime some apparently unimportant observations on the mixed colonies were being accumulated and the remarkable initiative of the queen ant in establishing her formicary began to be understood and appreciated. After vainly seeking the *raison d'être* of the mixed colonies in the behavior of the workers, an attempt was made to solve the problem by a study of the queen. This attempt proved to be so successful that we are now wondering how it could have taken so many years to perceive that a mixed colony or a simple colony, for that matter, can only be understood by tracing its development and history —its ontogeny, as the embryologist would say. And as all ant-colonies are started by queens, it would seem to be most natural to approach the subject by studying the behavior of these insects. But all problems appear to be simple after they have ceased to be problems. I described in Chapter XI the various methods of colony formation exhibited by ants in general. Before considering the mixed colonies it will be necessary not only to refer the reader to that description but also to present the subject from a somewhat different point of view.

In the great majority of ant species the colony arises and develops in the following manner: The single female, or queen, after mating during her marriage flight, descends to the earth, divests herself of her wings, digs a small cell in the soil, or enters some preformed cavity under a stone or in the tissues of a plant, lays a number of eggs, feeds the resulting larvæ with her salivary secretion, and guards and nurses them till they mature and constitute a brood of diminutive workers. These now proceed to enlarge the nest, to forage for food, both for themselves and their mother, and to care for the succeeding broods of young. The queen thenceforth gives herself up exclusively to feeding from the tongues of her offspring and to laying eggs. The colony grows apace, the workers increasing in number, size and polymorphism with successive broods. Eventually males and virgin queens are produced, though often only after the expiration of several years, when the colony may be said to have completed its ontogenetic development.

It will be seen from the foregoing summary that the mother queen lapses from the position of an independent organism with remarkable initiative to that of a parasite dependent on her own offspring. The latter stage in her life is of much longer duration than the former. This singular ontogenetic change in the instincts of the queen should be noted, as it foreshadows an important phylogenetic development exhibiting two different modifications, one of which is excessive, the other defective, in comparison with the primitive and independent type of colony formation. The excessive, or redundant, type is known to occur only among the Attiine ants of tropical America. These raise fungi for food and are quite unable to subsist on any other diet. The queens are often very large, especially in the typical genus *Atta,* and not only manage to bring to maturity a brood of workers, as has been shown (p. 329 *et seq.*), but at the same time have energy to spare to devote to the cultivation of a fungus garden. With the appearance of the first brood of workers, however, these queens, like those of most other ants, degenerate into parasites on their own progeny.

This dependent stage, which, as I have said, is of much greater duration than the independent stage in the long life of the queen, leads to a number of phylogenetic developments of the defective type. These first manifest themselves in the adoption of young queens by adult workers of their own species. A word of explanation will make this clear. In the colonies of many species of Formicidæ we find several queens—in fact, there are comparatively few ants whose adult colonies do not contain more than one of these fertile individuals. And a study of the growth of such colonies shows that the supernumerary queens are either daughters of the original single queen that founded the colony, or have been adopted from other colonies of the same species. Hence these queens are either virgins, or have been impregnated by their own brothers (adelphogamy of Forel) in the parental nest, or have been captured by the workers and carried into the nest after descending from their nuptial flight. This passive or forcible adoption leads necessarily to a complete suppression of the independent stage in the life of such queens. I have found that merely removing a queen ant's wings with tweezers will at once call forth the dependent series of instincts, and the same result is undoubtedly produced when the workers deälate the virgin or just-fertilized queens of their own or other formicaries. Such queens, finding themselves surrounded by a number of accomplished nurses, the workers, proceed at once to act like old queens that have already established their colonies and brought up a brood.

From this condition of facultative adoption to an obligatory adoption of the queen by workers of her own species is but a step. And here there are three possibilities: first, the queen can establish a colony only with the aid of workers of her own species and of the same colony. This condition seems not to obtain among ants, although it is well known in the honey-bees. Second, the queen must either be adopted by the workers of her own species of the same or another colony or by workers of an alien species. This is the case with many queen ants that have lost the power of establishing colonies unaided. Third, the queen must always be adopted by an alien species. This is the case in the highly parasitic forms that have lost their worker caste. The three conditions here enumerated clearly represent the transition from parasitism of the queen on the same to parasitism on an alien species. The latter alone is commonly regarded as true parasitism, but the former, which, of course, can occur only among social organisms or during social stages in the lives of solitary organisms, is parasitism in every essential particular.

Ant colonies are such closed and exclusive societies that the adoption of strange queens, even of the same species but from alien colonies, often meets with insuperable opposition on the part of the workers, and, as a rule, female ants have to overcome even greater hostility when they seek adoption in colonies of alien species. There are, nevertheless, at least three different methods of overcoming this hostility and of effecting an adoption, and each of these is characteristic of one of the forms of mixed colony. I shall consider these in this and the two following chapters under the heads of temporary social parasitism, dulosis, or slavery, and permanent social parasitism. The following diagram will serve to illustrate the foregoing account of the different types of adoption, their supposed phylogeny and their relations to one another. The relations will be made clearer by the facts recorded in the sequel.

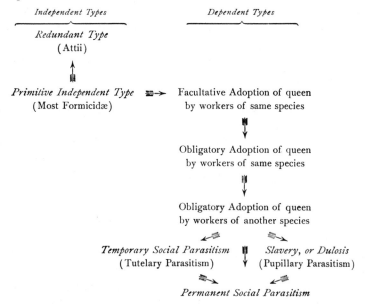

In the cases of temporary social parasitism the initiative of the queen ant is shown with great clearness. She actively seeks adoption in the colony of another species and permits the alien workers to bring up her first brood of young. The full benefits of this form of parasitism, however, can be secured only by the elimination of the queen of the host species, for if this insect remained in the colony she would continue to produce young and the nurture bestowed on these by the workers would seriously interfere with the development of the parasite's own progeny. As will be shown presently, different species seem to have developed different methods of getting rid of the host queen.

In the course of a year or two, the workers of these host species, being unable to reproduce, gradually die off and leave the parasitic queen and her offspring in possession of their nest, as a pure colony, and requiring no further assistance in its growth and development. The colony becomes populous and aggressive, with nothing to indicate that it began life as a parasitic community. This method of colony formation is adopted by some of the most powerful ants of temperate regions, and some of the most remarkable temporary parasites are members of the circumpolar genus *Formica.* Two groups of species in this genus, one embracing *F. rufa* and its allies, the other *F. exsecta* and its allies, are especially interesting in this connection. The workers of these various species are very similar. They have red heads and thoraces and black or brown gasters, but the cospecific females may exhibit extraordinary differences in size, sculpture, pilosity and coloration. According to size they may be divided into microgynous species, in which the female is little larger and sometimes even smaller than the worker, and macrogynous species, with the female considerably larger than the worker as in the members of other *Formica* groups. It is a singular fact that although the species in both of these subgroups are widely distributed and often very common in certain localities, no one has ever seen one of the females founding a colony independently. It is known, however, that in some of the species the colonies are often enlarged by adoption of females of the same species or even of a different subspecies. The microgynous species are most abundantly represented in North America. It was a study of these which first led me to the discovery of temporary parasitism as a regular or normal occurrence and to make the prediction (1904*h*) that it would be found to occur very generally in the *rufa* and *exsecta* groups on both continents. I will present the grounds for this prediction as succinctly as possible.

1. **Microgynous Formicæ of the Rufa Group.**—The commonest ants with minute females in the mountains of the Atlantic States are *F. difficilis* and its variety, *consocians.* The females of these are almost as small as the large workers and are fulvous yellow in color. In the Litchfield Hills of Connecticut I found that as a rule *consocians* lives in populous, independent formicaries under stones which it banks with plant débris. Like other members of the *rufa* group, it is a very pugnacious ant. During the course of several summers a number of small, incipient colonies were found, containing a *consocians* queen associated with workers of *F. incerta,* a variety of *schaufussi,* and sometimes also with a few *consocians* workers. *F. incerta* is a cowardly ant which forms numerous rather small formicaries in the same locality. The

workers are reddish-yellow and of about the same size as the *consocians* queen. I naturally inferred that the mixed colonies must owe their origin to the adoption of *consocians* queens by *incerta* workers. A number of experiments were performed, which left no doubt concerning the correctness of this inference. The account of one of these experiments may be repeated here:

July 21, 4.30 P. M., an artificially deälated *consocians* female was placed in a nest with twenty *incerta* workers and several worker

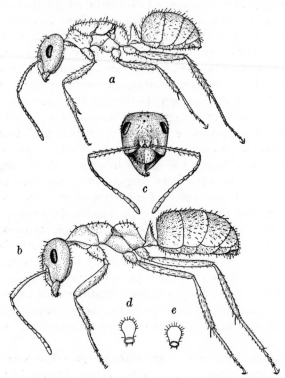

Fig. 262. *Formica microgyna.* (Original.) *a*, Deälated female; *b*, large worker drawn to same scale; *c*, head of worker; *d*, petiole of same from behind; *e*, petiole of female.

cocoons taken from one of the most vigorous colonies found during the entire summer. The workers were unusually large and more like the workers of pure *schaufussi,* but with the coloration and pilosity of *incerta.* The female seemed disinclined to approach the workers, which were brooding over their cocoons, but she moved towards them when the illumination of the chamber was reversed. She was at once seized by a worker and showered with formic acid. She escaped to a corner of the nest. By 5.15 P. M. she had returned, mounted the pile of cocoons and was licking the workers, who were submitting to this treatment as if it were a matter of course. A few moments later she fed one of the workers and then kept alternating between feeding and caressing them with comical rapidity and perseverance. The colony was watched till 7.45 P. M., but no hostilities were seen. July 22, 7 A. M.: The previous night had been cold and the female seemed to have passed it hanging from the roof pane in a corner of the nest. Later, as it grew warmer, she returned to the *incerta* and their brood, caressed and fed the workers and took food from their lips. Only once during the day was a worker seen to tug for a few moments at one of her antennæ. On the four following days (July 23 to 26) no hostilities were observed. The *consocians* female had been definitively adopted.

Numerous observations in the field have convinced me that the queen soon after her adoption lays eggs, the larvæ hatching from which are reared by the *incerta* workers. In this manner a mixed colony arises. While the queen keeps on laying eggs and producing more workers, the *incerta* gradually die of old age. Then, of course, a pure colony remains, and the *consocians* workers have become sufficiently numerous to enlarge and defend the nest and care for their queen and successive broods of their own species. The purpose of adoption and the signification of the small size and yellow color of the female are apparent. The queen pursues the same tactics as some of the myrme-cophilous beetles (*Lomechusa, Atemeles,* etc.) described in a previous chapter. She ingratiates herself with the workers by means of her mimetic resemblance to them, by her conciliatory and passive demeanor and by her neutral or soothing odor, and is thus able to exploit their blind philoprogenitive instincts for her own advantage and that of her offspring. Since she is thereby relieved of the necessity of nourishing her young with substances elaborated from her own tissues, she can be of diminutive stature, and this, in turn, represents a saving to her parental colony, for it is thus enabled to rear on a given amount of food a much greater number of queens than the macrogynous species. As a matter of fact, the adult *consocians* colony produces an enormous number of these dwarf females.

One important problem in the parasitism of *consocians* remains to be elucidated: What becomes of the mother queen of the *incerta* colony? Several possible answers suggest themselves. The *consocians* queen may succeed in obtaining adoption only in moribund and queenless colonies, or if she enters colonies provided with a queen, this insect may voluntarily forsake the nest, or she may be driven away or killed by her own workers or by the intrusive queen.   Observations on artificial colonies show that the *consocians* queen treats the host queen with indifference, even after she has been confined in the same nest for over a year, or as if she were one of the workers.   Moreover, the *incerta* queen displays no inclination to forsake her colony, and no hostilities develop between her and her own workers.   I deem it probable, therefore, that the parasite instinctively seeks out some impoverished or queenless colony of the host species.   We shall see, however, that this custom is by no means universal among the temporary parasites.

Other North American *Formicæ* of the *rufa* group known to have diminutive females as small as those of *consocians* or even smaller are: *microgyna* (Fig. 262), *rasilis, nevadensis, impexa, nepticula* and *dakotensis.*   As the nesting habit of these is very similar to that of *consocians,* and as I have found in Colorado two small mixed nests of *dakotensis* and *incerta,* I believe that there is little doubt that all these species are temporary social parasites.

2. **Macrogynous Formicæ of the Rufa Group.**—The forms included here are the typical European *rufa,* with its subspecies, *pratensis* and *truncicola,* and in America the subspecies *obscuriventris, obscuripes* and *integra,* with several varieties, and the species *ciliata, crinita, oreas, comata* and *specularis.*   In several of these forms the stature of the female is somewhat diminished and in *ciliata* (Fig. 263), *crinita,* etc., her color, pilosity or sculpturing are aberrant.   Small mixed colonies of *F. truncicola* and *fusca* have been known for some years.   Forel (1874) described one which he found near Loco, Switzerland; one was found by Zur Strassen in Saxony, and Wasmann (1901–'02, 1905d) has recently found three others in Luxemburg.   These mixed colonies were originally regarded as accidental or abnormal occurrences, but my observations (1904h, 1906c) indicated very clearly that they are merely incipient and transitory stages in the normal life of the *truncicola* colony and that the queen of this species is a temporary parasite.   After observing two of the mixed colonies in artificial nests Wasmann reached the same conclusion.   Recently (1908) Viehmeyer has shown that *truncicola* females are readily adopted by *fusca* workers.   Now as the North American *integra* and its varieties, *hæmorrhoidalis* and *coloradensis,* closely resemble the European *truncicola* in structure and nesting habit, and as I have succeeded in causing a female *integra* to be adopted by workers of *subsericea,* there can be little doubt that the huge formicaries of all these *rufa* forms have their beginnings in temporary parasitism.   Finally, the species with rich red or yellow, very glabrous or unusually

hairy females, like *ciliata, crinita, dakotensis* and *specularis,* probably have similar habits. Muckermann, in fact, discovered in Wisconsin some five colonies of *specularis* mixed with *subsericea,* and with females of the former species only. Although Wasmann has endeavored to make out that these nests represented cases of incipient slavery, there can be no doubt that the observations, as they stand, will bear no such interpretation, but point rather to temporary social parasitism.

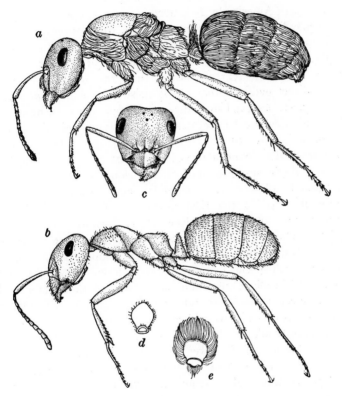

FIG. 263. *Formica ciliata.* (Original.) *a,* Deälated female; *b,* large worker drawn to same scale; *c,* head of worker; *d,* petiole of same seen from behind; *e,* petiole of female.

There are no published observations on the origin of *rufa* and *pratensis* colonies. It is not improbable, however, that these ants in the early stages of colony formation are parasitic on *fusca.* In Switzerland, during the summer of 1907, I found on two or three occasions a recently killed, but not mutilated, *pratensis* queen in the recesses of a *fusca* nest, and Professor Escherich showed me a typical *rufa* queen which he found near Strasburg living with a small number of *fusca* workers.[1] These facts, taken singly are rather insignificant, but conjointly they point very decidedly to the conclusion that most, if not all, the ants of the *rufa* group are temporary parasites.

3. **The Formicæ of the Exsecta Group.**—This group, which is characterized by having the head of the worker and female deeply excised behind, is represented in Europe by the typical *F. exsecta,* its subspecies *pressilabris* and *F. suecica,* a species recently discovered in Sweden by Adlerz; in North America by *F. exsectoides,* its subspecies *opaciventris* and *F. ulkei.* These ants build mound nests, often several to a colony, and sometimes of large size, especially in America (Figs. 109 and 181). The females are large in our forms, but smaller in *exsecta* and *pressilabris,* and scarcely larger than the workers in *suecica.* There is indirect evidence that all of these ants, except *ulkei,* which has not yet been observed in nature, are temporary parasites. In his "Fourmis de la Suisse" Forel described two small mixed colonies of *exsecta-fusca* and two of *exsectopressilabris-fusca.* During the summer of 1907 I also found a mixed colony of the latter composition, occupying a single small mound, on the slopes of Monte Generoso. Similar mixed colonies of *exsectoides* and *subsericea* have been repeatedly observed in the Eastern States. Forel observed one at Hartford, Conn., and the late Rev. P. J. Schmitt found five near Beatty, Pa. These invariably contained queens of *exsectoides* only, and all were obviously incipient, since they comprised not more than fifty workers, both species included. I have found two of these mixed colonies at Colebrook, Conn., and have observed the behavior of an *exsectoides* queen when she is introduced into a colony of *subsericea* workers. She is very passive and conciliatory and in one of my experiments was readily adopted by the alien colony. Considering the close taxonomic affinities of *F. ulkei* to *exsectoides* and the diminutive stature of the female *suecica,* we may assume that these species can hardly differ in their habits from the other members of the *exsecta* group.

4. **Bothriomyrmex.**—Among the mixed colonies recorded by Forel (1874) there was one composed of two species of Dolichoderine ants, *Bothriomyrmex meridionalis* and *Tapinoma erraticum,* which he found on the Borromean Islands in the Lago Maggiore. This colony, like the colonies of *truncicola-fusca* and *exsecta-fusca* above mentioned, had

[1] During the past summer (1909) I found three mixed colonies of *F. rufa* and *fusca,* which show very clearly that the former is a temporary parasite like *consocians.* Two of these, discovered in the Turtman Valley, in Switzerland, each consisted of a *rufa* queen and several *fusca* workers, the third, found at Zermatt, contained besides a *rufa* queen a few workers of the same species.

been regarded as an exceptional or abnormal occurrence till very recently, when Santschi (1906, Forel, 1906d) discovered several mixed colonies of varieties of these species (*B. atlantis* and *T. nigerrimum*) in the Tunisian desert, and showed by a series of surprising observations that they were cases of temporary parasitism. The *Bothriomyrmex* queen, on descending from her nuptial flight, wanders about on the ground till she finds a *Tapinoma* nest and then permits herself to be seized and "arrested" by the *Tapinoma* workers. These then proceed to drag her into their burrow by her legs and antennæ. After entering the nest the parasite may be attacked from time to time by the workers, but she takes refuge on the brood or on the back of the *Tapinoma* queen. In either of these positions she seems to be quite immune from attack. This observation throws light on certain peculiarities in the behavior of *F. consocians,* for this insect also mounts the brood pile as soon as she enters the *incerta* nest and when in this position is never molested by the alien workers. Santschi observed that the *Bothriomyrmex* queen often spends long hours on the back of the large *Tapinoma* queen and that while she is in this position she busies herself with sawing off the head of her host! By the time she has succeeded in accomplishing this cruel feat, she has acquired the nest odor and is adopted by the *Tapinoma* workers in the place of their unfortunate mother. The parasite thereupon proceeds to keep them busy bringing up her brood. They eventually die of old age and the nest then becomes the property of a thriving, pure colony of *Bothriomyrmex atlantis.* The queen of this species, as Santschi has shown, is mimetic like that of *consocians,* being but little larger than the *Tapinoma* workers and provided with an odor like that of the host species, though this odor is lacking in her own workers. Santschi has thus been able actually to witness the elimination of the host queen. But the method employed by *Bothriomyrmex* in accomplishing this is not universal among parasitic species, as we shall see when we come to his interesting observations on the permanent social parasite *Wheeleriella.*

5. **Aphænogaster.**—The female of the Myrmicine ant *Aphænogaster tennesseensis* (Fig. 264), in being deep red and of very small size, with a glabrous body and huge, flattened epinotal spines protecting the vulnerable abdominal pedicel, is so unlike the females of any other members of the genus *Aphænogaster* that she was originally described by Mayr as the type of a distinct species (*A. levis*). These peculiarities suggest temporary parasitism and this is borne out by the observations of Schmitt and myself (1901c). Schmitt found near Beatty, Pa., a small mixed colony of *A. tennesseensis* and *A. picea,* a variety of *fulva* and one of the commonest ants in the Northern States. He was impressed

with the fact that the nest of this colony was under a stone, because *tennesseensis* normally nests only in rotting wood. During the summer of 1902 I found near Rockford, Ill., two mixed colonies like that observed by Schmitt, except that the variety *picea* was represented by the variety *rudis*. Both colonies were of small size and situated under stones. In one of them a *tennesseensis* queen was unearthed. There can be little doubt, therefore, that the glabrous queens seek out small nests of some variety of *fulva* and start their colonies in them just as *consocians* does in the nest of *incerta*. This habit is also indicated by the sporadic distribution of *tennesseensis* and its occurrence only in

FIG. 264. In the first vertical row: virgin and deälated female of *Aphænogaster tennesseensis;* in the second vertical row: male and two workers of the same species; remaining figures: virgin female, male and workers of *Aphænogaster fulva.* × 1½. (Original.)

localities where some form of *fulva* is abundant. After the extinction of the host workers the pure *tennesseensis* colony evidently migrates into old logs and stumps and there attains its full development. A single adult colony of this species, like that of *consocians*, produces a great number of small females, whereas the non-parasitic *Aphænogaster* have all they can do to bring up a few of their large queens. Another *Aphænogaster* (*A. mariæ*), which is a rare species taken only in the Atlantic States and structurally closely related to *tennesseensis*, also has very small females (4.5 mm. long), with large epinotal spines. It is, in all probability, like this species, a temporary parasite in nests of *A. fulva*.

6. **Oxygyne.**—Forel has assigned to a special subgenus, *Oxygyne*, a series of *Cremastogaster* species (*emmæ, ebenina, soror, travancoren-*

sis, dalyi, aberrans, ranavolonæ, agnetis, daisyi, marthæ and *depressa*) from Madagascar, India and the Malayan region, because they have unusually small, glabrous females, with falcate, pointed or very oblique mandibles, abbreviated frontal carinæ and sometimes very strong epinotal spines and a robust abdominal pedicel. The workers of these various forms are much like those of the ordinary species of *Cremastogaster* with large queens. In one species of *Oxygyne* (*ranavalonæ*, Fig. 265), according to Emery (1897a), the aged female has the gaster enormously enlarged and subspherical like that of the mother queens of the permanently parasitic *Anergates* (Fig. 279, *b*). Forel has suggested that the structural peculiarities of the *Oxygyne* queens are probably correlated with peculiarities of habit. Comparison of a series of these insects, kindly given me by the eminent myrmecologist, with the microgynes of *Formica* and *Aphænogaster,* convinces me that they must be temporary parasites on other species of *Cremastogaster.* Their sickle-shaped mandibles, so much like those of *Polyergus* and *Strongylognathus* (Figs. 271, 273) point to a method of assassinating the host queen similar to that employed by *Bothriomyrmex.* The suggestion here advanced would, at any rate, constitute a good working hypothesis in carrying on further researches on the species of *Oxygyne.*

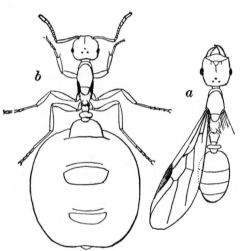

Fig. 265. *Female of Oxygyne ranavalonæ.* (Emery.) *a*, Virgin female, showing falcate mandibles; *b*, fertile female with enlarged ovaries and gaster.

While studying the foregoing known and hypothetical cases of temporary parasitism, one's attention is arrested by the following considerations of general interest:

1. Temporary social parasitism occurs in several unrelated species belonging to three of the five subfamilies of Formicidæ, and must therefore have originated independently on more than one occasion in the past history of the family.

2. Parasite and host are always members of the same genus or of closely allied genera. This seems to be necessary, because such inti-

mate symbiotic relations would be impossible between species of very diverse habits.

3. The host, being in all cases a very widely distributed and abundant species, forms an omnipresent substratum, so to speak, on which the sporadic parasitic forms manage to graft themselves. That the latter are either rare ants or abundant only in circumscribed localities, suggests that the adoption of their queens by alien workers is beset with many obstacles. The colonies of some of these ants, like those of *F. rufa* and *exsectoides,* when once established, may, indeed, grow to enormous dimensions and extend themselves over a number of nests by repeatedly adopting fertile queens of their own species, but the geographical distribution of these forms is never as continuous and uniform as that of the host.

4. The hosts of the temporary parasites are, as a rule, cowardly and prolific species. Both of these peculiarities fit them for being exploited, not only by these parasites, but also by the slave-making ants. And as ant colonies are the more timid and conciliatory the smaller they are, we find that the parasites prefer incipient or moribund colonies to the larger and more aggressive communities of the host species.

5. Temporary parasitism, being transitory, has not, as a rule, profoundly affected the morphological characters of the species. The workers, in fact, have remained unaffected, though the female, in whom the peculiar habit centers, certainly shows structural and instinctive peculiarities that can be interpreted only as adaptations to a parasitic life. Such are the dwarf stature, the mimetic coloration, the long yellow hairs of *F. ciliata* and *crinita,* so like the trichomes of many myrmecophilous beetles, and the conciliatory and insinuating behavior.

6. The production of a great number of dwarf females by pure adult colonies of *F. consocians* and *A. tennesseensis* bears a very interesting and suggestive resemblance to the production of a vast number of minute eggs by many nonsocial parasites like the ascarids, cestodes, *Sacculina,* etc. This has been universally regarded as an adaptation to the great destruction of individuals incident to the complicated and arduous efforts of the parasite to get a foothold on or in its host. The exception to this rule furnished by the macrogynous *Formicæ* of the *rufa* and *exsecta* groups may be due to the fact that in these species the queens are so often adopted by workers of their own opulent colonies, and the occasions on which they actually need to found colonies with the aid of alien species so infrequent, that they have not become dwarfed in stature and have not developed pronounced mimetic or myrmecophilous characters.

7. The elimination of the host queen in colonies invaded by the temporary parasites destroys the reproductive powers of the host colony. Hence this form of parasitism is strictly comparable to the castration induced in their hosts by many nonsocial parasites like *Sacculina* and *Stylops*. We may therefore designate cases like that of *Bothriomyrmex* and *Tapinoma* as examples of social castration. This term, as will be shown in the sequel, will apply also to most of the mixed colonies formed by dulosis and permanent social parasitism.

8. The future development of the temporary parasites may be supposed to lead most naturally in the direction of permanent parasitism. This, however, can eventuate only if the species limits and accelerates the growth of its colonies or foists itself only on well-developed colonies of the host. Contrariwise the parasite would outgrow the host colony, or the latter would die off prematurely unless its queen were retained in the nest. We shall see that such Malthusian practices are actually carried out by the permanent social parasites and have resulted in the complete extinction of the unnecessary worker caste.

CHAPTER XXV

THE SANGUINARY ANTS, OR FACULTATIVE SLAVE-MAKERS

"I shall next bring forward a scene still more astonishing, which at first, perhaps, you will be disposed to regard as the mere illusion of a lively imagination. What will you say when I tell you that certain ants are affirmed to sally forth from their nests on predatory expeditions, for the singular purpose of procuring *slaves* to employ in their domestic business; and that these ants are usually a ruddy race, while their slaves themselves are black."—Kirby & Spence, "Entomology," 6th ed., 1846.

"Ce fait choquant et hideux, tâchons du moins de le comprendre. Il est propre à quelques espèces; il est un incident particulier, un cas exceptionnel, mais rentrant au total dans une loi générale de la vie des fourmis."—Michelet, "L'Insecte," 1884.

The mixed colonies described in the last chapter are transitory consociations of two species merely formed as a means of establishing colonies, which, in their adult stages, are able to hold their own unaided in the struggle for existence. The cases to be described in this and the following chapters are more permanent symbiotic alliances, though they differ so much among themselves that it is difficult to include them in a single definition. With one or two exceptions, to be described in their proper places, these mixed colonies may be said to be formed by dulosis, or slavery, and this peculiar phenomenon may be defined as the habit of making periodical raids on particular alien species, seizing their worker larvæ and pupæ and rearing and adopting a portion of these. But neither the periodical raid nor the rearing of the alien ants alone constitutes slavery. Many of the species of *Eciton* make such raids on other ants and pillage their nests, but they attack any terrestrial ants indiscriminately and the young are all devoured. And even if some of these were permitted to hatch, a mixed colony would not result, because the Ecitons have no fixed home, but wander from place to place. Moreover, although the mixed dulotic colony certainly owes its origin to the rearing and adopting of the alien young, many nondulotic ants will do this if such young are placed in or near their nests. Forel (1874) long ago formed mixed colonies in this way, and more recently Miss Fielde (1903c) has shown the extreme to which this experiment can be carried. She succeeded in making triple and quadruple mixed colonies of ants belonging not only to different genera, but also to different subfamilies (Fig. 266). One of her experiments resulted in the formation of a colony comprising workers of *Stigmatomma pallipes* (Ponerine), *Formica subsericea* (Camponotine), and *Aphænogaster fulva* (Myrmicine); another was made up of such heterogeneous components as *Camponotus pennsylvanicus, Formica sanguinea, A. fulva* and *Cremastogaster lineolata.* In these artificial mixed colonies she found that

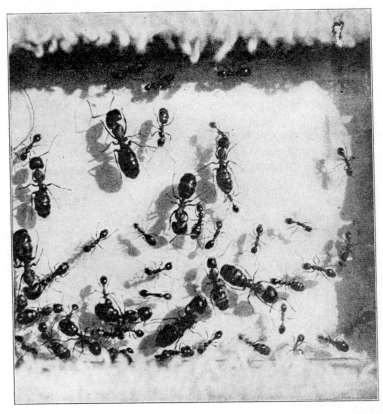

FIG. 266. Mixed colony consisting of workers of *Camponotus pennsylvanicus, Formica subsericea* and *Aphænogaster picea* reared by Miss A. M. Fielde. Photograph by J. G. Hubbard and Dr. O. S. Strong.)

"there is a close affiliation of ants of different species. Those of different subfamilies sometimes lick one another. Introduced young is carried about and taken care of without regard to its origin. Ants of one genus accept regurgitated food from those of another genus." She gives the following recipe for producing such colonies: "If one or more individuals, of each species that is to be represented in the future mixed nest, be sequestered within twelve hours after hatching, and each ant so sequestered touch all the others with its antennæ during the three ensuing days, these ants will live amicably together thereafter, although they be of different colonies, varieties, species, genera or subfamilies." Such experiments are of the greatest interest as showing the importance of the philoprogenitive instincts and the uniformity of their development in the workers of the most diverse species of Formicidæ, and adequately account for the presence of slaves in the mixed colonies, but they cannot be said to throw any light on the other essential peculiarities of slavery, namely, the raiding habit and its concentration on particular species. These peculiarities, as we shall see, must be referred to a different source.

Like the temporary parasites, with the possible exception of *Oxygyne,* the slave-making ants are confined to the north temperate zone and extend far up into boreal and alpine regions. Indeed, it is not improbable that the development of the slave-making habit is connected in some way with the long winters, short summers and small amount of food in the subarctic belt. All the known slave-makers are members of four genera: *Formica* (the species of the *sanguinea* group), *Polyergus, Strongylognathus* and *Harpagoxenus,* the first two comprising Camponotine, the last two Myrmicine ants. The habits of *Harpagoxenus* are imperfectly known, but the other genera form an interesting series, in which *Formica sanguinea* represents the slave-making habit in process of development, *Polyergus* its most specialized and *Strongylognathus* its involutionary or degenerate development. *F. sanguinea* and *Polyergus* have been studied by many observers. As Huber's and Forel's brilliant accounts of these ants have been extensively quoted in many accessible works, it will not be necessary to repeat them here. I shall therefore confine myself to a brief enumeration of the known slave-makers and to some observations of my own on the American forms. This will be the more advisable, since there are few published observations on our *sanguinea* and almost none on the expeditions of our *Polyergus.*

1. **The European Sanguinea.**—The typical form of this, the sanguinary, or blood-red slave-maker, which is easily distinguished by the median notch in the anterior border of its clypeus, is common throughout temperate Europe and probably also in northern Asia (Fig. 267). In Japan, the easternmost portion of its range, it has developed at least one variety, *fusciceps.* In Europe it lives under stones, in logs and stumps, or about the roots of plants and often accumulates considerable vegetable débris about its nest entrances. Those who have studied its habits are unanimous in regarding it as one of the most gifted and versatile of ants. It is certainly one of the most belligerent, and, at

least when living in large colonies, assails any intruder with its mandibles, simultaneously turning the tip of its gaster forward and injecting formic acid into the wound. *F. sanguinea* is, to use Wasmann's expression, a facultative slave-holder, for it sometimes lives in independent, slaveless colonies. As it has lost none of its essential formicine instincts, it is able to excavate a nest, secure its own food and bring up its own young without the aid of slaves. But even when these auxiliaries are present, much, if not most, of the labor of the

Fig. 267. The typical *Formica sanguinea* of Europe. (Original.) *a,* Deälated female; *b,* pseudogyne; *c,* worker; *d,* head of same, showing the notched clypeus.

colony devolves on the *sanguinea,* and there is nothing to show that the slaves contribute anything more to the communal activities than would be contributed by an equal number of small *sanguinea* workers.

The normal slaves of *F. sanguinea* are members of the *F. fusca* group, namely, *fusca, glebaria, rubescens, gagates, rufibarbis* and *cinerea,* but it occasionally enslaves members of the *rufa* group (*rufa, pratensis* and their varieties). Wasmann (1902a) has published statistics of 410 *sanguinea* colonies found nesting within an area of 4 sq. kilom. in Holland. In this region the ratio of slave-containing to slaveless colonies was as 40:1; that of colonies containing the normal slaves (*fusca, rufibarbis*) to those with *pratensis* and *rufopratensis* as 78.6:1; and that of the nests containing *fusca* only, *rufibarbis* only or both of these forms as 70.5:3. There can be no doubt that the typical *fusca* is the form most frequently enslaved in northern Europe and at higher elevations in the Alps, but in the valleys of Switzerland the varieties *glebaria* and *rubescens* and *F. cinerea* are the commonest slaves. In other words, *sanguinea* usually enslaves the common *fusca* form of its environment, and the ability of the slave-maker to live in a variety of different environments accounts for the diversity of its slaves. Wasmann's statistics therefore apply only to certain regions, as he himself admits, for he calls attention to the fact that in the vicinity of Luxemburg *rufibarbis* furnishes a greater number of slaves than in Holland. Forel (1874) mentions a number of slaveless colonies of *sanguinea* which he found at Maloja at the end of the Engadin, and near the same place (at Samaden and St. Moritz) I found two large areas in which the proportion of slaveless to slave-containing colonies must have been fully as 40:1, or the reverse of Wasmann's ratio. But even the slave-holding colonies of the European *sanguinea* contain comparatively few slaves, the average ratio of the *sanguinea* workers to that of the auxiliaries in 100 nests near Limburg being, according to Wasmann (1891) 3–5:1. He maintains that the youngest colonies, as a rule, have the greatest number of slaves and that it is usually the oldest colonies that are slaveless. In this respect the *sanguinea* colonies bear an interesting resemblance to those of the temporary parasites.

The tactics of *F. sanguinea* in procuring its slaves have been vividly described by Huber (1810), Forel (1874) and Wasmann (1891*h*). The sorties occur in July and August after the marriage flight of the slave species has been celebrated and when only workers and mother queens are left in their formicaries. According to Forel the expeditions are infrequent—"scarcely more than two or three a year to a colony." The army of workers usually starts out in the morning and returns in the afternoon, but this depends on the distance of the *sanguinea* nest from the nest to be plundered. Sometimes the slave-makers postpone their sorties till three or four o'clock in the afternoon. On rare occasions they may pillage two different colonies in succession before going home. The *sanguinea* army leaves its nest in a straggling, open phalanx sometimes a few meters broad and often in several companies or detachments. These move to the nest to be pillaged over the directest route permitted by the often numerous obstacles in their path. As the forefront of the army is not headed by one or a few workers that might serve as guides, but is continually changing, some dropping back while others move forward to take their places, it is not easy to understand how the whole body is able to go so directly to the nest of the slave species, especially when this nest is situated, as is often the case, at a distance of 50 or 100 m. We must suppose that the colony has acquired a knowledge of the precise location of the various nests of the slave species within an area of a hundred meters or more of its own nest.   This knowledge is probably acquired by scouts leaving the nest singly and from time to time for a period of several weeks, and these scouts must be sufficiently numerous to determine the movements of the whole worker body when it leaves the nest. This presupposes not only a high development of memory, but some form of communication, for the nest attacked is usually one of many lying in different directions from the *sanguinea* nest.

When the first workers arrive at the nest to be pillaged, they do not enter it at once, but surround it and wait till the other detachments arrive.   In the meantime the *fusca* or *rufibarbis* scent their approaching foes and either prepare to defend their nest or seize their young and try to break through the cordon of *sanguinea* and escape.   They scramble up the grass-blades with their larvæ and pupæ in their jaws or make off over the ground.   The sanguinary ants, however, intercept them, snatch away their charges and begin to pour into the entrances of the nest.   Soon they issue forth one by one with the remaining larvæ and pupæ and start for home.   They turn and kill the workers of the slave-species only when these offer hostile resistance.   The troop of cocoon-laden *sanguinea* straggle back to their nest, while the bereft ants slowly enter their pillaged formicary and take up the nurture of the few remaining young or await the appearance of future broods.

Forel is of the opinion that many of the young brought home by the *sanguinea* are eaten, for the number of those which eventually hatch and become auxiliaries is very small compared with the number pillaged during the course of the summer.   Wasmann believes, however, that the forays take place for the specific purpose of obtaining young to rear. This seems to be disproved by the fact that even small *sanguinea* colonies are quite able to get along without slaves and by the insignificant number of these individuals in many nests.   Darwin has interpreted the surviving and adopted workers as a kind of by-product, or as representing food which the ants failed to eat at the proper time, and such they would appear to be in the adult colony, though, as we shall see, they have an additional significance as the result of an instinct inherited by the *sanguinea* workers from their queen.   That the foray is, to some extent at least, due to the promptings of hunger, seems to be shown by the fact that *sanguinea* sometimes plunders the nests of ants which it could not adopt as slaves.   Thus Forel and others have described forays of *sanguinea* on *Lasius niger* and *flavus*.

Not only are the forays of *sanguinea* very similar to those of the nest-pillaging Ecitons, but the former ant also resembles the rapacious

Dorylines in its frequent change of dwelling. I have already mentioned the summer and winter nests of *sanguinea,* but this ant is also fond of changing its habitation in the same wood or field and of moving into nests which it has pillaged. Hence one often encounters *sanguinea* workers in the act of moving their young or sexual forms to new quarters. On such occasions they also carry their slaves in the same manner as they carry small workers of their own species; the ant carried being held by the mandibles while she coils herself up and remains motionless under the head and thorax of her carrier. It is not always easy at first sight to distinguish these changes of dwelling from dulotic expeditions.

2. **The American Sanguinea.**—The typical *sanguinea* does not occur in North America, but in its stead we have no less than six subspecies and varieties: *aserva, rubicunda, subnuda, subintegra* (Fig. 268), *puberula* and *obtusopilosa,* and two species: *pergandei* and *munda,* which, however, might be regarded merely as extreme subspecies. All of these forms have the clypeal border notched, a character which serves to distinguish them from our numerous other *Formicæ* of the *rufa, exsecta, fusca* and *pallide-fulva* groups. *F. munda* is confined to the Rocky Mountains, where it lives in rather small colonies and never makes slaves. *F. pergandei* is a more widely distributed species, but seems to be very rare, as only a few of its colonies have been seen. The one from which the types of the species were taken near Washington, D. C., contained also workers of *F. pallide-fulva,* and one which I found near Colorado Springs contained several workers of *subpolita.* The *sanguinea* subspecies and varieties cited above present a maze extremely difficult to disentangle taxonomically, and although I have made many observations on dozens of colonies in different parts of the country, I am quite unable to define their ethological peculiarities. I have no doubt that such peculiarities exist, but their accurate definition will require years of observation over a great area.[1] Some of the forms, such as *rubicunda, aserva* and *subnuda* are preëminently boreal or alpine, others, like *subintegra* and *puberula* prefer warmer latitudes and lower altitudes. In this general account I shall not endeavor to distinguish further between the habits of the various forms, but compare them as a whole with the single European type. This comparison will show that the American forms are peculiar in more than one particular.

The colonies of our *sanguinea* are quite as frequently slaveless as

[1] I have recently found (1908*f*) that the workers of one of our subspecies, *aserva,* are not slave-makers. The queens of this form of *sanguinea* establish their colonies by kidnapping the pupæ of *F. glacialis,* but the workers do not inherit this instinct. Hence the old colonies of *aserva* are pure, as Forel has observed (1900*e*).

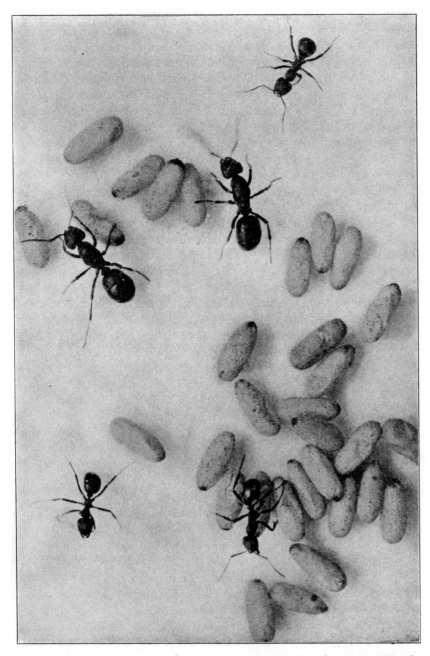

FIG. 268. Deälated queens, workers and cocoons of *Formica subintegra*, nearly twice the natural size. (Photograph by J. G. Hubbard and Dr. O. S. Strong.)

those of the typical form. In the Ute Pass and Florissant Canyon of Colorado I have found localities abounding in slaveless colonies like the localities in Maloja, Samaden and St. Moritz in the Engadin. As a rule, however, the colonies contain slaves and the ratio of these to the *sanguinea* is usually much greater than it is in Europe. The average ratio in seventy colonies on which I have made notes is 1.5 *sanguinea* to 4.5 slaves, which is practically the opposite of the ratio given by Wasmann for the European form. I have been unable to confirm his statement that the number of slaves decreases with the size of the colony, as I have seen many large colonies with numerous slaves and many small ones with few or none at all.

As the typical forms of the *fusca* group of *Formicæ* are confined to Europe, our *sanguinea* is found to enslave our peculiarly American varieties of the same group. Of these we have an extensive series, some of which are very local in their distribution. But still another group of *Formicæ*, that of *pallide-fulva*, not represented in Europe, is compelled to contribute slaves to our *sanguinea*. This group, including the typical *pallide-fulva, schaufussi, incerta, nitidiventris, fuscata*, etc., occurs only east of the Rocky Mountains. The following list includes the names of the *fusca* and *pallide-fulva* forms (cited in the order of their frequency) which I have taken as auxiliaries in the nests of our various *sanguinea:*

1. *F. aserva*—slaves: *F. subsericea, F. glacialis.*
2. *F. rubicunda*—slaves: *F. subsericea, neorufibarbis, subænescens, fuscata, neogagates.*
3. *F. subnuda*—slaves: *F. subsericea, argentata.*
4. *F. subintegra*—slaves: *F. subsericea, glacialis, subpolita, subænescens, nitidiventris, schaufussi, incerta, fuscata, neogagates.*
5. *F. puberula*—slaves: *F. subsericea, argentata, subpolita, neocinerea, neoclara, neogagates.*
6. *F. obtusopilosa*—slave: *F. argentata.*
7. *F. pergandei*—slaves: *F. pallide-fulva, subpolita.*

It will be seen that of the fourteen different slave forms in this list *F. subsericea* (Fig. 269) is far and away the most common. This, *F. glacialis* and *argentata* are also the most closely allied to the European *fusca*. The predominance of *subsericea* as a slave is due to its being the most abundant and widely distributed ant of its group in North America. The other forms are local: *F. cinerea*, e. g., occurring only in sunny meadows from Colorado to Illinois; *neorufibarbis* and *glacialis* in alpine and boreal regions; *neoclara* along the sandy water-courses of the Rocky Mountains; *subænescens* in the shady, deciduous woods of Wisconsin and the neighboring states, etc. These forms are enslaved only when *sanguinea* happens to be living in the particular regions where they are the dominant *fusca* forms. But as these regions are usually inhabited by *subsericea* to some extent, this ant never enjoys complete immunity if there are any slave-makers in the neighborhood. Occasionally *sanguinea* colonies are found to contain slaves of two or even three *fusca* or *pallide-fulva* forms. One small colony observed at the edge of a meadow in Colorado contained *neoclara, neocinerea* and *nitidiventris* workers in nearly equal proportions.

According to my observations, our *sanguinea* makes many more raids during the course of the summer than her European prototype. On

Fig. 269. Deälated females, workers, larvæ, nude and covered pupæ of *Formica subsericea,* nearly twice the natural size. (Photograph by J. G. Hubbard and Dr. O. S. Strong.)

several occasions I have seen a colony plunder a *subsericea* nest nearly every day for a week or a fortnight. Provided Forel's statement in regard to the typical *sanguinea* is correct, this peculiarity of the American forms would account for its having so many more slaves. This, however, is not the only reason: though individually smaller as a rule, less pugnacious and living in smaller and obscurer formicaries, our *sanguinea* enslaves *fusca* forms which are much more cowardly and docile than the typical European *fusca* and *rufibarbis*. This latter is, indeed, very far from being a gentle and tractable ant.

The slave-making tactics of our sanguinary ants are in the main very similar to those of the European form. They usually start on their raids in the morning and may return laden with booty before noon, or their expeditions may drag along for the remainder of the day or even over the following day if the colony to be pillaged is at some distance, of large size and belligerent, or contains a great number of larvæ and pupæ. Sometimes, however, the sortie is postponed till the afternoon. This was the case in the following instance which I take from a number of similar expeditions of which I have kept notes:

Rockford, Ill., July 14. At 4 P. M. I located a large colony of *F. fuscata* which was nesting under a piece of wood in a loose hazel thicket. On removing the wood I found a large, flat chamber, from the bottom of which a single opening 2 cm. in diameter led down into the subterranean galleries of the nest. The chamber was full of *fuscata* workers, winged females, larvæ and naked pupæ and the whole assemblage hastily poured down the opening out of sight. Looking up I saw a scattered army of *rubicunda* rapidly approaching the nest. When they reached the circle of grass immediately surrounding the earth just exposed by the removal of the wood, they stopped and completely surrounded the spot. They waited or kept advancing and retreating, but never entered the hole until the rear detachment had arrived. Even after the whole army, numbering at least 400 *rubicunda*, had assembled, they kept up this advancing and retreating movement for fully fifteen minutes, as if fearing the *fuscata*, which in the meantime were hiding in their nest. Now and then a *rubicunda*, bolder than her sisters, would enter the hole, but dart out again immediately. After twenty minutes more of this manœuvring, however, the slave-makers grew bolder and began to pour into the opening. For some time longer and at intervals of three to five minutes a *rubicunda* would emerge from the nest with a larva or pupa and start for home. As soon as one of these lucky individuals appeared, four or five of the workers on the outside of the nest would try to wrest away her booty. Sometimes one of them was successful and at once started off for her nest. Finally, at 4.35 P. M., thirty-five minutes after the nest had been surrounded, a winged *fuscata* female shot out of the opening, immediately followed by fully fifty others and a flood of *fuscata* workers carrying larvæ and pupæ in their jaws. They scattered at once in all directions, breaking through the *rubicunda* cordon and making for the grass beyond. The *rubicunda* instantly fell upon both females and workers and tore the larvæ and pupæ from the jaws of the latter. The long-legged *fuscata,* however, all managed to escape unscathed and with a few of their young. The wildest excitement prevailed till all the *fuscata* were out of the nest, but not one of them remained on the premises ten minutes after the first winged female had emerged from the opening. The *rubicunda* then proceeded to pillage the nest at their leisure, bringing out the deserted larvæ and pupæ and making for home. I followed them as they hurried off over a very tortuous path under the hazel bushes to their formicary, which was covered by a pile of twigs and dead leaves, some 40 meters from the nest they had pillaged. Loitering about the *rubicunda* nest were a number of slaves, large *subsericea* and an occasional small *fuscata.* These seemed to show great interest in the larvæ and pupæ with which the *rubicunda* were constantly arriving. I returned to the *fuscata* nest. It was now 5.25 P. M. and the last straggling *rubicunda* were just starting home with the last of the pupæ. In the meantime the *fuscata* had established themselves under a bunch of dead leaves around the roots of a hazel bush about two meters from their old quarters. They had transported thither the rescued larvæ and pupæ and were very busy carrying in the workers and females that had strayed about in the grass. This was done with marvellous dispatch and precision. The whole raid had been accomplished in an hour and a half, without the death or injury of a single ant, showing that the *rubicunda,* like her European congener, accomplishes her purpose by surprising and terrorizing rather than by killing the colonies on which she preys. The unharmed *fuscata* could at once set to work to raise another large brood to be pillaged in turn at a later date, and this is as it should be—from the *rubicunda* point of view.

F. *fuscata,* like the other members of the *pallide-fulva* group, is even more cowardly than *subsericea,* so that the raid above described is not typical in all respects. Large *subsericea* or *neoclara* colonies offer a much more hostile resistance to the invading slave-makers, and the battle may continue for hours or even days before the latter succeed in pillaging the nest. At such times the *sanguinea* will not hesitate to use her mandibles and the ground may be strewn with the corpses of both species. Colonies that have been attacked and plundered repeatedly season after season seem to submit to the affliction more passively than those attacked for the first time. Owing to the great differences in the size and condition of the colonies of both the slaves and the slave-makers, the forays of the latter present an enormous range of variability, and it would be desirable to record many more observations on them, both in Europe and North America.

Like the typical *sanguinea,* our American forms may also pillage the nests of ants belonging to strange genera. I once witnessed a ridiculous foray of a large *rubicunda* colony on a woodland variety of *Myrmica scabrinodis* near Rockford, Ill. The foray was carried out exactly as if it had been directed against one of the normal auxiliary species. After killing or putting to flight the *scabrinodis,* the *rubicunda* returned to their nest with the small larvæ and pupæ of an ant belonging to an entirely different subfamily. In another *rubicunda* nest in the same wood, I found two of the flat chambers full of uninjured pupæ of *scabrinodis.* These had evidently been set apart from the *rubicunda* young and from those of the normal auxiliaries (in this case *F. subœnescens*). Forel (1874) made a similar observation on a *sanguinea* nest in which *Lasius niger* and *L. flavus* cocoons had been stacked up in a chamber by themselves. Near Rockford, Ill., a large number of *subintegra* workers were seen one morning to make a normal assault on a *Lasius americanus* colony and to return with a number of cocoons in their jaws and many *Lasius* workers hanging to their legs and antennæ. These forays, which are probably not at all infrequent and are, moreover, undoubtedly undertaken by colonies of considerable size and of some experience in capturing the normal auxiliaries, point to hunger as one of the impulses which compels them to undertake their expeditions. We can hardly suppose that *sanguinea* workers, even after some practice in making slaves, have any definite ideal association between the kidnapped pupæ and the slaves that hatch from them or they would not make forays on such unsuitable species.

3. **The Founding of the Sanguinea Colony.**—How do the mixed colonies of the facultative slave-makers arise? As no one had been able to observe the behavior of the *sanguinea* queen just after descending from her nuptial flight and while establishing her colony, Forel and Wasmann supposed that she must either be adopted by some colony of the slave species or bring up unaided a brood of her own which could then by dulosis make the mixed colony. During the summer of 1905 I performed a number of experiments on young, artificially deälated queens, introducing them into nests containing several *subsericea* workers with their brood. I here transcribe the account of one of these experiments from my paper " On the Founding of Colonies by Queen Ants " (1906c):

July 8, 9 A. M. A *rubicunda* female was placed in a nest containing 33 *subsericea* workers, small and large, 150 cocoons, and a few larvæ. The workers at once seized their cocoons and fled into the light chamber. One or two of them attacked the female, but she shook them off and killed one of them. In the meantime some of the workers kept stealing into the dark chamber for the purpose of securing cocoons and carried them to the remotest corner of the light chamber. As the morning wore away the female gradually became more and more excited. By 1 P. M. she had killed five more workers and was busy carrying the cocoons back from the illuminated into the dark chamber, where she had already stored most of them in a corner. In a few minutes she had secured all the cocoons in the light chamber, 36 in number. She interrupted this task twice, each time for the purpose of killing a worker that came within her reach. Finally she retired to the dark chamber and began to collect the cocoons into a more compact pile. Two of the workers persisted in stealing in and hurrying back with a cocoon taken from the edge of the pile. The female soon perceived this, however, and dispatched both of them. The whole performance resembled a dulotic expedition in miniature, carried out by a single virgin queen instead of by an army of *rubicunda* workers. In killing the *subsericea* workers she was quite as ruthless as the workers of her own species, but more sure on account of her larger size and greater strength. She exhibited very beautifully what may be called the "prancing" movement, so characteristic of the females in this stage of their activities. She moved in a jerky fashion, taking a few steps in one direction, then turning her body and taking a few steps more. July 9, 8 A. M., only two of the workers survived. They had regained possession of 30 of their cocoons, however, and were guarding them in a remote corner of the light chamber, while the female was watching over the great bulk of the brood in a corner of the dark chamber. By 10.30 she had entered the light chamber, recaptured all but 6 of the cocoons, carried them into the dark chamber and placed them on her pile. The two workers were wandering about in a state of "abulic dejection." At 11.30 one of them was seen to enter the dark chamber and approach the female, but the latter opened her mandibles and the worker fled. The female had stacked her cocoons in a compact heap and was bent on defending them. Apparently she had not forgotten the 6 cocoons still remaining in the light chamber. At any rate, she secured 4 of them by 12 M. She took up her position on the pile of cocoons, and whenever light was admitted into the dark chamber, opened her mandibles and went to prancing about as if looking for an enemy. By 1.15 P. M. she had secured one of the remaining cocoons in the light chamber. July 10, 6 A. M. In the night the female had killed the two remaining workers and had taken their last cocoon. Throughout the day she kept closely to the brood, prancing whenever the light was admitted into the chamber and fiercely seizing a straw or my finger whenever either was held near her. She seemed to display a much greater interest in the pupæ than in the larvæ. July 11 to 15 she remained *in statu quo*. Whenever the nest was uncovered she hastily took up a cocoon and tried to conceal it. July 16, 7 A. M., five callow workers had hatched during the night. One larva had been partially eaten by the female. At 1.40 she was surprised in the act of opening a cocoon. She used her fore and middle feet to hold the cocoon while she tore a large, elliptical hole with her mandibles in the portion of its wall overlying the concave ventral surface of the pupa. Through this hole the worker was later drawn after it had thrust out its antennæ and legs. Whenever the nest was uncovered throughout this and the following of the first days, the female could nearly always be detected in the act of either opening a cocoon or removing the pupal envelope from a callow just released. By the afternoon of July 16 some of the callows began to assist the female in releasing their sister workers so that the number of callows now began to increase rapidly. On the morning of July 17 there were 19 altogether, by 5 P. M. 24, by 7.30 A. M., July 18, 30, and by 7.30 A. M., July 19, 50. On the following days the numbers ran thus: July 20, about 60; July 21, about 75; July 22, about 100; July 23 and 24, about 130. This completed the callow brood, as some of the cocoons failed to hatch. The female took the greatest interest in her black family, and they bestowed on her every attention. Soon after they had begun to feed and clean her another marked change supervened in her instincts. Instead of defending herself and brood when the nest was uncovered she slunk away, or at any rate attempted to conceal herself among the mass of workers. She had become highly photophobic and behaved exactly like the old queens, that invariably make for the galleries whenever the nest is disturbed or illuminated. This experiment was concluded and the ants were liberated in the garden on July 26.

The above experiment shows very clearly that the female *rubicunda,* when placed with a small number of *subsericea* workers and their pupæ, displays a chain of instincts that result in her gaining possession of the latter. To all appearances she is quite ready to be amicably adopted by the *subsericea,* but when received with marked hostility, as is probably almost invariably the case, her animosity is very quickly kindled, and she slays the *subsericea* with all possible dispatch, thus manifesting instincts very similar to those of her own workers when engaged in a dulotic raid. Owing to her powerful mandibles and closely knit frame she is always a match for several workers and may kill as many as twenty-one of these in a very short time. Before she has killed them all, however, she becomes much interested in their brood, eagerly collects and secretes it in some favorable corner and guards it with open mandibles till the callows are ready to hatch. These she skilfully divests of their cocoons and pupal envelopes. Their advent in considerable numbers appears to be the signal for another marked change in the instincts of the female. She now becomes very timid, fleeing whenever the nest is disturbed and taking refuge in the darkest and remotest corner of the nest. In this instinct phase the female remains throughout the remainder of her life. The reactions displayed in the foregoing experiment are, moreover, so definite, uniform and purposeful even in artificial nests that one can hardly doubt that they are similarly manifested in a state of nature. It is evident that, especially in timid, incipient, wild colonies of *F. subsericea,* the females may meet with less opposition and therefore with greater and more immediate success. Still the fact that *rubicunda* is a local ant and by no means one of our most abundant species shows that the successful establishment of colonies in a state of nature must be attended with considerable difficulties. The search of the *rubicunda* female for weak or incipient *subsericea* colonies, even in regions where the latter ant is very abundant, must often be vain or illusory. This is tantamount to saying that the element of chance must enter very largely into the life of the *rubicunda* queen, just as it does into the lives of most parasitic animals.

If it should happen that the *rubicunda* queen enters a *subsericea* nest with a queen of its own, the latter must be eliminated. In one of my artificial nests there was a queen cocoon among the worker cocoons of *subsericea* appropriated by the *rubicunda.* She eventually hatched and lived unmolested for a time. In the course of some weeks, however, the *subsericea* workers began to pull their sister about by the legs and antennæ in a vicious manner. One morning, probably as a result of this treatment, she was found dead in the nest. This assassination of a queen by her sister workers acquires a new significance in the light of Santschi's observations on *Wheeleriella* and *Monomorium salomonis* to be described in Chapter XXVII. Perhaps in many cases the *subsericea* queen is simply driven out of the nest or killed by the intrusive *rubicunda* queen. Which of these two methods is commonly adopted can be determined only by further observations and experiments. It is certain, however, that queens of the slave species are not permitted to live in mixed dulotic colonies of the *sanguinea* and *Polyergus* type. In this respect these colonies resemble the mixed colonies of the temporary and permanent social parasites.

My experiments and conclusions were received with skepticism by Wasmann (1906h) and Escherich, because they had been performed on unfertilized queens. These authors argued that fecundated queens in their natural environment would probably behave differently. Wasmann performed several experiments with such queens and found that they were adopted by the slave species without hostility. Viehmeyer, however, has recently (1908) found that the fecundated European *sanguinea* behaves in precisely the same manner as *rubicunda,* and still more recently (1908*b*) Wasmann has repeated his experiments with this same result. A number of experiments which I performed during the summer of 1907 with queens of *F. aserva* and *subintegra* showed that these insects behave precisely like *rubicunda* (Wheeler, 1908*f*).

Although the young colony of *sanguinea* resembles that of the temporary parasites like *F. consocians* and *tuncicola,* it differs in one important respect: the alien workers which it contains are younger, whereas in the incipient colony of the temporary parasite, they are older than the queen. Santschi (1906) therefore calls the former a " pupillary," the latter a " tutelary " parasite. Wasmann and Santschi believe that slavery has arisen from temporary parasitism, but although I was the first to advance this opinion, I have been compelled to abandon it. Wasmann found that a colony of *F. truncicola,* which he has shown to be a temporary social parasite in all essential particulars like *F. consocians,* accepted and reared *fusca* pupæ placed in its nest. This, however, is not dulosis. In order to establish his case he would have to prove that the *truncicola* workers can also make periodical forays on *fusca* for the sake of capturing their young, and there is no more evidence that *truncicola* can do this than there is of similar behavior on the part of *consocians.* Santschi, if I understand him correctly, believes that the *sanguinea* colony restricts its forays to the scattered fragments of the original *fusca* colony from which the queen secured her first supply of auxiliaries, and that the slave-making expeditions cease when these fragments are exhausted. This assumption seems to explain the fact that old *sanguinea* colonies are sometimes slaveless and pure, like the adult colonies of *consocians, truncicola,* etc. It is, however, rendered highly improbable by the fact that both in Europe and in North America *sanguinea* colonies not infrequently contain slaves of two or more different species or varieties. There is also some evidence that the same colony may have slaves of different species at different times (see p. 472). The similarity between old *sanguinea* colonies and adult colonies of temporary parasites like *F. consocians* may be due to various causes: in the slave-makers to a dearth of suitable nests to pillage, or adaptation to an independent life owing to sufficiency of other food (dead insects, honey-dew, etc.), or to a lapsing of the predaceous instincts with age; in the temporary parasites the purity of the colony is brought about, as has been shown, by a gradual extinction of the tutelary workers. In my opinion both temporary parasitism and dulosis have arisen independently from the practice of *F. rufa* and *F. sanguinea* of adopting fertilized queens of their own species, and to this extent my views coincide with those of Wasmann and Santschi.

Great difficulty was formerly experienced in accounting for the various dulotic instincts, because these were supposed to be the exclusive property of the sterile workers. On this assumption they could be transmitted only through the queen and she was supposed not to manifest them. The discovery in the queen of a type of behavior essentially like that of the workers solves this problem, for these instincts are seen to be primarily important in the establishment of the colony. They are naturally inherited by the workers, but in this caste they have been modified and intensified by fusion with the foraging instincts. Thus instincts which in the reproductive caste are useful in establishing the colony are useful in the sterile caste in procuring food and incidentally, perhaps, in adding to the working personnel of the colony. The differences in the display of the instinct by the two castes is due to the fact that the workers make their forays in concert and on populous colonies of the slave species, which the female could probably not enter. The discriminative character of dulosis, that is, its concentration on particular slave species, may be readily explained by the fact that both worker and queen *sanguinea* have been reared by the slave-workers, or at any rate have become familiar with them in the parental nest. What is more natural, therefore, than that both *sanguinea* queens and workers should seek out colonies of the familiar species, the queens for the purpose of nidification, the workers for the purpose of obtaining food? If we adopt Wasmann's view that the young of the slave species are pillaged for the purpose of being reared instead of eaten, we may suppose that the pure colonies of these species in the vicinity of the *sanguinea* nests appear to these ants as so many detached and refractory portions of their own colony and therefore to be brought together in the one nest. I have already given my reasons for dissenting from Wasmann's view, although I admit that the *sanguinea* workers of the same or different colonies may inherit in very different intensities their mother's instinct to pillage larvæ and cocoons for the sake of rearing them, and that the number of slaves in a colony may represent the degree to which this instinct on the part of the workers preponderates over that of hunger. Hunger and affection are such closely linked emotions in all animals that we cannot doubt that queens and workers alike possess them. They are, moreover, displayed by all ants in their tendency to eat their own larvæ and pupæ. It is certain, however, that a rational explanation of slavery can be formed only by recognizing it as a form of parasitism in which the slaves are the host.

But as the slaves are brought together from different colonies, the host is really synthetic. Santschi expresses this conception when he says: " In fine, slavery reduces itself to a form of pupillary parasitism that perpetuates and extends itself beyond the confines of the nest." The dulotic raid and synthetic character of the host sharply distinguish the slave-makers from the temporary parasites.

CHAPTER XXVI

THE AMAZONS, OR OBLIGATORY SLAVE-MAKERS

" L'histoire des fourmis amazones et de leurs auxiliaires, nous prouve encore, que si l'éducation peut effacer la haine qui existe entre des espèces différentes, et par conséquent ennemies, elle ne sauroit changer leur instinct et leur caractère, puisque les amazones et leurs esclaves, élevées avec les mêmes soins et par les mêmes nourrices, vivent dans la fourmilière mixte sous des lois entièrement opposées."—P. Huber, " Recherches sur les Moeurs des Fourmis Indigènes," 1810.

The observations recorded in the last chapter show that the European and American sanguinary ants represent two different stages in the development of slavery, and suggest the question as to which is the more advanced or specialized. The greater variation and usually smaller size of the New World forms indicate a more primitive or inchoate condition, but, on the other hand, the greater number of slaves and more frequent expeditions, except in *F. aserva,* indicate a higher and more specialized development of the dulotic instincts. A very similar problem confronts us in the obligatory slave-makers of the genus *Polyergus,* the amazons, whose distribution parallels in an interesting manner that of *F. sanguinea. Polyergus,* too, is circumpolar, with only a single representative in Europe, the typical *P. rufescens,* whereas North America has at least four subspecies and a few undescribed varieties. The subspecies are: *P. breviceps,* ranging from the Rocky Mountains eastward to Illinois and Kansas; *mexicanus* in Mexico; *bicolor,* known only from Wisconsin and Illinois, and *lucidus,* ranging from the Atlantic seaboard, north of the Carolinas, to the eastern slopes of the Rocky Mountains. The genus is therefore represented by the greatest number òf different forms in the Middle West.

1. **The European Amazons.**—*P. rufescens* was the first slave-making ant to be described by P. Huber (1810). His splendid observations were confirmed and extended by Forel in 1874 and little of importance has since been added. Unlike *sanguinea, rufescens* is, on the whole, a rare ant, especially in northern Europe. In Switzerland, however, along the shores of Lake Leman, where Huber and Forel carried on their investigations, one may be sure of finding a number of its colonies without difficulty. It is one of the most beautiful of ants, the worker and female being of a rich brownish-red color, slightly tinged with

purplish, while the male is coal-black with white wings. The worker is extremely pugnacious, and, like the female, may be readily distinguished from the other Camponotine ants by its sickle-shaped, toothless, but very minutely denticulate mandibles. Such mandibles are not adapted for digging in the earth or for handling thin-skinned larvæ or pupæ and moving them about in the narrow chambers of the nest, but are admirably fitted for piercing the armor of adult ants. We find therefore that the amazons never excavate nests nor care for their own young. They are even incapable of obtaining their own food, although they may lap up water or liquid food when this happens to come in contact with their short tongues. For the essentials of food, lodging and education they are wholly dependent on the slaves hatched from the worker cocoons that they have pillaged from alien colonies. Apart from these slaves they are quite unable to live, and hence are always found in mixed colonies inhabiting nests whose architecture throughout is that of the slave species. Thus the amazons display two contrasting sets of instincts. While in the home nest they sit about in stolid idleness or pass the long hours begging the slaves for food or cleaning themselves and burnishing their ruddy armor, but when outside the nest on one of their predatory expeditions they display a dazzling courage and capacity for concerted action compared with which the raids of *sanguinea* resemble the clumsy efforts of a lot of untrained militia. The amazons may, therefore, be said to represent a more specialized and perfected stage of dulosis than that of the sanguinary ants. In attaining to this stage, however, they have become irrevocably dependent and parasitic. Wasmann believes that *Polyergus* is actually descended from *F. sanguinea,* but it is more probable that both of these ants arose in pretertiary times from some common but now extinct ancestor. The normal slaves of the European amazons are the same as those reared by *sanguinea,* viz: *F. fusca, glebaria, rubescens, cinerea* and *rufibarbis;* and of these *fusca* is the most frequent. But the ratio of the different components in the mixed nests is the reverse of that in *sanguinea* colonies, there being usually five to seven times as many slaves as amazon workers. The simultaneous occurrence of two kinds of slaves in a single nest is extremely rare, even when the same amazon colony pillages the nests of different forms of *fusca* during the same season. This is very probably the result of the slaves' having a decided preference for rearing only the pupæ of their own species or variety and eating any others that are brought in. Two slave forms may, however, appear in succession in the same nest. Near Morges, Switzerland, Professor Forel showed me an amazon colony which during the summer of 1904 contained only *rufibarbis* slaves, but during 1907 contained only *glebaria*.

Unlike *sanguinea, rufescens* makes many expeditions during July and August, but these expeditions are made only during the afternoon hours. One colony observed by Forel (1874) made 44 sorties on thirty afternoons between June 29 and August 18. It undoubtedly made many more which were not observed, as Forel was unable to visit the colony daily. He gives the following statistics on these 44 expeditions: "On 4 of them the army separated into two columns, from 6 it returned without having found a nest to plunder (through fatigue or losing the trail), on 3 the amazons found only formicaries containing neither larvæ nor cocoons, from 6 they brought back only a meager supply of these, from 25 a great number. Of the 44 attacks, 19 were on *fusca* colonies and 19 on *rufibarbis*. Three of the latter were unsuccessful because they yielded no booty. The same formicary was visited repeatedly: the ants visited altogether 7 colonies of *fusca* (one 6 times, one 4 times, one 3 times, two twice and two once), and 8 *rufibarbis* colonies (one 5 times, two 4 times, one twice and four once)." Forel estimated the number of amazons in the colony at more than 1,000 and the total number of pupæ captured at 29,300 (14,000 *fusca,* 13,000 *rufibarbis* and 2,300 of unknown provenience, but probably *fusca*). The total number for the summer (1873) was estimated at 40,000. This number is certainly above the average, as the amazon colony was an unusually large one. Colonies with only 300 to 500 amazons are more frequent, but a third or half of the above number of pillaged cocoons shows what an influence the presence of a few colonies of these ants must have on the *Formica* colonies of their neighborhood. Of course, only a small proportion of the cocoons are reared. Many of them are undoubtedly injured by the sharp mandibles of the amazons and many are destroyed and eaten after they have been brought home.

The tactics of *Polyergus,* as I have said, are very different from those of *sanguinea*. The ants leave the nest very suddenly and assemble about the entrance if they are not, as sometimes happens, pulled back and restrained by their slaves. Then they move out in a compact column with feverish haste, sometimes, according to Forel, at the rate of a meter in 33⅓ seconds or 3 cm. per second. On reaching the nest to be pillaged, they do not hesitate like *sanguinea* but pour into it at once in a body, seize the brood, rush out again and make for home. When attacked by the slave species they pierce the heads or thoraces of their opponents and often kill them in considerable numbers. The return to the nest with the booty is usually made more leisurely and in less serried ranks.

The observer of one of these forays cannot fail to be impressed with the marvellous precision of its execution. Although the ants may occasionally lose their way and have to retrace their steps or start off in a different direction, they usually make straight for the nest to be plundered. They must, therefore, like *sanguinea,* possess a keen sense and memory of locality. There can be little doubt that they often leave the nest singly and make a careful reconnoissance of the slave colonies in the vicinity. "This year [1873]," says Forel, "I kept seeing the amazons of my colony leaving the nest one by one and going great distances (as much as fifty paces from the nest), marching a short distance at a time. I saw some in little squads of four or five inspecting the nests of *F. fusca* situated at more than thirty paces from their own. They hunted out the openings and carefully scrutinized the surroundings. These facts prove more and more that each amazon worker studies the slave-nests around its own and on its own account, and this permits the army as a whole to direct itself in a mass and to reach a decision at a given moment."

It is an interesting fact that the slaves take on certain peculiarities, apparently by imitation, from the amazons with which they are living. The timid *fusca, e. g.,* becomes fierce and aggressive, a peculiarity which it also acquires when dwelling with *sanguinea.* In *rufibarbis* the change in behavior is less apparent, because this ant, even when living alone, is very belligerent. The behavior of the amazons seems also to be influenced by their slaves. According to Forel, those with *rufibarbis* slaves leave their nests more frequently and earlier and later in the day and move in denser armies and more rapidly than amazons with *fusca* slaves. It is rather difficult to account for these colonial idiosyncrasies. Perhaps only the more vigorous *Polyergus* succeed in enslaving *rufibarbis,* while feebler or more languid colonies have to content themselves with the more tractable *fusca.* While in its nest *rufescens* is under the tutelage of its slaves. These sometimes prevent the warriors from making a foray or go out and meet them, when they have gone astray and carry them home. When the colony moves to a new nest the slaves take charge of matters and carry the amazons. We have seen that when the *sanguinea* colony changes its headquarters, it is the slaves that are carried.

2. **The American Amazons.**—I have been able to observe all our American subspecies of *rufescens* in a living condition, except *mexicanus,* which is known only from a few cabinet specimens. Even the precise locality from which these came is unknown, but it must have been either in the northern portion of Mexico, or if further south, at a considerable altitude. The worker of this subspecies resembles that of

breviceps very closely, judging from Forel's description (1899*a*) and a couple of type specimens which he has generously given me. The Mexican form differs only in having very few or no hairs on the dorsal surface of the body, and is hardly more than a variety of *breviceps*. Its slaves are unknown but are in all probability some form of *fusca*. I take from my note books the following observations on our other amazons:

(*a*) *Polyergus breviceps.*—This subspecies, which I shall call the occidental amazon, is not uncommon in several localities in the mountains of Colorado and New Mexico at altitudes between 2,000 and 2,500 m. I have also seen a few specimens that were taken at much lower elevations in Illinois and Kansas. Of all our subspecies *breviceps* resembles the European type most closely. Its color, pilosity and sculpture are practically the same, it forms rather large formicaries and its slaves are much like those of *rufescens*. These comprise *F. argentata, subsericea* and *neocinerea,* ants so similar in size and color that they would be regarded as identical by any one but a myrmecologist. *F. neocinerea* occurs only in rich meadows, the two others on dryer ground. The ratio of slaves to *breviceps* workers is the same as that of *fusca* to *rufescens* in Switzerland. During the summer of 1903 and 1906 I witnessed several forays of *breviceps* in Cheyenne Canyon near Colorado Springs and in Florissant Canyon, west of Pikes Peak. One of the most typical of these forays was seen in the former locality. An unusually large colony, containing fully 1,000 *breviceps* workers, was found nesting under some large stones near the top of the steep bank of Cheyenne Creek. The formicary extended out under the stones and must have covered an area of fully 2.5 sq. m. Under the edge of one of the stones was the single entrance, about 2 cm. in diameter. July 20 at 1 P. M., after seeing a few *breviceps* and their slaves (*subsericea*) loitering about the entrance, I stationed myself at the nest in the hope of witnessing a foray. After waiting nearly an hour (at 1.55 P. M.) I saw the beautiful red ants boil up, so to speak, in the opening. In a few moments they came rushing out in great numbers and kept running about just outside the entrance till 2.15, when they started in a compact army up the embankment and obliquely in a south-westerly direction. Soon, however, they returned to the nest as if changing their minds and again started out due south and straight up the bank. The procession formed with great alacrity and then pushed ahead at the rate of one m. in forty seconds, over smooth ground, but requiring about one minute to make the same distance over the dead oak leaves. There was no leader, the army being headed by a few workers which were continually being passed by workers overtaking them from the rear. They neither hesitated nor stopped till they reached a large *subsericea* nest about 25 m. from their own, on the top of the embankment. This nest was under and around a couple of large, flat stones, and had two entrances a short distance apart. There were a few *subsericea* sauntering about the entrance, but as soon as they scented the approaching army they scampered into their nest. The amazons arrived at 2.40 P. M. and at once poured into the two entrances in a mass like wine being poured into a couple of funnels. Two minutes later the first *breviceps* emerged with a cocoon in her jaws and was at once followed by a file of others similarly laden. They started for home in great precipitation. One that was timed made the entire distance of 25 m. in a little more than four minutes. As the army must have comprised fully 1,000 workers, there was soon a long file, each carrying a larva, nude pupa or cocoon. I returned to the *subsericea* nest in time to see a few workers of this species rush out of the opening with larvæ, run the gauntlet of the amazons and make off to the open ground beyond. From time to time a *breviceps* would emerge from the nest carrying a *subsericea* worker, take it a few centimeters from the opening and put it down. To my surprise the black ant scrambled to her feet and ran away uninjured. I saw this performance repeated more than a dozen time by different amazons. Not a single *subsericea* was killed or even maimed! The plundering of the nest continued, the *breviceps* returning repeatedly from their own nest to get more pupæ. By 2.55 the number of these brought out of the nest had dwindled considerably and at 3.06 the supply ceased altogether. Nevertheless the *breviceps* kept entering the nest and coming out with empty jaws till 3.15 when they began to straggle home. The last ones left the pillaged formicary at 3.30 and moved away slowly or sauntered about as if reluctant to return home without booty. The feverish excitement so apparent in these insects a few moments before had suddenly subsided. At the entrance of their own formicary the slaves were running about in considerable numbers and seemed to be greatly excited over the quantities of booty that were being brought in. Soon, however, both slaves and *breviceps* entered their nest and all was quiet. I again went back and found the *subsericea* cautiously returning to their pillaged nest. On raising the stones I found a great many unharmed workers in the galleries but not a single larva or pupa. These ants must have remained in their nest during the whole time that the rape of their brood was in progress! The foray was remarkable on account of the behavior of both species, for the *subsericea,* though abundant, had made no attempt to protect the young which they had for weeks been rearing with infinite solicitude, and the *breviceps* had been more courteous and considerate than their vocation of professional kidnappers would seem to permit.

In the neighborhood of Colorado Spring *breviceps* is rare and sporadic, but in the subalpine meadows about Florissant it is as common as the typical *rufescens* in the meadows on the shores of Lake Leman. The nests of *neocinerea* in which *breviceps* lives at Florissant are grass-covered mounds like those of the European *glebaria* and *rubescens,* but larger (sometimes nearly a meter in diameter and 2–3 dcm. high). On the slopes surrounding the meadows, however, the western amazon also lives in the nests of *argentata,* which are usually found under stones or logs. The abundance of these slave-makers at such an altitude (2,500 m.) indicates that they belong to the Canadian zone and that they will also be found in the southern portions of British America. This distribution is significant in connection with their close structural and ethological relationship to the European and probably also Asiatic *rufescens.*

(*b*) *Polyergus bicolor.*—This subspecies was simultaneously discovered by Father Muckermann at Prarie-du-Chien, Wis., and myself at Rockford, Ill., and has not been recorded from any other localities. It is closely related to *breviceps,* but differs in its smaller size and in having the gaster of the worker and female black, instead of red, like the remainder of the body. We may therefore call it the black and red amazon. Like *breviceps* it often forms rather large colonies and its slave (*F. subænescens*) is closely allied to the typical European *fusca* and *gagates.* *F. subænescens,* according to my observations, occurs only in rich, shady woods, and prefers to nest in logs or stumps so rotten as to be easily broken apart. The six colonies of *bicolor* which I have found in widely separated localities near Rockford, were all in such logs or stumps in shady spots where the undergrowth had been removed. The average ratio of *bicolor* to *subænescens* workers in the mixed colonies was at 1 : 3. The following notes were made on a single colony of these ants late in July and early in August, 1902:

July 24, 2 P. M., I came upon a troop of about 300 *bicolor* in the act of pillaging a rather large *subænescens* colony that was nesting in a small rotten stump under some hickory trees. The stump was cautiously broken open and the *bicolor* were seen rushing about the galleries, biting the shining, black *subænescens,* or even the bits of wood in a kind of insensate " Mordlust." The *subænescens* seemed to be more dismayed than injured. The *bicolor* seized the larvæ and pupæ with tremulous eagerness and began to leave the nest. Soon the whole troop, laden with booty, was under way, in an open phalanx, threading the grass and pattering over the dead leaves. By 2.20 they had reached their own nest, which was in a dead branch only 8 cm. in diameter, concealed under a pile of old oak leaves. Some of the ants made one or two journeys back to the *subænescens* nest, which was some 20 m. from their own, for the purpose of bringing the remaining pupæ. The *subænescens* workers were left wandering about their stump disconsolately and by 2.30 all the *bicolor* had entered their branch under the leaves.

July 26, I again visited the *bicolor* nest, but a shower came up, so that no observations could be made. July 27, the rain continued and although it cleared off in the afternoon the amazons remained in their nest.

July 29 was warm and sunny. I reached the nest at 1.35 P. M., just as the straggling rear of the army was issuing from under the leaves covering the dead branch. The main body had advanced only 2.5 m. from the nest and was soon joined by the stragglers. The ants moved rapidly at a rate of 1.3 m. per minute in a rather compact body 2.3 m. long and 5–15 cm. broad. They seemed to be greatly excited and hastened on in frenzied eagerness. When about 10 m. from the nest they halted as if they had lost their way and scurried about wildly in all directions over and under the dead leaves. This lasted nearly fifteen minutes. Then the troop again formed and advanced even more rapidly than before in the direction of the stump where I first saw it July 24 in the act of pillaging a *subænescens* nest. But when the ants had come within about 1.5 m. of the stump they veered off to the left to a pile of dead leaves. At this point a few *subænescens* workers were running about and it seemed as if there must be a nest of these ants in the immediate vicinity. Such was evidently also the impression of the amazons, for the troop halted and began to scurry about under the leaves. The few *subænescens* did not desert the premises, but fell upon the amazons and pulled them about by the legs and antennæ. Fully fifteen minutes were consumed in this feverish search. Then the amazons seemed to have gained the impression that there was no nest at this spot. The column turned back slowly, with movements indicative of disappointment or fatigue. After retreating about 2 m. in the direction of their own nest, an offshoot of the troop suddenly started to the right and after covering about 60 cm. came upon a nest. I raised the leaves slightly and found a small hollow in the vegetable mould containing several hundred *subænescens* workers huddled about some twenty larvæ and pupæ. This undoubtedly represented a colony that had been previously pillaged, probably the one I had seen attacked July 24. The poor ants had moved first to the spot where the *bicolor* had first scented them, but had again decamped and were now detected. The amazons pounced upon the disheartened band, part of which scattered in all directions with a few of the larvæ. Many, however, stood their ground resolutely and attacked the invaders. These lashed themselves into a kind of fury, pierced the heads and thoraces of the *subœnescens* with their sickle-shaped jaws and strewed the leaves with their jet-black corpses. There were very few larvæ and pupæ to take home, but many of the amazons seized uninjured *subœnescens* and joined the ranks of the homeward bound procession. They moved back in a long, loose file, very unlike the compact troop on its outward journey, and over a different path. They arrived at their nest by 2.35 P. M. The whole foray had taken little more than an hour and only a quarter of this time had been spent in pillaging the temporary *subœnescens* nest.

July 30. I remained in the vicinity of the *bicolor* nest from 1.10 to 4.30 P. M., but there was no sortie, although the weather was propitious.

July 31. There was no sortie, but I stayed near the nest and made the following observations: At 2 P. M. a single amazon left the branch and by her apparent determination arrested my attention. She hurried on in a southeasterly direction over a rather irregular course, making short excursions to the right and left, and exploring every hole and cavity in the ground and under the dead leaves. I followed her for a distance of nearly 25 m. to a pile of dead leaves heaped about the base of an old stump. Here she slipped out of sight. After waiting some minutes for her to reappear, I removed the leaves and found, a few cm. from the spot where I had lost sight of her, a large *subœnescens* nest containing many larvæ and pupæ. The galleries ran under the dead leaves and up into the stump. This nest had evidently not been pillaged during the course of the summer, and I inferred that the amazon was a scout that had succeeded in locating a treasure. She failed to reappear and must have returned to her nest unnoticed. About half an hour later another amazon left the nest in the branch and made off in a direction at a right angle to the first. She went about 2 m. in one direction, then turned abruptly and continued 2.3 m. in another direction to a large rotten stump surrounded by dead leaves. Like the first scout she slipped under the leaves and failed to reappear. As several *subœnescens* were running about on the stump, there must have been a nest in the immediate neighborhood, but I failed to find it. After watching the amazon nest for some time longer without observing any further developments, I went home.

August 1. On reaching the *bicolor* nest at 1.10 P. M. I noticed no unusual activity. A few of the amazons and slaves emerged from time to time from the mass of oak leaves covering the branch and anon reëntered the nest. At 1.15 a *bicolor* scout emerged and went in the direction taken by one of the scouts on July 31. I followed her for about 6 m. when she disappeared under the dead leaves. I returned to the nest in time to see another scout start out and move away in the opposite direction. When about 4 m. from the nest she also disappeared under the leaves. At 1.35 the *bicolor,* about 300 strong, came pouring out of the nest as if in response to some sudden signal. They were not restrained by the slaves loitering about the entrance, but moved around rather leisurely for some minutes like a crowd assembling. Then at 1.40 P. M. they started and soon detached themselves completely from the nest. I expected to see them make for one of the stumps that had been reconnoitered by the scouts July 31, but they took the opposite direction. They moved very rapidly, in a more crowded body than they had presented on previous occasions, and four to six abreast. They soon reached the spot where some twenty minutes before I had seen the first scout disappear. Here they halted for a few moments and assembled, then they turned at a right angle and proceeded about half a meter and forthwith began to disappear under the leaves. Two *subænescens* suddenly darted out with larvæ in their jaws and fled. I raised the leaves and found in a depression of the soil about 500 *subænescens* workers and two deälated queens all huddled together with only six or eight pupæ in their midst. This was certainly a temporary nest in which the ants had taken refuge after being plundered by the amazons on some previous afternoon. The *bicolor* fell upon them, tore away their few remaining pupæ and by 1.50 P. M. were starting home. At first the *subænescens* did not flee, but hung about as if thoroughly disheartened or indifferent. Some of them attacked the amazons, but these for some reason showed very little animosity. Finally the *subænescens* dispersed and the amazons filed home, many of them carrying uninjured *subænescens,* apparently because they did not wish to leave the nest with empty jaws. By a few minutes past two the slave-makers were all in their branch under the oak leaves and all was quiet in the neighborhood.

August 2. Arriving at the *bicolor* nest at 1.20 P. M. I saw the last members of the troop just leaving the dead oak leaves. I followed the stragglers and found that the army had assembled at the spot to which I had traced the first scout August 1. The ants were ferreting in some galleries in the vegetable mould under the leaves, but there were no *subænescens* to be seen. They seemed to be very reluctant to leave the spot, but they finally spread apart and began to investigate the oak leaves in the vicinity. They soon reached the stump that had contained the flourishing *subænescens* colony reconnoitered by the scout, climbed about on it and thrust their heads into every cranny. It was all to no purpose—the *subænescens* had moved away with their fine lot of young. Slowly and in what seemed to be a crestfallen and disappointed spirit the amazons assembled and returned with empty jaws to their nest. They had all entered the dead branch before 2 P M.

August 5. At 1.45 P. M. I visited the *bicolor* nest for the last time. Carefully removing the dead oak leaves I broke open the branch, but it was empty. The colony had moved to some other spot and I searched for it in vain in the neighborhood.

These observations are recorded in detail because they illustrate so many of the interesting peculiarities of the amazons. The behavior of

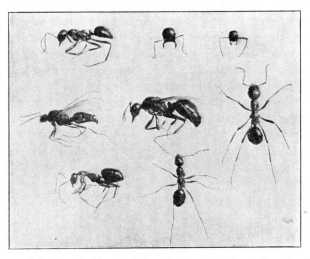

Fig. 270. *Polyergus lucidus* and its slave, somewhat enlarged. (Original.) In the upper row: worker of *P. lucidus,* head of same and head of *Formica schaufussi;* in the middle row, male, virgin female and worker of *P. lucidus;* in the lower row workers of *F. schaufussi.*

the scouts confirms Forel's opinion of the way in which the location of slave nests is ascertained, and the behavior of the amazon troup and of the harassed *subænescens* colonies on successive days shows how complicated are the environmental conditions which these insects have to meet and the intricacy of the problems with which the observer has to deal. The slave colonies are repeatedly plundered and driven from pillar to post, till they probably emigrate to other localities in sheer desperation. Then the *Polyergus,* too, finding no nests to pillage, are compelled to seek a new field for their persistent and pernicious activities. Surely Fabre is right in maintaining that the life of a predatory parasite is not a bed of roses. The amazons have indeed acquired brilliant military instincts, but if these ants were capable of reflection they might occasionally regret having abandoned the quiet pastoral life which their ancestors probably led.

(c) *Polyergus lucidus* (Figs. 270 and 271).—This is the largest, handsomest and most graceful of our amazons, and even surpasses the European form in its brilliant red coloring and gleaming surface. It may be called the shining amazon. Owing to its wide distribution in the Eastern States it has been known for some time. Mrs. Treat (1877) and McCook (1880b) saw its colonies, but Burrill (1908) is the only author who has described one of its forays. In the Atlantic States it is very rare and sporadic. During the past five years I have seen only four of its colonies in New York and New Jersey, and these were at great distances from one another. It is more frequently met with on the warm eastern slopes of the Rocky Mountains in Colorado, where, unlike *breviceps,* it occurs only at lower elevations. It is the furthest removed of all of our subspecies from the European type in its smooth surface, in the coloring of its queens, which, in eastern colonies, at least, have the head and thorax nearly black, in the small size of its communities and the character of its slaves. These are not members of the *fusca,* but of the *pallide-fulva* group of *Formicæ,* and are represented by *schaufussi,* or the closely allied *incerta* or *nitidiventris.* The very small size of the colonies of these ants may account for the same peculiarity in *lucidus.* The slave species makes obscure crater nests in sunny, open pastures and such places are therefore also the home of the shining amazons. The ratio of these to slaves in the mixed colonies is about 1:5 or 6. It is an interesting fact that *lucidus* resembles its slaves in having a smooth, shining surface, a slender, elegant stature and long legs, whereas *breviceps* and *bicolor* resemble the *fusca* forms which they enslave, in having a more pilose and pubescent surface, more thickset stature and shorter legs. These resemblances may therefore be regarded as mimetic.

Near my former home in Bronxville, N. Y., there was an unusually fine *lucidus-incerta* colony, which I had under observation for five years. During four years this colony produced numbers of males and females, both winged and ergatoid, and the winged females lingered for weeks in the nest without deälation. The first week of April 1908, I found the whole community with its larvæ and mother queen enjoying the spring warmth in the superficial galleries just under the large flat stone with which I covered the nest in September 1903. I captured the queen and part of the colony and transferred them to an artificial nest. August 9 I again visited the nest, and to my surprise, found it teeming with several hundred males clinging to the lower surface of the stone, but with no winged or deälated females. Besides the males I found only a single large ergatoid female, several dozen workers and slaves, and half a dozen cocoons enclosing nearly mature male pupæ. Without doubt, the ergatoid had usurped the rôle of the mother queen and, being unfertilized, had produced only male offspring. The comparatively small number of slaves had been able to rear an enormous number of these little creatures, although the absence of *incerta* pupæ in the nest indicated that the *Polyergus*

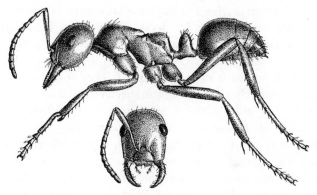

Fig. 271. *Polyergus lucidus.* (Original.) *a,* Worker in profile; *b,* head from above.

workers had made no forays during the summer of 1908. The following is a description of one of the forays made by this colony July 31, 1904, while it was still in a normal condition:

On reaching the nest at 2.20 P. M. I found the *lucidus* pouring out of it in numbers. They ran about on the stones and surrounding soil till 2.37, when a troop of nearly 200 had congregated and began to move away from the nest, slowly at first and then with feverish paces. At 2.45 they reached, by a direct path through the grass, an obscure crater nest of *incerta,* situated some fifteen meters from their own. They at once poured into the opening, slaughtering or putting to flight the *incerta* that were loitering about or issuing from the galleries. One minute later (at 2.46) the first *lucidus* emerged with a cocoon. Then followed a stream of these ants, each similarly laden, and started for home. Several were unable to secure sound pupæ, but grabbed up empty cocoons and pupal exuviæ and fell in line. Some also brought out recently hatched and callow *incerta* and slaughtered them on the nest crater. The last cocoon was brought out at 3.13 and a few moments later the last amazon left the nest and joined the returning troop. During the pillage some of the *incerta* endeavored to defend their nest, but were promptly dispatched by the *lucidus*. The corpses were dragged away by a lot of *Myrmica sabuleti* that had their nest about the roots of a plant within 30 cm. of the *incerta* nest. By 3 P. M. the last *lucidus* had disappeared into her nest. The whole expedition therefore consumed only forty minutes.

During the summer of 1902 I found near Rockford, Ill., a fine *lucidus-nitidiventris* colony. Thirty of the amazons were transferred to an artificial nest furnished with a wet sponge and a dish of honey, for the purpose of studying their behavior when isolated from their slaves. In the course of a few days the ants were famished and kept vainly begging one another for food. They often licked the water from the surface of the sponge and two that had accidentally stumbled into the honey head foremost, so that their tongues were brought in contact with it, lapped it up with avidity. They soon began to die of hunger and when only sixteen of them survived I wished to see whether they would adopt alien workers of *subsericea* and *nitidiventris* taken from a garden far removed from any *lucidus* colony. At two o'clock one afternoon three of the former (*A'*, *B'*, *C'*) and three of the latter (*A, B, C*) were placed in the nest. They began to run about in great dismay, especially when they happened to touch one of the amazons with their antennæ. From the first, however, the *subsericea* seemed to be much more frightened and to irritate the amazons more than did the *nitidiventris*. One large *lucidus* that had lost her right antenna and right tarsus seemed to be in a particularly vicious frame of mind, possibly because she had been spending much of the day trying to comb an imaginary antenna with an imaginary strigil and had repeatedly tumbled over while attempting this feat. This ant pounced on *A'* and *B'* like a cat and killed them in quick succession. She pierced the gaster of *A'* with her sharp jaws till its contents flowed out on the floor of the nest. *B'* she pierced through the thorax. For some time the surviving *subsericea* (*C'*) succeeded in evading the amazons, which in the meantime had worked themselves up into such a fury that they even attacked one another. I saw one of them grab a sister worker by the neck and hold on for three quarters of an hour. The amazons, though visibly irritated by the *nitidiventris*, did not seize them by the body, but only by the legs and antennæ. The smallest individual (*A*) lost its left middle leg in such an encounter. At this point the observations were interrupted.

At 9 P. M. both *A* and *B* were found dead, and *C* and *C'* were running about. *C'* skulked in the corners of the nest, but *C* was seen to walk up to one of the amazons, protrude her tongue, and feed the famished creature for several minutes, then go to the food chamber, take a draught of honey, return and feed a number of them in succession. For an hour she thus moved back and forth between the amazons and the honey till all had been fed. At 8 A. M. on the following morning the amazons were huddled together on the sponge, as if asleep, and in their midst was the *nitidiventris, C,* also resting peacefully. The *subsericea, C',* still alive but distrustful, was lurking in the furthest corner. I tapped the nest gently to arouse its inmates. *C* immediately ran into the food chamber, imbibed a lot of honey, returned and began to feed the *lucidus,* like a solicitous mother who wakens early and sets about getting breakfast for a large family. The friendly relations between *C* and the amazons continued throughout the day. Early the following morning *C'* was found dead in a corner and *C* was ministering to the amazons. Before noon, however, I found her lan-

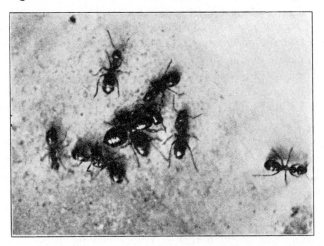

Fig. 272. Queen of *Polyergus rufescens* and her incipient colony of *Formica fusca* workers. (Photograph by Prof. C. Emery.)

guidly dragging her body about the food chamber. Her head had been pierced by one of the stupid and ungrateful *lucidus.* She died in a few hours.

At 3 P. M. twenty large *subsericea* workers, with a number of larvæ and pupæ, were placed in the light chamber. The sixteen amazons entered the chamber and began to attack the black intruders in a perfect frenzy of valor. To my surprise the *subsericea* stood their ground, took the offensive and were soon driving the amazons around the nest like a herd of sheep. They seized the *lucidus* by the legs and antennæ, showered them with formic acid, mauled them about, gnawed off their legs and left them in a pitiable plight. This victory for the *subsericea* was not only a surprise, but coming so soon after the death of the self-sacrificing *nitidiventris,* made me feel much as I felt when a boy on reading of the death of the suitors in the Odyssey.

These observations on *lucidus,* with many others which space forbids relating, show that this subspecies is much more belligerent and of a more vicious disposition than *breviceps* or *bicolor.* This is the more surprising because the ants which it enslaves are more cowardly and docile than the slaves of the other subspecies. The behavior of the ministering *nitidiventris* also shows that this form and not *subsericea* is the natural slave of *lucidus.*

3. **The Founding of Amazon Colonies.**—Most authors have inferred from the absence of the domestic instincts in the amazons that the queens of these ants would be unable to establish a formicary without the aid of alien workers. Forel and Wasmann have therefore insisted that the *rufescens* queen must be adopted by a band of *fusca,* and they have published several observations which go to show that such an adoption can be rather easily brought about in artificial nests. These observations have been recently confirmed and extended by Viehmeyer (1908). In this respect *Polyergus rufescens* resembles the temporary parasites. Several experiments in which I introduced artificially deälated queens of *lucidus* into nests containing *incerta* workers with their brood gave rather conflicting results. In some cases the *lucidus* queens behaved like *sanguinea* queens under similar conditions, to the extent of killing the alien workers, but they paid absolutely no attention to the brood. In other cases they were more passive and conciliatory, but equally indifferent to the *incerta* cocoons. It will be necessary, therefore to study this question further before making definite statements in regard to the method employed by our American amazons in establishing colonies. But even if the method of *rufescens* should be found to obtain also in our subspecies, we should not be justified in deriving it from that of the temporary social parasites, for we might conceive it to have arisen secondarily by involution or degeneration from that employed by *sanguinea.*[1]

[1] Professor Emery, in a paper just received (Nuove Osservazioni ed Esperimenti sulla Formica Amazzone. *Rend. Sess. R. Accad. Sci. Inst. Bologna,* 1909, pp. 31–36), records an experiment which goes a long way towards solving the problem here considered. July 13 he placed a deälated *P. rufescens* queen in a Janet nest containing a *F. fusca* queen, fourteen workers and a few pupæ. The *rufescens,* on being attacked by the workers, offered no resistance, but showed great interest in the *fusca* queen, who received her amicably. By July

The dulotic instincts reach the apogee of their development in *Polyergus.* This ant is, however, at the same time a permanent social parasite on its host, the slaves, and replete with degenerate tendencies. These, in the further course of evolution, may be expected to gain the upper hand, and, overwhelming and supplanting the predatory instincts, lead to the peculiar conditions to be described in the next chapter.

20 the attacks had ceased and both queens were living on friendly terms with two of the workers. On the morning of July 22 the *fusca* queen was found dead in the nest. Her head had been perforated by the mandibles of the *Polyergus,* who was now adopted and courted by all the workers. Fig. 272 is taken from a photograph of the diminutive colony that arose in this manner. This experiment indicates that *P. rufescens* founds its colonies in the same manner as *Bothriomyrmex* (*vide supra*, p. 447).

CHAPTER XXVII

THE DEGENERATE SLAVE–MAKERS AND PERMANENT SOCIAL PARASITES

"Concluons donc que le parasitisme n'est inoffensif qu'accidentellement et que son effet normal est de nuire. Il faut par conséquent considérer comme aussi éloigné que possible de l'union sociale tout être qui se nourrit de la substance d'un autre. Au point de vue physiologique sa fonction est en opposition avec celles de sa victime; au point de vue psychologique il n'entre dans la sphère de sa conscience que pour y causer de la douleur, autre signe non moins manifeste d'opposition. Il appartient à un optimisme plus courageux que clairvoyant de chercher une harmonie au sein de la plus âpre concurrence. Mais le parasitisme ne nuit pas seulement à la victime, il nuit au parasite lui-même, sinon immédiatement dans l'individu, du moins par accumulation dans l'espèce."
—Espinas, "Des Societés Animales," 1877.

The true slave-making ants, both facultative and obligatory, are closely allied members of the Camponotine subfamily. The ants to be considered in the present chapter, however, are all Myrmicinæ and cannot, therefore, have arisen from such forms as *sanguinea* and *Polyergus*. Considered by themselves they represent a heterogeneous assemblage of remotely related genera, which may be described in the order of increasing degeneration. Several of these ants resemble their respective hosts so closely that it is from these that some authors suppose them to have been derived. But this supposition, though plausible, is, nevertheless, open to doubt, for the resemblance between host and parasite may be due to mimicry and therefore to convergence rather than to true morphological relationship. We have seen that many myrmecophiles, some of the temporary parasites, like *Formica consocians,* and some of the amazons simulate their hosts, and it is conceivable that parasites as extreme as those we are about to consider, might show even more striking resemblances as the result of a long process of adaptation and association. Very similar resemblances are also known to obtain between many parasitic bees of various genera and their respective hosts.

The symbiotic ants with which we are here concerned, fall naturally into two groups. Those which I shall call the degenerate slave-makers, resemble *Polyergus* in certain respects, but differ in permitting the queens of the host species to survive and reproduce in the mixed colonies. The permanent social parasites, on the contrary, live in host colonies whose queens have been eliminated, and differ, moreover, from all the other social parasites in lacking the worker caste. The ants of both groups are throughout life dependent on their hosts and are, therefore, permanent social parasites, but I would restrict this term to the workerless species, since they represent the most extreme type.

A. **The Degenerate Slave-makers.**—This group embraces only two genera, *Strongylognathus* and *Harpagoxenus*, formerly known as *Tomognathus*. *Strongylognathus* is a strictly palearctic genus, confined, so far as known, to Europe, western Siberia, Asia Minor and the southern shores of the Mediterranean. It contains only two species, *testaceus* and *huberi*, but the latter has several subspecies and varieties (*christophi, rehbinderi, afer* and *cæciliæ*). These ants are very small, measuring only 2.5–4.5 mm. in length, and of a yellowish or dark brown color. The head of the worker and female is more or less excised behind, with very prominent posterior corners and subparallel sides. The mandibles are toothless, narrow, pointed and sickle-shaped, like those of *Polyergus*, but without denticles. All of the forms occur only in nests of *Tetramorium cespitum* (Fig. 273, *d*), a very common ant which they closely resemble in size and appearance.

1. *Strongylognathus huberi* (Fig. 273, *c*).—This species was origi-

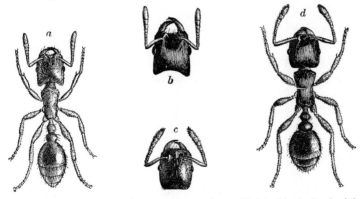

FIG. 273. *a, Strongylognathus testaceus* worker. (Original.) *b*, head of female of same ; *c, S. huberi,* head of worker ; *d, Tetramorium cespitum* L. host of *S. testaceus* and *huberi.*

nally described by Forel (1874) from specimens taken in Canton Vallais, Switzerland, on a warm slope near Fully, in the valley of the Rhone. More recently (1900*d*) he has published additional observations on a colony from the same locality. He found that the workers of *huberi* are very numerous, that they will go forth in a closed phalanx, much like that of the amazons, and pierce the heads of strange *Tetramorium* workers placed near their nests and that they will also take up the pupæ of the strange ants and carry them home. In his more recent observations Forel found that the strange pupæ thus brought in were carried out by the host workers and cast away. This behavior and the fact that no one has witnessed a spontaneous foray of *huberi,* seem to indicate that these ants never voluntarily leave the nest and pillage the *Tetramorium* colonies in their neighborhood. It is probable, therefore, that the habits observed by Forel are vestigial. In other respects, however, *huberi* is less degenerate than the amazons, for it occasionally excavates the soil.[1]

2. *Strongylognathus afer.*—This is merely a variety of *huberi* from Spain and Algiers. It was originally described by Emery (1880) from the female only. Forel discovered its colonies in Algiers and found that they resemble those of the typical *huberi* in having numerous workers.

3. *Strongylognathus christophi.*—Emery (1889a) described this subspecies from female specimens collected at Sarepta on the Volga. Ruzsky (1905) has recently taken the workers at Turgai in western Siberia and Astrachan.

4. *Strongylognathus rehbinderi.*—This robust variety of *christophi* was found by Rehbinder (Forel, 1904a) in a convent garden at New Athos near the foot of the Caucasus. The workers were running along a path, apparently carrying pupæ in their jaws. Forel believes that they must have been on a foray. If this is true, we should have to admit that *Strongylognathus* is still able to make forays on *Tetramorium* like those of the amazons on *F. fusca,* but we must await further observations before accepting this inference.

5. *Strongylognathus cæciliæ.*—Only the male and female of this form are known. It was based by Forel on specimens taken in Spain.

6. *Strongylognathus testaceus* (Fig. 273, *a* and *b*).—This species is widely distributed in Europe and is not uncommon in certain portions of Germany and Switzerland. Its habits have been studied by Schenck (1852), von Hagens (1866), Forel (1874), Wasmann (1891h), Viehmeyer (1906, 1908) and others. It is of a yellowish color and distinctly smaller and feebler than *huberi* and its varieties. Moreover, the workers are so much reduced in numbers as to represent a mere vestige of their caste. Forel is, therefore, of the opinion that they are on the verge of disappearing and leading to a condition in which the species is represented by males and females only. It is certain that these workers no longer make spontaneous

[1] During July, 1909, I found near Zermatt, in the valley of the Visp, seven colonies of *S. huberi.* Some experiments, performed on the largest of these, confirmed Forel's conclusions.

forays on alien colonies of *Tetramorium*. When the latter are brought near a mixed colony and a conflict ensues, the *testaceus* endeavor to kill the strange workers, but are too feeble to pierce their armor, and, if the mixed colony is victorious, this is due to the efforts of the host workers. The *testaceus,* though able to excavate and to feed independently, contribute little or nothing to the structure of the nest and probably obtain most of their food from the tongues of the *Tetramorium*. The broods of both species are cared for by the host, since the parasites have ceased to interest themselves in the education of their own young. Unlike many parasitic ants, *S. testaceus* is often found in vigorous and populous colonies of the host species. The flourishing condition of such colonies, a number of which were shown me by Mr. Viehmeyer in the heaths near Dresden, must be due either to the retention of the *Tetramorium* queen or to the adoption of the *Strongylognathus* queen at a very late stage in the development of the colony. That we must accept the former alternative is proved by the following observations: In Bohemia, Wasmann found a large mixed colony which contained 15,000–20,000 *Tetramorium,* some thousand *Strongylognathus* and pupæ of both species. About 70 per cent. of the pupæ were males and females of the parasitic species, the remainder were worker pupæ, and there were two large male pupæ of the host. This nest contained a fertile queen of *Tetramorium* and one of *Strongylognathus,* living side by side. During June, 1907, Professor Forel and I were able to confirm this discovery. We found a similar *testaceus-Strongylognathus* colony on the Petit Salève, near Geneva. This colony, though much smaller than the one described by Wasmann, contained a fertile *Tetramorium* queen. The diminutive *Strongylognathus* queen was not found, but must have been present, as there were in the nest young worker pupæ in addition to the imagines of this species. Wasmann is inclined to believe that these mixed colonies arise through the alliance of a *testaceus* and a *Tetramorium* queen, but it is more probable that the former enters a colony of the latter after it has been established and become rather populous, since the founding of colonies even by pairs of queens of the same species is an extremely rare occurrence (see p. 190). Although the host and parasitic queens come to live side by side in the mixed colonies, the offspring of the latter are exclusively workers, the two male pupæ found by Wasmann being the only known exception to this rule. Forel (1900*d*) explains this absence of the male and female offspring of the host queen as the result of a regulatory instinct: " The females and males of *Strongylognathus* are smaller and less troublesome to nourish. This is evidently sufficient to induce the *Tetramorium* workers to rear them in the place of their own enormous queens and males, the larvæ of which they therefore undoubtedly devour or neglect, as they do in the case of all that seems to be super-fluous." The absence of the conspicuous males and females of the host species in nests infested with *testaceus* aids the investigator in search-ing for the parasites, especially during late June and early July, when the host species is rearing the sexual brood, for nests containing male or female larvæ or pupæ of the *Tetramorium* may be quickly passed over and attention concentrated on the nests in which these are absent. Wasmann has shown that *testaceus* is more resistant to unfavorable conditions than its host. This suggests the feasibility of introducing it into America, where *T. cespitum* has become thoroughly acclimated and rather abundant, especially in some parts of the Atlantic States.

II. *Harpagoxenus* (*Tomognathus*).—The two known species of this genus are rare and very local ants, allied to *Leptothorax*, the genus to which their hosts belong. The workers are small, dark-brown, with short legs and hairy bodies and are easily recognizable by their broad, toothless mandibles and their peculiarly elongated frontal carinæ, which extend back to the vertex and there bend outward, forming scrobe-like depressions for the short antennæ.

1. *Harpagoxenus sublevis* (Fig. 274).—The habits of this ant have been studied by Adlerz (1886, 1896) and Viehmeyer (1906, 1908). It

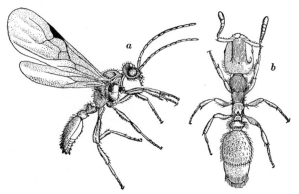

FIG. 274. *Harpagoxenus sublevis.* (Adlerz.) *a*, Male; *b*, ergatoid female.

was formerly supposed to be confined to boreal Europe, having been discovered in Finland by Nylander (1848) and taken in Denmark by Meinert (1860), and in Sweden by Stolpe (1882) and Adlerz (1886, 1887, 1896), but Viehmeyer has recently shown that it also inhabits the heaths near Dresden. In the locality last mentioned it is always found in the nests of *Leptothorax acervorum,* and although this is its common host in northern Europe, Alderz has observed it also in the nests of *L. muscorum* and *L. tuberum*. The mixed colonies may contain males and females as well as workers of both the host and parasitic species. The males of *sublevis* are so much like those of *Leptothorax* that Adlerz failed to distinguish them till he published his final paper (1896). All the females which he found were wingless and ergatoid, with a thorax like that of the worker, but with ocelli and a receptaculum seminis. He naturally took these ergatoids to be the only females of the species, but in addition to these Viehmeyer has discovered winged females in some of the colonies in Saxony. Adlerz's observations seem to show that *sublevis* secures its auxiliaries by attacking *Leptothorax* colonies, driving away the adult ants and taking possession of their nests and young. The latter are then reared as auxiliaries, or hosts. It is not impossible, however, that *sublevis* may recruit the number of its auxiliaries by making occasional sorties like *Polyergus*, for Adlerz succeeded in finding one nest in which the parasites were living with two species of *Leptothorax* (*acervorum* and *muscorum*). The domestic instincts of *sublevis* are very much blunted or obsolescent. It rarely or never excavates, and although it is able to feed itself if food is within reach, it does not go in quest of it, but leaves this to its host. A number of *sublevis* which Adlerz isolated with a number of larvæ and some food managed to live for 135 days, but the larvæ shriveled up or died. It seems probable, therefore, that this ant depends on its slaves for the nurture of its young. When the mixed colony moves to a new nest the *sublevis* are carried by the *Leptothorax;* very rarely are the rôles reversed. Sometimes when the *sublevis* endeavor to leave the nest they are restrained by their slaves in much the same manner as *Polyergus*. Adlerz observed the males mating with the ergatoid females, but this occurred only between individuals belonging to different colonies. The larvæ of *sublevis* are so much like those of their hosts that he could not distinguish them. They are nourished both with regurgitated liquid food and with pieces of insects, a method of larval feeding which was also observed by Viehmeyer. This author believes that *sublevis* was originally lestobiotic like *Solenopsis,* that is, that it once robbed and devoured the young of an ant in whose neighborhood it nested without forming a mixed colony. The following are his views on the phylogeny of *sublevis* and its method of establishing colonies: " The starting point of the development was represented by an ant allied to *Leptothorax*, with males and females, both winged, and, like many other ants, with a predilection for eating the larvæ and pupæ of allied species. This habit, practiced only occasionally at first, became established and the ants took to nesting near other ants, which at first tolerated these thieves unwillingly (compound nest). The thief ants then gradually became marauders (mixed colony). With increasing dependence on their auxiliaries, which showed itself in the dwindling of the worker instincts and the disappearance of the mandibular teeth, the difficulty of founding colonies by means of winged females increased and led to the development of the ergatoid forms. In these the ancient lestobiotic and predatory instincts united with the newly acquired female instincts, so that the ergatoids became incomparably better fitted for founding colonies than the winged forms, which therefore tended to extinction. We must still, however, endeavor to explain why the winged females have never been found in the colonies of northern Europe. This may be accounted for in two ways. We may regard the winged female either as a reversion or as the lingering vestige of a not yet completely eliminated winged form. The latter alternative seems to be indicated by the remoteness of the locality in which this form occurs from the true

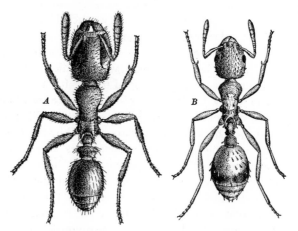

Fig. 275. *A, Harpagoxenus americanus* worker and *B,* its host, *Leptothorax curvispinosus* worker. (Original.)

geographical range of the species. The development of this sex would probably be unequally advanced in two regions differing so much in climate and other conditions. But we must wait to see whether this ant does not occur also in other regions, perhaps in northern Germany."

2. *Harpagoxenus americanus* (Fig. 275, *A*).—This species, which is smaller and of a darker brown color than *sublevis,* seems to be extremely rare. To my knowledge it has been taken on only three occasions. The type specimens, describe by Emery (1893-'94), were found by Pergande at Washington, D. C., in a nest of *Leptothorax curvispinosus* (Fig. 275, *B*), but no observations on the relations

of the two species were recorded. Schmitt found a few specimens while sifting vegetable mould for beetles near Beatty, Pa., and I found it during the summer of 1905, in a rich, boggy wood near Bronxville, N. Y. Here there were several fine *L. curvispinosus* colonies nesting in the hollow twigs of elder bushes, and in three of these colonies there were specimens of *H. americanus*. One contained only a single worker, another six, and a third eight workers and a queen of the parasitic ant. The latter insect was not ergatoid, but decidedly larger than the workers, with well-developed ocelli and a typical, though small, female thorax, showing distinct traces of having borne wings. All three colonies contained larvæ and pupæ, presumably of the parasitic species, but no *Leptothorax* queens. When confined in artificial nests the *americanus* were very inactive and paid no attention to the brood. All the colonies were too small to admit of the supposition that they had been formed by repeated forays on the part of *Harpagoxenus*. This ant, in fact, has every appearance of having reached a more abject stage of parasitism than its European congener. In the same locality I found a mixed queenless colony of the yellow *L. curvispinosus* and the black *L. longispinosus* inhabiting a hollow elder twig. If a deälated queen of *H. americanus* happened to establish her colony in such a nest as this, we should have a case like Adlerz's *sublevis* living with both *L. acervorum* and *muscorum,* but the inference that this indicated repeated slave-making forays on the part of *americanus* would be erroneous.

B. **The Permanent Social Parasites.**—The ants included in this group are all small and nearly all of them belong to monotypic genera. The absence of workers makes it difficult to assign definite positions to these genera in our classifications, which are based very largely on the worker forms.

1. *Wheeleriella santschii* (Fig. 276).—This is a small, dark-brown species, the female of which measures 4–4.7 mm. in length, the male only 3.5–3.8 mm. It was discovered by Santschi in the cactus fields near Kairouan, Tunis, and lives in the nests of the most abundant of all the North African ants, *Monomorium salomonis* and its varieties. The female *Wheeleriella* resembles *Strongylognathus testaceus* in having the posterior border of the head deeply excised and its posterior corners projecting as blunt horns. Santschi's interesting observations have been published by Forel (1906d) and may be briefly summarized. Although both sexes have well-developed wings, mating seems to take place, at least as a rule, in the outer galleries of the nest and between brothers and sisters (adelphogamy). After fecundation the deälated female roams about over the surface of

the soil in search of *Monomorium* nests. When near the entrance of one of these, she is "arrested," to use Santschi's expression, by a number of *Monomorium* workers, which tug at her legs and antennæ and sometimes draw her into the galleries. At other times she may be seen to dart into the nest entrance suddenly, so that she is arrested within the nest itself. There are no signs of anger on the part of the *Monomorium* and she is soon able to move about in the galleries without restraint. The workers forthwith feed and adopt her. In the course of a few days she begins to lay eggs which are received and cared for by the *Monomorium* workers. Santschi observed that the colonies infested with *Wheeleriella* were usually of small size, had an impoverished appearance and lacked queens of the host species, and he was able to account for these peculiar conditions. The *Wheeleriella* queen pays no attention to the much larger *Monomorium* queen, but this insect is assassinated by her own workers and the parasitic queen is adopted in her place. Forel believes that this singular perversion of instinct is due to the preference of the workers for a smaller fertile individual, just as the *Tetramorium* workers prefer to rear the small males and females of *Strongylognathus* instead of their own bulky sexual phases. This explanation is not very satisfactory, however, for, as we have

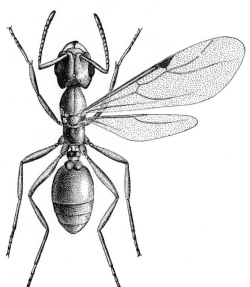

FIG. 276. *Wheeleriella santschii* of Tunis; female; (Original.)

seen, the huge mother *Tetramorium* is retained in the nest, whereas it is precisely this individual that is destroyed in the infested *Monomorium* colonies. Hence there must be some other reason for the assassination of the host queen by her own progeny.

2. *Epixenus andrei* and *creticus.*—These ants have been recently described by Emery (1908*a*), the former from females taken between Jaffa and Jerusalem in a nest of *Monomorium venustum,* and originally referred to this species by Ern. André (1881*b*), the latter from a single

male taken in Crete. As both species are related to *Wheeleriella santschii*, Emery believes that they lack the worker caste.

3. *Sympheidole elecebra* (Fig. 277, *A*).—This species, which is much smaller than *Wheeleriella* (female 2.75–3 mm.; male 2.5–2.75 mm.), lives in the nests of *Pheidole ceres*, a common ant in the mountains of Colorado and New Mexico at altitudes between 2,500 and 3,000 m. The parasites and host are very similar, but the female of the former is much smaller, has a more rounded head and a very broad post-petiole. I have seen only two females: one taken by Schmitt in a *ceres* nest at Boulder, Colo., the other with eighteen males, taken by myself August 17, 1903, in the Ute Pass, near Manitou in the same state. The *ceres* colony in which I found these ants was carefully examined, but contained only workers and soldiers of the host species, and besides the adult parasites, a number of their pupæ. No workers of the latter species could be detected, though from what we know of other ants, they should have been in the nest, if they exist at all, at the time of maturity of the males. When the nest, which was under a stone, was first disturbed, the *Pheidole* workers seized the parasites and their pupæ and quickly carried them into the galleries. As there are usually from one to five deälated queens in the uninfested colonies of *ceres*, their absence in this nest shows that they must have been eliminated. And as the *elecebra* queens are very small and feeble compared with the *ceres* queens (which measure 5–5.5 mm.), it is probable that the latter are killed by their own workers and soldiers.

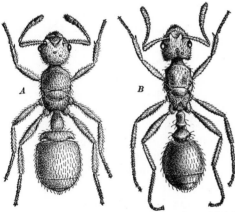

FIG. 277. Parasites of *Pheidole*. (Original.) *A*, Deälated female of *Sympheidole elecebra; B*, deälated female of *Epipheidole inquilina.*

4. *Epipheidole inquilina* (Fig. 277, *B*).—Like the *Sympheidole*, this ant resembles its host, which is also a common *Pheidole* (*P. pilifera*). Emery (1893–'04) saw the small queen of *Epipheidole* (length 3–3.3 mm.) among some soldiers and workers of *pilifera* collected in Nebraska, but he regarded the insect as an unusually microgynic *Pheidole*. During late July and early August, 1903, I found near Colorado Springs three colonies of *Ph. coloradensis*, a subspecies of

pilifera, containing males and females of the *Epipheidole.* In these colonies the *coloradensis* queens were absent, as in the case of the *ceres* and *Sympheidole.* It is probable, therefore, that they are eliminated by their own workers after the intrusion of the parasite.

5. *Epœcus pergandei* (Fig. 278).—This species is known only from the types, a number of small black males and females taken by Pergande in a nest of *Monomorium minimum* near Washington, D. C., and described by Emery (1893–'04). According to Pergande's statement, the nest contained the winged sexes of the host in addition to those of the parasite, but as he also found that when both species were put in the same vial the *Epœcus* queens attacked and killed some of the *Monomorium* males, I am inclined to believe that there is some confusion in his observations. He may have mixed two *Monomorium* colonies that were nesting very close together, one of which may have been pure and have contained the winged sexes, whereas the other consisted of male and female *Epœcus* and *Monomorium* workers. During the past eight years I have examined hundreds of *M. minimum* nests, but have never succeeded in finding *Epœcus.* This is not surprising, however, as all the workerless parasites are rare and very local in their distribution.

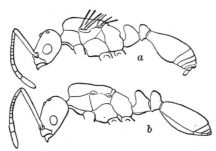

Fig. 278. *Epœcus pergandei.* (Emery.)
a, Male; *b,* deälated female.

6. *Anergates atratulus* (Fig. 279).—This extraordinary ant, like the preceding, is far from common, though it is widely distributed in continental Europe. For this reason it is better known than any of the other workerless parasites. Its host is *Tetramorium cespitum.* Studies on its habits have been published by Schenck (1852), von Hagens (1867), Forel (1874), Adlerz (1886), Wasmann (1891*h*) and Janet (1897*e*). Both male and female are peculiarly modified. The former is 2.7–3 mm. long, of a pale, sordid yellow color, wingless and pupa-like, with the gaster strongly curved downward at the tip. Although its legs are rather well developed, it moves very slowly and with a dawdling gait. The fore legs are furnished with strigils which are pectiniform in specimens from certain localities (Switzerland), but in those from other localities (Sweden, Holland, France) the teeth are lacking and the strigils may be vestigial or absent. Janet has shown that the mandibular glands are well developed, though the mandibles are very small and feeble. The black, winged female is of the same size as the male

and has the gaster of normal dimensions, but with a longitudinal dorsal groove before fecundation. After entering the *Tetramorium* nest, however, the ovaries become greatly enlarged and the gaster expands till it bcomes a flattened sphere 4 mm. in diameter, on which are seen, in the form of little plates, isolated by the enormous distention of the articular membranes, the strongly chitinized rings, which, in the virgin, constitute the whole external surface of the gaster. Both male and female have 11-jointed antennæ and large ocelli, but the eyes are rather poorly developed. Owing to the apterous condition and sluggish movements of the male, mating takes place in the nest among the offspring

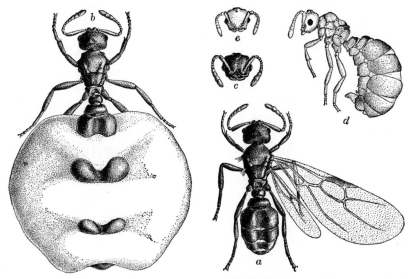

Fig. 279. *Anergates atratulus.* (Original.) *a*, Virgin female; *b*, old queen; *c*, head of same; *d*, pupoid male; *e*, head of same.

of the same mother (adelphogamy). This can be readily observed both in natural and artificial nests. The couples are so firmly united that they can be killed, without separating, in warm alcohol. After fecundation the females fly out of the nests, so that the nuptial flight, though vestigial and unisexual in this ant, still subserves the important function of disseminating the species. *Tetramorium* colonies infested with *Anergates* contain only the workers of the host species. Adlerz and Wasmann have shown that these pay very little attention to the virgin *Anergates*, but carry the males about and lick them assiduously, and that during these operations the latter assume a characteristic, motionless attitude. Both the male and female parasites are, of course, fed by their hosts, as they are quite unable to eat independently.

Adlerz and Wasmann have made some experiments with a view to ascertaining the method whereby the female *Anergates* becomes associated with the *Tetramorium*. Adlerz in Sweden placed several unfertilized *Anergates* queens in a strange nest of the host species. They moved about among the workers as if unperceived. Nearly the same results were obtained on placing unfertilized *Anergates* in a normal colony containing a *Tetramorium* queen. He also placed several larvæ, pupæ and male and female imagines of *Anergates* in a normal *Tetramorium* colony which was living in an artificial nest. In every case the strangers were almost at once amicably received. Similar observations were made by Wasmann in Holland. He found that strange *Tetramorium* workers did not in the least injure the male and female *Anergates,* whereas they killed without mercy a number of *Strongylognathus testaceus* males and females which he placed in the nest.

The experiments of Adlerz and Wasmann were not carried far enough to throw any light on the permanent adoption of the *Anergates* and the fate of the *Tetramorium* queen. It now seems probable that the latter insect is killed by her own workers soon after the colony is invaded by the parasitic queen. Since the publication of Santschi's notes on *Wheeleriella,* renewed observations on young *Anergates* queens in the presence of alien *Tetramorium* colonies, and under natural conditions, have become a desideratum. June 6, 1907, at 2 P. M., while collecting ants near Vaud, in the very meadow in which Forel as a very young man made many of his classical observations on *Formica sanguinea, Polyergus, Strongylognathus testaceus* and other species of his " Fourmis de la Suisse," I discovered a medium-sized *Tetramorium* colony from which female *Anergates* were escaping in considerable numbers. The nest was around the roots of a plantain, and the females issued one by one from the entrances, climbed the leaves to their tips and flew away in all directions over the sun-lit grass. At 3.30 P. M. Professor Forel joined me and we excavated the nest with great care. It contained, besides the obese mother queen of *Anergates* and several thousand *Tetramorium* workers, more than a thousand winged queens, a few hundred of the pupa-like males, several pupæ and a few larvæ of the parasitic species. In the galleries of the nest dozens of couples were united in the act of mating. The *Tetramorium* workers picked up the single males and hurried away with them, but they paid little attention to the females. The colony was placed in a bag and on the following day used for experiments on *Tetramorium* colonies in Professor Forel's garden at Chigny. On opening the bag I found several of the *Anergates in copulâ,* but most of the females had either lost their wings or were ready to drop them at the slightest touch. Eight *Tetra-*

morium colonies that had large nests with multiple craters in the paths
of the garden were selected and the females were placed near them one
at a time on the ground. In all cases when they were placed within
a few centimeters of the openings, they entered the nests almost immediately; when placed at a greater distance they wandered about demurely
till they found an opening and then at once crept into it. Seven of the
nests were thus entered by numbers of the queens without creating
the slightest excitement among the *Tetramorium* workers. These
merely stopped when they happened to meet a female, seized her by
the wings, thorax or pedicel, but at once dropped her and went about
their work. In no case was one of the queens injured. In three of
these colonies they were seized by single workers and carried into the
nest as fast as I could set them on the craters. Both males and females
were placed near the openings of one of these nests. The males were
seized with signs of keen interest and some animosity, to judge from
the way in which the workers bent their gasters forward and tried to
sting the helpless creatures. They were not killed, however, but carried
a few decimeters from the nest and then thrown away, sometimes from
the top of a pebble or lump of earth. This was being done while other
workers were carrying the females into the nest. One vigorous colony
exhibited a different behavior: All the parasites, both male and female,
were at once seized, pulled about by the legs, wings and antennæ, and
then carried away and dumped on the ground at some distance from
the nest. In this instance several of the parasites of both sexes were
injured so that they could not walk. Strange *Tetramorium* workers
placed on any of the nests above mentioned were suddenly pounced
upon and killed. These observations show that the *Anergates* queens
are, as a rule, treated with great lenity and even carried into the nests,
but that the males are rejected. They also show that certain colonies
are positively hostile to both sexes of the parasites. In all cases, however, the behavior of the *Anergates* queens was very uniform: they
sought and entered the *Tetramorium* nests as if these belonged to them,
offered no resistance when seized, and, when roughly handled, merely
curled up and feigned death. The experiments were continued throughout the morning. With the gradually increasing temperature towards
noon the *Tetramorium* became more numerous and active outside their
nests, but their treatment of the *Anergates*, which I was continually
giving them, remained the same. Late in the afternoon the experiments were repeated on two of the colonies, which, during the morning, had been entered without protest by a number of the parasitic
queens. The workers were out in a multitude, excavating and dragging
in insect food. When male, female or pupal *Anergates* were placed

on these nests, the males and pupæ were promptly seized and thrown away and the females were also seized, but less promptly, and also rejected. Some of the latter that had managed to enter the nests were soon brought out and dumped at a distance of several decimeters from the entrances. I watched the nests for some time and although a few of the females were not brought out, I am, of course, unable to state whether they were subsequently adopted, killed in the galleries, or ejected. It appears, therefore, that the acceptance of the parasites by the *Tetramorium* under natural conditions is not as immediate and simple as the observations of Adlerz and Wasmann on artificial nests would lead one to suppose. The fact that *Anergates* is so rare an ant, notwithstanding its sporadic colonies produce enormous numbers of females in regions inhabited by myriads of *Tetramorium* colonies, shows that permanent adoption is not easily effected. Were the contrary the case, *Tetramorium cespitum* would itself become a rare, if not extinct, species.

There can be no doubt that of the seven permanent social parasites above enumerated, *Anergates* is the most specialized and degenerate. This is clearly shown in the ergatoid and nymphoid structure of the male and the structure of the head in both sexes. All the other species agree in being in a less advanced stage, although they, too, have lost the worker caste. This loss may be said to be due to disuse, but it followed necessarily upon the reduction in size of the male and female, and this condition in turn was probably initiated by the same causes that have led to the dwarfing of the queens among the temporary parasites. Forel, Lubbock and Wasmann are inclined to believe that *Anergates* represents a form that was once dulotic. Lubbock says: "In *Anergates,* finally, we come to the last scene of this sad history. We may safely conclude that in distant times their ancestors lived, as many ants do now, partly by hunting, partly on honey; that by degrees they became bold marauders and gradually took to keeping slaves; that for a time they maintained their strength and agility, though losing by degrees their real independence, their arts, and even many of their instincts; that gradually even their bodily force dwindled away under the enervating influence to which they had subjected themselves, until they sank to their present degraded condition—weak in body and mind, few in numbers, and apparently nearly extinct, the miserable representatives of far superior ancestors, maintaining a precarious existence as contemptible parasites of their former slaves." This interpretation of *Anergates* as a very degenerate dulotic ant seems to have been suggested by the obvious dwindling of the worker caste in *Strongylog-*

nathus testaceus, but there is nothing in the structure of *Anergates* or of any of the other workerless ants to prove that they are descended from slave-making species. More probable is the supposition that they have been derived from temporary parasites or xenobiotic forms with habits like those of *Leptothorax emersoni.* The *Anergates* or *Wheeleriella* colony differs from those of species like *Formica consocians* in reaching its complete development, that is, the stage in which the sexual offspring of the mother queen mature, in a much shorter period of time. This period must fall within the lifetime of the *Tetramorium* or *Monomorium* workers and can therefore hardly exceed three or four years. This acceleration of colonial development is made possible by a suppression of the useless worker caste and a dwarfing of the sexual individuals, although there is a concomitant increase in their numbers. And all of these interesting compensatory developments are necessitated in turn by the castration of the host colony, for this is what the elimination of the host queen amounts to. As this is a mortal injury to the host colony and a serious injury to the host species, it is not surprising that the intrusion of the parasites is resisted and that the latter, as Lubbock says, are " few in number and apparently nearly extinct." In other words, extreme parasitism in ants, as in other organisms, tends continually to defeat its own ends and to undermine its own existence.

The zoölogist, as such, is not concerned with the ethical and sociological aspects of parasitism, but the series of ants we have been considering in this and the four preceding chapters cannot fail to arrest the attention of those to whom a knowledge of the paragon of social animals is after all one of the chief aims of existence. He who without prejudice studies the history of mankind will note that many organizations that thrive on the capital accumulated by other members of the community, without an adequate return in productive labor, bear a significant resemblance to many of the social parasites among ants. This resemblance has been studied by sociologists, who have also been able to point to detailed coincidences and analogies between human and animal parasitism in general.[1] Space and the character of this work, of course, forbid a consideration of the various parasitic or semi-parasitic institutions and organizations—social, political, ecclesiastical and criminal—that have at their inception timidly struggled for adoption and support, and, after having obtained these, have grown great and insolent, only to degenerate into nuisances from which the sane

[1] *Cf., e. g.,* Massart and Vandervelde's interesting paper: " Parasitisme Organique et Parasitisme Social," *Bull. Sci. France et Belg.,* XXV, 1893.

and productive members of the community have the greatest difficulty in freeing themselves.[2]

[2] Besides the mixed colonies of ants considered in this and the two preceding chapters, there are a few cases of a very exceptional and problematic character. These are:

1. A mixed colony comprising workers of *Lasius niger* and *L. flavus* found by Adlerz (1896*b*) in Sweden.

2. Two small mixed colonies comprising workers of *L. nearcticus* and *L. americanus* found near Rockford, Ill. (Wheeler, 1905*i*).

3. Four small mixed colonies comprising workers of *L. latipes* and *L. americanus* found near Colebrook, Conn. (Wheeler, 1905*i*).

4. The small mixed colony of *Leptothorax curvispinosus* and *L. longispinosus* mentioned on p. 495.

5. A colony consisting of a male, two winged females and several workers of *Pseudomyrma flavidula* and several workers of *Ps. elongata,* found in a hollow *Cladium* culm in the Bahamas (Wheeler, 1905*b*).

Adlerz believed that his mixed *Lasius* colony had been formed by dulosis, but Wasmann suggested that it was probably the result of an accidental alliance between fertilized queens of different species. I am inclined to believe that neither this nor the other colonies above enumerated arose in either of these ways, but by the accidental irruption of one colony into the contiguous brood galleries of another, followed by the pillaging and rearing of a number of alien worker larvæ or pupæ. This is not dulosis, but as I have shown (p. 452), merely one of its conditions.

CHAPTER XXVIII

THE SENSATIONS OF ANTS

"Il faut donc, bon gré mal gré, étudier la psychologie et la physiologie en rapport l'une avec l'autre, en comparant leurs résultats, en tâchant de trouver les relations les plus exactes possibles, entre leurs notions et les termes qui s'y rapportent, même au risque de retomber souvent dans l'anthropomorphisme sans le vouloir. Si nous connaisons ce dernier danger, et si nous le combattons sans relâche, le corrigeant sans cesse, nous marcherons, d'erreur corrigée en erreur corrigée, lentement mais sûrement vers la vérité relative que seule nous pouvons connaître. Si pas contre, ne voyant qu'un côté de la question, nous nous obstinons à vouloir d'un coup faire de la mécanique soi disant objective là ou toutes les bases nous manquent pour le faire, nous tomberons dans l'absurde et n'arriverons à rien."—Forel, "Sensations des Insectes," V, 1901.

To close our survey of the ants without a more coherent treatment of the subject of their behavior than is represented by the scattered references to "reactions," "habits" and "instincts" in the preceding chapters, would be to turn aside from the very *fons et origo* of our interest in these insects. For structure and development, distribution in time and space, and the multifarious ethological relationships we have been considering are merely the more obvious aspects of an intricate and subtle behavior that enables these creatures to lead their balanced, but nevertheless plastic, social life amid an environment made up of refractory matter and more or less indifferent or hostile organisms.

In endeavoring to gain an insight into the behavior of any animal, two courses are open to us. These may be designated as the intellectual and the intuitional, and it depends on the temperament and training of the observer which he will follow, or whether he will be inclined to follow both. The intellectual course is the one usually pursued by the scientist pure and simple, and is especially exalted by those most thoroughly embued with the spirit of our laboratories, where living organisms are best loved when they are dead, or, at any rate, when they can be subjected to the methods of investigation that have yielded such valuable results to the development of physics and chemistry. In this environment the intellect proceeds on her clean path, according to her peculiar method, first cutting up the indiscerptible, flowing process, which is the life of every organism, into stationary concepts, and then combining these congealed and partial abstractions into a system that will have "explanatory" value—in obedience to Goethe's well-known dictum:

> "Wer will was Lebendig's erkennen und beschreiben
> Sucht erst den Geist herauszutreiben;
> Dann hat er die Theile in seiner Hand,
> Fehlt leider nur das geistige Band."

Nor is the intellect able to proceed in any other manner, and that her ways are right and justifiable is shown by her triumphs. To extoll these in this place is unnecessary, but it should be remarked that the intellect, as Bergson has so beautifully shown, was evolved as an instrument of action and fabrication, and not for the purpose of understanding or explaining an inorganic flux or movement, much less a durational and creative flux, like that which we call life.[1]

The intuitionist, in dealing with the behavior of animals, proceeds along the path of æsthetic insight, sympathy and introspective knowledge of our own internal processes. His method is, therefore, essentially psychological and metaphysical. He does not deal with things or quantities, but with the living creative movement as immediately experienced in his own consciousness. He attempts to place himself *en rapport* with the organism and to move in the stream of its vital current. Being an animal organism himself, he may, therefore, be said to feel something of what must be taking place in other animals. This experience cannot be expressed, or can be expressed only through indirect or artistic channels, because language is essentially a work of the intellect. Thus the intellectual course is definite and concise, but its prime object is to eventuate in action or practice, whereas the intuitional course is vague, contemplative and ineffable, but is nearer reality.

To the narrow scientific mind the intuitional method of contemplating animal behavior has always been as great an abomination as is the self-sufficient, geometrical and mechanical method of the scientist to the nature lover. Both methods, when carried to extremes, lead to false or inane, or, at best, very partial interpretations—the scientific to a kind of animal phoronomy, like the reflex-theories of Bethe and

---

[1] "Modern science, no less than ancient science, proceeds according to the cinematographic method. It cannot do otherwise; all science is subject to this law. It is, in fact, of the essence of science, to manipulate *signs,* which it substitutes for the objects themselves. These signs undoubtedly differ from those of languages in their greater precision and higher efficacity, but they are none the less subject to the general condition of the sign, which is to denote a fixed aspect of reality under an arrested form. In order to think movement, an incessantly renewed effort of the mind is necessary. Signs are made for the purpose of dispensing with this effort by substituting for the moving continuity of things an artificial recomposition which is their equivalent in practice and has the advantage of being easily manipulated."—Henri Bergson, "L'Évolution Créatrice," 4th ed., Paris, Félix Alcan, 1908, p. 356. See also the other works of this remarkable philosopher: "Essai sur les Données Immédiates de la Conscience," 6th ed., 1908, and "Matière et Mémoire," 5th ed., 1908.

Uexküll, the intuitional to the humanizing of animals and all the perversities of the American "nature-fakers." It is generally easy to class a particular observer according to his temperament and training. The scientist is prone to follow the intellectual method till he ends in rank atomic materialism, but he deserves admiration and sympathy for his consistency and his whole-souled confidence in his method. The intuitionist tends to become a panpsychist and though he may humanize the brute, we must remember that this is not a penal offence and that it does credit to his heart if not to his head. The scholastic will naturally adopt the intellectual method because he is used to working among concepts and abstractions as if they were realities, but if he be a member of some religious body, he will not be averse to using the intuitional method, though in his hands it will be curbed and more or less perverted in the interests of dogma. He who enters on the study of animal behavior in the right spirit will strive to avoid both the narrowness of the laboratory worker and the superficial emotionalism of the nature-lover. That he will always adopt the proper attitude between these extremes is not to be expected of human nature, but it is possible to cultivate a critical and catholic spirit. If I decline to join the ranks of those whose only ambition is to describe and measure the visible movements of animals, and am willing to resort to a comparative psychology in which inferences from analogy with our own mental processes shall have a place, I do this, not because I believe that the former course would be altogether unfruitful or uninteresting, but because the latter seems to me to promise a deeper and more satisfactory insight into the animal mind.

In attempting to give a comprehensible account of such complicated phenomena as those of animal behavior, it is necessary to follow the course of the intellect and classify the various processes involved according to certain salient characters. Some authors have dwelt on the simplicity of certain processes, the complexity of others, while other authors have laid greater stress on automaticity and plasticity as differentiæ. It is, indeed, convenient to distinguish first, simple responses to sensory stimuli, *i. e.*, reflex behavior; second, instinctive behavior, which has been referred by some to chains or series of such reactions—melodies, so to speak, of which the reflexes are but single notes or chords—and third, plastic or modifiable behavior, that is, behavior which is not stereotyped and automatic like the typical reflexes and instincts, but varies adaptively in response to the exigencies of the environment, and is more or less influenced by the previous experience of the individual organism. By many this modifiable activity is supposed to be essentially intelligent. While such a treatment of

the subject is convenient and will be followed in this and the two succeeding chapters, it must be borne in mind that it is very artificial and
schematic, as is clear from the fact that the psychical process in
animals, the source of its visible activities, is neither a unity nor a
multiplicity.   Whatever views may be entertained concerning the nature
of this process and the best method of studying it, all authors agree
in regarding the simple sensory reactions as the basis of any scientific
study of behavior and that this should be supported in turn by a morphological study of the sense organs.   I shall, therefore, follow this
course in our study of the ants, referring the reader to Chapter IV
for the necessary data on the structure of the sense organs.   For
many interesting details, which lack of space compels me to omit, the
reader must also be referred to the works of the following authors,
who have contributed to our knowledge of sensation in ants: Huber
(1810), Forel (1874, 1878*d*, 1886, 1900–'01), Lubbock (1881), Bethe
(1898, 1900, 1902), Janet (1893*b*, 1894), Wasmann (1899*g*), von
Buttel-Reepen (1900), Miss Fielde (1901*a*, 1901*b*, 1902, 1903*a*, 1903*b*,
1904, 1905), Miss Fielde and Parker (1904), Viehmeyer (1900),
Piéron (1904, 1905, 1906, 1907), and Turner (1907*b*).

The study of the sensory responses of ants is beset with grave
difficulties, first, because these responses are more numerous, complex
and obscure than in many lower animals; second, because several senses
may be coimplicated in what appears as a single response, and third,
because the sense organs of ants are merely analogous and by no means
homologous with our own.   These conditions prevent the observer and
experimenter from isolating a single sense.   Both the structure of the
sense organs and experiment show, moreover, that ants respond to
stimuli to which our own senses are irresponsive.   It has, therefore,
been suggested by Bethe and others that we abandon the terminology
of human sensation with its subjective connotations and adopt a new
one of purely objective import, that we speak of photorecepting instead
of seeing, chemorecepting instead of smelling, tasting, etc.   The
reasons given for adopting these terms are not very cogent.   Strictly
speaking, we should have to use them for the higher animals and our
fellow-men.   As Forel remarks: " One ought not to say, ' My wife
has a headache.'   One should say, ' This animal machine which I
believe to be my wife exhibits certain facial cortortions and emits
certain articulate sounds that correspond with those emitted by myself
when I have a headache, but I have no right to say that she has a
headache.' "   The difficulties above mentioned are not to be avoided
by adopting a new nomenclature, but by further and more persistent

experimentation and observation. I have emphasized them because they seem to have been ignored by some investigators.

Although touch is one of the most important senses of ants, it has not been thoroughly studied in these insects. Its great delicacy is attested by the number, distribution and structure of the tactile hairs or sensillæ. As these are extremely fine and abundant on the antennal funiculi, we are justified in concluding that the latter are the principal organs of touch and as the moving ant continually palpates and explores the surfaces over which she travels, it is not improbable that she gleans perceptions of the forms of objects. But it is impossible to dissociate this mechanical sense from the chemical or olfactory sense, since the organs of both are not only situated in the same antennal joints, but are intermingled with one another. It is probable that ants also perceive tactile stimuli to the general chitinous integument where it is not furnished with hairs. That these insects have a very delicate temperature sense, although the location and nature of its organs are quite unknown, is shown by many of their habits, notably by the way they regulate their hours of activity and the way they place their brood in the best situations for utilizing the warmth of the earth and stones. That ants are capable of feeling pain hardly admits of doubt, for, as Forel says: " They often exhibit unequivocal signs of discomfort, especially when their antennæ are pinched, or when their nerve terminations come in contact with certain corrosive or strongly irritating substances." But the quiet manner in which an ant, that has just had an antenna, a leg or even her abdomen cut off, will gorge herself with honey, shows that her sensation of pain must differ profoundly, both in quality and intensity, from that which we should suffer from similar operations.

Much more attention has been devoted to the study of the sense of smell than to that of touch. Forel (1874, 1878d), the pioneer in this field of investigation and the one who has established all the important facts, found that many ants, when deprived of their antennæ, not only do not attack alien ants, but even lick them, that they cannot care for the young or excavate the nest, and are able to eat only when they stumble on their food by accident. Such ants also make unusual movements with their legs and palpi in attempting to substitute these organs for their missing antennæ. Forel believes that the prostrate, club-shaped sensillæ (see Chapter IV, p. 62) are the principal olfactory organs, because they are the ones best developed in insects with the keenest sense of smell (*e. g.,* in Ichneumon flies). Ants are able to perceive odors diffused in the air as well as those dissolved in liquids; for even the blind species often stop and wave their funiculi about in a peculiar manner when within a short distance of an odorous body. It is probable, however, that the odor stimulates the delicate end organs only when it is dissolved in the thin film of glandular secretion covering the antennal club. When the antennæ actually touch the surface of a body, however, the ant, in all probability, receives both tactile and olfactory stimuli, and these probably fuse to produce a single sensation, which Forel calls the topo-chemical, or contact-odor sensation. He believes, therefore, that the ant has a sense of odor-shape. To make this clear he suggests that we fancy ourselves to be blind or in total darkness and in possession of delicate olfactory organs in our finger-tips. Then, if we moved about, touching objects to the right and left along our path, our environment would appear to us to be made up of shaped odors, and we should speak of smells that are spherical, triangular, pointed, etc. Our mental processes would be largely determined by a world of chemical configurations, as they are now by a world of visual (*i. e.*, color) shapes. Blind ants are, of course, permanently in the condition here described, and as all other ants spend most of their time in the dark recesses of the nest, and, with the exception of very few species, rely but little on their eyesight, we can see how different must be our own mental processes from those of these insects.

In order to understand many of the commonest reactions of ants, such as the recognition of friends and foes, the homing instincts of the worker and the development of certain peculiarities of myrmecophiles, we must suppose that ants have not only extremely acute powers of odor-discrimination, but no less extraordinary powers of odor-association. Even the degenerate human olfactories can detect the different species and in some cases even the different castes of ants (*Eciton*) by their odors, but these insects carry the discrimination much further. They not only differentiate the innate odors peculiar to the species, sex, caste and individual and the adventitious or " incurred " odors of the nest and environment, but, according to Miss Fielde, they can detect " progressive odors," due to change of physiological condition with the age of the individual. She believes that " as worker ants advance in age their progressive odor intensifies or changes to such a degree that they may be said to attain a new odor every two or three months." Miss Fielde is also convinced that different antennal joints are specialized for the perception of different odors. This conclusion was reached by cutting off the joints one at a time and studying the subsequent behavior of the ant. She says: " The organ discerning the nest-aura, and probably other local odors, lies in the final joint of the antenna, and such odors are discerned through the air; the progressive odor or the incurred odor is discerned by contact, through the penultimate joint; the scent

of the track by the antepenultimate joint, through the air; the odor
of the inert young, and probably that of the queen also, by contact,
through the two joints above, or proximal to those last mentioned,
while the next above these by contact also discerns the specific odor."
This statement not only lacks confirmation by other observers, but seems
to be the only one which implies that the olfactory organs of an animal
may exhibit regional differentiations.   This has not even been claimed
for dogs, which, nevertheless, possess extremely delicate powers of
odor discrimination and association.   This would be no serious objection, however, if we were able to discover the slightest support for
Miss Fielde's hypothesis in the structure of the antennæ.   We do,
indeed, find in the funiculi a variety of sensillæ, as has been shown in
Chapter IV, but none of these is confined to a single joint or to two
joints.   Miss Fielde, moreover, completely ignores the tactile organs
of the antennæ and makes this surprising statement: "During five
years of fairly constant study of ants I have seen no evidence that their
antennæ are the organs of any other sense than the chemical sense."
And still she observed that ants that had lived in a Petri dish for over
a year felt perfectly at home in any new Petri dish to which they were
transferred.   For an interpretation of such a case of "recognition"
one would certainly turn to a mechanical rather than to a chemical
sense.   Many of her interpretations of the behavior of ants with mutilated antennæ are open to the obvious objection that she tacitly denies
the existence of perception where there is no visible response or where
the animal inhibits certain of its activities.   If we add to this objection
the very limitations of the method, *i. e.,* the necessity of removing all
the joints distal to the one whose function is being tested, and the consideration that the hypothesis is not needed in explaining the facts, it
will be seen that we are not sufficiently justified in regarding the ants'
antenna as an organ made up of a series of specialized "noses."

It is not always easy to distinguish taste from smell in our own
sensory experience, and in ants, where even the structure of the sensillæ in the antennæ and mouthparts are very similar, the difficulty is
greatly enhanced.   That the rows of sensillæ on the maxillæ and at
the base and tip of the tongue are the organs of taste seems to be
proved by the observations of Forel (1886–'88, 1900–'01).   He found
that "when morphine or strychnine are mixed with honey, the ants fail
to detect these substances with their antennæ.   The odor of the honey
attracts them and they begin to eat it.   But as soon as their mouth-
parts come in contact with it they at once turn away.   It is easy to
observe the preferences of ants for certain viands; they will partake
of some and not of others, but they will neglect everything, sometimes

even their duties and the defence of the nest, in order to partake of honey, so inordinate is their fondness for this substance." Forel has seen ants that were attacked in their nest and in imminent danger of being overpowered by their enemies, nevertheless stop a moment and imbibe a little of the honey which he was holding out to them. The fondness of nearly all ants for sweets, such as the excreta of plant-lice, and their dislike of ill-smelling things, such as carrion and the feces of mammals, is very pronounced.[2] Taste is evidently the sense in which these insects approach most closely the higher animals and man.

Whether or not ants are able to perceive the stimuli that we call auditory, has been much debated. In Chapter II I have shown that stridulatory organs are well developed in the Ponerinæ and Myrmicinæ and are present in a rudimental form also in the Dorylinæ; and that the ants possessing these organs actually emit very shrill sounds— usually of so high a pitch as to be inaudible to us—has been observed more or less clearly by a number of investigators, notably by Swinton (1878, 1879), Wroughton (1892), Sharp (1893), Janet (1893b), Emery (1893h), Wasmann (1893a), Adlerz (1895) and myself (1903f). Forel (1874) and Wasmann (1893h) have shown that the workers of European *Camponoti* make sounds also by striking the walls of their nest repeatedly with their gasters, and Gounelle (1900) observed that workers of the Brazilian *Camponotus mus,* which nests in the twigs and dried leaves of the bamboo, produce, when disturbed, a very audible, metallic and whirring sound like that of a rattlesnake, by repeatedly striking the walls of the nest with their heads. In Chapter IV attention was called to the fact that all ants (even the Camponotinæ and Dolichoderinæ!) possess in all their tibiæ, and probably also in other parts of their bodies, structures built on the same fundamental plan as the famous chordotonal organs of the stridulating crickets and katydids. This fact renders it extremely probable that ants perceive not only the stridulatory vibrations of their fellows, but also other vibrations. All students of these insects would doubtless agree to this statement. At this point, however, opinions begin to diverge. Huber (1810) and Forel (1874) deny that ants hear sounds, and the latter, while admitting that they respond easily to grosser mechanical shocks, failed to obtain any response to sounds of a very high pitch. Lubbock (1881), on the other hand, believed that they react to such sounds, but he failed to obtain any experimental evidence for his view. Parker and Miss Fielde (1904) failed to observe any reactions to "aërial

[2] I have seen *Eciton cæcum* visiting carrion, but this was evidently for the purpose of feeding on the larvæ of flies, Silphids, etc. A correspondent informs me that the ants of the Philippines have similar habits and are very important agents in reducing the number of flies at certain seasons of the year.

sound waves from a piano, violin and Galton whistle, which collectively gave a range of from 27 to 60,000 vibrations per second." The insects reacted, however, to vibrations reaching them through the soil and other solids. These vibrations were received through the legs, as they were perceived even when the antennæ, head, abdomen and any one or two pairs of legs were removed. In contradiction to this view and that of Forel, several authors have recently maintained that ants do perceive aërial vibrations. That this is the case has been stated by Weld (1899) for *Cremastogaster lineolata, Lasius americanus* and *Aphænogaster* sp., and by Metcalf (1900) for "a small black ant." Wasmann (1891*f,* 1899*g*) has recorded similar, rather inconclusive observations. I have also virtually expressed myself in favor of such a view in one of my papers (1903*a*), in a passage which as been over-looked or misunderstood by some recent students of this subject, and may therefore be repeated in this place: " Stridulation, at least among the Myrmicinæ, Ponerinæ and Dorylinæ, is an important means of com-munication, which Bethe has completely ignored and even Forel and other myrmecologists have failed to appreciate. It readily explains the rapid congregation of ants (Myrmicinæ) on any particle of food which one of their number may have found, for the excitement of finding food almost invariably causes an ant to stridulate and thus attract other ants in the vicinity. It also explains the rapid spread of a desire to defend the colony when the nest is disturbed. This is especially notice-able in species of *Pheidole, Myrmica* and *Pogonomyrmex.* It is the secret of being able in a short time to catch ants like *P. molefaciens* in great numbers by simply burying a wide-mouthed bottle up to its neck in the mound of the nest. An ant approaches and falls into the bottle. It endeavors to get out, and failing, begins to stridulate. This at once attracts other ants which hurry over the rim and forthwith swell the stridulatory chorus till it is audible even to the human ear. More ants are attracted and soon the bottle is filled. If it be corked and shaken for the purpose of still further exciting its contents, and then held over another *Pogonomyrmex* colony whose members are peacefully sauntering about on the dome of the nest, the wildest excite-ment will suddenly prevail, as if there had been a call to arms—or to dinner. Even more remarkable is the stridulation in a colony of *Atta fervens* (= *texana*), the Texan leaf-cutting ant. Here the different ants, from the huge females through the males, large soldiers and diminishing castes of workers to the tiny minims, present a sliding scale of audibility. The rasping stridulation of the queen can be heard when the insect is held a foot or more from the ear. To be audible the male and soldier must be held somewhat closer, the largest workers

still closer, whereas the smallest workers and minims, though stridulating, as may be seen from the movements of the gaster on the postpetiole, are quite inaudible to the human ear. It is not at all improbable that all this differentiation in pitch, correlated as it is with a
differentiation in the size and functions of the various members of
the colony, is a very important factor in the coöperation of these insects
and of ants in general. The contact-odor sense, important as it
undoubtedly is, must obviously have its limitations in the dark, subterranean cavities in which the ants spend so much of their time, especially when the nests are very extensive like those of *Atta*. Under
such conditions stridulation and hearing must be of great service in
maintaining the integrity of the colony and of its excavations." If
the view of Miss Fielde and Parker be accepted, we must suppose that
the *Pogonomyrmex* in the experiment above described, were thrown
into agitation by vibrations passing from the bottle of stridulating ants
through my body to the soil of the nest. It seems to me much
more probable that the ants perceived the stridulation directly as
aërial vibrations. More numerous experiments, however, have been
recently performed by Turner (1907*b*). Although he worked only
with Camponotine ants (*Formica fusca* and *F. sanguinea*), which
are not known to stridulate, he found that they responded to vibrations as low as 256 and as high as 4,138 per second. "The responses, in the form of zigzag movements, were usually slight
for pitches higher than 3,000 vibrations per second and sometimes
slight for other pitches; but, to most pitches under 3,000 vibrations
per second, the ants usually responded in a pronounced manner, usually
darting about as though much excited." Turner believes that he took
sufficient precautions, by resting the nest on cotton and felt, to exclude
the transfer to the ants of vibrations through the floor, table and walls
of the nest. It is, however, extremely difficult to prove that such
vibrations were excluded, and for this reason we cannot, with the data
at hand, reject the statements of Miss Fielde and Parker. As these
authors say: "It has long been recognized by physiologists, if not by
the scientific public, that touch and hearing in the vertebrates are very
closely related. The apparent separateness of these senses in us is due
to the fact that the air waves by which our senses are usually stimulated are too slight to affect our organs of touch. If, however, we
transfer our experiments to water, we at once meet with a medium in
which, as has long been known, vibrations can be both heard and felt.
In dealing with a like question among the lower animals it therefore
seems to us misleading to attempt to distinguish touch from hearing,
and we shall be more within the bounds of accuracy if we discuss the

question from the standpoint of mechanical stimulation rather than attempt to set up questionable distinctions based upon human sensations."

In Chapter IV attention was called to the fact that the eyes of ants, especially those of the workers, exhibit remarkable differences of development in different species. That this implies an equally wide range in the reactions of these insects to light is proved by observation and experiment. There can be little doubt that these reactions are both phototropic and visual; in other words, that they involve not only an adaptive orientation of the ants' movements as a whole with reference to the direction of the light rays, but also some discrimination of colors and objects. We are not surprised to find that the workers of hypogæic ants, like the smaller species of *Solenopsis,* all species of *Acanthomyops* and *Dorylus* and certain species of *Eciton,* which are virtually cave-dwellers and either have no eyes or mere vestiges of these organs, are strongly photophobic, or negatively phototropic; whereas certain tropical tree ants (*Gigantiops, Dimorphomyrmex, Myrmoteras, Gesomyrmex* and *Pseudomyrma*), which have large convex eyes, are positively phototropic. The workers of the common ants of temperate regions (*Camponotus, Formica, Lasius, Myrmica*) stand about midway between these two extremes in the development of the eyes, but are, on the whole, rather strongly photophobic. This is shown by their actions when suddenly exposed to the light, especially when they happen to be in possession of their brood. However slowly or reluctantly they may react to sudden illumination when alone, they make the greatest haste to remove their brood to a dark place.

The phototropic response, both in the workers and the sexual forms, may be reversed rather suddenly, apparently as the result of changes in physiological condition. This is very clearly seen in the males and females, which in their callow stages are negatively phototropic, but as the time for the marriage flight approaches, exhibit a strong positive phototrophism, as Loeb (1890) has shown. After their marriage flight and the loss of their wings, the females again become negatively phototropic and this reaction seems to become the more pronounced the longer the insect lives. It is evident that these reactions are all highly adaptive and depend on important physiological changes in the wing-musculature and reproductive organs. The dependence of the phototropism of the workers on physiological conditions is not so clear. It is possible, however, that hunger may have something to do with changing the usual negative to a positive phototropism and impelling the worker to leave the nest and forage, while repletion or exposure to the light for several minutes may reverse the reaction and induce the ant to return to the nest. But this is, perhaps, too simple an explanation, for it is certain that prolonged exposure causes many ants to become indifferent to light, and I know two species (*Hypoclinea mariæ* and *gagates*) which seem to be normally in this condition.

That the eyes of our common ants are sufficiently developed to enable their possessors to discriminate colors and forms has been maintained by several observers. Lubbock (1882), Forel (1886–'88, 1900–'01), Forel and Dufour (1902) and Miss Fielde (1902) have made many experiments to test the ants' power of discriminating light of different wave lengths. Lubbock found that ants avoid the ultra-violet rays of the spectrum, and Forel, by hoodwinking ants, showed that these rays were perceived through the eyes and not through the general integument as Graber (1883–'85) had maintained. Miss Fielde summarizes her results, which agree with those of Lubbock and Forel, in the following words: "The ants manifested no liking for any of the rays of light. If obliged to stay in light rays of some sort, the rays of longer wave-lengths are preferred to those of shorter wave-lengths. Dividing the spectrum, as we know it, into red, green and violet, we may say that to the ants' eyes red and green are most like the darkness that they prefer and that violet is to them most luminous; or that the red and green are less visible to them than is violet. In this regard the eyes of the ant appear to be the reverse of our own. Our eyes perceive in the spectrum three fundamental colors—red, green and violet. The eyes of the ant perceive there only two fundamental colors—one made up of the red and green rays, the other of the violet and ultra-violet rays." She says further: "It appears that the eye of the ant is not well-adapted to the reception of light-rays whose wave-length is longer than in the violet rays; that it receives blue and indigo more perfectly than red, orange, yellow and green; and that there is a sudden increase of luminosity in the light rays at that point in the spectrum where violet begins for our eyes. The ants may discern colors, and yet have no preferences among the colors discerned. Color is determined by the wave-length in the light-ray, and since the ants discriminate between rays of different wave-lengths, they probably perceive color in the rays. Sensitivity to the length of the wave indicates perception of color."

Forel and Dufour also experimented on ants with Roentgen rays. These were directed up through the bottom of an artificial nest, and although they were allowed to act on the ants and their brood for fifteen minutes, the insects made no response. Moreover, a week later, they showed no signs of having sustained any injury from the experiment.

If we accept Exner's view that the compound eye of insects forms of an object a single upright image, which is the more definite the greater the number of ommatidia and the more convex the surface of the eye, it is very probable that only ants with well developed eyes, like *Formica, Pseudomyrma,* etc., can distinguish objects by means of these organs. Wasmann's experiments (1899*g*) indicate that workers of various species of *Formica* can see resting objects as large as a finger at a distance of 5–10 cm., but that they are unable to see small objects, like beetles, at a greater distance than 4–5 mm. My own observations tend to confirm these statements. Moving objects are, of course, much more readily perceived. Indirect evidence of visual discrimination in ants is furnished by the mimetic coloration and form of certain myrmecophiles (see Chapters XXI and XXII). Undoubtedly male ants, which always have very large, convex eyes, are able to see the flying females at a considerable distance. The function of the ocelli, so highly developed in the males and females, has not been determined. It has been suggested that they may be of use in seeing objects at very close range and in dark places, like the galleries of the nest.

On the whole, we are led to conclude that vision in worker and female ants is very poorly developed, compared with the chemical and mechanical senses (contact-odor and the perception of vibrations). Indeed, ant behavior is so profoundly influenced by these senses, that it may be said to differ fundamentally, not only from the behavior of man and the higher mammals, but even from that of such closely allied Hymenoptera as the bees and wasps.

CHAPTER XXIX

THE INSTINCTIVE BEHAVIOR OF ANTS

"Est sind keine anderen als die Erscheinungen des thierischen Instinctes, die für jeden nachdenkenden Menschen zu den allergrössten gehören—wahrer Probirstein ächter Philosophie."—Schelling, "System der gesammten Philosophie," I Bd.

"Der Instinkt ist nicht Resultat bewusster Ueberlegung, nicht Folge der körperlichen Organisation, nicht blosses Resultat eines in der Organisation des Gehirns gelegenen Mechanismus, nicht Wirkung eines dem Geiste von aussen angeklebten todten, seinem innersten Wesen fremden Mechanismus, sondern *selbsteigene* Leistung des Individuums, aus seinem innersten Wesen und Charakter entspringend."—E. von Hartmann, "Philosophie des Unbewussten," 9th ed., 1882.

If ants exhibited merely the reflexes, or such brief and simple responses to sensory stimuli as we have been considering in the preceding chapter, their lives would flow on with the same monotonous regularity as those of many other insects and the lower invertebrates in general. In addition to these reflexes, however, ants manifest more complicated trains of behavior, the so-called instincts; and both these and the reflexes may be affected with a certain modifiability or plasticity which, in its highest manifestations, has been called intelligence. Leaving for my last chapter a consideration of this latter aspect of behavior, I shall here confine myself to the instincts.

Many attempts have been made to define instinct, but it is evident that none of these could be completely successful, because instinct transcends intelligence and has its mainspring in the depths of the life-process itself. Perhaps as good a formal definition as I am able to give is the following: An instinct is a more or less complicated activity manifested by an organism which is acting, first, as a whole rather than as a part; second, as the representative of a species rather than as an individual; third, without previous experience; and fourth, with an end or purpose of which it has no knowledge. This definition will satisfy the person of scholastic mind, but to the biologist it is a mass of obscurities; for it is certain that the man lives not who can tell where the whole begins and the part leaves off in a living organism, or can frame a satisfactory definition of a living individual or a species; and the intellect abdicates when it is called upon to grasp an activity that is unconsciously purposeful.

In all probability these very obscurities have attracted many students to the study of instinct. At any rate, there is no end of the literature on the subject.[1] Instinct could not, of course, be studied by so many authors without much controversy, and the employment of the word in many different senses. This is pardonable, at least to some extent, since the subject itself presents no less than four aspects, according as it is studied from the ethological, physiological, psychological or metaphysical points of view. From the first two of these instinct is open to objective biological study in the form of the " instinct actions." These may be studied by the physiologist merely as a regularly coördinated series of movements depending on changes in the tissues and organs, and by the ethologist to the extent that they tend to bring the organism into effective relationship with its living and inorganic environment. But that these movements have a deeper origin in psychological changes may be inferred on the basis of analogy from our own subjective experience which shows us our instincts arising as impulses and cravings, the so-called " instinct-feelings "; and these in turn yield abundant material for metaphysical and ethical speculation.

Modern biological writers naturally wish to restrict the term instinct to the instinct-actions, whereas scholastic, psychological, metaphysical and theological writers throw the emphasis on the instinct-feelings. That this was the original meaning of the word is shown by its derivation from the Latin *instinguere,* to incite, and its probable relation to the Greek ἐνστίζειν. The contrast between the subjective and objective aspects of instinct is brought out sharply in Descartes' notion of the animal as an automaton, a conception which has profoundly affected biological and even theological thought. The following passage, quoted from the Seventh Bridgewater Treatise by the Rev. William Kirby, will make this clear: " An eminent French zoölogist [Virey] has illustrated the change of instincts resulting from the modi-

[1] During the past ten years I have read a small library of books on instinct. Among these the following have been most suggestive from the physiological point of view: Chapter XIII of Loeb's " Physiology of the Brain," Driesch's " Die ' Seele' als Elementarer Naturfaktor," and the second volume of his " Science and Philosophy of the Organism "; from the psychological point of view: G. H. Schneider's " Der Thierische Wille," Wundt's " Vorlesungen uber die Menschen- und Thierseele," Chapter XXIV of the second volume of Wm. James's " Principles of Psychology," and Groos's " Die Spiele der Thiere "; from the metaphysical point of view: Chapter XXVII of the second volume of Schopenhauer's " Welt als Wille and Vorstellung," Chapter III of von Hartmann's " Philosophie des Unbewussten " and Chapter II of Bergson's " L'Évolution Créatrice "; from the scholastic and doctrinaire points of view: Reimarus's " Allgemeine Betrachtungen uber die Triebe der Thiere " (1798), Joly's " L'Instinct, ses Rapports avec la Vie et avec l'Intelligence," Wasmann's " Instinct und Intelligenz im Thierreich," and Supplement A of Maher's " Psychology: Empirical and Rational."

fication of the nervous system, which takes place in a butterfly in the
transit to its perfect or imago state from the caterpillar, by a novel and
striking simile. He compares the animal to a portable or hand organ,
in which, on a cylinder that can be made to revolve, several tunes are
noted; turn the cylinder and the tune for which it is set is played;
draw it out a notch and it gives a second; and so you may go on till
the whole number of tunes noted on it have had their turn. This,
happily enough, represents the change which appears to take place in
the vertebral cord and its ganglions on the metamorphoses of the
caterpillar into the butterfly, and the sequence of new instincts which
result from the change. But if we extend the comparison, we may
illustrate it by the two spheres of organized beings that we find on
our globe, and their several instinctive changes and operations. We
may suppose each kingdom of nature to be represented by a separate
cylinder, having noted upon it as many tunes as there are species differing in their respective instincts—for plants may be regarded, in some
sense, as having their instincts as well as animals—and that the constant impulse of an invisible agent causes each cylinder to play in a
certain order all the tunes noted upon it; this will represent, not inaptly,
what takes place with regard to the development of instincts in the
vegetable and animal kingdoms, and our simile will terminate in the
inquiry, whose may be that invisible hand that thus shakes the sistrum
of Isis, and produces that universal harmony of action, resulting from
that due intermixture of concords and discords, according to the will
of its Almighty Author, in that infinitely diversified and ever-moving
sphere of beings we call *nature.*" Kirby concludes that the powers
which turn the hand organ of instinct are " the physical Cherubim of
the Holy Scriptures, or the heavens in action, which under God govern
the universe."

This specimen, extracted from the theological dust-bin, derives its
interest from the fact that it is a caricature of views that are still held
on the subject of instinct. It is, in fact, more like the scholastic conception of instinct than would appear at first sight. Considering for
the present only the objective, or hand organ, portion of the above
simile, and neglecting the " physical Cherubim," who keep turning the
handle, we see that the peculiarity of instinct—the combination of
complexity with automatic or mechanical fixity—that impressed earlier
thinkers is the one that still arrests our attention. Indeed, this peculiarity is responsible both for the " lapsed intelligence " and the
" reflex " hypotheses of instinct. The former of these seems to be
moribund, the latter, according to which instincts are merely chain
reflexes (" Kettenreflexe "), still flourishes, at least, in our biological

laboratories. Spencer, Loeb, Bethe, Driesch and others have supported this hypothesis with much clean-cut argument; but the way to its conception was prepared long ago by Claude Bernard in his description of certain complex physiological activities, like those of the alimentary tract, as "mouvements reflexes régulièrement enchaînés." The difficulty with the hypothesis is its schematism, for while we may admit that an instinct may be described as a compound reflex, we must also admit that it is more than this, since the reflexes are not merely strung along in sequence, but constitute an organized system of coördinated activities which coimplicate and interpenetrate one another, so to speak, and grow and change by modification *in toto,* or by intersusception and not by simple apposition of new activities.

Biologists find it increasingly difficult to draw a hard and fast line between instinct and reflexes, or between either of these and the simple vital activities of protoplasm. The definition of instinct cited above is perfectly applicable to a unicellular organism, or to a single Metazoan cell, considered as a whole. It is difficult or impossible, moreover, as Loeb and Driesch have insisted, to dissociate the instinctive activities from those of growth and development. This is due to the fact that instinct is so intimately and inextricably involved in the structure of the organism. As Bergson says: " It has often been remarked that most instincts are the prolongation, or better, the achievement, of the work of organization itself. Where does the activity of instinct begin? Where does that of nature end? It is impossible to say. In the metamorphoses of the larva into the nymph and into the perfect insect, metamorphoses which often require appropriate adaptations and a kind of initiative on the part of the larva, there is no sharp line of demarcation between the instinct of the animal and the organizing work of the living matter. It is immaterial whether we say that instinct organizes the instruments which it is going to use, or that the organization prolongs itself into the instinct by which it is to be used." The spinning of the cocoon by the larval ant is a good example of the kind of instinct to which Bergson refers. From one point of view this is merely an act of development, and the cocoon, or result of the secretive activity of the sericteries and of the spinning movements of the larva, is a protective envelope. But an envelope with the same protective function may be produced by other insect larvæ simply as a thick, chitinous secretion from the whole outer surface of the hypodermis. Here, too, we have an activity which, though manifested in a very different way, is even more clearly one of growth and development. And when the workers of *Œcophylla* or *Polyrhachis* use their larvæ for weaving the silken envelope of the nest, as described in Chapter XIII, we have a further extension and modification of the cocoon-spinning activities. In this case the spinning powers of the larva are utilized for the purpose of producing an envelope, not for its individual self, but for the whole colony. In conventional works this latter activity would be assigned a prominent place as a typical instinct, the spinning of the cocoon might also be included under this head, but the formation of the puparium, or pupal skin, would be excluded as a purely physiological or developmental process, yet this last, no less than the two other cases, has all the fundamental characteristics of an instinct.

Viewed in this light there is nothing surprising about the complexity and relative fixity of an instinct, for it is inseparably correlated with the structural organization, and in this we have long been familiar both with the dependence of the complexity and fixity of parts on heredity and the modifiability of these parts during the life-cycle of the individual. Fixed or instinctive behavior has its counterpart in inherited morphological structure as does modifiable, or plastic, behavior in well-known ontogenetic and functional changes.

There is no better group for the study of instinct, both as a stereotyped heredity activity and in its correlation with structure, than the ants. Wundt and others have called attention to the fact that all instincts center about alimentation and reproduction, and that in these processes themselves we have the most typical instincts. As alimentation may be regarded as subservient to reproduction, we may say that all instincts converge towards the propagation of the species. This statement meets with no exception in the ants on account of their social organization. On the contrary, this merely lends it greater emphasis. All the foraging, nest-building and other activities revolve about the care and education of the brood, and, as has been shown in Chapters XIX, XXI and XXII, even the extravagant and aberrant activities that these insects exhibit in their tolerance and care of myrmecophiles and parasites, have their origin in the same obsessional generative instincts.

The ant colony, as many authors have suggested, is analogous to a single large organism, in which the soma is represented by the body of workers, the reproductive organ by the fertilized queen. It follows, of course, from this conception that the differentiation of the colonial soma into castes is merely the visible result of a psychological and physiological division of labor. It is also noticeable that in the ant colony the closer instincts come to those of pure growth, development and reproduction, the more fixed and mechanical they appear, whereas the ancillary and more remote ethological instincts, like those of foraging and nest building and those relating to other organisms such as alien ants, myrmecophiles and parasites, are much less constant and universal. Here, too, the analogy of the colony to a Metazoon is apparent, for in the latter we also find that growth, ontogeny and reproduction are very rigidly determined as compared with the activities that bring the organism into relation with its multiform and changing environment.

The castes have often been cited as fine examples of the correlation of instinct and structure, but it is only recently that we have come to feel the full force of this assertion. As I have discussed this subject at some length in Chapter VII, I may here confine myself to a few remarks. The male and female ant present an extraordinary contrast in the development of their instincts; the male, though possessing very highly developed eyes and antennæ, having such abortive instincts that he scarcely ranks above many lowly organized, solitary insects, whereas most female ants may be said to be richly endowed with all the instincts of their respective species. For this reason, and also because the queen ant, while forming her colony leads a solitary life and is not disconcerted by being kept in confinement, she is an extremely favorable object for the study of instinct. Her activities, as an individual, are so methodical that they strike the observer, who first witnesses them, as a beautiful example of the catenary or compound reflex. Beginning with deälation, which seems to be the necessary initiatory stimulus, she goes through a regular routine, excavating a small cell in the earth, closing its opening, laying eggs, feeding the larval workers with her own secretions, guarding them, burying them when mature till they have spun their cocoons, unearthing them and eventually assisting them to hatch, all as if she were merely a machine wound up and set in motion by definite external and internal stimuli. But closer study of her reflexes, especially under changed conditions, shows that matters are not so simple as they seem. Gaps may be formed in the series of activities without affecting the outcome. Thus the excavation of the nest may be omitted if the insect finds some preëxisting cavity under a stone, in a gall or in an artificial nest, or when she is adopted by a number of workers of her own or another species, without in the least disturbing her subsequent reactions. Or, if food is placed in the nest, the young may be fed with it instead of with the maternal secretions, or some of the eggs or larvæ may be devoured by the mother for the sake of nourishing the remainder of the brood, etc. Moreover, the young may not all mature at the same time and must, therefore, be treated differently, according to their respective ontogenetic stages. In short, the activities, though all tending towards one end, the maturation of the brood, are, nevertheless, organically and very flexibly combined. This is even more apparent when we come to compare the instincts of different queen ants representing not only the common method of colony formation just considered, but also the methods adopted by the fungus-growers, the temporary and permanent social parasites and the slave-makers. In these latter cases the aim still remains the same—the bringing to maturity of the first brood—and undoubtedly they have developed out of the common type of colony formation. This development, however, could not have taken place by a mere omission or addition of single reflexes, but only through a more or less profound modification of the instinct theme as a whole.

With the exception of the parasitic females, we find that ants of this sex exhibit all the instincts of their species and it would seem that, like the queen bee, even the parasitic queens must virtually possess, although they never manifest, the worker instincts. This statement, of course, can have no meaning to those who limit instinct to the instinct actions. Yet we must suppose that the parasitic queen ant, like the degenerate queen of the honey-bee, is capable of transmitting to her worker offspring the tendency to forage and construct, although she never manifests this tendency in her own person. We should expect the worker, as an abortive female, to exhibit an abridgment of her mother's instincts, and this, generally speaking, is found to be the case. In the workers, however, under normal conditions, certain of the queen's activities, especially those of nidification, foraging and defence, are exaggerated, while others, such as those of reproduction, are suppressed or kept in abeyance. This intensification of certain tendencies and suppression of others is, of course, eminently purposeful and adaptive.

In the structural differentiation of the various castes of workers, so elaborately carried out in the species of *Atta s. str., Pheidologeton, Camponotus,* etc., we see a corresponding differentiation of instincts. But, as I have shown in Chapter VII, even monomorphic workers exhibit a tendency to separate into groups of individuals that temporarily or permanently perform specific functions in the life of the colony. Both this and the fact that some queen ants that have become parasitic, show as yet in their size and external structure no visible effects of these peculiarities, indicate that instinct leads with changes in the more delicate texture of the nervous system and tissues of the body generally, and that the grosser structures follow more slowly in the wake of these modifications.

Some authors have laid considerable stress on the deferred instincts, but it is obvious that these, too, are merely instincts that are unable to manifest themselves till the necessary structural apparatus has been developed. Male, female and worker ants all have deferred instincts.

The males and females do not attempt the nuptial flight till they are thoroughly mature, and the queen does not begin to start a colony till her wings have been removed. The worker will not forage or take part in excavating or guarding the nest till its integument has hardened and taken on the adult coloration. As a callow, it remains in the nest and functions only as a nurse. The tendency of certain old workers to become sexually mature and to act as gynæcoids may also be regarded as a deferred instinct, depending on unusual powers of assimilating food and the ripening of eggs in the ovaries. To the same category we may also assign the behavior of old queens that shun the light and merely assimilate food and lay eggs, without paying any attention to the brood or to the adult workers.

As additional evidence of the intimate correlation between instinct and structure we may point to the vestigial, decadent and deceased instincts and the analogy between form regulation and instinct regulation. Ants furnish abundant examples of all of these, especially of activities that must once have been of the greatest importance to the species, but have since fallen into desuetude and been overlaid or all but completely replaced by more recently acquired tendencies. Cases of this description are most obvious in the parasitic species, or in those that have changed their nesting habits within comparatively recent times. Forel (1900d, 1904f) has called attention to vestigial slave-making instincts in *Strongylognathus huberi* and *rehbinderi,* ants now living as permanent parasites in the nests of *Tetramorium cespitum* (see Chapter XXVII), but in all probability descended from slave-makers like *Polyergus rufescens,* which they still resemble in the peculiar falcate structure of their jaws. *P. rufescens,* too, has its vestigial instincts. As we have seen, the workers of this species are no longer able to take food except from the tongues of their slaves, and perish when these attendants are removed, but the queens have retained to a very slight degree the ability to feed independently. This case and many others that might be cited, are interesting as proving that the castes may show different stages in the decay of the same instinct. In other words, we not only find the ants exhibiting vestigial instincts as species, but a certain caste within the species may show vestiges of instincts whose full exercise is the normal prerogative of a different caste. Thus, under extraordinary circumstances, the usually sterile worker may lay eggs, like the female, or the female may forage like the workers or accompany them on slave-making expeditions. In *Leptothorax emersoni* I have observed a very striking example of an obsolescent feeding habit (see Chapter XXIII). This ant when living with its host, *Myrmica canadensis*—and in a state of nature it is always found in this association—obtains its food only from the tongues of the *Myrmica* workers (*i. e.*, by regurgitation), or by licking their oily bodies, but when it is separated from the *Myrmica* in an artificial nest, it begins to visit the food dish and feeds, rather awkwardly at first, but eventually quite like the nonparasitic species. In this case, an instinct, which would certainly be put down by the casual observer as completely absent, can be resuscitated under experimental conditions. The nidification of ants also furnishes examples of vestigial activities. *Cremastogaster lineolata, e. g.,* a common North American ant which nests in the ground or in rotten wood, belongs to a largely tropical, arboreal genus, many species of which construct great paper or carton nests, roughly resembling the nests of certain social wasps (see Chapter XIII). On very rare occasions, however, and in moist localities which somewhat resemble the jungles of the tropics, *C. lineolata* constructs small carton nests or diminutive "sheds" of the same material over the plant-lice and mealy bugs on whose excrement it feeds. This is obviously a feeble reminiscence of formerly well developed carton-building instincts.

That the instincts of ants may become pathological, or, at any rate, result in the production of diseased individuals, was shown in Chapter XXII, where I described the habits of *Lomechusa* and *Xenodusa*. The presence of these parasitic beetles in the nest causes the ants to neglect their own brood and even to rear abnormal or defective individuals (pseudogynes), which are of no use to the colony. A similar aberration of instinct is seen in the rearing and toleration of the mermithergates in nests of *Pheidole commutata,* and perhaps also in the production of workers of the intermediate type in nests of *Ph. instabilis* infested with *Orasema.*

All of these parasites eventually bring about the decay of the colony in which they establish themselves, through a disturbance of its trophic status, or balance. This balance is an extremely delicate adjustment to the food supply and any change in it is very soon reflected in the growth or decay of the colony as a whole. Such growth or decay is best gauged by the appearance or disappearance of the brood, or of certain castes which require an unusual amount of food for their maintenance. Favorable trophic conditions show themselves first in the increase and growth of the brood, and unfavorable conditions in the arrest of its growth and its disappearance. The second indication of prosperity in a colony is the increase in the number of large workers or soldiers and the appearance of virgin queens. Pricer and I have shown that incipient colonies of ants contain only minim workers and that the major and maxima forms and the queens appear only after the colony has been in existence for some years. A decline in the food supply, continuing after the elimination of the larvæ leads, as I have observed in artificial nests, to a suppression, first, of the soldier forms, and then of the males and supernumerary females. Thereupon, the smaller workers gradually die off, leaving only the queen surviving as the most resistent and most important individual in the colony. These facts indicate that there is an instinctive regulation of the personnel of the colony, but there are others which point in the same direction. In colonies infested with the Lomechusine beetles, if we accept Wasmann's interpretation, there is an endeavor on the part of the ants to replace the workers, which the parasites have destroyed, by converting female larvæ into workers. Like many form regulations, this effort fails, since it results in the nonviable pseudogynes, but it is, nevertheless, sufficiently successful to indicate the presence of regulation. Another phase of regulation is seen when the queen of the colony disappears. When this happens one of the workers may become gynæcoid and assume her functions, as Wasmann and I have found in *Polyergus* colonies. In a few ants (*Leptogenys* and perhaps *Diacamma* and *Champsomyrmex*) this condition has become permanent, so that winged queens are no longer produced. Another case which shows the resemblance between instinct regulation on the one hand and form regulation and regeneration on the other has been observed by Janet. He found that if the workers of a very young colony be removed, the queen, instead of lapsing into the impassive, egg-laying stage characteristic of her sex in old colonies, proceeds at once to produce and rear another brood, thus restoring or regenerating the lost part of the colony, just as many mutilated animals and plants restore their missing organs. Many cases of parasitism among ants probably depend on the regulation of instincts. The killing of the queen *Monomorium* by her own workers in colonies that have been entered by *Wheeleriella* queens (Chapter XXVII), and the elimination of the host queen in many other cases, may depend on a tendency to preserve the individual that is able to reproduce on the smallest amount of food. This, I take it, is the significance of Forel's hypothesis that the hosts prefer the small parasitic to their own much larger queens. Simpler examples of regulation in instinct are seen in the rebuilding in typical form of the disturbed nests and fungus-gardens of ants. In such cases a part of the nest is repaired with reference to the whole, just as if it were part of a living body undergoing regeneration.

Among recent writers Driesch (1903, 1908) is one of the few who have given some thought to the nature of the stimuli which set the instinct actions going. He distinguishes two kinds of stimuli, the

" simple," meaning " light of different wave-lengths, or heat, or moisture, or chemical compounds, etc.," and " individualized " stimuli, by
which he understands " specific typical bodies," or objects.   That many
instinct actions are called into existence by simple stimuli admits of
no doubt, but it is an open question whether this may be accomplished
by individualized stimuli.   In this connection Driesch (1908) says:
" It is very important to notice that, *if an actual case of a specific individualized stimulus of an instinct should become known, the limits of
the possibility of a mechanical explanation would be exceeded.*   They
would be exceeded and an autonomic or vitalistic factor would be at
work, because we could by no means understand how the specifically
combined or ' individualized ' stimulus could be *received* by the organism in such a way as to become the cause of a specific and fixed series
of motions in the organism.   Supposing that any organism were specifically affected in its instinctive movements by the mere *sight* of any
other typical organism, say of the same species, but of the other sex,
and that this affection were the same, whether the organism which
forms the stimulus were seen from before or from behind, or from
the side or at any angle whatsoever, what would follow from such a
fact?   A machine could only be fitted to receive the specific complicated stimulus in a few typical positions, but how could a machine be
imaginable if an infinite variety of aspects had the same invariable
instinctive effect? "   It seems probable, as Driesch suggests, that the
sexual instincts, at least in the higher animals, may be set going by
individualized stimuli.   He cites in support of this supposition the
observations of Mayer and Soule (1906) who found that female moths,
unless deprived of their sight, would not copulate with male moths
that had their wings removed.   I am at a loss to see how the question
raised by Driesch can be answered satisfactorily through a study of
the ants.   It is, of course, possible that many of their instincts are
initiated by individualized stimuli, such as perceptions of the young
in various stages and of the various castes as typical bodies, but as
the dominant senses of ants are mechanical and chemical, it is at least
equally probable that these objects may call forth appropriate instinctive
reactions merely as tactile and olfactory sensations, and hence as simple
stimuli.[2]

With a description of the instinct actions and their stimuli the
ethological and physiological consideration of instinct is exhausted.   I

[2] Probably many authors would be inclined to doubt the dependence of instincts on individualized stimuli on the ground that " purely inherited responses
can be adapted only to certain broad, roughly distinguished classes of stimuli,
for these are common to the experience of all members of the species" (Miss M.
F. Washburn, 1908).

do not wish to intimate that this task has been accomplished in any group of animals, much less in the ants, which offer an endless field for further investigations.   But it will be necessary before leaving the subject to admit openly what has been somewhat covertly assumed in the preceding pages—the existence of some factor which directs and coördinates the instinct actions in their adaptive course.   Such a factor has been postulated under a variety of names by a host of thinkers and speculators on the subject of instinct.   It is the " physical Cherubim " of the Rev. William Kirby in the passage cited above.   Aristotle calls it the ψυχὴ αἰσθητική, the school-men dubbed it the *vis æstimativa,* Wasmann calls it the " sinnliches Erkenntniss- und Strebevermögen," Driesch calls it the " entelechy," while some modern psychologists, considering the matter from the introspective and therefore necessarily human standpoint, are satisfied to speak of it as the " instinct-feeling," " Trieb," " craving " or " impulse."

It is evident that the best way to know what instincts are is to experience, that is, to live them.   Such experience shows that they arise as primitive volitions or cravings, or what the Germans call " Triebe " —a word for which we have no exact equivalent in the English language—and that they are inseparable from certain pleasurable or painful emotions.   The question then suggests itself as to whether there is anything to indicate that ants experience similar internal states. We are, of course, working here merely with analogical inferences and probabilities, and may, therefore, incur the contempt of a whole school of German physiologists, but, as has been often stated by other authors, we must either proceed in this manner or abandon animal psychology altogether.   I admit that it is very easy and very reprehensible to read one's own psychology into an animal, but after a patient, and, I believe, unprejudiced study of the ants, I have reached the same conclusions as Forel, Wasmann and others, namely, that these insects show unequivocal signs of possessing both feelings and impulses.   In my opinion they experience both anger and fear, both affection and aversion, elation and depression in a simple, " blind " form, that is, without anything like the complex psychical accompaniment which these emotions arouse in us.   Whether a stinging ant or hornet merely exhibits a pure reflex or has a feeling of anger besides, is a nice problem.   I have unintentionally sat on nests of *Vespa germanica* and *Pogonomyrmex barbatus,* and while I have no doubt that I myself acted reflexly under the circumstances, it will take quite an army of physiologists to convince me that these creatures were acting as nothing but reflex machines.

As would be expected, instinct, in its teleological and unconscious aspect, has appealed very powerfully to the philosopher.   He has, in fact, been inclined to regard it as a brilliant manifestation of the principle conceived to lie at the heart of his particular metaphysical system. Thus Schopenhauer and many of his followers have regarded instinct as a vivid revelation of the " will to live," and von Hartmann finds in it a striking activity of the " unconscious." More recently Bergson has defined it as " divinatory sympathy." This is, of course, in no sense a scientific definition, but it suggests an interesting line of reflection. May it not enable us to understand why ants live as parasites on particular hosts, tolerate particular myrmecophiles or attend certain aphids and Lycænid larvæ? On any other view these relationships, in which one organism acts as if it had an intimate and innate knowledge of the structure and activities of another, seem to depend too much on accident or chance. Bergson's conception may also explain why the investigator who puts himself into sympathetic *rapport* with an animal is more likely to interpret its behavior correctly than one who uses it merely as so much material for the solution of some laboratory problem.

CHAPTER XXX

THE PLASTIC BEHAVIOR OF ANTS

"Die Ameisen sind weder intelligente Miniaturmenschen noch blosse Reflexmaschinen. Sie sind mit dem Vermögen der sinnlichen Empfindung und willkürlichen Bewegung ausgestattete Wesen, deren sinnliche Triebe (Instinkte) durch sinnliche Wahrnehmung und Empfindung in ihrer Ausführung geleitet werden und je nach der Verschiedenheit der augenblicklichen Wahrnehmungen und Empfindungszustände, sowie zum Theile auch durch den Einfluss früher gemachter Erfahrungen in mannigfaltiger Weise modificirt werden können. Das ist eine Auffassung des Ameisenlebens, die mit den Thatsachen übereinstimmt und den Thieren weder zu viel noch zu wenig zuerkennt."—E. Wasmann, "Die psychischen Fähigkeiten der Ameisen," 1899.

While there has long been unanimity of opinion in regard to the predominant rôle of instincts in the lives of ants, there is still considerable diversity of opinion in regard to the plasticity or modifiability of behavior in these insects. This plasticity is what Hobhouse calls "the power of an organism to adapt action to requirement without the guidance of a hereditary method of adjustment." It may also be defined as action on the basis of individual, *i. e.,* ontogenetic experience ("historische Reaktionsbasis" of Driesch), and as such is commonly designated as "intelligence." Scholastic writers, like the Jesuit Wasmann, and a few modern psychologists, like Wundt, however, restrict this term to reasoning, or ratiocination, the highest type of plastic behavior. Though not in conformity with general usage, Wasmann's preference for using the term in this sense is not a serious matter, but when he persists in comprising under instinct also the modifiable activities of organisms, he clearly reveals his zeal to minimize the difference between automatic and plastic behavior on the one hand, and to increase the gap between the latter and ratiocination on the other, in order to save one of the old Thomistic dogmas concerning the nature of the human soul. While I am quite as unable as all his other non-scholastic critics (Forel, Emery, Escherich, Bethe, von Buttel-Reepen, Driesch, etc.) to accept Wasmann's terminology, I nevertheless find myself in rather close agreement with his interpretation of the facts of ant behavior. This interpretation, however, is not original with Wasmann, but is essentially that of Forel, as outlined in his earliest myrmecological work (1874) and since developed in a number of his publications.

In addition to instinct, two types of plastic behavior may be distin-

guished in ants: first, random behavior, like that observed by Jennings,
Holmes, Yerkes and others in so many of the lower invertebrates and
by Lloyd Morgan, Thorndike, Hobhouse and others in the higher
animals. Random, or "trial and error" movements, occur, so to speak,
in the very bosom of the instincts, as, for example, when an ant goes
out to forage for food that has not as yet been located. She moves
along slowly and in a very irregular course, palpating all the elevations
and depressions in her path, till she happens on some bit of food. Then
her demeanor suddenly changes, she seizes the food and returns with
it rapidly to the nest. Of course, there are also random movements
of a more primitive type, such as the righting movements, or those performed by an ant that is trying to extricate herself from some sticky
substance, from the jaws of another ant, or from under a pebble or
bit of earth that has fallen on her body. Such movements have the
same teleological significance which they have in other animals: they
greatly increase the likelihood of escape and survival, and through what
Jennings calls the "readier resolution of physiological states after
repetition" they have a prospective value in relation to future circumstances of a similar character.

A second type of behavior is that in which the organism when confronted with a new situation does not proceed to make random movements, but at once adapts itself to the situation by a process which some
authors (Loeb, Turner) have called associative memory. The nature
of this process is, of course, a matter of conjecture and on this account
it is differently conceived by different authors. Before considering
this matter, however, we may pass in review the main facts that compel
us to postulate the existence of some form of memory in ants. These
facts may be grouped under the heads of foraging and homing, recognition of nest mates and aliens, communication, imitation, coöperation
and docility.

1. **Foraging and Homing.**—Forel was the first to show that ants
are guided in their foraging and homing excursions very largely by
their sense of contact-odor, *i. e.,* that they recognize by means of their
antennal sense-organs the odor-form, and hence also the direction of
the trails laid down by their own feet and those of their nest mates.
He showed also that some blind or small-eyed ants, like the Dorylines
and *Lasius,* ants which habitually forage in files, stick very close to
their odoriferous trails and therefore rely mainly or altogether on their
topochemical sense in finding their way back to the nest, whereas
others, like the species of *Formica,* use their eyes as well, and therefore often abandon the sinuosities of the trail and make straight for
their feeding grounds or for the nest. These observations have been

fully confirmed by Wasmann. Lubbock, Viehmeyer and, more recently, Turner, have found some evidence that ants may also be guided by the direction of the light rays. Turner, especially, has emphasized this point, but he seems to overlook the fact that it can have only subordinate significance, as many of our ants forage as readily at night or in the dark store-rooms of houses, the holds of ships, etc., as they do in the daylight, that many tropical and desert species are nocturnal at certain seasons, and that others are permanently nocturnal or hypogæic. We are compelled, therefore, to regard the topochemical, or contact-odor sense as all important in the foraging and homing behavior of ants, although it must be admitted that other senses may be relied upon to some extent. Bethe (1898), with a rather superficial knowledge of the habits of ants and of the literature pertaining to them, has endeavored to show that these insects follow the odor trail from and to the nest in a purely reflex manner and therefore neither exhibit nor require even a rudiment of memory. Like a true physiologist, he selected for his studies the first ants that came to hand—*Lasius niger, L. emarginatus* and *Myrmica scabrinodis*—all species which adhere closely to their trails and, overlooking Forel's important studies, postulated a "polarization" of the paths as more acceptable to the scientific mind than any explanation involving a psychical factor. Wasmann, in a comprehensive work on the mental endowment of ants (1899*g*), has adequately demonstrated the falsity of Bethe's position. To this work and to Forel's controversial articles (1900–'01, 1903*e,* etc.) the reader is referred for the further arguments on the subject. Here it will suffice to quote a passage in which Forel gives some of his reasons for assuming the existence of memory in the insects under discussion: "An ant may perform an arduous journey of thirty meters from her ruined nest, there find a place suitable for building another nest, return, orienting herself by means of her antennæ, seize a companion who forthwith rolls herself about her abductrix, and carry her to the newly selected spot. The latter then also finds her way to the original nest, and each carry back another companion, etc. The memory of the suitable nature of the locality for establishing a new nest must exist in the brain of the first ant, or she would not return, laden with a companion, to this very spot. The slave-making ants (*Polyergus*) undertake predatory expeditions, led by a few workers, who for days and weeks previously have been searching the neighborhood for nests of *Formica fusca*. The ants often lose their way, remain standing, and hunt about for a long time till one or the other finds the topochemical trail and indicates to the others the proper direction by rapidly pushing ahead. Then the pupæ of the

Formica fusca nest which they have found are brought up from the depths of the galleries, appropriated and dragged home, often a distance of forty meters or more. If the plundered nest still contains pupæ, the robbers return on the same or following days and carry off the remainder, but if there are no pupæ left they do not return. How do the *Polyergus* know whether there are pupæ remaining? It can be demonstrated that smell could not attract them from such a distance, and this is even less possible for sight or any other sense. Memory alone, *i. e.,* the recollection that many pupæ still remain behind in the plundered nest can induce them to return." The same reasoning, of course, applies to the cases of simple foraging, and the attendance of ants day after day on the same plant-lice.

2. **Recognition of Nest-mates and Aliens.**—Bethe has also endeavored to show that the mutual recognition of ants is a mere chemoreflex, without a trace of sensation or perception, but in this he has failed even more signally than in his reflex interpretation of the homing behavior. The existence of mixed colonies like those of the slave-holders and other social parasites shows very clearly that ants, both young and adult, not only learn to accept alien ants as friends, but may actually treat as enemies members of their own colony from which they were separated as pupæ. These facts and their bearing on Bethe's contention have been clearly analyzed by Wasmann as follows: "An ant could be born only with the amicable reaction to the odoriferous secretions of those ants with whom she is connected by descent. No one would be willing to state that the amicable reaction towards any kind of odor of an alien colony or alien species is innate, for this would patently contradict the observed facts. Therefore we can regard as innate only the amicable reaction of an ant towards the family odor of her own species and her own colony, from which she is descended, but not the amicable reaction to the odor of alien ant colonies and species, which are in fact recognized as "enemies" by their different odors. Now the auxiliaries that are reared in the colonies of predatory ants react amicably to the odor of the alien species (the so-called mistresses in the colony), but are hostile to the odor of their own sisters, from whose colony they were kidnapped as pupæ. Therefore the amicable reaction of ants to the odor of their own colony is not innate, but is acquired individually by the single ants. This individual acquisition occurs during the period in which the young, freshly developed worker begins to harden and take on her adult coloration. During this period her own definite individual odor first develops, and during this period there develops in her antennæ the olfactory sense, by means of which she is able to distinguish the odor of her own nest-mates from those

of other ants. Hence the ant's ability to distinguish between " friend " and " enemy " does not depend on inherited reflexes, but on the sensory perception of the olfactory impressions she receives during the first days of her life as an imaginal worker." These facts have been placed beyond doubt by the experiments of Forel, Wasmann, Miss Fielde, myself and others. The ease with which, as I have shown, colonies will adopt adult queens of alien species, and the immediate adoption of strange myrmecophiles by some of the ants observed by Wasmann, show that reflexes are very far from offering a satisfactory explanation of the facts and that we must suppose ants to be capable of remembering odors and of regulating their behavior accordingly.

3. **Communication.**—We are not surprised to find among both scientific and lay observers a very general belief in the existence of some power of communication among ants, for the social organization of these insects is alone sufficient to suggest such a belief. That it is of long standing is shown by several passages in the ancient writers, and by Dante's simile (Purg. xxvi, 34) :

> " Così per entro loro schiera bruna
> S'ammusa l'una con l'altra formica,
> Forse a espiar lor via e lor fortuna."

I believe that no one who has watched ants continuously and under a variety of conditions will doubt that they actually communicate with one another. This is clearly indicated by the rapidity with which they congregate on a spot where one of their number has found food, or retire from any spot in which a few of their number have been killed or injured. That there is often a desire on the part of ants to coerce their companions into performing certain acts is shown by the way in which they drag their queens about by the mandibles, or transport one another bodily to new nests or back to the old nest. And the compliance or obedience of the ants thus treated shows that they grasp the meaning of this conduct on the part of their nest-mates. Forel, Wasmann and myself have also interpreted the rapid antennary vibrations, the minatory divarication of the jaws, the butting with the head, the supplicatory posture of the body, the striking of the floor of the nest with the gaster, etc., as so many signs which may be understood and acted on by other ants. In Chapter XXVIII I gave some reasons for concluding that stridulation, at least in the Myrmicinæ and Ponerinæ, also serves as an important method of communication. I grant that one is in very imminent danger of falling into gross anthropomorphisms in interpreting these various movements, but they are so clearly associated with certain needs in the lives of ants and, moreover, meet with such uniform response from other members of the colony, that they

soon come to have the same significance to the observer as the characteristic attitudes and cries, or what have been called " the expressions
of the emotions " in our domestic animals. Of course, all the signs or
signals employed by ants and other animals in conveying their impressions to other members of their respective species are concrete and
instinctive, or what Bergson calls " adherent," and not " movable " or
rational signs like those of language and mathematics.

 4. **Imitation and Coöperation.**—These are very closely connected
with communication, for the object of much of the interchange of
impressions in an ant colony is to secure coöperation through imitation.
This is clearly observed in the carrying out of foraging expeditions,
like those of the slave-makers and Dorylines, in bringing in large and
unwieldy booty, in the removal of the brood when danger threatens,
in the construction of nests, aphid-tents and covered ways, in defending the colony against intruders, in storing seeds in particular chambers,
in building and cultivating fungus-gardens, in restraining the males
and females from leaving the nests for their nuptial flight till the propitious time arrives, etc. Many of these activities can be studied in
artificial nests. Under such conditions one usually sees a particular
activity started by one or a few workers, which have more initiative
or respond more quickly to a change of conditions than the great bulk
of the colony. The movements of such individuals attract the attention of others in their immediate neighborhood and these forthwith
proceed to imitate their more alert companions. Then the activity
spreads like a conflagration till it has seized on most or all the members
of the community. Imitation and coöperation of this description, which
is really a form of learning by experience, is best seen in a colony that
is moving into an artificial nest placed in the Forel arena or on a
Lubbock island (see Appendix A). Sometimes it is difficult to decide
whether a particular change of condition has simultaneously stimulated
a great number or only a few workers to perform an appropriate reaction. Such doubtful cases are most liable to arise when the stimulus
acts continuously and for a long time, as when a colony is situated in
an unfavorable locality, or in one that makes it necessary to construct
a peculiar form of nest. Then it may be doubtful whether the nest
modification is initiated by one or a few workers that are imitated by
the remainder, or whether all or nearly all the workers simultaneously
alter the style of architecture. Even in such cases, however, I am
inclined to regard the former supposition as the more probable. There
has been much discussion as to whether or not coöperation among ants
extends to the succoring of companions in danger or distress. Reuter
(1888) claims to have found positive evidence of such acts of sym-

pathy, but the observations of most myrmecologists have yielded only doubtful results. My own observations are negative, except in a single instance. Several years ago I kept a large colony of *Eciton schmitti* in a Lubbock nest surrounded by a water moat. Workers repeatedly fell into the water and on several occasions I saw other workers reach down and pull them out. Forel, Lubbock and Wasmann relate instances of ants nursing and caring for crippled or mutilated companions. But if we reject all such observations as too infrequent or doubtful to have any value, there still remain a great many easily observed cases that can be explained only on the supposition that ants respond quickly by imitating the purposeful activities which they perceive in their nest-mates. The stimulus in these cases would seem to be highly individualized, to use Driesch's expression, and entirely unlike those which call out reflex and instinct actions. By certain critics of the general position here taken much has been made of the numerous cases in which ants of the same colony work at cross-purposes, or in opposition to one another. Such cases naturally arise on account of the powerful initiative of the individual ants, but they eventually resolve themselves into coöperation, or, at any rate, into a lack of opposition, through a weakening or reversal of the tactics of one of the contending parties, These contentions are, in fact, merely slight temporary disturbances or maladjustments analogous to those which are continually occurring among the different organs and tissues of a Metazoan body.

5. **Docility.**—Although the facts recorded in the preceding paragraphs indicate very clearly that ants are capable of learning by experience, and that they must, therefore, possess memory, this becomes even more evident when it is shown that they can actually be trained like many of the higher animals. Wasmann (1899g) succeeded in the course of a few days in training workers of *Formica rufibarbis* and *fusca* to come for food to his finger, from which they at first fled. Ernst (1905) obtained similar results with a *fusca* worker, which he taught to come out of a test-tube and take food from his finger while it was in motion. Turner (1907b) has recently described some experiments in which *Myrmica punctiventris* and *F. subsericea* trained themselves to drop from a stage with a pupa and to carry it to the nest. These ants then permitted him to replace them on the stage with a pair of tweezers. This act was repeated over and over again. More interesting is the following experiment in which he taught *F. subsericea* to use a section lifter as an elevator on which to pass to and from a stage connected with an island nest by an incline: "On this occasion two marked workers, *A* and *B,* were being experimented upon at the same time. The one I have called *A* readily learned the way down

and up the incline, but to *B* this was an insoluble problem. It continued for a long time to move at random over the stage, reaching down over first one edge and then over another, as though it were reaching for a support that was not to be found; but nothing prompted it to pass down the incline. In experiments where the time required to learn the trick was not the point to be investigated, I had sometimes helped ants to learn the way by forcing them with forceps or spatula to move in the right direction. I thought I would thus help *B* to learn. So with my forceps I pushed it along. Several times I succeeded in getting it to the incline, but nothing that I did would induce it to go down. I had failed, but this was not the first time I had failed in similar attempts with other ants.

"Prompted by another thought, I shoved the section-lifter under the ant and transferred it to the island. The ant then stepped off and carried the pupa into the nest. As soon as *B* returned to the island, I shoved the section-lifter under it and transferred it to the stage. *B* stepped off and picked up another pupa. With the section-lifter I again transferred it to the island. After this had been repeated several times, the moment I presented the section-lifter, whether on the island or on the stage, the ant immediately mounted it and rested quietly thereon until it had been removed to the stage or to the island; then it stepped off and picked up a pupa or else went into the nest. I usually held the section-lifter from two to four millimeters above the surface of the island or stage. In this manner the industrious creature passed to and from the stage about fifty times in something less than two hours.

"Whenever I presented the section-lifter to other ants of the same colony they would attack it or avoid it, or else mount it and roam over blade and handle and sometimes even my hand. When the same section-lifter was presented to *A* (the one that all this time had been carrying pupæ down the incline) it would avoid it and pass on.

"Thus I had two individuals of the same colony, at the same time and under identical external conditions, responding to the same stimulus in quite different ways. To the one the incline had no psychic value, to the other it was a stimulus to pass to and from the stage. To the one the section-lifter was a repellent stimulus, to the other an attractive stimulus. Each had acquired a different way of accomplishing the same purpose and each had retained and utilized what it had gained by experience."

While the foregoing considerations leave little doubt that ants have memory, in the general sense of the word, it is, for obvious reasons, no easy matter to form a satisfactory conception of the psychic processes which this involves. At least three different views may be entertained on the subject. First, it may be said that ants not only have images or ideas as the result of sensory stimulation, but are able to recall them at will, and to refer them to the past. This would imply that ants, like man, not only have memory ($\mu\nu\dot{\eta}\mu\eta$ in the Aristotelian, *memoria sensitiva*, in the scholastic sense) but also recollection ($\dot{\alpha}\nu\dot{\alpha}\mu\nu\eta\sigma\iota\varsigma$, *reminiscentia*). Second, it may be maintained that ants have images only as the result of sensory stimulation, but are unable to call them up at will, much less to refer them to the absent or to the past. This would imply that the insects have sensory association but not recollection. Third, it may be maintained that ants are unable to form images or ideas and are hence devoid of memory. This is really Bethe's view, which will not be discussed, as it obviously contradicts the facts. Of the two other views I believe that the second does not go further than the facts warrant, and is far and away the more plausible. I am unable to find anything in the observations above recorded, or in many others, which the limits of this volume prevent me from presenting, that would compel us to believe that ants can recollect in the true sense of the word. There is, indeed, much doubt as to the existence of such a capacity even in the higher animals (Thorndike). "We must admit," as Miss Washburn says, "that it is not easy to prove the possession by any animal of memory in the sense of *having ideas of absent objects,* rather than in the sense of *behaving differently to present objects because of past experience with them.* The dog shows clearly that he remembers his master in the latter sense by displaying joy at the sight of him. Can we be sure that he has remembered him in the former sense during his absence; that is, that he has had a memory image of him?" Although it seems to be necessary to assume that ants have images or ideas, it must not be supposed for a moment that these bear anything but the remotest resemblance to our own. The fact that the ant's sense-impressions are, almost exclusively, those of odors, contacts and vibrations, make it evident that her mental imagery must differ enormously from ours, in which visual and auditory images luxuriate to the almost complete exclusion of others. To appreciate this difference we have only to contrast with our dull powers of olfaction the ants' exquisite perception, recognition and association of odors. A dog that is born deaf and nearly blind would probably resemble an ant rather closely in its psychical processes, but would be inferior in lacking the ant's fine tactile sense and her power of associating tactile with olfactory impressions.

If this moderate estimate of the memory of ants be correct, it follows that they must be incapable of reasoning—of " focusing the wherefore," to use Lloyd Morgan's expression, for a mere association of sense impressions is not deducing conclusions from premises. There are in the literature, however, many startling accounts in which ants are described as reasoning like human beings, or as acting in such a manner as to make any other interpretation of their behavior seem impossible. These accounts may be separated into two classes; those involving a demonstrable misinterpretation of facts and those whose main or only value at the present time is to suggest lines of experimental investigation. In the first class belong such cases as the following:

Several writers have described ants as building earthen bridges over sticky bands that at first prevented them from climbing trees (Leuckart), over water moats surrounding their nests (Turner, 1907*b*), or over the surface of honey placed in their nests (Ern. André, 1894). In each of these cases the observer, a trained zoölogist, regarded the act as due to reasoning, or, at least, as the result of a " practical judgment." In reality, however, nothing more than a reflex or simple instinct was manifested in any of these cases. If the observers had had a more intimate acquaintance with ants, they would have known that these insects almost invariably throw earth, empty cocoons, or particles of débris on any liquid or viscid substance in their immediate environment. Such actions result in covering the whole surface of a small amount of liquid, so that the ants are able to cross over to the other side on what was never intended to be a bridge. That this is the true interpretation of the foregoing observations is shown by experiments like those performed by Wasmann. He placed near a nest of *Formica sanguinea* a watch glass full of water, with a number of pupæ on an island in the middle. The ants threw sand into the water till they had made a bridge to the island and then carried away the pupæ. Later he placed near the nest a watch glass full of water, but without pupæ, and the ants filled it with grains of sand as before! The significance of this reflex or simple instinct which may be observed in any artificial nest in which the ants are provided with liquid food and a little earth or detritus, is not altogether clear. Escherich (1906) interprets it as an instinct of cleanliness, but I am inclined to believe that it represents an effective method of dealing with water that may soak into the galleries of the earthen nests during showers.

Another case that has been interpreted as an example of reasoning is the behavior of the fungus-growing *Atta sexdens* queen while she is founding her colony, and of the workers of this species during inundations. These are such complicated bits of behavior that von Ihering (1898) can scarcely be blamed for saying that the insects are " fully conscious of the fact that the cutting of leaves is not sufficient, but that a portion of the fungus mass itself is necessary for the growth of the fungus garden." And yet a critical examination of the facts since brought to light by J. Huber and related in Chapter XVIII, shows that only typical instincts are manifested. The queen feeds on fungus hyphæ before leaving the nest for her nuptial flight, and as this food is solid, it is packed into the hypopharyngeal pocket, which also receives the dirt scraped from her body by her strigils. The pellet thus formed is not expelled till she has excavated her cell in the ground. Then it is cast out like the hypopharyngeal pellets of other ants. It contains enough extraneous substance to cause the hyphæ to proliferate and the presence of these evidently stimulates the ant to attend to their cultivation and to manure them with the only substance at her disposal, namely, her feces. There is no point in this series of activities where it is necessary to postulate a process of reasoning on the part of the insect. The saving of portions of the fungus garden by the workers when the nest is inundated is also quite as instinctive as the rescuing of the larvæ and pupæ by these and other insects under the same circumstances.

Here belongs also the following case of a wasp described by Erasmus Darwin ("Zoonomia," I, p. 183): "One circumstance I shall relate which fell under my own eye and showed the power of reason in a wasp, as it is exercised among men. A wasp on a gravel walk had caught a fly nearly as large as himself; kneeling on the ground I observed him separate the tail and the head from the body part, to which the wings were attached. He then took the body part in his paws, and rose about two feet from the ground with it; but a gentle breeze wafting the wings of the fly turned him around in the air, and he settled again with his prey upon the gravel. I then distinctly observed him cut off with his mouth, first one of the wings, and then the other, after which he flew away with it unmolested by the wind. Go, thou sluggard, learn arts and industry from the bee, and from the ant! Go, proud reasoner, and call the worm thy sister!" Some knowledge of the ways of wasps would have taught Erasmus Darwin that they instinctively cut off the legs, wings, head, etc., of their insect prey before carrying the more nutritious portion of it to their young, and that they perform these activities with machine-like regularity whether the wind happens to be blowing or not. This case may be regarded as the type of a large number of ant, bee and wasp stories. The recorded facts are often perfectly accurate, but the inferences are false and misleading, owing to ignorance or insufficient knowledge of the normal behavior of the animals under consideration.

The second class of accounts that are supposed to demonstrate the power of reasoning in ants cannot be adequately considered in this place. It must suffice to give examples of the many references to ants dropping food from high places to other ants at a lower level, and to ants themselves dropping from ceilings onto tables when they have been prevented from climbing up for food. Of the former behavior the following anecdote recorded by Romanes ("Animal Intelligence," 1892, p. 99) is an example: "In Herr Gredler's monastery, one of the monks had been accustomed to put food regularly on his window sill for ants coming up from the garden. In consequence of Herr Gredler's communications, he took it into his head to put the bait for the ants, pounded sugar, in an old ink-stand, and hung this by a string to a cross-piece of the window and left it hanging freely. A few ants were in the bait. They soon found their way out over the string with the grains of sugar and so their way back to their friends. Before long a procession was arranged on the new road from the window sill along the string to the spot where the sugar was, and so things went on for two days, nothing fresh occurring. But one day the procession stopped at the old feeding place on the window sill and took the food thence without going up to the pendent sugar jar. Closer observation revealed that about a dozen of the rogues in the jar above were busily and unwearyingly carrying the grains of sugar to the edge of the pot and throwing them over to their comrades down below." Turner (1907b), who quotes this observation, attempts to explain the separation of the continuous procession of workers into two coöperating companies as due to the accidental falling of sugar heaped on the edge of the jar. I am inclined to believe that the ants in the jar were burrowing in the sugar and that they acted just as if the bottle were partially filled with sand. Under such circumstances they would certainly carry the excavated sand to the edge of the bottle and throw it down. But this is mere supposition, and both in this and in similar cases which I have met with in the literature, the data are insufficient to prove rational coöperation.

Of the many observations on ants dropping from ceilings in order to reach food, I will cite only the following, which was made by a young entomologist, Mr. E. S. G. Titus (1905) on the Argentine ant (*Iridomyrmex humilis*) in New Orleans: "An experiment was tried with some sugar syrups on a table which stood against the wall. The ants came up the wall to reach the table. When it was removed from the wall they came up the legs. Next morning the legs were wrapped with cloths soaked in coal-oil and the table removed some distance from the wall. That day the ants were persistent in their efforts to reach the food, constantly climbing up and down the legs, but only a few attempted to cross the oiled bandages and these were not successful. The following morning the table was well covered with ants. They had gone up the wall over the first trail and passed on up to the ceiling, then over that diagonally until they were over the table, when they dropped down onto it. Very few ants were noticed returning from the ceiling, but a constant stream of them was going up. At the point where the table had formerly touched the wall quite a number of ants were clustered, evidently at a loss to know where to go. The ants, on leaving the table, usually went down one of the legs and were crossing the coal-oil bandages with apparently little or no injury to themselves. Some dropped directly from the table top to the floor." The facts related by Titus are not to be questioned, but the same criticism applies to this case as to the preceding: the whole series of events was not observed. Moreover, although ants are often seen to drop from plants or walls, either voluntarily or when disturbed, we know nothing as yet about the various instinctive adaptations which such behavior may involve. It may be a much more frequent method among ants of clearing vertical distances than has been supposed. Hence, I believe that instead of attributing such acts to reasoning, it would be wiser to suspend judgment till careful experimental data are available.

In conclusion it may be noted that all the activities of ants, their reflexes and instincts, as well as their plastic behavior, gain in precision with repetition. In other words, all their activities may be secondarily mechanized to form habits, in the restricted sense of the word. This is tantamount to saying that even the reflexes and instincts are not so stereotyped but that they may become more so by exercise during the lifetime of the individual. And not only do ants thus form habits, but, as several myrmecologists have observed, these habits when once formed are often hard to break. It is certain that many instincts among the higher animals are at first incomplete or indefinite and are guided into their proper course by stimuli that affect the organism at a later period. This is probably true also of many formicine instincts. There is little doubt, moreover, that the more fixed or stereotyped instincts are phylogenetically the older. This fact, and the close superficial resemblance of habits to instincts, has led many authors to derive the latter from the former. The views on the origin of automatic behavior, however, are so diverse and conflicting that they cannot be satisfactorily considered without entering into a discussion of the doctrines of the Neodarwinians, Neolamarkians and those who believe in coincident, or organic selection. In my opinion we have little to gain at the present time from such a discussion. As Bergson says: " It is

a remarkable fact that the scientific theories of instinct keep oscillating
back and forth between the *intelligent* and the merely *intelligible,* that
is to say, between the likening of instinct to a ' lapsed ' intelligence
and the reduction of instinct to a pure mechanism.   Each of these two
explanatory systems triumphs in its criticism of the other, the former
when it proves to us that instinct cannot be a pure reflex, the latter
when it asserts that instinct is something different from intelligence,
even when this has lapsed into the unconscious.   Does not this mean
that we have here two symbolisms equally acceptable from certain
points of view, and from other points of view equally inapplicable to
their object?"   It is, in fact, quite futile to attempt a phylogenetic
derivation of the automatic from the plastic activities or *vice versa,*
for both represent primitive and fundamental tendencies of living protoplasm, and hence of all organisms.   As instinct, one of these tendencies reaches its most complex manifestation in the Formicidæ, while
the other blossoms in the intelligent activities of men.

APPENDIX A

METHODS OF COLLECTING, MOUNTING AND STUDYING ANTS

Most of the methods of collecting and preserving ants, both in the entomological cabinet and as living objects in artificial nests, are so simple that they would be devised by almost anyone who undertakes a serious study of these insects. Nevertheless it may save some of my readers, who may wish to study ants, considerable time and experimentation if I give a condensed account of the methods I have found to be most useful.

The collecting outfit (Figs. 280 and 281), which may be readily carried in a large pocket, or in a small bag such as hunters use for ammunition, consists of the following: a small but very strong trowel, or a

short, broad chisel, for digging into the nests, a pair of tweezers with rounded, flat and smooth, i. e., not transversely ridged points, for picking up the insects, a number of homœopathic or shell vials of strong glass, three quarters full of commercial alcohol (about 95 per cent.)[1] for preserving the specimens, some absorbent cotten, blank labels, a large handkerchief or napkin, and some small bags made of strong

[1] Wood alcohol, denatured alcohol or even strong whiskey may be used as a preservative if commercial alcohol cannot be obtained. Formaline should be avoided as it makes the specimens very rigid and refractory and has other disagreeable qualities.

cloth.   Small wads of the cotton are used for separating the specimens from different colonies in the same vial of alcohol, so that
there may be no possible confusion of the often very closely related
species and varieties.   The handkerchief is spread upon the ground
and small nests may be dug up hastily and placed in the middle of
it and broken apart.   The ants can then be readily seen and captured before they can reach the periphery of the cloth and escape.
The bags are used as temporary receptacles for living colonies or
portions of them, to be transferred to artificial nests by a method
to be described below, or for transporting ants from one region and
dumping them near the nests of the same or other species in other

Fig. 281.   Outfit for collecting ants; including bottles, lens, tweezers and labels, and
showing manner of separating catches from different nests by means of cotton.

localities.   In the battles which inevitably ensue the ants display
many instinctive peculiarities that might otherwise be overlooked.
Forel has used this method with great success in his studies of the
Swiss ants.   In order to secure material for such experiments, or for
artificial nests, the ants, together with their brood and portions of their
nest, are hastily shoveled into the bag, which is then tied with a string
and carried without shaking.   It is well before filling the bag to put
in it a few twigs or leaves to prevent the pebbles and earth from
moving about and crushing the ants.   If several days must elapse before
the contents of the bag can be transferred to an artificial nest, the earth

should be occasionally moistened with water, or the ants will die. Large, wide-mouthed bottles or vials that can be plugged with cotton are often more useful than bags, especially for the accommodation of small colonies. Each colony from which specimens are taken, either for the cabinet or for the artificial nest, should be given a number and all the important data concerning it should be entered in a note book.

Nothing is easier than to find ants in the fields and woods. The most convenient place to seek them is under stones and logs, but many specimens rarely or never nest in such situations and must be sought under or in bark, in rotten wood, hollow twigs, old galls and rootstocks, in vegetable mould, about the roots of plants, or in the open soil of the woods and fields. The nests of many small species which form diminutive colonies, are extremely difficult to find unless individual workers are first located on the soil or vegetation and then carefully followed while they are returning to their nest.

For study large series, illustrating all the obtainable phases in a colony, should be mounted dry, and the greatest care should be taken to avoid mixing specimens from different nests and localities. Ants should always be carded and in no case—no matter how large the specimens—should they have pins run through their thoraces. Some myrmecologists prefer to glue the specimens on small triangular, or rather trapezoidal pieces of card, in such a position that the body of the ant lies at right angles to the long axis of the card and across its shortest side, which is turned to the left and should be broad enough to support at least the posterior portion of the thorax, the whole pedicel and the base of the gaster. A stout insect pin is then run through the middle of the broad right-hand end of the card. It is convenient and economical to mount three such specimens, one above the other, on the same pin. The size of the trapezoidal cards must, of course, be adapted to the size of the ants. Other myrmecologists prefer to glue the ants singly, or in a series, on a square or oblong card, and to run the pin through the card behind instead of to the right of the specimens. I would earnestly insist on the advantages of mounting ants in one or both of these ways because the method of pinning them, as if they were flies or bees, entails an enormous loss of valuable material in collections. Ants mounted in this way are almost sure, sooner or later, to break at the neck or pedicel and lose the head or gaster, or both. Many specimens in the great number of collections that have been sent to me for study from various parts of the United States have been rendered worthless by this vicious method of mounting. No matter how thoroughly one may know our ants, there is little satisfaction in identifying a species which is represented only by a thorax or a few legs, the former destroyed by being spitted on a pin, and the whole enveloped in a mass of grease and verdigris.

While collecting ants and making every endeavor to secure all their phases, it is important to collect all the parasites and myrmecophiles that may occur in their nests. These insects are most easily found in the early spring when they seek the warmth in the upper galleries, or

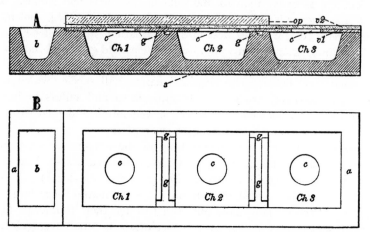

Fɪɢ. 282. Janet nest of porous material such as plaster, terra cotta, soft stone, etc. (Janet.) *B,* Seen from above with covers removed; *A,* in vertical section: *a,* block with three chambers; *b,* water chamber which is filled once or twice a week; Ch. 1, dark and very moist chamber; Ch. 2, dark and somewhat humid chamber inhabited by the ants; Ch. 3, dry chamber, exposed to light and containing the manger; *g,* communicating galleries in the walls separating the chambers. v^1, large plate of glass covering all the chambers, pierced with a hole (*c*) over the center of each chamber; v^2, three separate pieces of glass which close the openings in the large plate; *op,* opaque cover (felt, cardboard or plaster) serving to darken chambers 1 and 2; *s,* plate of glass placed under the nest to prevent the moisture of the nest from reaching the table on which it stands.

on the lower surfaces of stones. They should always be mounted on the same pins with one or more specimens of their host. The same rule should be followed in the case of all parasitic or inquilinous ants, which are also myrmecophiles. I find it best not to mix the myrmecophiles in with the general collection of ants, but to keep them by themselves in a systematically arranged collection, in which the ants are represented merely as hosts.

The student will find that the new Zeiss pocket microscope, consisting of a couple of lenses of rather long focal distance and magnifying some sixteen and twenty-seven diameters respectively suffices for the taxonomic study of most ants. In the examination of some of the smaller species, however, especially in counting the antennal and palpal joints, the ommatidia and teeth of the mandibles, it will be found necessary to use a compound microscope.

I am convinced that there is no form of entomological work more fascinating than collecting ants, for these insects are everywhere abundant and no two of their colonies ever present the same picture to the observer. Hence one is always coming upon new and interesting facts in the commonest species, and even in localities in which one has been diligently collecting for years. Certainly there is no more delightful avocation for the man who desires a not too strenuous employment that will keep him in the open air. Many years ago Moggridge called attention to the value of myrmecology to the valetudinarian and the convalescent, and it is surprising that physicians have so seldom recommended it to patients who need to spend much time out of doors and to have some intellectual interest that will make this seem worth while.

Although field study is absolutely essential to an understanding of the taxonomy and ethology of ants, it must be supplemented by observations on colonies kept in artificial nests. And while such colonies are necessarily prevented from manifesting all their instincts in a perfectly normal manner, this disadvantage is more than outweighed by the great ease and thoroughness with which nearly all of their activities can be observed. Artificial nests must, in fact, be used in all studies on the relations of myrmecophiles to their hosts and the behavior of ants towards their young.

Various artificial nests have been devised, but these are all of two types—those with and those without earth. Ants kept in nests of the former type are, of course, removed from one of the most important elements of their natural environment. Nevertheless, this does not interfere with their other activities; the excavating instinct simply remains in abeyance without inconveniencing the insects. Naturally, the nests containing earth were the first to be devised and the conclusion that this substance can be dispensed with is of comparatively recent date.

The earliest account of an artificial nest I have seen is in Swammerdam's " Biblia Naturæ." This remarkable entomologist placed the ants in a quantity of earth in a flat dish and surrounded this with a strip of wax, which was five fingers broad, hollowed out and filled with water. This served as a moat and prevented the ants from escaping. A modification of Swammerdam's nest has been recently recommended and will often prove to be useful when it is necessary to construct a nest on very short notice. It consists of a dish containing some earth covered with a pane of glass and set in a larger dish containing water.

Huber (1810) describes two artificial nests which he used in his researches. One of these consisted of a box mounted on legs, not unlike those of a sewing machine, and covered with a large bell-jar.

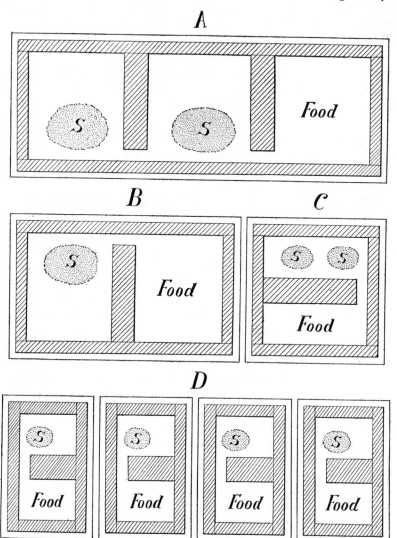

FIG. 283. Bases of Fielde nests of different sizes made to fit into shelves of portable case. (Miss Fielde.) The shaded portions represent the walls of the nest built up with strips of glass. *S*, slice of sponge.

A colony of *Formica rufa* that was placed in the box built up its mound of sticks under the bell-jar and tunneled in the earth of the box. The other nest consisted of a wooden frame twenty inches long and ten inches broad, with glass on the two sides separated by a distance of ten lines. The space thus enclosed was subdivided into two equal and very flat compartments by a perforated sheet of tin placed parallel with the glass panes. The space between the glass and tin on each side was filled with earth. An opening with a sliding door was made at one end of the frame, to permit the ants to enter and leave the apparatus, and there was also an opening in the top of the frame for the introduction of food (honey) and water. These were simply poured upon the soil. The frame was placed vertically on the ground.

Lubbock combined the water-moat of Swammerdam with Huber's frame nest, which he placed horizontally and simplified by omitting the perforated tin and bringing the two panes of glass close together. A detailed description of this nest, with a figure, is given on pp. 2–4 of Lubbock's well-known book on " Ants, Bees and Wasps."

Wasmann uses a Lubbock nest, to which he attaches Florence flasks and other glassware to serve as play-grounds, dumping-grounds and mangers for the ants. Although he dispenses with the water-moat, his nest is clumsy and not readily moved about. He has published figures and descriptions of it in several of his papers, notably in the one entitled: " Die psychischen Fähigkeiten der Ameisen," 1899, Pl. I.

Janet's nest (1897d) differs considerably from the types that have just been described (Fig. 282). It consists of an oblong block of colored plaster of Paris, containing a series of disk-like depressions in its upper portion. One of these, isolated at the end of the series, is smaller than the others, and is used as a water reservoir, the others, which are inhabited by the ants, are connected with one another by short galleries and are covered with glass plates and in part also with opaque covers. The water diffuses from the reservoir through the porous plaster block in such a manner that there is a gradation of moisture in the different chambers. This permits the ants to station themselves and their brood at the spot where the conditions are most favorable. Janet has also constructed some large and elegant plaster nests that can be hung on the walls like pictures, but these did not prove to be successful, owing to the crumbling of the moist plaster.

Viehmeyer (1905c) has improved on the Janet nest by enclosing it in a zinc box and adding metal strips across the top for the purpose of preventing the glass covers from slipping. In this form the nest, though rather clumsy and heavy, can be more readily transported.

Miss Fielde has devised a very useful glass-nest, which is compact and light and has many advantages over the nests of the Lubbock and Janet patterns. This she first described in 1900, but more recently

(1904*f*) she has published more detailed directions for its construction. These I give in her own words, together with some of her figures (Figs. 283–285) :

" The floor of the nest is a pane of double-thick, transparent glass. This is laid upon very thick, white blotting-paper, giving an elastic bed to the pane of glass and the best background for observation of the ants. The paper has just the area of the glass, but is not fastened thereto.

" The outer walls of the nest are laid a quarter of an inch, or six millimeters, from the edge of the pane. They consist of two strips of double-thick glass, a half inch, or thirteen millimeters, wide, the one

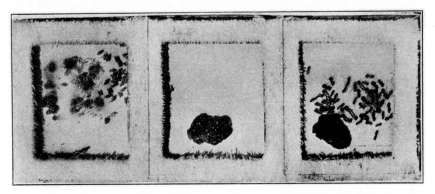

FIG. 284. Fielde nest of three chambers seen from above, with opaque covers removed. (Photograph by J. G. Hubbard and Dr. O. S. Strong.)

superimposed on the other. Both are held in place by crockery cement. The wall is smoothly laid up, with no interstices where an ant may hide or escape.

" The partitions are double the width of the wall, which they otherwise copy. At one end of every partition a space is left whereby the ants may pass from room to room. This passageway is covered by a thin celluloid film, or a piece of mica. It is desirable that this covering be transparent, so that the passageway underneath it may be scanned from above, on lifting the end of the towelling which is to overlay it.

" After the cement is well dried, the edge of the floor-pane and the outside of the walls are covered with a cambric impervious to light. Cloth serves better for this purpose than does paper, the edges of the nest being subject to much handling. Le Page's or some other good liquid glue is used for securing the fabric upon the walls.

" The walls and partitions are topped by Turkish towelling of a sleazy sort, folded over one layer of cotton wadding so that the edges of the strip of towelling meet in the center of the underside of the wadding. The wadding is cut to the same width as the wall or the partition. The towelling is just twice the width of the wadding, and its edges are basted evenly together, making a cushion of even thickness. It serves the double purpose of admitting air into the nest and preventing the escape of the ants between the roof and its supports. It is held taut and is made level; it is fitted snugly at the corners, exhibits no ravelings to afflict the ants and is firmly glued to the glass beneath it. When a cushion becomes soiled by long use of the nest, the glue may be softened, by soaking and the cushion may be removed and be replaced by a new one. The ends of the cushions are fringed out a half inch or more, and are left open so that the enclosed wadding may be adjusted to present a perfectly level surface.

" There is a glass roof-pane for each room in the nest. The glass is thin; extends to the middle of the partition and to the outer edges of the walls on which it rests; prevents the exit of the ants and permits observation of their behavior. The glass may be without color, or it may be of a red or orange tint that will partially exclude ultra-violet rays of light. Ants perceive only such rays of light as are of short wave-length, and, by use of a spectroscope, a glass roofing may be selected which renders the ants visible within the nest, while it protects them from such light-rays as they instinctively shun. If such glass is used for roofing the nest, the ants will behave as if in the darkness where they habitually live.

" An outer roofing of blotting paper makes the interior of the nest wholly dark. The food-room should be light, as it represents the ants' outside world.

" When any room in the nest requires cleaning, it is covered only with transparent glass, and then the ants withdraw from it with their young into a dark room, which may in its turn be made light.

" The food-room is dry, and in cool weather requires attention but once a forthnight. Sponge-cake, merged in a little honey or molasses, banana, apple, mashed walnut, and the muscular parts of larvæ of insects are among their favorite edibles. Food is constantly attainable in the nest, but is introduced in tiny morsels that it may not vitiate the air.

" Since moisture encourages the growth of mould, no water is put into the food-room. But ants often drink, and they require a humid atmosphere. All other rooms than that allotted to their food are made humid by laying a flake of sponge on the floor and keeping the sponge saturated with clean water dropped twice a week from a pipette. The proportion of the floor which is covered by the sponge depends on the degree of moisture in the soil usually chosen as the habitat of the species. The sponges are kept clean by weekly washing and an occasional immersion in alcohol. Sponges of fine, tough texture render the best service, as they offer no apertures where the ants may conceal their eggs. The flake of sponge is so thin as to permit the ants to pass between it and the roof-pane.

"The completed nest is less than half an inch, or thirteen millimeters, in its interior height, and does not exceed three-fourths of an inch, or two centimeters, in its exterior height. A low-power lens is easily focused upon the ants within the nest."

Miss Fielde makes her nests of such sizes as to fit snugly into the

FIG. 285. Portable case showing three Fielde nests on shelves. (Photograph by J. G. Hubbard and Dr. O. S. Strong.)

shelves of a portable box like the one represented in the figure (Fig. 285). This box has an interior length of seventeen inches, a width of seven inches and a height of four and three-fourth inches. In a case of these dimensions a number of nests can be carried safely for long distances.

I have used with considerable success a combination of the Janet and Fielde nests. The glass base and sides of the latter are replaced by a single thin block of colored plaster of Paris, but the height and arrangement of the chambers, their communications, the towelling and roof-panes are those of the Fielde nest. Other details of construction may be readily inferred from an examination of Fig. 286 and its legend.

Miss Edith Buckingham (Amer. Natur., Oct., 1909, pp. 611–614) has described a nest of the Fielde pattern, in which the weight is greatly diminished by replacing the glass base by one made of sheet aluminum.

Dr. F. Santschi has given me directions for making a nest which he has used with excellent results in his studies on small ants, such as *Oxyopomyrmex, Leptothorax, Monomorium, Tapinoma* and the parasitic *Bothriomyrmex* and *Wheeleriella*. It is quickly constructed merely with wet plaster of Paris and glass plates, such as those used in photography. Onto the surface of a plate of the required dimensions the plaster is poured in the form of the walls of two oblong or square chambers and a short connecting gallery. Then another plate of the same dimensions, with its surface oiled, is pressed down somewhat onto the plaster before it sets, leaving a space of a few millimeters between the two plates. As soon as the plaster has set, the upper plate is removed and may be cut into two pieces to serve as the covers of the chambers. The plaster is sufficiently porous to admit the air, and the walls leave no spaces for the escape of the ants. This nest is so shallow that it can be placed on the stage of the compound microscope and its inhabitants studied under a low objective.

All of the various artificial nests here described have both admirable qualities and serious defects, so that anyone who wishes to gain a thorough knowledge of the ants will do well not to pin his faith to any one of them, but will select the form best adapted to the special problem in hand. For small colonies very simple nests consisting of Petri or flat stender dishes will often answer every purpose. In all nests, however, there should be plenty of moisture, food and fresh air, as ants soon sicken and die when the supply of these essentials is insufficient. The food should be varied. Fresh insects and honey are nearly always acceptable. I have kept colonies for many months on a thick mixture of raw yolk of egg, honey and sugar, with an occasional mess of hashed meal-worms, or of the larvæ and pupæ of alien ants. The harvesting ants (*Pogonomyrmex, Pheidole*) are fond of our various breakfast foods, but these species also thrive best on an occasional diet of fresh insects.

Ants are readily induced to move with their brood into the nests of the Lubbock, Janet and Fielde patterns. This is accomplished by using the water-moat or the Forel arena. I prefer the latter, which is very easily constructed. On a table or large board a circular or elliptical enclosure a few feet in diameter is made by laying down a wall of dry, powdered plaster of Paris about two or three inches broad and an inch high. The inner edge of this wall is made smooth and steep with the aid of a putty or case knife. The artificial nest, with its chambers moistened and darkened, is placed in this arena. Then the colony to be installed, together with its brood and the earth of its nest, is dumped from the collecting bag into the arena just as it was brought in from the field. The ants are at first much excited and

FIG. 286. Combination Janet and Fielde nest used by the author. The roof-pane of the light, or food chamber is removed. *r,* Plaster of Paris base cast in a single piece; *c,* entrance, to be plugged with cotton after the admission of the ants from the Forel arena; *m,* glass roof-pane, resting on strips of Turkish towelling (*s*); *a,* opening between the two chambers; *n,* manger, a cup-shaped depression in the plaster base; *e,* slice of sponge, which is kept wet. The plaster base measures 20 × 25 cm. and is heavily coated with varnish over its entire surface.

wander about in the enclosure, but are unable to scale its crumbling walls. They soon learn to avoid the powdery plaster, find the entrance of the nest and migrate into it with their whole brood and any myrme-cophiles they may have This migration is hastened by spreading out the earth from their old nest so that it may dry. When the colony has entered, the nest opening is plugged with cotton and the nest is removed from the arena. Small colonies or colonies of small and deli-cate species, which, as I have said, are best collected in bottles plugged with cotton, may be hastily poured directly into one of the chambers of the nest. By illuminating this chamber the ants may be induced to move into the adjoining dark chamber and the fragments of the original nest can then be removed.

APPENDIX B

KEY TO THE SUBFAMILIES, GENERA AND SUBGENERA OF THE NORTH AMERICAN FORMICIDÆ, FOR THE IDENTIFICATION OF THE WORKERS

1. Cloacal orifice ventral, slit-shaped; sting well developed or vestigial; abdominal pedicel consisting of one or two segments..................... 2.
   Cloacal orifice terminal, circular, surrounded by a fringe of hairs; abdominal pedicel consisting of only a single segment; no constriction between the first and second gastric segments; pupæ usually enclosed in cocoons. Subfamily Camponotinæ.
2. Sting developed; sometimes very small but nevertheless exsertile; abdominal pedicel consisting of one or two segments; when of only one there is a distinct constriction between the first and second gastric segments...... 3
   Sting vestigial; abdominal pedicel consisting of a single segment; no constriction between the first and second gastric segments; anal glands which produce a secretion with a peculiar rancid-butter odor ("Tapinoma odor") are often present; pupæ naked................ Subfamily Dolichoderinæ.
3. Pupæ always enclosed in cocoons; abdominal pedicel consisting of a single segment; gaster with a distinct constriction between its first and second segments; frontal carinæ separated or close together; when close together they are dilated to form oblique or horizontal laminæ partly covering the insertions of the antennæ ....Subfamily Ponerinæ.
   Pupæ naked; abdominal pedicel consisting of two segments in the American species (excepting *Cheliomyrmex* of Central America)................ 4.
4. Frontal carinæ very close together, almost vertical, not at all covering the antennal insertions. Eyes always very small or absent; tropical and subtropical ....Subfamily Dorylinæ.
   Frontal carinæ of a different conformation and covering the antennal insertions. Eyes rarely vestigial or absent; cosmopolitan. Subfamily Myrmicinæ.

Subfamily PONERINÆ

1. Frontal carinæ closely approximated; antennæ inserted very near the oral margin; tip of gaster strongly deflected downward................... 2.
   Frontal carinæ of a different conformation; tip of gaster not deflected downward .... 3.
2. Front of clypeus projecting in the middle; petiole nodiform. *Sysphincta* Roger.
   Clypeus not projecting in the middle; petiole surmounted by a scale. *Proceratium* Roger.
3. Mandibles linear, inserted close together at the middle of the oral border; petiole terminating in a point or spine above........*Odontomachus* Fabr.
   Mandibles inserted at the corners of the head; petiole rounded or flattened above .... 4.
4. Antennæ very thick and robust.. 5.
   Antennæ not greatly thickened.. 6.
5. Pygidium with a row of prominent prickles on its lateral border; last antennal joint not greatly enlarged........................*Acanthostichus* Mayr.
   Pygidium without prominent prickles on its lateral border; last antennal joint greatly enlarged..*Cerapachys* F. Smith; subgen. *Parasyscia* Emery.

6. Mandibles long and slender with coarse, bidenticulate teeth; clypeus with numerous teeth on its anterior border; petiole not constricted posteriorly ....*Stigmatomma* Roger.
  Of a different conformation.. 7.
7. Claws pectinate .... 8.
  Claws simple .... 9.
8. Mandibles edentate, slender; without apical masticatory border.
  Leptogenys Roger s. str.
  Mandibles broader, generally toothed; with distinct masticatory border at apex ....Subgen. *Lobopelta* Mayr.
9. Median spur of middle and hind legs alone developed, lateral spurs lacking; small species with vestigial eyes...........................*Ponera* Latr.
  Both spurs of the middle and hind legs well-developed; medium or large species, with larger eyes... 10.
10. Cheeks with a longitudinal carina.......................*Neoponera* Emery.
  Cheeks without a carina... 11.
11. Clypeus flat, separated from the frontal carinæ by a scarcely perceptible suture or none at all; body opaque....................*Platythyrea* Mayr.
  Clypeus separated from the frontal carinæ by a distinct suture; body subopaque or shining.. 12.
12. Pronotum more or less marginate on the sides; middle tibiæ not abbreviated nor beset with prominent bristles..............*Pachycondyla* F. Smith.
  Pronotum not marginate on the sides; middle tibiæ short, with prominent bristles on their extensor surfaces.
  Euponera Forel; subgen. *Pseudoponera* Emery.

Subfamily DORYLINÆ

1. Claws toothed ....*Eciton* Latr.
  Claws simple ....Subgen. *Acamatus* Em.

Subfamily MYRMICINÆ

1. Workers absent..*Epœcus* Emery; *Sympheidole* Wheeler; *Epipheidole* Wheeler.
  Workers present .... 2.
2. Clypeus not extending back between the frontal carinæ, which are closely approximated; antennæ 12-jointed.................*Pseudomyrma* Guérin.
  Clypeus almost always extending back between the frontal carinæ, which are more or less separated, in the opposite case the antennæ are 11-jointed.. 3.
3. Antennal fossæ prolonged as grooves for the antennal scapes along the sides of the head dorsal to the eyes and covered by the expanded lateral margins of the head; antennæ 11-jointed.....................*Cryptocerus* Fabr.
  Antennal fossæ of a different conformation or antennæ of a different number of joints .... 4.
4. Postpetiole articulated to the dorsal surface of the gaster which is flattened dorsally, more convex ventrally and acutely pointed..*Cremastogaster* Lund.
  Postpetiole inserted at the anterior end of the gaster which is of the usual shape .... 5.
5. Antennæ 6-jointed; head cordiform, antennal fossæ as long as the scapes.
  Strumigenys F. Smith.
  Antennæ with more than six joints................................... 6.
6. Antennæ 11-jointed; without a distinct club, or with a club consisting of only a single joint... 7.
  Antennal club consisting of several joints, or the antennæ not 11-jointed.. 10.
7. Integument rough, bearing stiff or hooked hairs........................ 8.
  Integument smoother; hairs scale-like and appressed..*Cyphomyrmex* Mayr.

8. Large species; workers highly polymorphic; head with only one pair of occipital spines; thorax with three pairs of dorsal spines or tubercles.

Atta Fabr. s. str.

    Smaller species; workers monomorphic or feebly polymorphic; thoracic dorsum with four pairs of spines or tubercles.......................... 9.

9. Head broad, with rounded occipital lobes, without supraocular spines or tubercles ....Subgen. *Mœllerius* Emery.

    Head narrow, with angular occipital lobes; body rough, covered with small tubercles ....Subgen. *Trachymyrmex* Forel.

10. Antennæ with a 2-jointed club... 11.

    Antennal club, when developed, with more than two joints.............. 12.

11. Antennæ 10-jointed; epinotum unarmed.................*Solenopsis* Westw.

    Antennæ 11-jointed; epinotum dentate..............*Erebomyrma* Wheeler.

12. Posterior margin of clypeus elevated in the form of a welt or ridge bordering the antennal fossa in front.. 13.

    Posterior border of clypeus not thus elevated........................... 15.

13. Portion of clypeus in front of the antennal insertion narrow but not reduced to a mere ridge (antennæ of male 10-jointed)....................... 14.

    Portion of the clypeus in front of antennal insertion reduced to a mere ridge (antennæ of male 13-jointed).......................*Myrmecina* Curtis.

14. Antennæ 12-jointed ....*Tetramorium* Mayr. s. str.

    Antennæ 11-jointed ....*Xiphomyrmex* Forel.

15 Antennæ 11-jointed ·· 16.

    Antennæ 12-jointed ··· 19.

16. Thorax and petiole without any traces of teeth or spines; pronotum never angular .... 17.

    Epinotum armed with spines or teeth............................... 18.

17. Petiole distinctly pedunculate........................*Monomorium* Mayr.

    Petiole not pedunculate...............................*Xenomyrmex* Forel.

18. Mesoëpinotal constriction distinct; males ergatomorphic.

Symmyrmica Wheeler.

    Mesoëpinotal constriction faint or lacking...............*Leptothorax* Mayr.

19. Workers strongly dimorphic, usually without intermediates connecting the extreme forms; antennal club 3-jointed, longer than the remainder of the funiculus ....*Pheidole* Westwood.

    Workers monomorphic or polymorphic, *i. e.,* with mediæ intermediate between the major and minor forms; antennal club indistinct or shorter than the remainder of the funiculus.. 20.

20. Last three antennal joints much shorter than the remainder of the funiculus and not forming a distinct club.................................... 21.

    Last three antennal joints forming a distinct club nearly as long as the remainder of the funiculus....................................... 26.

21. Thoracic dorsum impressed at the mesoëpinotal suture; promesonotal suture usually distinct .... 22.

    Thoracic dorsum without any traces of suture or impression

Pogonomyrmex Mayr.

22. Posterior tibial spurs pectinated ....*Myrmica* Latr.

    Posterior tibial spurs simple .... 23.

23. Small hypogæic species, with vestigial eyes and two keels on the clypeus.

Stenamma Westwood.

    Medium sized species, with well-developed eyes and no keels on the clypeus .... 24.

24. Workers monomorphic .... 25.

    Workers polymorphic ....*Messor* Forel.

25. Cosmopolitan species with moderately slender thorax and legs.

Aphænogaster Mayr. s. str.

Tropical and subtropical species with very slender thorax and legs.

Subgen. *Ischnomyrmex* Mayr.

26. Clypeus armed with a pair of ridges which project forward in the form of teeth, rarely without teeth, but then the epinotum is quite unarmed; mesoepinotal suture marked ....*Monomorium* Mayr.

Clypeus of a different conformation; rarely 2-toothed, but then the mesoëpinotal suture is indistinct .... 27.

27. Postpetiole campanulate, not constricted behind but applied with its whole posterior surface to the first gastric segment.........*Macromischa* Roger.

Postpetiole constricted behind ....*Leptothorax* Mayr.

Subfamily DOLICHODERINÆ

1. Chitinous integument hard and brittle, declivity of epinotum strongly concave.

Dolichoderus Lund; subgen. *Hypoclinea* Mayr.

Chitinous integument thin and flexible, smooth or very finely sculptured, declivity of epinotum not strongly concave........................... 2.

2. Scale of petiole very small, strongly inclined forward, or even altogether absent .... 3.

Scale of petiole more or less inclined but well-developed................. 4.

3. Scale of petiole small but indistinct; gizzard with a convex, 4-lobed calyx.

Forelius Emery.

Scale vestigial or absent; gizzard with a depressed calyx, without lobes.

Tapinoma Foerster.

4. Epinotum with a conical elevation......................*Dorymyrmex* Mayr.

Epinotum without a conical elevation.................................. 5.

5. Body not conspicuously hairy or pubescent; gizzard very short, with a large reflected calyx; ocelli absent........................*Iridomyrmex* Mayr.

Body densely pubescent; gizzard at least as long as broad; ocelli usually present in large workers...........................*Liometopum* Mayr.

Subfamily CAMPONOTINÆ

1. Antennæ 9-jointed ....*Brachymyrmex* Mayr.

Antennæ with more than 9 joints.................................... 2.

2. Workers di- or polymorphic... 3.

Workers not polymorphic though often of variable size................. 4.

3. Workers polymorphic, *i. e.,* with forms (mediæ) intermediate between the largest and smallest workers; head of largest workers not sharply truncated anteriorly ....*Camponotus* Mayr. s. str.

Workers dimorphic, *i. e.,* without intermediate forms; head of largest workers sharply truncated anteriorly..........Subgen. *Colobopsis* Mayr.

4. Clypeal fossa distinctly separated from the antennal fossa................ 5.

Clypeal fossa confluent with the antennal fossa........................ 6.

5. Antennal scapes and tibiæ without erect hairs; mesonotum strongly constricted and subcylindrical......................*Prenolepis* Mayr. s. str.

Antennal scapes and tibiæ with erect hairs; mesonotum constricted but not subcylindrical ....Subgen. *Nylanderia* Emery.

6. Joints 2–5 of the funiculus shorter or not longer than the succeeding joints; ocelli usually absent... 7.

Joints 2–5 of the funiculus longer than the succeeding joints; ocelli distinct .... 8.

7. Maxillary palpi 6-jointed.............................*Lasius* Fabr. s. str.

Maxillary palpi 3-jointed...................Subgen. *Acanthomyops* Mayr.

8. Fourth joint of maxillary palpi nearly as long as the fifth.

Myrmecocystus Wesmael.

Fourth joint of maxillary palpi a little longer than the fifth............ 9.

9. Mandibles with broad, dentate, masticatory border.........*Formica* Linn.

Mandibles narrow, falcate and pointed.................*Polyergus* Latreille.

APPENDIX C

A LIST OF DESCRIBED NORTH AMERICAN ANTS

Subfamily PONERINÆ

Genus STIGMATOMMA Roger

pallipes Haldeman. — Canada to Texas.
—— subsp. *oregonense* Wheeler. — Oregon.

Genus ACANTHOSTICHUS Mayr.

texanus Forel. — Texas.

Genus CERAPACHYS F Smith

Subgenus *Parasyscia* Emery

augustæ Wheeler. — Texas.

Genus SYSPHINCTA Roger

melina Roger. — Atlantic States.
pergandei Emery. — Atlantic States.

Genus PROCERATIUM Roger

croceum Roger. — Southern States to Texas.
silaceum Roger. — Atlantic States.
crassicorne Emery. — Atlantic States.
—— var. *vestitum* Emery. — Atlantic States.

Genus PLATYTHYREA Roger

punctata F. Smith. — Texas.

Genus PACHYCONDYLA F. Smith

harpax Fabr. — Louisiana to Texas.

Genus EUPONERA Forel

Subgen. *Pseudoponera* Emery

stigma Fabr. — Florida.

Genus NEOPONERA Emery

villosa F. Smith. — Texas.

Genus PONERA Latreille

gilva Roger. — " North America."
coarctata Latr. subsp. *pennsylvanica* Buckley. — Northeastern States, Canada.
opaciceps Mayr. — Texas.
trigona Mayr. var. *opacior* Forel. — Texas.
inexorata Wheeler. — Texas to Colorado.
ergatandria Forel. — Texas.

Genus LEPTOGENYS Roger

Subgenus *Lobopelta* Mayr

elongata Buckley. — Texas.

Genus ODONTOMACHUS Latreille

hæmatodes L. subsp. *insularis* Guérin. — Florida.
clarus Roger. — Georgia to Texas.

Subfamily DORYLINÆ

Genus ECITON Latreille

Subgen. *Eciton* s. str.

cæcum Latreille. — Texas.
esenbecki Westwood. — Texas.

Subgenus *Acamatus* Emery

sumichrasti Norton. — Texas.
schmitti Emery. — Texas to Missouri and Colorado.
californicus Mayr. — California.
opacithorax Emery. — Texas to Missouri.
carolinensis Emery. — North Carolina.
wheeleri Emery. — Texas.
pilosus F. Smith. — Texas.
pauxillus Wheeler. — Texas.
commutatus Emery. — Texas.
arizonensis Wheeler. — Arizona.
oslari Wheeler. — Arizona.
minor Cresson. — Texas.
melsheimeri Haldeman. — Utah to Texas.
harrisi Haldeman. — Utah to Texas.
nigrescens Cresson. — Kansas to Texas.
mexicanus F. Smith. — Texas.

Subfamily MYRMICINÆ

Genus PSEUDOMYRMA Lund

gracilis Emery var. *mexicana* Roger. — Texas.
pallida F. Smith. — Florida to Texas.
flavidula F. Smith. — Florida to Texas.
brunnea F. Smith. — Florida to Texas.
elongata Mayr. — Florida.

Genus MYRMECINA Fabr.

graminicola Fabr. subsp. *americana* Emery. — Northeastern States
—— —— var. *brevispinosa* Emery. — Northeastern States.
—— subsp. *texana* Wheeler. — Texas.

Genus MONOMORIUM Mayr

pharaonis L. — United States (introduced).
minimum Buckley. — Atlantic, Southern States, Texas.
ergatogyna Wheeler. — California.
floricola Jerdon. — Florida (introduced).
destructor Jerdon. — Southern States (introduced).

Genus XENOMYRMEX Forel

stolli Forel subsp. *floridanus* Emery. — Florida.

Genus EPŒCUS Emery

pergandei Emery. — District of Columbia.

Genus SOLENOPSIS Fabricius

geminata Fabr. — Southern States.
—— var. *xyloni* McCook. — Texas.
—— var. *diabola* Wheeler. — Texas.
—— subsp. *rufa* Jerdon. — Florida (introduced).
aurea Wheeler.— Texas to California.
salina Wheeler. — Texas.
krockowi Wheeler. — New Mexico.
pilosula Wheeler. — Texas.
molesta Say. — Northern and Eastern States.
—— var. *validiuscula* Emery. — Western States.
—— var. *castanea* Wheeler. — Colorado and New Mexico.
texana Emery. — Texas.
—— var. *catalinæ* Wheeler. — California.
—— subsp. *carolinensis* Forel. — North Carolina.
—— subsp. *truncorum* Forel. — North Carolina.
pergandei Forel. — North Carolina.
picta Emery. — Florida.

Genus EREBOMYRMA Wheeler

longi Wheeler. — Texas.

Genus PHEIDOLE Westwood

megacephala Fabricius. — Florida (introduced).
pilifera Roger. — Eastern and Northern States.
—— var. *simulans* Wheeler. — Atlantic States.
—— subsp. *coloradensis* Emery. — Colorado.
—— —— var. *neomexicana* Wheeler. — New Mexico.
ceres Wheeler. — Colorado to Texas.
kingi Ern. André subsp. *instabilis* Emery. — Texas, Mexico.
proserpina Wheeler. — Arizona.
soritis Wheeler. — New Mexico.
sitarches Wheeler. — Texas.
—— var. *transvarians* Wheeler. — Texas.
—— subsp. *rufescens* Wheeler. — Texas.
—— —— var. *campestris* Wheeler. — Texas.
sciophila Wheeler. — Texas.
xerophila Wheeler. — Texas.
—— subsp. *tucsonica* Wheeler. — Arizona.
—— —— var. *gilvescens* Wheeler. — Arizona.
barbata Wheeler. — California.
macclendoni Wheeler. — Texas.
rhea Wheeler. — Arizona.
desertorum Wheeler. — Texas, Arizona.
—— var. *comanche* Wheeler. — Texas.
—— var. *maricopa* Wheeler. — Arizona.
morrisi Forel. — South Atlantic States.
—— var. *impexa* Wheeler. — Texas.
—— var. *vanceæ* Forel. — North Carolina.

dentata Mayr. — Southern States to Texas.
—— var. *commutata* Mayr. — Southern States to Texas.
—— var. *faisonica* Forel. — North Carolina.
crassicornis Emery. — Southern States to Texas.
—— *diversipilosa* Wheeler. —
—— subsp. *porcula* Wheeler. — Texas.
—— —— var. *tetra* Wheeler. — Texas.
titanis Wheeler. — Texas.
hyatti Emery. — Texas to California.
—— var. *ecitonodora* Wheeler. — Texas.
cockerelli Wheeler. — New Mexico.
texana Wheeler. — Texas.
californica Mayr. — California.
oregonica Emery. — Oregon.
bicarinata Mayr. — Wisconsin and Illinois.
davisi Wheeler. — New Jersey.
tysoni Forel. — New York to North Carolina.
vinelandica Forel. — Eastern States.
—— var. *longula* Emery. — Colorado, Texas.
—— subsp. *leviuscula* Emery. — Missouri.
—— subsp. *buccalis* Wheeler. — Arizona.
flavens Roger subsp. *floridana* Emery. — Florida.
anastasii Emery. — Florida.
casta Wheeler. — Texas.
humeralis Wheeler. — Texas.
marcidula Wheeler. — Texas.
pinealis Wheeler. — Texas.
constipata Wheeler. — Texas.
lauta Wheeler. — Texas.
nuculiceps Wheeler. — Texas.
metallescens Emery. — Florida.
—— subsp. *splendidula* Wheeler. — Texas.
lamia Wheeler. — Texas.

Genus SYMPHEIDOLE Wheeler

elecebra Wheeler. — Colorado.

Genus EPIPHEIDOLE Wheeler

inquilina Wheeler. — Colorado, Nebraska.

Genus CREMASTOGASTER Lund

lineolata Say. — Northern States and Canada.
—— var. *cerasi* Fitch. — N. Atlantic States.
—— var. *lutescens* Emery. — Atlantic States.
—— var. *subopaca* Emery. — South Atlantic States.
—— subsp. *pilosa* Pergande. — South Atlantic States.
—— subsp. *leviuscula* Mayr. — Texas.
—— —— var. *californica* Emery. — California.
—— —— var. *clara* Mayr. — Texas to Arkansas.
—— subsp. *coarctata* Mayr. — California.
—— —— var. *mormonum* Emery. — Utah.
—— subsp. *opaca* var. *depilis* Wheeler. — Texas, New Mexico, Mexico.
—— —— var. *punctulata* Emery. — Colorado to Texas.
ashmeadi Mayr. — South Atlantic States.

vermiculata Emery. — California.
arizonensis Wheeler. — Arizona.
victima F. Smith subsp. *missouriensis* Pergande.
minutissima Mayr. — Texas.

Genus STENAMMA Westwood

brevicorne Mayr. — Northern States.
—— subsp. *diecki* Emery. — Northern States.
—— —— var. *impressum* Emery. — New York, Vermont.
—— subsp. *impar* Forel. — Virginia, Pennsylvania.
—— subsp. *schmitti* Wheeler. — Pennsylvania.
nearcticum Mayr. — British Columbia.

Genus APHÆNOGASTER Mayr

Subgen. *Aphænogaster* s. str.

subterranea Latr. subsp. *occidentalis* Emery.— Western States eastward, to
    Colorado.
patruelis Forel.— Lower California.
—— subsp. *bakeri* Wheeler. — California.
mariæ Forel. — South Atlantic States.
treatæ Forel. — South Atlantic States, north to Connecticut and west to Texas.
—— var. *ashmeadi* Emery. — Florida.
lamellidens Mayr. — South Atlantic States.
fulva Roger. — Northeastern States.
—— subsp. *aquia* Buckley. — Northeastern States.
—— —— var. *picea* Emery. — Northeastern States.
—— —— var. *rudis* Emery. — Northern States.
—— —— var. *texana* Emery. — Texas.
mutica Pergande. — Texas.
tennesseensis Mayr. — Northeastern States.
—— var. *ecalcarata* Emery. — Vermont.

Subgenus *Ischnomyrmex* Mayr

albisetosus Mayr. — Texas.
cockerelli Ern. André. — Texas to Arizona.

Genus MESSOR Forel

julianus Pergande. — Lower California.
carbonarius Pergande. — Lower California.
stoddardi Emery. — California.
pergandei Er. André. — Arizona, California.
andrei Mayr. — California.

Genus POGONOMYRMEX Mayr

Subgen. *Pogonomyrmex* s. str.

barbatus F. Smith var. *molefaciens* Buckley. — Texas.
—— var. *fuscatus* Emery. — Texas to Colorado.
—— var. *nigrescens* Wheeler. — Texas.
—— var. *marfensis* Wheeler. — Texas.
—— subsp. *rugosus* Emery. — Arizona to California.
occidentalis Cresson. — Wyoming, Colorado, Kansas, New Mexico, Arizona.
—— var. *subnitidus* Emery. — California.

comanche Wheeler. — Texas.
subdentatus Mayr. — Arizona to California.
desertorum Wheeler. — Texas to Arizona.
californicus Buckley. — Texas and California.
—— var. *estebanius* Pergande. — Lower California.
—— subsp. *longinodis* Emery. — California.
badius Latreille. — South Atlantic States.
apache Wheeler. — Texas.
sancti-hyacinthi Wheeler. — Texas.

Subgenus *Ephebomyrmex* Wheeler

imberbiculus Wheeler. — Texas.
pima Wheeler. — Arizona.

Genus MYRMICA Latreille

mutica Emery. — Northwestern States.
bradleyi Wheeler. — California.
punctiventris Roger. — North Atlantic States.
—— subsp. *pinetorum* Wheeler. — Middle Atlantic States.
rubra L. subsp. *brevinodis* Emery. — Colorado.
—— —— var. *sulcinodoides* Emery. — Utah, Colorado, New Mexico.
—— —— var. *frigida* Forel. — British Columbia.
—— —— var. *whymperi* Forel. — British Columbia.
—— —— var. *canadensis* Wheeler. — Northeastern States and Canada.
—— —— var. *subalpina* Wheeler. — Colorado.
—— —— var. *decedens* Wheeler. — Colorado.
—— —— var. *brevispinosa* Wheeler. — Colorado.
—— subsp. *levinodis* Nyl. — Mass. (Introduced.)
—— —— var. *bruesi* Wheeler. — Mass. (Introduced.)
—— subsp. *neolevinodis* Forel. — New York. (Introduced.)
—— subsp. *champlaini* Forel. — Canada.
—— subsp. *scabrinodis* Nyl. var. *fracticornis* Emery. — Northeastern States.
—— —— var. *sabuleti* Meinert. — Northern States.
—— —— var. *schencki* Emery. — Northern States.
—— —— var. *detritinodis* Emery. — Northern States.
—— —— var. *lobifrons* Pergande. — Alaska.
—— —— var. *glacialis* Forel. — British Columbia.

Genus LEPTOTHORAX Mayr

Subgen. *Leptothorax* s. str.

acervorum Mayr. subsp. *canadensis* Provancher. — Northern States and British America.
—— —— var. *yankee* Emery. — Northwestern States.
—— —— var. *kincaidi* Pergande. — Alaska.
—— —— var. *obscurus* Viereck. — New York.
hirticornis Emery. — District of Columbia.
muscorum Nyl. var. *sordidus* Wheeler. — Colorado.
provancheri Emery. — Canada.
emersoni Wheeler. — New England.
—— subsp. *glacialis* Wheeler. — Colorado.
schaumi Roger. — Atlantic States.
fortinodis Mayr. — Atlantic States.
—— var. *melanoticus* Wheeler. — Illinois.
—— var. *gilvus* Wheeler. — Texas.

longispinosus Roger. — North Atlantic States.
curvispinosus Mayr. — North Atlantic States.
—— subsp. *ambiguus* Emery. — Northern States.
—— subsp. *rugatulus* Emery. — S. Dakota, Colorado.
—— —— var. *cockerelli* Wheeler. — New Mexico.
—— subsp. *annectens* Wheeler. — Colorado.
schmitti Wheeler. — Colorado.
nitens Emery. — Utah.
—— var. *heathi* Wheeler. — California.
—— subsp. *occidentalis* Wheeler. — Washington.
texanus Wheeler. — Texas.
—— subsp. *davisi* Wheeler. — New Jersey.
neomexicanus Wheeler. — New Mexico.
obturator Wheeler. — Texas.
nevadensis Wheeler. — Nevada.
melanderi Wheeler. — Idaho.
terrigena Wheeler. — Texas.
tricarinatus Emery. — South Dakota.
furunculus Wheeler. — Colorado.
andrei Emery. — California.

Subgenus *Dichothorax* Emery

pergandei Emery. — Southern States and California.
floridanus Emery. — South Atlantic States.

Genus SYMMYRMICA Wheeler

chamberlini Wheeler. — Utah.

Genus HARPAGOXENUS Forel

americanus Emery. — Atlantic States.

Genus MACROMISCHA Roger

subditiva Wheeler — Texas.

Genus TETRAMORIUM Mayr
Subgen. *Tetramorium* s. str.

cespitum L. — North Atlantic States (introduced).
guineense Fabr. — Florida (introduced).

Subgenus *Tetrogmus* Roger

simillimum Roger. — Florida (introduced).

Genus XIPHOMYRMEX Forel

spinosus Pergande. — Texas to Arizona.

Genus CRYPTOCERUS Fabricius

varians F. Smith. — Florida.
angustus Mayr. — Texas.

Genus STRUMIGENYS F. Smith

louisianæ Roger. — Gulf States.
pergandei Emery. — Atlantic States.

pulchella Emery. — Atlantic States.
ornata Mayr. — Atlantic States.
clypeata Roger. — Atlantic States.
—— var. *pilinasis* Forel. — Atlantic States.
rostrata Emery. — Atlantic States.
margaritæ Forel. — Texas.

Genus ATTA Fabricius
Subgen. *Atta* s. str

texana Buckley. — Texas.

Subgenus *Mœllerius* Emery

versicolor Pergande. — Arizona.
—— subsp. *chisosensis* Wheeler. — Texas.

Subgenus *Trachymyrmex* Forel

septentrionalis McCook. — New Jersey.
—— var. *obscurior* Wheeler. — Gulf States.
turrifex Wheeler. — Texas.
arizonensis Wheeler. — Arizona.

Subgenus *Mycetosoritis* Wheeler

hartmani Wheeler. — Texas.

Genus CYPHOMYRMEX Mayr

wheeleri Forel. — Texas to California.
rimosus Spinola var. *comalensis* Wheeler. — Texas.
—— subsp. *minutus* Mayr. — Florida.

Subfamily DOLICHODERINÆ
Genus DOLICHODERUS Lund
Subgenus *Hypoclinea* Mayr

mariæ Forel. — South Atlantic States.
—— var. *davisi* Wheeler. — New Jersey.
taschenbergi Mayr. — Louisiana.
—— var. *gagates* Wheeler. — Atlantic States.
plagiata Mayr. — Northeastern States.
—— var. *inornata* Wheeler. — Atlantic States.
—— subsp. *pustulata* Mayr. — Atlantic States.
—— —— var. *beutenmuelleri* Wheeler. — Atlantic States.

Genus LIOMETOPUM Mayr

apiculatum Mayr. — Texas, New Mexico.
—— var. *occidentale* Emery. — Colorado to California.
—— subsp. *luctuosum* Wheeler. — Colorado to Arizona.

Genus DORYMYRMEX Mayr

pyramicus Roger. — Southern States.
—— var. *niger* Pergande. — Southern States.
—— var. *flavus* Pergande. — Southern States.
—— var. *bicolor* Wheeler. — Texas to Arizona.

Genus TAPINOMA Förster

sessile Say. — Northern States.
littorale Wheeler. — Florida.
pruinosum Roger. — South and Middle Atlantic States.

Genus IRIDOMYRMEX Mayr

analis Ern. André. — Southern States.
humilis Mayr. — Louisiana, California (introduced).

Genus FORELIUS Emery

maccooki Forel. — Texas.

Subfamily CAMPONOTINÆ

Genus BRACHYMYRMEX Mayr

heeri Forel subsp. *depilis* Emery. — Northeastern States.
nanellus Wheeler. — Texas.

Genus PRENOLEPIS Mayr

Subgen. *Prenolepis* s. str.

imparis Say. — New England to California.
—— var. *testacea* Emery. — Middle Atlantic States.
—— var. *minuta* Emery. — Middle Atlantic States.

Subgenus *Nylanderia* Emery

parvula Mayr. — Northeastern States.
fulva Mayr. subsp. *pubens* Forel. — District of Columbia (introduced).
longicornis Latreille. — Florida (introduced).
bruesi Wheeler. — Texas.
arenivaga Wheeler. — Texas to New Jersey.
guatemalensis Forel. — Arizona.
vividula Nyl. subsp. *melanderi* Wheeler. — Texas.

Genus LASIUS Fabricius

Subgen. *Lasius* s. str.

niger L. var. *neoniger* Emery. — Northern States.
—— var. *americanus* Emery. — Northern States.
—— var. *sitkaënsis* Pergande. — Alaska, British America, Colorado.
brevicornis Emery. — North Atlantic States.
flavus L. subsp. *nearcticus* Wheeler. — Northeastern States.
umbratus Nyl. subsp. *mixtus* Nyl. var. *aphidicola* Walsh. — Northern States.
—— subsp. *minutus* Emery. — Atlantic States.
—— subsp. *subumbratus* Viereck. — New Mexico.
—— subsp. *speculiventris* Emery. — Northern States.

Subgenus *Acanthomyops* Mayr

interjectus Mayr. — Northern States.
claviger Roger. — Northern States.
—— var. *subglaber* Emery. — Northern States.
latipes Walsh. — Northern States.
murphyi Forel. — Northern States.
occidentalis Wheeler. — Colorado.

Genus Formica L.

pergandei Emery. — Northern States.
munda Wheeler. — Colorádo, New Mexico.
sanguinea Latr. subsp. *aserva* Forel. — Canada and Northern States.
—— subsp. *rubicunda* Emery. — Northern States.
—— subsp. *subintegra* Emery. — Northern States.
—— subsp. *subnuda* Emery. — British America.
—— subsp. *puberula* Emery. — Colorado, S. Dakota.
—— subsp. *obtusopilosa* Emery. — New Mexico.
moki Wheeler. — Arizona.
adamsi Wheeler. — Isle Royale, Lake Superior.
rufa L. subsp. *obscuriventris* Mayr. — Northeastern States.
—— —— var. *gymnomma* Wheeler. — Northern States.
—— —— var. *integroides* Emery. — California to Nebraska
—— subsp. *obscuripes* Forel. — Northwestern States, British America.
—— —— var. *rubiginosa* Emery. — Nebraska, Colorado, Dakota.
—— —— var. *melanotica* Emery. — Wisconsin.
—— —— var. *whymperi* Forel. — British America.
—— subsp. *integra* Nylander. — Northeastern States.
—— —— var. *hæmorrhoidalis* Emery. — Dakota, Colorado.
—— —— var. *coloradensis* Wheeler. — Colorado.
oreas Wheeler. — Colorado.
ciliata Mayr. — Colorado.
crinita Wheeler. — Colorado.
comata Wheeler. — Colorado.
dakotensis Emery. — S. Dakota, Colorado.
specularis Emery. — Wisconsin.
morsei Wheeler. — Massachusetts.
difficilis Emery. — Middle Atlantic States.
—— var. *consocians* Wheeler. — New England.
microgyna Wheeler. — Colorado.
—— var. *rasilis* Wheeler. — Colorado.
nevadensis Wheeler. — Nevada.
nepticula Wheeler. — New England States.
impexa Wheeler. — Michigan to Massachusetts.
exsectoides Forel. — Northeastern States.
—— var. *opaciventris* Emery. — Colorado.
ulkei Emery. — Nova Scotia to S. Dakota.
pallide-fulva Latreille. — Southern States.
—— var. *succinea* Wheeler. — Texas.
—— subsp. *schaufussi* Mayr. — Northern States.
—— —— var. *meridionalis* Wheeler. — Texas.
—— —— var. *incerta* Emery. — Northern States.
—— subsp. *nitidiventris* Emery. — Northern States.
—— —— var. *fuscata* Emery. — Northern States.
rufibarbis Fabr. var. *occidentalis* Wheeler. — Western States.
fusca L. var. *subsericea* Say. — Northern States
—— var. *argentata* Wheeler. — Northern States.
—— var. *densiventris* Viereck. — New Mexico.
—— var. *subænescens* Emery. — Northern States.
—— var. *glacialis* Wheeler. — North Atlantic States, Nova Scotia.
—— var. *neorufibarbis* Emery. — British America, Alaska, Colorado. Mass.
—— var. *neoclara* Emery. — Colorado, Mass.
—— var. *gnava* Buckley. — Texas to Colorado.
subpolita Mayr. — Northern States.

—— var. *neogagates* Emery. — Northeastern States.
—— var. *montana* Emery. — Nebraska.
—— var. *perpilosa* Wheeler. — Texas to Arizona.
lasioides Emery. — South Dakota.
—— var. *picea* Emery. — South Dakota.
cinerea Mayr. var. *neocinerea* Wheeler. — Colorado to Illinois.
pilicornis Emery. — California.
rufiventris Emery. — California.

Genus POLYERGUS Latreille

rufescens Latr. subsp. *breviceps* Emery. — Colorado to Arkansas and Illinois.
—— subsp. *bicolor* Wasmann. — Wisconsin.
—— —— var. *foreli* Wheeler. — Illinois.
—— subsp. *lucidus* Mayr. — New York to Colorado.

Genus MYRMECOCYSTUS Wesmael

melliger Forel. — Texas.
—— subsp. *orbiceps* Wheeler. — Texas to Arizona.
—— subsp. *mendax* Wheeler. — Colorado, Arizona.
—— —— var. *comatus* Wheeler. — Texas.
—— subsp. *mimicus* Wheeler. — Texas to Arizona.
—— —— var. *jesuita* Wheeler. — Texas.
—— —— var. *depilis* Forel. — California.
—— subsp. *semirufus* Emery. — Arizona, New Mexico and California.
—— —— var. *testaceus* Emery. — California.
mexicanus Wesm. var. *horti-deorum* McCook. — New Mexico and Colorado.
—— subsp. *navajo* Wheeler. — New Mexico.
—— subsp. *mojave* Wheeler. — California.
lugubris Wheeler. — California.

Genus CAMPONOTUS Mayr

Subgen. *Camponotus* s. str.

socius Roger. — Florida.
abdominalis Roger subsp. *floridanus* Buckley..— Florida.
fumidus Roger var. *festinatus* Buckley. — Texas.
—— var. *fragilis* Pergande. — Texas.
—— var. *pubicornis* Emery. — Texas.
levigatus F. Smith. — Rocky Mts., California.
maculatus Fabr. subsp. *vicinus* Mayr. — California.
—— —— var. *nitidiventris* Emery. — Western States.
—— —— var. *semitestaceus* Emery. — California.
—— subsp. *tortuganus* Emery. — Florida.
—— subsp. *ochreatus* Emery. — California.
maccooki Forel. — California, Arizona, Colorado.
—— var. *sansabeanus* Buckley. — Texas.
castaneus Latreille. — Atlantic States.
—— subsp. *americanus* Mayr. — Northeastern States.
herculeanus L. var. *whymperi* Forel. — British America, Colorado.
—— subsp. *pennsylvanicus* De Geer. — Canada to Texas and Louisiana.
—— —— var *semipunctatus* Kirby. — California.
—— —— var. *ferrugineus* Fabr. — New York to Illinois.
—— subsp. *ligniperdus* Latr. var. *noveboracensis* Fitch. — Canada, Northeastern States.
—— —— var. *rubens* Wheeler. — Maine and Michigan.

planatus Roger. — Florida and Texas.
mina Forel. — Arizona.
frontalis Pergande. — Texas.
texanus Wheeler. — Texas.
schæfferi Wheeler. — Arizona.
fallax Nyl. var. *nearcticus* Emery. — Northeastern States.
—— var. *minutus* Emery. — Northeastern States.
—— var. *decipiens* Emery. — Middle States to Texas.
—— subsp. *subbarbatus* Emery. — Atlantic States.
—— —— var. *paucipilis* Emery. — Atlantic States.
—— subsp. *rasilis* Wheeler. — Texas.
—— subsp. *discolor* Buckley. — Texas.
—— —— var. *clarithorax* Emery. — California.
—— —— var. *cnemidatus* Emery. — District of Columbia.
sayi Emery. — Arizona.
hyatti Emery. — California.
—— var. *bakeri* Wheeler. — California.

Subgenus *Colobopsis* Mayr

impressa Roger. — Florida.
abdita Forel var. *etiolata* Wheeler. — Texas.
pylartes Wheeler. — Texas.

APPENDIX D

METHODS OF EXTERMINATING NOXIOUS ANTS

In houses, gardens, orchards and fields several of our imported, and a few of our native ants, may become such intolerable nuisances that measures must be taken to exterminate them. Merely killing off their workers is, as a rule, quite ineffectual, since their place is soon filled by a fresh brood reared from the eggs and larvæ remaining in the nest. Hence the only proper method is to destroy the whole colony, and this can be accomplished only by killing the queen. But as ant colonies often contain a number of queens, and as these habitually lurk in the deepest and most inaccessible portions of the nest, total eradication of a colony is often difficult or impossible. The usual method of treatment, apart from digging up the nest completely—which is often impracticable—consists in forcing into the nest a liquid or gaseous insecticide that will permeate all the chambers and galleries and kill their occupants. Our noxious ants may be divided into four groups, which are here very briefly characterized, together with some of the most approved methods that have been recommended for their extermination.

1. **House Ants.**—The most prevalent species are *Monomorium pharaonis,* a small reddish-yellow ant, with well-developed eyes and 3-jointed funicular club; *Solenopsis molesta,* an even smaller, more yellowish species, with vestigial eyes and 2-jointed funicular club; *Tetramorium cespitum,* the small, black or dark brown "pavement ant" and the large, black "carpenter ant," *Camponotus pennsylvanicus,* or some of the allied varieties (*C. ferrugineus* and *noveboracensis*). The *Monomorium, Solenopsis* and *Tetramorium* nest in crevices of the woodwork, tiling and masonry and forage in pantries, store-rooms and kitchens, where they often become a great nuisance, not because they consume much of the food, but because they crawl into it. The carpenter ants have similar habits and in addition sometimes do considerable damage by weakening or destroying old woodwork in which they mine their galleries. On account of their habits it is often very difficult to get at the nests of these various house ants, but they may sometimes be exterminated by pouring or injecting boiling water, benzine, gasoline, or, preferably, carbon bisulphid, into the crevices which they inhabit. Their numbers can often be greatly diminished by placing

on their foraging grounds small sponges saturated with sugar-water. The ants collect on these and can be killed by dropping the sponges into hot water. This process can be repeated till no ants come to the sponges. *Solenopsis molesta* seems not to be attracted by sweets, but it can be entrapped and killed in the same manner by using bones or rags saturated with grease instead of sponges. This is, however, merely a makeshift, for as long as the queens remain in their nests in the wood-work and masonry of the house, the colonies may be regenerated.

Newell (Journ. Econ. Entom. II, 1909, pp. 324–332) has recently shown that the Argentine ant (*Iridomyrmex humilis*) which has be-come a serious house-hold pest in Louisiana and California, and prom-ises to overrun all the warmer portions of the United States, has a unique habit. This ant nests both out of doors and in the masonry and woodwork of houses. On the approach of winter numerous colo-nies, that have inhabited a considerable area during the summer, come together and unite to form a single huge colony, which may contain, at "a conservative estimate," upwards of 1000 fertile queens! In the spring this colony splits up into numerous smaller colonies which move out and again cover an extensive territory. For ridding the premises about houses of these insects, Newell suggests the use of a trap consisting of a dry goods box about $2 \times 2 \times 3$ feet, filled with cotton seed and straw or other porous vegetable material. The top of the box is left open so that its contents are exposed to the weather. The interior of the compost mass becomes warm through decomposi-tion and as winter approaches attracts the ant colonies. During Jan-uary, after the colonies have assembled in the box, its cracks are closed, a pound or two of carbon bisulphide is poured into the compost and the whole is covered with a water-proof canvas till the ants are asphyxiated.

2. **Garden Ants.**—The ants that most frequently disfigure our lawns and garden beds with their untidy earth-works are, in the Northern States, *Lasius americanus, Formica subsericea,* and, occa-sionally, *Prenolepis imparis* and *F. subintegra,* and various species of *Pheidole* (especially *Ph. dentata*), *Dorymyrmex pyramicus* and the "fire-ant," *Solenopsis geminata,* in the Southern States. The fire-ant stings viciously and is often a serious pest in gardens, dooryards and barn-yards. The most effective method of dealing with all of these ants is that described by Hinds (Farmers' Bulletin, No. 145, U. S. Depart-ment of Agriculture): "The treatment consists in making one or more holes in the nest with a stick or iron bar to the depth of from one to two feet, and pouring into each hole one or two ounces of carbon bisulphid. The hole may be closed immediately by step-

ping on it, or, as many writers suggest, the vapor may be exploded at the mouth of the hole with a match, in order to drive the fumes deeper into the chambers. If the latter method is adopted, the hole should be covered with fresh earth immediately after the explosion, in order to put out the fire and confine the fumes. If this is not done, a large portion of the gas will be burned and the efficiency of the treatment be lessened thereby. Right at this point an added word of caution must be given. After the explosion the vapor continues to burn with a colorless flame. It is therefore invisible, but its presence may be easily perceived by holding the hand over the opening or by blowing into it. This point should be carefully noted, for if the operator, thinking the fire had ceased and desiring to make the extermination of the insects doubly certain, should attempt to recharge the hole from a can or bottle, an explosion would surely follow, with possibly fatal results. Explosion does not appear to add to the efficacy of the treatment, and is not at all necessary. If it is not attempted, it may be well to cover the nest with a wet blanket, which will aid greatly in confining the fumes. If any considerable area is infested, as is often the case in lawns, the holes should not be more than one and one-half feet apart each way, and, after the close of the application, the surface treated may be thoroughly watered, as the wet surface will add to the efficiency of the treatment by preventing the rapid diffusion of the fumes into the air." A method recently recommended by Woglum and Wood (Journ. Econ. Entom., 1908, p. 348) would probably prove to be very effective in dealing with the various ants above mentioned. These authors use a solution of potassium cyanide (one ounce of the salt to a gallon of water). Holes are dug and the solution is poured into them in the same way as when bisulphid is used. The ants are killed by the very poisonous cyanide fumes and probably also by getting the liquid into their mouths when they attempt to clean themselves. Kerosene oil may also be used like the cyanide and bisulphid, but greater quantities are required, as it kills only by contact.

3. **Harvesting Ants.**—In the Southwestern States two species of *Pogonomyrmex* (*P. molefaciens* and *P. occidentalis*) often occupy so much space with their large mounds and cleared areas in the fields, sidewalks and yards, and sting so viciously on the slightest provocation, that it becomes necessary to exterminate their colonies. This is most easily accomplished by means of the bisulphid method described above. Headlee and Dean (Kans. Exper. Station Bull. No. 154, 1908), however, have recently recommended the following modification of this method, which they found to be very successful in dealing with *P.*

occidentalis, in Kansas: "Start fumigation when gateways are open; take a vessel, such as a galvanized-iron wash-tub, and place it bottom side up in such a manner as to cover the openings and as much of the mound as possible; if there are more openings than the tub will cover, they should be closed by throwing some of the surrounding soil on them; place under the tub, in a shallow pan or dish, near the opening, one to three ounces of carbon bisulphid, depending on the size of the nest, quickly pack soil around the edge of the tub, making it as nearly air-tight as possible; allow to stand thus for about five hours." It was found that "breaking open the mound before setting the fumigation is of no advantage, nor did the practice of pouring the fluid into the broken-up mound give any better results than that of evaporating it from a shallow pan." The method here recommended would probably give equally good results with the Texan harvester, *P. molefaciens.*

4. **Leaf-cutting Ants.**—The only Attiine ant which is at all a serious menace to gardens, orchards or forage crops in the United States is *Atta texana,* which seems to be confined to certain portions of Texas. Mexico, Cuba, Central and South America have similar pests in *A. mexicana, insularis, sexdens* and *cephalotes.* The nests of these ants, as I have shown in Chapter XVIII, are often of huge dimensions and their colonies when once established are difficult to eradicate. A common method of dealing with *A. texana* is to dig up the nest till the large queen is found and can be destroyed, but this is an arduous task. The sulphur method, which I have not seen in operation, is sometimes employed in Texas, Cuba and South America. Dr. C. L. Marlatt, who has seen it in operation on the ranch of Mr. E. L. Sanborn, Jr., at Artamisa, Pinar del Rio, Cuba, describes it (*in litteris*) as follows: "It consists in digging a large hole six feet deep by three or four feet wide in the midst of the colony. This hole is filled with dry brush or shed palm leaves and a great roaring fire started. Into this is then poured a bucketful of powdered sulphur. The opening is closed with a large iron plate. Through a hole in the center of this plate air is forced down into the burning mass with a large bellows two or three feet in diameter, and by this means the fumes of the sulphur are driven out through the ramifications of the colony around the nest to a distance of several rods, thoroughly destroying all inmates. The escape of the fumes can often be seen from holes which are at a long distance from the point of operation. It is a rather expensive process, but seems to be effectual." Dr. Marlatt also describes another treatment which has recently come into use in Cuba. This is known as the bichlorid of lime and sulphuric acid treatment. "The bichlorid of lime

is made into a paste so that it may be easily poured. The sulphuric acid solution is made by putting four ounces of crude acid into a gallon of water. The amount used of the two mixtures will vary with the size of the nest. Equal quantities of each are employed. First pour the bichlorid into the main entrance to the nest through a funnel and follow with an equal quantity of the diluted sulphuric acid. Close all the entrances to the nest and the chlorin gas generated penetrates through the galleries of the nest and kills the ants. At least this is the belief of the exploiters of this remedy."

APPENDIX E

LITERATURE

Note: In the following pages, the number in parentheses, thus (5), refers to series; the first number not in parentheses, to volume or year; the next number, if preceded by a comma, to part, number, Abteilung, Heft, Lieferung, etc.; and the numbers preceded by a colon (:) to pages. The references preceded by an asterisk (*) contain materials bearing on myrmecophily, symbiosis, parasitism, etc.

ACLOQUE, A., 1900. *Les hôtes Fourmilières. Le Cosmos,* N. S., 43: 393–397, 5 figg.

Adlerz, G., 1884. *Myrmecologiska Studier. I Formicoxenus nitidulus, Nyl. Öfversigt af Kongl. Vet.-Akad. Förh.* 8: 43–64, pls. 27–28. — **1886.** *Myrmecologiska Studier. II Svenska Myror och deras Lefnadförhållanden. Bih. till K. Svenska Vet.-Akad. Handl.* 11, 18: 1–329, pls. 1–7. — **1895a.** *Om en myrliknande svensk Spindel. Ent. Tidskr.* 16: 249–253. — **1895b.** Stridulationsorgan och ljudförnimmelser hos myror. *Ofvers. Vet.-Akad. Förh. Stockholm* 10: 769–782. — **1896a.** *Myrmekologiska Studier. III Tomognathus sublævis Mayr. Bih. Svensk. Vet.-Akad. Handl.* 21, 4: 76 pp., 1 pl. — **1896b.** Myrmecologiska Notiser. *Ent. Tidskr.* 17: 129–141. — **1902.** *Formica suecica n. sp. Eine neue schwedische Ameise. Öfvers. Vet.-Akad. Förh. Stockholm* 59: 263–265. — **1908.** *Zwei Gynandromorphen von Anergates atratulus Schenck. Arkiv Zool.* (5), 2: 1–6, pls. 1–2.

Adolf, E., 1880. Uber das Flügelgeäder des Lasius umbratus. *Bonn.* 1 pl.

Afzelius, A., 1798. *Observations on the genus Paussus, and description of new species. Trans. Linn. Soc. London* 4: 243–275.

v. Aigner-Abafi, Ludw., 1898. *Myrmekophile Lycæna-Raupe. Illustr. Zeitschr. Ent.* 3: 185–186. — **1899.** *Ueber die myrmekophile Orion-Raupe. Ibid.* 4: 124. — **1900.** *Lycæna jolas O. Ibid.* 5: 225–227.

Aitken, E. H., 1890. Red Ants' Nests. *Journ. Bombay Nat. Hist. Soc.* 5, 4: 422.

Alberts, K., 1900. Die Ameisen. *Die Natur.* 49: 268–270.

Alcott, W. P., 1899. Battles of the Black Ants. *Bull. Essex Inst.* 29: 64–70.

Aldrovandus, U. (with Michel Gehler). Encomia Formicarum. *Amphitheatr. Dornavii.* 1.

Alfken, J. D., 1904. Beitrag zur Insectenfauna der Hawaiischen und Neuseeländischen Inseln. (Ergebnisse einer Reise nach dem Pacific. Schauinsland, 1896/97). *Zool. Jahrb. Abt. Syst.* 19: 561–628, 1 pl. — **1905.** *Die von P. Knuth auf seiner 1898/99 unternommenen Reise nach Java, Japan und Kalifornien gesammelten Lepidopteren und Hymenopteren und die von diesen besuchten Pflanzen. Abh. Nat. Ver. Bremen* 18: 132–138.

Allen, J. A., 1866. *Notice of a foray of a colony of Formica sanguinea Ltr. upon a colony of a black species of Formica, for the purpose of making slaves of the latter. Proc. Essex Inst.* 5, 1: 14–16.

Amoreux, P. J., 1800. Observations on Ants and on the Poison of these Insects. *Philos. Mag.* 7: 152–157.

Andersson, J., 1901. Myror såsom skadedjur i trädgården. *Ent. Tidskr.* 22: 60–62.

André, Ed. *Relations des Fourmis avec les pucérons et les gallinsectes.*

Bull. d'Insect. Agri. Ann. 7, 3–7.—**1888.** Le Nid du Lasius fuliginosus. *Le Nat.* (2) 1: 33–36.—**1891.** *Species des Hyménoptères d'Europe et d'Algérie. 4. Braconides. *Beaune.*

André, Ern., 1874. *Manuel descriptif des Fourmis d'Europe pour servir à l'étude des insectes myrmécophiles. *Revue Mag. Zool.* (3) 2: 152.—**1881–1885.** Species des Hyménoptères composant le groupe des Formicides d'Europe, etc. *Gray*, pls. 1–25, 8 suppls.—**1881a.** Description de trois nouvelles espèces de fourmis. *Ann. Soc. Ent. France* (6) 1. Bull. pp. XLVIII–L.—**1881b.** Catalogue raisonné des Formicides provenant du Voyage en Orient de M. Abeille de Perrin et description des espèces nouvelles. *Ibid.* (6) 1: 53–78.—**1881c.** Description du Monomorium Abeillei. *Annal. Mus. Civ. Stor. Nat. Genova* 16: 531.—**1881d.** *Species des Hyménoptères d'Europe et d'Algérie. Les Fourmis 2. *Beaune.*—**1884.** Le Monde des Fourmis. *Feuill. Jeun. Nat.* 15: 7–9; 19–21.—**1885.** *Les Fourmis. *Paris.* 345 pp.—**1887.** Description de quelques fourmis nouvelles ou imparfaitement connues. *Rev. d'Ent.* 6: 280–298.—**1889.** Hyménoptères nouveaux appartenant au groupe des Formicides. *Ibid.* 8: 217–231.—**1890.** Matériaux pour servir à la faune Myrmécologique de Sierra-Leone. *Ibid.* 9: 311–327.—**1892a.** Matériaux myrmécologiques. *Ibid.* 11: 45–56.—**1892b.** (Notes sur une collection de Fourmis de Bornéo.) *Bull. Soc. Zool. France* 16, 9/10: 238–239.—**1892c.** Voyage de M. Chaper à Bornéo. Catalogue des Fourmis et description des espèces nouvelles. *Mèm. Soc. Zool. France* 5, 1: 46–55, 5 figs.—**1893a.** *Description d'une nouvelle espèce de Fourmi. *Bull. Soc. Ent. France* p. 191.—**1893b.** Description de quatre espèces nouvelles de Fourmis d'Amérique. *Rev. Ent. France* 12: 148–152.—**1894a.** Un nouvel example d'intelligence chez les Fourmis. *Feuille Jeunes Natural.* 24: 190.—**1894b.** Nouvelle Espèce de Fourmis de Tunisie. *Ann. Soc. Ent. France* 62, 3 Bull.—**1895a.** Notice sur les fourmis fossiles de l'ambre de la Baltique et description de deux espèces nouvelles. *Bull. Soc. Zool. France* 20: 80–84.—**1895b.** Formicides de l'Ogooué (Congo français). *Rev. Ent. France* 14: 1–5.—**1896a.** Fourmis nouvelles d'Asie et d'Australie. *Rev. Ent.* 15: 251–265.—**1896b.** *Description d'une nouvelle Fourmi de France. *Bull. Soc. Ent. France,* pp. 367–368.—**1896c.** Fourmis recueillies dans les serres du Muséum. *Bull. Mus. Hist. Nat. Paris* 1: 24.—**1898.** Description de deux nouvelles Fourmis de Mexique. *Bull. Soc. Ent. France* pp. 244–247.—**1899.** Les Fourmis champignonnistes. *Bull. Soc. Grayioise d'Emul.* 2: 271–280.—**1900.** Sur le femelle de l'Anomma nigricans Ill. *Bull. Mus. Hist. Nat.* pp. 364–368.—**1902.** Description de deux nouvelles Fourmis du Pérou. *Bull. Soc. Ent. France* pp. 14–17.—**1903a.** Description d'une nouvelle espèce de Dorymyrmex et tableau dichotomique des ouvrières de ce genre. *Zeitschr. Syst. Hymenopt. Dipt.* 3: 364–365.—**1903b.** Hyménoptères Formicides, récoltés au Japon par M. J. Harmand. *Bull. Mus. Hist. Nat. Paris* p. 128.

Armit, W. E., 1878. Agricultural Ants. *Nature* 19: 643.

Arnold, F., 1906. Das Leben im Tierstaat. (Unsere Ameisen.) *Natur u. Haus* 14: 205–207; 216–220.

Arnold, N., 1881. *Paxylloma Cremieri Breb. *Horæ Soc. Ent. Ross.* 16: 146–149.

Ashmead, W. H., 1890. On the Hymenoptera of Colorado. *Bull. Col. Biol. Ass.* 1: 1–47.—**1893.** *A Monograph of the North American Proctotrupidæ. *Bull. U. S. Nat. Mus.* 45: 1–472, 18 pls.—**1896.** The Phylogeny of the Hymenoptera. *Proc. Ent. Soc. Washington* 3, 5: 323–336.—**1900.** *Report upon the Aculeate Hymenoptera of the Islands of St. Vincent and Grenada, with additions to the Parasitic Hymenoptera and a List of the Described Hymenoptera of the West Indies. *Trans. Ent. Soc. Lond.* Part 2 (July): 207–367.—**1904.** Descriptions of New Genera and Species of Hymenoptera from the Philippine Islands. *Proc. U. S. Nat. Mus.* 28: 127–158. — **1905a.** Additions to the Recorded Hymenopterous Fauna of the Philippine Islands, with Descriptions of New Species. *Ibid.* 28: 957–971. — **1905b.** New Hymenoptera from the Philippines. *Ibid.* 29: 107–119. — **1905c.** A Skeleton of a New Arrangement of the Families, Subfamilies, Tribes and Genera of the Ants, or the Superfamily Formicoidea. *Canad. Ent.* 37: 381–384. — **1906.** Classification of the Foraging and Driver Ants, or Family Dorylidæ with description of the Genus Ctenopyga Ashm. *Proc. Ent. Soc. Washington* 8: 21–31, 1 fig.

Assmuth, J., 1907. *Einige Notizen über Prenolepis longicornis Latr. *Zeitschr. Wiss. Insekt.-biol.* 3, 10–12: 301–309; 328–334; 357–368.

Atkinson, E. T., 1890. *Catalogue of the Family Paussidæ. (Cat. of the Insecta of the Oriental Region No. 6. Coleoptera.) *Journ. Asiat. Soc. Bengal* 59, 2, suppl. nos. 1 and 2: 156–163.

Atkinson, G. F., 1886. *Descriptions of some new Trap-door Spiders, their nests and food habits. *Ent. Amer.* 2, 6–8. — **1887.** Singular Adaptation in Nest-making by an Ant, Cremastogaster lineolata Say. *Amer. Nat.* 21: 770; 771, pl. 26.

Aubé, C., 1833a. *Pselaphorum Monographia. *Magaz. Zool. de Guérin* 78–94. — **1833b.** *Note sur la famille des Psélaphiens. *Ann. Soc. Ent. France* 2: 502. — **1837.** *Essai sur le genre Monotoma. *Ibid.* 453–469.

Audouin, J. V., 1825-27. Explication sommaire des planches d'insectes de l'ouvrage de la commission d'Egypte (*Voy. Savigny*).

Aurivillius, C., 1884. *(On the occurrence of pupæ of Lycæna argus in nests of Lasius niger). *Ent. Tidskr.* 5: 190–227. — **1887.** *Ytterligare om Lycænidernas Larver och Myrorna. *Ibid.* 8: 63–65.

Azam, C., 1884. *(Observations on Amorphocephalus Coronatus.) *Soc. d'Études Scient. Archéol. Dragnignan.* Séance du 26 Mai. **1893.** *(Notes on Amorphocephalus Coronatus with "Lasius niger.") *Bull. Soc. Ent. France* 62: xi.

Axmann, A., 1895. Vorbeugungsmittel gegen die Beschädigungen durch Lasius flavus Latr. *Zentralbl. ges. Forstwesen* 21: 249–252.

BACH, M., 1851. *Ueber Ameisen und ihre Gäste. *Stett. Ent. Zeitg.* 12: 303–304. — **1859a.** *Der Keulenkäfer, ein Hausgenosse der Ameisen. *Natur u. Offenbar.* 5: 385–389; *Studien u. Lesefrüchte* 1, 5: 215–222. — **1859b.** *Ueber gewisse Veränderungen und Auswüchse an verschiedenen Pflanzentheilen, welche durch den Einfluss der Insecten bewirkt werden (pp. 250–263); die Ameisen (pp. 363–372; 385–394); die Wespen (pp. 446–452); die Hummeln (pp. 452–454); Kann man Insecten auch abrichten und zähmen? (pp. 505–510) *Natur u. Offenbar.* 5. — **1867.** *Ameisenkolonien. *Ibid.* 13: 110–116; *Studien u. Lesefrüchte* 4: 194–202.

Bachmetjew, P., 1896. Eine Episode aus dem Leben der Ameisen. *Soc. Ent.* 11: 25–26.

Bacon, F., 1623. De Dignitate et Argumentis Scientiarum. 5, 2.

Baer, G. A., 1903. *Note sur un Membracide myrmécophile de la Republique Argentine. *Bull. Soc. Ent. France* pp. 306–308.

von Baerensprung, F., 1857. *Myrmedobia und Lichenobia, zwei neue einheimische Rhynchotengattungen. *Berl. Ent. Zeitschr.* pp. 161–168.

Bagnall, R. S., 1906. Formicoxenus nitidulus, Nyl. ♂, as British. *Ent. M. Mag.* (2) 17: 210.

Ball, W. P., 1894. Neuter insects and Lamarckism. *Nat. Sci.* 4: 91–97.

Ballerstedt, M., 1904. Zurückziehung einer Ameisenkolonie durch den Mutterstaat. *Nat. Wochenschr.* 19: 824–825.

Banks, Charles S., 1906. Problems in Economic Entomology in the Philippines. *Philip. Journ. Sc.* 1: 1067-1074.

Banks, N., 1891. *Mimicry in Spiders. *Proc. Ent. Soc. Wash.* 2, 2: 174.— **1895.** *A list of the Spiders of Long Island, N. Y., with Descriptions of New Species. *Journ. N. Y. Ent. Soc.* 3: 76-93.— **1898.** *Three Myrmecophilous Mites. *Canad. Ent.* 30: 265-266.

Barboteau, 1776-'77. Essai sur la Fourmi. *Journ. Phys.* 8: 383-395; 9: 21-36; 88-96.

Bargagli, P., 1870. Escurcione entomologische sulla montagna di Cetona (Toscana). *Boll. Soc. Ent. Ital.* 2: 171-178.— **1893.** Notizie intorno alle abitazioni della Formica rufa L. *Ibid.* 25: 42-45.

Barker, E. E., 1903. The Bull-ants of Victoria. *Victorian Natural.* 20: 104-111.

Barlow, E., 1899. Notes on Insect Pests from the Entomological Section, Indian Museum. *Indian Mus. Notes* 4: 118-142; 180-221, 3 pls., 3 figg.— **1900.** Id. *Ibid.* 5: 14-34; 39-54, 1 pl.

Bates, H. W., 1892. The Naturalist on the River Amazon. *Ed. by Clodd, London.*

Baudoin, M. (*recte* Baudouin?), 1898. L'emploi des fourmis en médecine opératoire. *Rev. Scient. Bourbonn.* pp. 252-253.

Beard, J. C., 1901. Some New Features in Ant Life. *Scient. Amer.* 84: 265-266, 5 figg.

Beccari, O. *Piante ospitatrici ossia piante formicarie della Malesia et della Papuasia. *Malesia* 2.

Bedel, L., 1872. *(Capture of Trichonyx sulcicollis in the environs of Paris.) *Ann. Soc. Ent. France* p. 51.— **1881.** *(Note on Eroticoris rufescens in the environs of Paris.) *Ibid.* (6) 1: cxlvi.— **1884.** *(A new species of Claviger.) *Ibid.* (6) 4: 124.— **1885.** *(Description of a new Cerambycid from the eastern coast of Algiers.) *Ibid.* (6) 5: 131.— **1899.** *Un nouvel Histéride myrmécophile, des Basses-Alpes. *Bull. Soc. Ent. France* pp. 183-184.

Bedot, Maurice, 1907. Fourmis de Tunisie capturées en 1906, par F. Santschi. *Rev. Suisse Zool.* 15, 2, 7 figg.

Beeker, H., 1893. Geschmacksinn der Ameisen. *21 Jahrb. Westfäl. Prov. Ver.*

Bellevoye, A., 1870. *Note sur quelques Hémiptères myrmécophiles. *Pet. Nouv. Ent.* 16: 62.

Bellevoye, M. A., 1888-'90. (Observations on Monomorium Pharaonis Latr. domestica Schenck.) *Ann. Soc. Ent. France* (6) 8, Bull. pp. clxxvii-clxxxi. Transl. and condensed in *Insect Life* 2: 230-233.

Belon, M.-J., 1881. *Histoire Naturelle des Coléoptères de France. (Mulsant, etc.) Lathridiens. *Lyon.*— **1890-'91.** *Viaggio di Leonardo Fea in Birmania e regione vicine 38. Lathridiidæ. *Ann. Mus. Civ. Stor. Nat. Genova* 30: 877-880.

Belon, 1896. *Sur la place systématique du genre Belonilla Wasm. *Rev. Ent.* 15: 266-268.

Belt, T., 1874. *The Naturalist in Nicaragua. *London.*

Benson, W. H., 1846. *Description of four new species of the Coleopterous Family Paussidæ, and a notice of a fifth species, forming the type of a new genus. *Calcutta Journ. Nat. Hist.* 6, 24: 459-470.— **1847-'49.** *Notes on the capture of Paussi, at the Cape of Good Hope. *Trans. Ent. Soc. London* (1) 5: 30.

Berg, Carlos, 1881. Formicidæ de la Expedicion al Rio Negro. *Informe Oficial de la Comision Cientif.,* etc., 1., Zool. *Buenos Ayres.*— **1890.** Enumeración sistematica de los Formicidos Argentinos, Chilenos y Uruguayos. *Buenos Ayres Estr. Soc. Cient. Argent.* 29: 5-43.

Bergroth, E., 1892a. *On an Indian Ant-mimicking Hemipteron (Dulichius Wroughtoni n. sp.). *Ent. M. Mag.* (2) 3: 107.— **1892b.** Note on Dulichius

Wroughtoni (inflatus Kirby). *Ibid.* (2) 3: 126. — 1903. *Neue myrme-cophile Hemipteren. · *Wien. Ent. Zeitg.* 22: 253–256.

Berlese, A., 1881. *Indagini sulle metamorfosi di alcuni Acari insetticoli. *Atti. R. Ist. Venet. Sc. Lett. ed Arti.* — 1882-'92. *Acari Myriopoda et Scorpiones hucusque in Italia reperta. Ordo Mesostigmata (Gamasidæ) *Patavii.* — 1899-'01. Osservazioni su fenomeni che avvengono durante la ninfosi degli insetti metabolici. *Riv. di Patologia Vegetale* 8; 9; 10 — 1900. Considerazioni sulla fagocitosi negli Insetti metabolici. *Zool. Anzeig.* 23: 441–449. — 1901. Vorgänge, welche während der Nymphosis d. metabolischen Insecten vorkommen. *Ibid.* 24: 515–521. — 1904. *Illustrazione iconografica degli Acari mirmecofili. *Redia* 2, 2: 299–474, 14 pls.

Bertkau, P., 1899. *Ueber die Larven von Microdon. *Sitzgbr. Niederrhein. Gesell. Nat. Heilk.* p. 58.

Bethe, A., 1898. Dürfen wir den Ameisen und Bienen psychische Qualitäten zuschreiben. *Arch. Gesam. Physiol.* 70: 15–100, pls. 1 and 2, 5 text-figg. — 1900. Noch einmal über die psychischen Qualitäten der Ameisen. *Ibid.* 79, 1 and 2: 39–52. — 1902. Die Heimkehrfähigkeit der Ameisen und Bienen, zum Teil nach neuen Versuchen. *Biol. Centralb.* 22: 193–215, 234–238.

Bethune, C. J. S., 1877. Insects of the Northern Parts of British America. Compiled from Kirby's Fauna Boreali-Americana: Insecta, Fam. Formicidæ. *Canad. Ent.* 9: 151. — 1881. Ants. *Eleventh Ann. Report Ent. Soc. Ontario, 1880, Toronto* pp. 76–89. — 1901. *Caterpillars attended by Ants (editorial). *Canad. Ent.* 33: 279–280.

Beyer, O. W., 1890. Der Giftapparat von Formica rufa, ein reduziertes Organ. *Jen. Zeitschr. Naturwiss.* 25: 26–112, pls. 3, 4.

Bickford, E. E., 1895. Ueber die Morphologie und Physiologie der Ovarien der Ameisen-Arbeiterinnen. *Zool. Jahrb. Abth. Syst.* 9: 1–26, pls. 1 and 2.

Bignell, G. C., 1881. Lasius mixtus Nyl., an Ant new to Britain. *Entomologist* 14: 11. — 1892. Myrmica ruginodis making war on its own species. *Ent. M. Mag.* (2) 3: 135. — 1894. Formica rufa strengthening its nest by taking workers from other nests. *Ibid.* (2) 5: 267. — 1895. Prenolepis vividula, an introduced Ant new to Britain. *Ibid.* (2) 6: 6. — 1901. Corsican Ants, etc. *Ibid.* (2) 12: 8.

Bilberg, 1690. Dissertatio historialis de formicis. *Resp. J. Hammarus.* Upsala.

Billups, T. R., 1887. (Tapinoma melanocephalum in Kew Gardens.) *Trans. Ent. Soc. London* p. 27.

Bingham, C. T., 1899. Note on Diacamma, a Ponerine Genus of Ants, and of the Finding of a Female of D. vagans Smith. *Journ. Bombay Nat. Hist. Soc.* 12: 756–757. — 1903. The Fauna of British India, including Ceylon and Burma. Published under the authority of the Secretary of State for India in Council. Hymenoptera. II. Ants and Cuckoo-Wasps. *London* 19, 506 pp., 1 pl., 161 figg. — 1906. A Plague of Ants in the Observatory District, Cape Town, South Africa. *Trans. Ent. Soc. London* pp. xxiii–xxvi. — 1907. *The Fauna of British India, including Ceylon and Burma. Butterflies 2. *London, Taylor & Francis.*

Biró, L., 1885a. Hangya-háború. *Rovartani Lapok.* 2, 4: 81. — 1885b. Bataille des Fourmis. Suppl. contenant la revue des articles dans les Rovartani Lapok. 2: 14. — 1897a. Pattogó hangyák — Springende Ameisen. *Rovart. Lap.* 4: 73–74. — 1897b. Biologische Mittheilungen aus Neu-Guinea. 3 Springende Ameisen. *Berl. Ent. Zeitschr.* 42: 136, 137.

Blake, J., 1873. On the structure of the Honey-bag in the Honey-making Ant Myrmecocystus Mexicanus. *Proc. Calif. Acad. Sc.* Pt. 2: 98.

Blanford, Fotheringham and Lewis, 1882. (Sound-producing Ants.) *Nature* 25: 32; 266.

Blochmann, F., 1884. Ueber eine Metamorphose der Kerne in den Ovarialeiern und über den Beginn der Blastodermbildung bei den Ameisen. *Verh. Ver. Heidelb.* (2) 3: 243–247. — **1885.** Ueber die Gründung neuer Nester bei Camponotus ligniperdus Latr. und anderen einheimischen Ameisen. *Zeitschr. Wiss. Zool.* 41: 719–727. — **1886.** Ueber die Reifung der Eier bei Ameisen und Wespen. *Festschr. Ruperto-Carola Heidelb. Naturhist.* pp. 143–170, pl.

Blochs, D., 1776. Beitrag zur Naturgeschichte des Kopals. *Beschäft. Berlin Gesell. Naturf. Freunde.* 2: 91–196, pls. 3–5.

Le Blond, 1793. Kurze Beschreibung verschiedener neuen oder wenig bekannten Thiere welche Herr Le Blond der naturforschenden Gesellschaft zu Paris aus Cayenne als Geschenk überschickt hat. In *Reich. Mag. Thierreichs* 1: 128–134. *Erlangen.*

Boerner, I. C. H., 1774. Naturgeschichte der Ameisen. *Boerner Samuel* 1: 179–196.

Boethius, J., 1763. Försökt medel at afhålla Myror ifrån Bi stockar och Träd. *Vetensk. Acad. Handl.* 25: 32–34. German trans. **1766.** 25: 34–36. *Füessy Neu Magaz.* 3: 52–53.

Boheman, C. H., 1844. *Om insecter som lefva bland Myror. Öfvers K. Sv. Vet.-Akad. Förh.* pp. 155 seq. — **1850.** *Scydmaenii, Pselaphii och Clavigeri, fauna i Sverige. Ibid.* 10.

Bolívar, Ignacio, 1901. *Un neuvo ortóptera mirmecófile Attaphila bergi. Com. Mus. Nac. Buenos Ayres* 1: 331–336, 1 pl.

Bonatelli F., 1897. Il ponte volante delle formiche. *Atti Ist. Veneto Sc. Lett. Arti* 54: 930–931. *Boll. Natural. Siena* 17: 8–9.

Bonnet, C., 1779–'83. Observations sur de petites Fourmis qui s'etoient établies dans la tête d'un chardon à bonnetier. *Oeuvres d'Histoire Naturelle et de Philosophie.* Neuchâtel, I: 523.

Bos, H., 1886. Bijdrage tot de Kennis von den lichaamsbouw der roode boschmier, Formica rufa L. mang. diss. 111 pp. 2 pls. *Groningen* 1885. — **1887.** Iets over de nederlandsche Mierenfauna. *Tijdschr. Ent.* 30: 181–198. — **1888a.** Waarenmingen omtrent mieres. *Nederl. Ent. Verien.* 30, 2: cviii–cx. — **1888b.** *Mieren en Bladluizen. Tijdschr. Ent.* 31: 235–244. — **1893.** Een nest van Lasius fuliginosus. *Ibid.* 36: 230–239, pl. 7.

Bos, J. R., 1893. Die Pharao-Ameise (Monomorium pharaonis). *Biol. Centralb.* 13: 244–255.

Bosc d'Antic, Louis Aug. Guil, 1813. Rapport sur l'ouvrage de Huber fils intitulé: Recherches sur les mœurs de Fourmis indigènes. *Journ. Phys.* p. 14.

Bostock, J. A., 1837. On the Domestic Habits of a minute species of Ant. *Trans. Ent. Soc. London* (1) 2: 65–67.

Bothe, H., 1901. Aus dem Leben der Ameisen. *Neudamm.*

Bourgeois, J., 1904. L'origine des fourmillières, état actuel de la question d'après les communications faites au congrès international de zoologie tenu à Berne en août 1904. *Bull. Soc. Hist. Nat. Colmar,* N. S., 7: 121–127.

Bower, F. O., 1887. *On Humboldtia laurifolia as a Myrmecophilous plant. Proc. Phil. Soc. Glasg.* 18: 320–326, pl. 10.

Boyes, W. J. E., 1843. *Extract from a note-book regarding the genus Paussus. Journ. Asiat. Soc. Bengal.* (2) 1: 421–437, 4 pls.

Brandes, G., 1893. *Die Blattläuse und der Honigthau. Zeitschr. Naturw.* 66: 98–103. — **1898.** Der Intellect der Ameisen. *Ibid.* 71: 238–241, 1 fig.

Brandicourt, V., 1902. *Pucerons et fourmis. La Nature* 30, 2: 202.

Branner, J. C., 1900. Ants as Geologic Agents in the Tropics. *Journ. Geol. Chicago* 8: 151–152, 3 figs.

Braselmann, J. E., 1845. *Ueber das Vorkommen und die Verwandlung der Larven von Cetonia aurata. Verh. Nat. Ver. Rheinl. Westf.* 2: 38–41.

Brauns, J., 1901. Ueber die Lebensweise von Dorylus und Ænictus. *Zeitschr. Syst. Hymenopt. Dipter.* 1: 14–17. — **1903.** Ueber das Weibchen von Dorylus (Rhogmus) fimbriatus Shuck. *Ibid.* 3: 294–298, 4 figg.

Breddin, G., 1904. *Rhynchoten aus Ameisen-und Termitenbauten. *Ann. Soc. Ent. Belg.* 48: 407–416, 1 fig.

Brendel, E., and H. F. Wickham, 1890. *The Pselaphidæ of North America. (Part II) *Bull. Lab. Nat. Hist. Iowa* 2, 1: 1–84.

Brenske, E., and E. Reitter, 1884. *Neuer Beitrag zur Käferfauna Griechenlands. *Deutsch. Ent. Ztschr.* 28: 17–100.

Brent, C., 1886. *Notes on the Œcodomas, or Leaf-cutting Ants of Trinidad. 7 cuts. *Am. Nat.* 20, 2: 123–131. Extr. *Naturforsch.* 19, 23: 237–239.

Brinkmann, A., 1890. *Ueber die Ameisengäste (Myrmekophilen). *Verh. Gesell. Naturf. Aerzte Leipzig,* 63, 2: 154–159.

Brisout de Barneville, C., 1860. *Coléoptères nouveaux. *Ann. Soc. Ent. France* pp. 335–350. — **1880.** *Descriptions de Coléoptères nouveaux d'Europe. *Ibid.* pp. 230–235.

Britton, W. E., 1906. Fifth Report of the State Entomologist of Connecticut. *Rep. Conn. Agri. Exper. Stat.* 1905, 4: 189–262, 12 pls., 6 figg.

Britton and Forbes, 1875–'80. *(Pheidole javana Mazo? Galleries in Myrmecodia). *Proc. Linn. Soc.* p. 53.

Brodie, R. P., 1895. Tertiary fossil ants in the Isle of Wight. *Nature* 52: 570.

Brues, C. T., 1901. *Two New Myrmecophilous Genera of Aberrant Phoridæ from Texas. *Amer. Nat.* 35: 337–356. — **1902a.** *Two New Texan Ant and Termite Guests. *Ent. News* p. 184. — **1902b.** *New and little-known Guests of the Texan Legionary Ants. *Amer. Natur.* 36: 365–378. — **1903a.** *Description of new ant-like and myrmecophilous Hymenoptera. *Trans. Am. Ent. Soc.* 29: 119–128, pl. 1. — **1903b.** *Notes on some California Myrmecophiles. *Ent. News* 14: 147–149. — **1903c.** *The structure and significance of vestigial wings among insects. *Biol. Bull.* 4: 179–190. — **1903d.** *A Monograph of the North American Phoridæ. *Trans. Am. Ent. Soc.* 29: 331–404, pls. 5–9. — **1906.** *Genera Insectorum, Phoridæ p. 22, 2 pls. — **1907.** *On the Phorid Genera Plastophora and Pseudacteon. *Ent. News* 18, 10: 430.

Brullé, A., 1836. Expédition scientifique de Morée. Section des Sciences physiques 3, 1 (Insectes): 326. — **1839.** Animaux articulés recueillis aux iles Canaries, par MM. Webb et Berthelot. *Paris.*

Brunner von Wattenwyl, C., 1883. *Ueber hypertelische Nachahmungen bei den Orthopteren. *Verh. Zool. Bot. Gesell.* 33: 247–249, pl. 15.

Bruner, L., 1884. *Two new Myrmecophilæ from the United States. *Canad. Ent.* 16, 3 (March): 41–43, fig.

Bruyant, C., 1890. Les Fourmis de la France Centrale. *Soc. d'Edit. Sci., Paris,* 60 pp., 4 pls.

Bryan, G. H., 1899. Harvesting Ants. *Nature* 60: 174.

Büchner, Ludw., 1876. Aus dem Geistesleben der Tiere. *Berlin.*

Bucholz, F. H., 1782. Von der Bereitung des Ameisenäthers. *Crelle Chem. Entdeck.* 6: 55.

Buckley, S. B., 1860. *The Cutting Ant of Texas. (Œcodoma Mexicana Sm.) *Proc. Acad. Nat. Sc. Phila.* p. 233. *Ann. Mag. Nat. Hist.* (3) 6: 386–389. — **1861a.** Myrmica (Atta) molefaciens, "Stinging Ant" or "Mound-making Ant" of Texas. *Proc. Acad. Nat. Sc. Phila.* (1860) pp. 445–447. — **1861b.** Note on Ants in Texas. *Ibid.* p. 10. — **1866–'67.** Descriptions of New Species of North American Formicidæ. *Proc. Ent. Soc. Phila.* 6: 152–172; 7: 335–350.

Buckton, G. B., 1881–'83. *Monograph of British Aphidæ. 3 and 4.

Budde-Lund, G., 1885. *Crustacea Isopoda Terrestria Hafniæ.

Bünemann, J. L., 1754. Beantwortung der Fragen betreffend Mittel gegen Ameisen, Heimchen und Holzwürmer. *Hannöv. Gel. Anzeig.* 4: 1417–1420.

Burbridge and Masters, 1875–'80. *(Black ant visiting pitcher plants in Borneo for the sake of entrapped insects.) *Proc. Linn. Soc.* p. 53.

Burrill, A. C., 1908. *A Slave-making Foray of the Shining Amazon (Polyergus lucidus Mayr). Jour. N. Y. Ent. Soc.* 16, 3: 144–151.

Buscaglioni, L., and J. Huber, 1900. *Eine neue Theorie der Ameisenpflanzen. Bot. Centralb.* 9, 2.

Büsgen, M., 1891a. Der Honigtau. Biologische Studien an Pflanzen und Pflanzenläusen. *Biol. Centralb.* 11: 193–200. — **1891b.** *Der Honigtau. Biol. Studien an Pflanzen u. Pflanzenläusen. Jen. Zeitschr. Nat.* 25: 339–428, pls. 15–16. Summary. *J. R. Micr. Soc. 1892,* p. 33.

Butler, E., 1899. Two Rare Ants at Gomshall. *Ent. M. Mag.* (2) 10: 12.

von Buttel-Reepen, H., 1905a. Soziologisches und Biologisches vom Ameisen- und Bienen-Staat. Wie ensteht eine Ameisen Kolonie? *Arch. Rassen. Gesell. Biol.* 2, 1: 1–16, 1 fig. — **1905b.** Biologische und soziologische Momente aus den Insektenstaaten. *C. R. 6me Congr. Internat. Zool. Berne* pp. 462–482. — **1907.** Psychobiologische und biologische Beobachtung an Ameisen, Bienen und Wespen. *Naturwiss. Wochenschr.* 22: 465–478, 3 text.-figg.

Buxbaum, L., 1888. Das Einsammeln der Ameisenpuppen. *Zool. Garten* 29, 4: 124–126.

CABRERA, AN., 1893. Formicidos de la Laguna, Tenerife. *Anal. Soc. Espan. Hist. Nat.* 1 (XXI), 3.

Cameron, P., 1887. On a New Species of Strumigenys from Japan. *Proc. Manch. Lit. Phil. Soc.* 25: 229–232. — **1888-'89.** *Hymenoptera Orientalis; or Contributions to a Knowledge of the Hymenoptera of the Oriental Zoological Region. Mem. Proc. Manch. Lit. Phil. Soc.* 2 sess. — **1890-'91.** *Hymenopterological Notices. Ext. from id. 4 sess. — **1891.** Hymenoptera in E. Whymper's Supplementary Appendix to Travels amongst the Great Andes of the Equator. *London* 22: 147 pp. — **1892.** Synonymical Notes on Cynipidæ and Formicidæ. *Ent. Mag.* (2) 3: 67. — **1901.** On a Collection of Hymenoptera made in the Neighborhood of Wellington by Mr. G. V. Hudson, with Descriptions of New Genera and Species. *Trans. Proc. New Zealand Inst.* 33: 104–120. — **1903.** A List of the Hymenoptera of New Zealand. *Ibid.* 35: 290–299. — **1907.** Hymenopterological Notices. *Ann. Scott. Nat. Hist.* pp. 221–223.

Canestri, G., 1873. Atti della Societa Veneto-Trientina di Scienze Naturali. 1, 1: 52.

Canestrini, R., 1881. *Contribuzione allo studio degli Acari parassiti degli Insetti. Atti. Soc. Venet.-Trient. Sc. Nat.*

Carpenter, G. H., 1893. Some Recent Researches on the Habits of Ants, Bees and Wasps. *Nat. Sci.* 3: 267–272. — **1894.** Further notes upon the habits of Insects. *Ibid.* 4: 365–370.

Carpentier, L., 1881. *Chasses d'hiver dans les Fourmilières. Bull. Soc. Linn. Nord France* 5, 104: 212–214. — **1886-'88.** *Insectes myrmécophiles. Ibid.* 7: 70–78. — **1893.** *Insectes myrmécophiles. Ibid.* 11, 258: 371–377.

Carré and Soniners. Geschichte der Ameisen. *Natururkund. Verh. Amsterdam* 1–2.

Casey, T. L., 1884-'86. *New Genera and Species of California Coleoptera. Bull. Calif. Acad. Sc.* 1: 283–336. — **1886-'87.** *Descriptions of North American Coleoptera I. Ibid.* 2: 157 seq. — **1889.** *Notes on the Pæderini. Ent. Am.* 5, 9: 183–184. — **1893.** *Coleopterological Notices V. Ann. New York Ac. Sc.* 7: 281–606.

Castles, John, 1790. Observations on the Sugar Ants. *Philos. Trans.* 80: 346–358. *Voigt. Mag.* 81, 3: 90–100.

Cecconi, G., 1908. *Contributo alla Fauna delle Isole Tremiti. Boll. Mus. Zool. Anat. Comp.* 23: 53.

Chapman, T. A., 1902. *On the Larva of Liphyra brassolis Westw. *Entomologist* 35: 225–228; 252–255, pl. 4.

Charsley, R. S., 1877. Ponera tarda nov. sp. found in Britain. *Ent. M. Mag.* (1) 14: 162.

Chatin, J., 1887. Recherches Morphologiques sur les Pièces Mandibulaires, Maxillaires et Labiales des Hymenoptères. *Paris* 40 pp. 2 pl.

Chatrain, Nic., 1886. La fourmi Sauva. *Rev. Scientif.* (3) 38, 12: 371–372.

de Chaudoir, M., 1845. *Notices entomologiques sur le gouvernement et la ville de Kiew. *Bull. Soc. Imp. Nat. Moscou* 3: 158 seq.

Chevrolat, A., 1835. *Mémoire sur un Coléoptère Tétramère de la famille des Xylophages et observations sur plusieurs espèces de cet ordre rencontrées dans diverses fourmilières. *Rev. Ent. (Silbermann)* 2: 263 seq. — **1870.** *(Note on Fourmilla Chevrolatii.) *Ann. Soc. Ent. France* p. 65.

Cholodkowsky, N., 1899. Ein interessanter Ameisen-Instinkt. *Illustr. Zeitschr. Ent.* 4, 23: 363.

du Choul, J., 1556. Dialogus formicæ, muscæ, aranæi et papilionis. *Lugduni, Rovillius.*

Christ, I. L., 1791. Naturgeschichte, Klassification und Nomenclatur der Insekten vom Bienen-, Wespen- und Ameisengeschlecht. 60 pls. *Frankfurt a. M. Hermann.*

Chun, C., 1903. Aus den Tiefen des Weltmeeres. 2 *(Jena)*: 129.

Clarkson, F., 1883. Formica Sanguinea. *Canad. Ent.* 15: 217.

Clément, A. L., 1902. La destruction des fourmis. *La Nature* 30, 2: 155–158, 4 figg.

Cobelli, R., 1887. Gli Imenotteri del Trentino. Notizie preliminari. 1 Formicidæ. *Rovereto* pp. 1–10. — **1902.** Il senso del gusto nel Lasius emarginatus Oliv. *Verh. Zool.-Bot. Gesell. Wien* 52: 254–257. — **1903a.** I veleni ed il Lasius emarginatus Oliv. *Ibid.* 53: 18–21. — **1903b.** L'ibernazione delle Formiche. *Ibid.* 53: 369–380. — **1906a.** *Il Pachylomma cremieri de Romand ed il Lasius fuliginosus Latr. *Ibid.* 56: 475–477. — **1906b.** Le formiche del promontorio di Sezza (Istria). *Ibid.* 56: 477–480.

Cockerell, T. D. A., 1890. *Hetærius morsus Lec., an entomological tragedy. *Ent. M. Mag.* (2) 1: 158. — **1891a.** *Case-making Coleopterous Larvæ. *Ibid.* (2) 2: 190. — **1891b.** *The use of Ants to Aphids and Coccidæ. *Nature* 44, 1226: 608. — **1893.** The Entomology of the Mid-Alpine Zone of Custer County, Colorado. *Trans. Am. Ent. Soc.* 20: 305–370. — **1896.** Insect Pests in Madeira. *Garden and Forest* pp. 518, 519. — **1898.** *Miscellaneous Notes. *Proc. Ent. Soc. Washington* 4, 2: 64–65. Discussion pp. 65–66. — **1903.** *Five new Coccidæ from Mexico. *Entomologist* 36: 45–48. — **1904.** The Bee-genus Apista and Other Notes. *Canad. Ent.* 36: 330–331. — **1905.** *Tables for the Identification of Rocky Mountain Coccidæ (Scale Insects and Mealy bugs). *Univ. of Colorado Studies* 2, 3: 189–203. — **1906.** A New Fossil Ant. *Ent. News* 17: 27–28.

Cockerell, T. D. A., and G. B. King, 1897. *New Coccidæ Found Associated with Ants. *Canad. Ent.* 29: 90–93.

Cockerell, Mrs. W. P., 1903. *Some Aphids Associated with Ants. *Psyche* Oct.–Dec. pp. 216–218.

Collett, Edw. P., 1883. *Myrmecophilous Coleoptera in the Hastings District. *Ent. M. Mag.* (1) 20: 40.

Comstock, J. H., 1886. *Relations of Ants and Aphids. *Am. Nat.* 21, 4: 382.

Conway, C., 1834. Ants conveying in their mouths other ants of their species; Courage of the Wood or Fallow Ants (Formica rufa). *Mag. Nat. Hist.* (1) 7: 266–267.

Cook, B., 1882. Myrmica lævinodis. *Natural. Yorkshire* 8: 30.

Cook, O. F., 1904a. Report on the Habits of the Kelep, or Guatemalan Cotton-Boll-Weevil Ant. *U. S. Dept. Agric. Div. Ent. Bull.* 49: 15 pp. — **1904b.**

Professor William Morton Wheeler on the Kelep. *Science* N. S. 20: 611–612. — 1904c. An Enemy of the Cotton-Boll-Weevil. *Ibid.* 19 · 862–864. — 1904d. Pupation of the Kelep Ant. *Ibid.* 20: 310–312. — 1905. Progress in the study of the Kelep. *Ibid.* 21: 552–554.

Cooke, M. C., 1892. *Vegetable Wasps and Plant Worms. A Popular History of Entomogenous Fungi, or Fungi Parasitic upon Insects. *London and N. Y. Soc. Prom. Christ. Knowl.* pp. 31–39.

Cope, E. D., 1893. Heredity in the social colonies of the Hymenoptera. *Proc. Acad. Nat. Sc. Phila.* pp. 436–438.

Coquillett, D. W., 1903. *The Occurrence of the Phorid genus Ænigmatias in America. *Canad. Ent.* 35: 20–22. — 1907. *A New Phorid Genus with Horny Ovipositor. *Ibid.* June p. 207.

Cori, C. I., 1892. Review of Wasmann: Die zusammengesetzten Nester und gemischten Kolonien der Ameisen. *Biol. Centralb.* 12: 123–126.

Costa, A., 1888. Notizie ed osservazioni sulla Geofauna Sarda. *Mem. Sec. Atti Acc. Nap.* (2) 1, 9: 56.

Cotes, E. C., 1896. Miscellaneous Notes from the Entomological Section. *Indian Mus. Notes* 3, 6: 1–23, 50 figg.

Couper, W., 1863. *Remarks on the Tent-building Ants. *Proc. Ent. Soc. Phil.* pp. 373–374.

Coupin, H., 1897. *Les parasites des fourmis et des fourmilières. *La Nature* 25, 2: 81–83, 2 figg. — 1898. *Les plantes myrmécophiles. *Ibid.* 27: 70–74, 2 figg. — 1904. *Le monde des fourmis. *Paris,* Delagrave, 160 pp. (Rev. *Nature* 70: 29.)

Courtiller, 1863. Formica 4-maculata. *Mém. Soc. Linéenne Dép. Maine-et-Loire.*

Cresson, E. T., 1865. Catalogue of Hymenoptera in the Collection of the Entomological Society of Philadelphia from Colorado Territory. *Proc. Ent. Soc. Phila.* pp. 242–313; 426–488. — 1872. Hymenoptera Texana. *Trans. Amer. Ent. Soc.* 4: 153–292.

Crowther, H., 1878. *Clivina fossor myrmecophilous. *Ent. Month. Mag.* 15: 19.

Csiki, Ernö., 1899. *A Myrmecophile Pselaphidak. Die Myrmekophilen Pselaphiden. *Rovart. Lapok* 6: 10–12.

Cunningham, J. T., 1894. Neuter Insects and Darwinism. *Nat. Sc.* 4: 281–289.

Curtis J., 1829. Myrmica Latreillei. *Brit. Entomology* 6. — 1854. On the Genus Myrmica and other Indigenous Ants. *Trans. Linn. Soc. London* 21, 3: 211–220.

Cox, E. W., 1878. Intellect in Brutes. (On Ants.) *Nature* 20, 509: 315–316.

Czwalina, Dr., 1878. Neues aus dem Leben der Ameisen. *Schriften Phys. Oekon. Gesell. Königsberg* 17 and 18.

DAHL, FR., 1901. Das Leben der Ameisen im Bismarck-Archipel, nach eigenen Beobachtungen, etc. *Mitth. Zool. Mus. Berlin* 2, 1: 1–69, 1 pl.

Dale, C W., 1892. *On the Occurrence of Ripersia tomlini with Formica nigra in the Chesil Bank. *Ent. M. Mag.* (2) 3: 219. — 1895. *Ants and their Companions. *Entomologist* pp. 97–100.

Dale, J. C., 1834a. Ants and their Carnivorous Habits; a mode of Destroying Ants in Gardens. *Mag. Nat. Hist.* (1) 7: 268–269. — 1834b. A Battle between Ants of the Species Myrmica rubra and M. cæspitum. *Ibid.* (1) 7: 267–268.

von Dalla Torre, K. W. 1888. *Die Thysanuren Tirols. *Ztschr. Ferdin.* (3) 32: 145–161. — 1892. Hymenopterologische Notizen. *Wien. Ent. Zeitg.* 11: 89–93. — 1893. Catalogus Hymenopterorum hucusque descriptorum systematicus et synonymicus. 7 (Formicidæ): viii + 289. *Leipzig.* — 1907. Die Ameisen von Tirol und Vorarlberg. *Ent Jahrb.* 17: 170–171.

Dalla Torre, K. W., u. H. Friese, 1899. Die hermaphroditen und gynandromorphen Hymenopteren. *Ber. Naturwiss-med. Ver. Innsbruck.* 24: 3–96, 1 pl.

Daniell, G., 1852. Notice on the Habits of Myrmica domestica Schuck., together with some account of a means of turning the industry of this minute Ant to account in the preparation of Skeletons of small animals. *Linn. Soc.* 2: 172–177. *Ann. of N. H.* (2) 10: 457–461. — **1854.** Notes on the habits of the common garden ant, Formica nigra L. *Proc. Linn. Soc.* 2: 290–291.

Dankler, M., 1898. Die Ameisen. *Die Natur* 47: 259–260.

Darwin, C., 1861. On the Origin of Species by means of Natural Selection. (3d ed.) *London. John Murray.* — **1873a.** Instinct. Perception in Ants. *Nature* 7: 443–444. — **1873b.** The Habits of Ants. *Ibid.* 8: 244. — **1901.** The Life and Letters of Charles Darwin. Edited by his son Francis Darwin. 2 Vols. — **1902.** Journal of Researches into the Natural History and Geology of the Countries visited during the Voyage of H. M. S. Beagle round the World. New Ed., *New York, Appleton & Co.*

Davis, W. T., 1907. Nests of the Carpenter Ant. *Proc. Staten I. Ass. Arts and Sci.* 2: 10–12.

Day, F., 1883–'84. On the Habits of Ants. *Proc. Cheltenham Soc.* pp. 71–103.

Dedekind, J. J. W., 1778. De Remediis contra Formicas. *Litteræ ad Acad. Reg. Parisi. Helmst.*

De Geer, K., 1778. Mémoires pour servir à l'histoire des insectes 7.

Delpino, F., 1872. *Sui Rapporti delle Formiche colle Tettigometre e sulla genealogia degli Afidi e dei Coccidi. *Bull. Soc. Ent. Ital.* p. 343. — **1875.** *Altre osservazioni sui Rapporti tra Cicadelle e Formiche. *Ibid.* p. 61. — **1886.** *Funzione mirmecofila nel Regno vegetale. Prodromo d'una monografia delle piante formicarie. *Mem. Acc. Bologna* (4) F: 215–323.

Denny, H., 1825. *Monographia Pselaphidorum et Scydmænidarum Britanniæ. *Norwich.*

Devaux, F., 1892. (Widerstandsfähigkeit der Ameisen gegen das Ertrinken.) *Bull. Soc. Philom. Paris.* Ext. *Naturwiss. Rundschau.* 7, 18: 231–232.

Devaux, H., 1890. Sur quelques expériences concernant le sens du goût chez les Fourmis. *C. R. Soc. Philom. Paris.* No. 17. — **1892.** Le sens du goût chez les Fourmis. *Bull. Soc. Philom. Paris* (8) 3, 3: 159–160. (Rev. in *Naturwiss. Rundschau.* 7, 22: 284.)

Dewitz, H., 1877. Ueber Bau und Entwickelung des Stachels der Ameisen. *Zeitschr. Wiss. Zool.* 28: 527–556. — **1878a.** Beiträge zur postembryonalen Gliedmassenbildung bei den Insecten. *Ibid.* 30: suppl. pp. 78–105. — **1878b.** Ueber die Bildung der Brustgliedmassen bei den Ameisen. *Sitzb. der Gesell. Naturf. Freunde. Berlin* pp. 122–125. — **1878c.** Nachtrag zu "Beiträge zur postembryonalen Gliedmassenbildung bei den Insecten." *Zeitschr. Wiss. Zool.* 31: 25–28. — **1879.** Insectenmisbildung. *Zool. Anz.* 2: 134–136, 1 fig.

Deyeux, 1778. Sur la Dissertation de l'abbé Fontana sur l'acide formique. *Jour. Phys. de Rosier.*

Diehl, A., 1903. Die Sitten und Nester einiger Ameisen der Sahara bei Tugurt und Biskra. *Mitth. Schweiz. Ent. Gesell.* 10: 453–459.

Dilger, J. S., 1684. Rempublicam formicarum favente Divino nomine sub praesidio Joh. Andreas Schmidt explicabit Jo. Simon Dilger, Ulmensis, auctor respondens. *Jenæ, Bauhofer.* 28 pp., 1 pl.

Dodd, F. P., 1902a. *Notes on the Queensland Green Tree Ants (Œcophylla smaragdina, Fab.?). *Victorian Nat.* 18: 136–140. [Caterpillars living with them.] — Suppl. Notes pp. 141–142. — **1902b.** *Contribution to the Life History of Liphyra brassolis Westw. *Ent.* 35: 153–156. — **1906.** *Notes upon some remarkable parasitic insects from North Queensland. With an appendix containing descriptions of New Species by Col. Chas. T. Bingham and Dr. Benno Wandolleck. *Trans. Ent. Soc. London* pp. 119–132, 2 figg.

Doflein, F., 1905. Beobachtungen an den Weberameisen. (Œcophylla smaragdina.) *Biol. Centralb.* 25: 497–507, 5 figg. — **1906.** Ostasienfahrt. *Leipzig u. Berlin, Teubner.*

Doherty, W., 1886. *A List of Butterflies taken in Kumaon. Journ. Asiat. Soc. Bengal* 55, 2, 2: 103–140. — **1889.** *(Description of the singular Lycænid, Liphyra brassolis.) *Ibid.* 58: 409.

Dohrn, C. A., 1876a. *Zur Lebensweise der Paussiden. *Stett. Ent. Zeitg.* 37: 333–336. — **1876b.** *Ueber australische Paussiden. *Journ. Mus. Godeffroy* 12: 48–55. — **1886.** *Paussidische Nachreden. *Stett. Ent. Zeitg.* 47: 120 seq. — **1888.** *Passus adiuventus Dhn. *Ibid.* 49: 393. — **1891a.** *Die zusammengesetzten Nester und gemischten Kolonien der Ameisen. *Ibid.* 52: 304–351. — **1891b.** *Bengalische und Afrikanische Paussiden. *Ibid.* 52: 386–388.

Dollfus, A., 1887. *Catalogue provisoire des espèces françaises d'Isopodes terrestres. *Rennes.* — **1889.** *Crustacea Neerlandica, door P. C. Hoek. III Isopoda. *Tidjschr. Ned. Dierk. Vereen.* (2) 2: 3–4. — **1890.** *Notice sur les Isopodes terrestres de Marseille et de Salon, par I. J. Marius Aubert et Adr. Dollfus. *Soc. Ent. Sc. Paris Juillet.* — **1892.** *Catalogue raisonné des Isopodes terrestres de l'Espagne. *Ann. Soc. Españ. Hist. Nat.* 21: 161–190. — **1893.** *Voyage de M. Ch. Alluaud aux Iles Canaries. Isopodes terrestres. *Extr. Mém. Soc. Zool. France* 6: 45–56.

Dombey, J., 1777. Mémoire pour détruire les fourmis de l'île de la Martinique. *Journ. Phys.* 10: 226–228.

Dominique, J., 1900. Fourmis jardinières. *Bull. Soc. Sc. Nat. Ouest, Nantes* 10: 163–168, 3 figg.

Donisthorpe, H. S. J., 1896. *Hints on Collecting Myrmecophilous Coleoptera. *Ent. Month. Mag.* pp. 44–50. — **1897.** *Myrmecophilous Coleoptera in 1897. *Ent. Rec. Journ. Var.* 9: 246–247. — **1900a.** *Myrmecophilous Orthoptera. *Ibid.* 12: 162–163. — **1900b.** *A few notes on Myrmecophilous Coleoptera. *Ibid.* 12: 172–176. — **1900c.** *The Guests of Ants and Termites. Extracts from E. Wasmann's "Die Gäste der Ameisen und Termiten." *Ent. Rec. Journ. Var.* 12: 41–43, 72–75, 87–89, 117–119, 147–150, 204–206, 1 pl. — **1901a.** *Evolution of our Knowledge of Myrmecophilous Coleoptera. *Ibid.* 13: 51–56. — **1901b.** *On some Experiments with Myrmecophilous Coleoptera and an observation nest of Formica rufa. *Ibid.* 13; 349–353. — **1901c.** *On the Origin of, and Progress in, the Study of Myrmecophilous Coleoptera. *Trans. Leicester Lit. Phil. Soc.* 6: 1–15. — **1902.** *The Life-history of Clythra quadri-punctata, L. *Trans. Ent. Soc. London,* pp. 11–23, 1 pl. — **1903.** *Further Experiments with Myrmecophilous Coleoptera, etc. *Ibid.* 15, 1: 11–12. — **1905.** *The Myrmecophilous Coleoptera of Great Britain. *Proc. Lanc. Chesh. Ent. Soc.* pp. 1–11. — **1906.** *Dinarda pygmæa, Wasmann, a Species of Myrmecophilous Coleoptera new to Great Britain. *Ent. Rec.* 18: 2 pp. — **1906-'07.** *Myrmecophilous Notes for 1906. *Ibid.* 18: 288–289; 317–319. 19: 4–7, 1 pl. — **1907a.** *Notes on Dinarda. *Trans. Ent. Soc. London* 1906 pp. lxxi–lxxii. — **1907b.** *British Myrmecophilous Acarina. *Hastings and E. Sussex Nat.* 1, 2: 65–67. — **1908a.** *A Few Notes on Myrmecophilous Spiders. *Zoologist,* Nov.: 419–425. — **1908b.** *The Life History and Occurrence as British of Lomechusa strumosa, F. *Trans. Ent. Soc. London* pp. 415–420, 8 figg. — **1908c.** *Notes on the Life-histories of two supposed Ants'-nest Beetles. *Ent. Rec.* 20, 5: 2 pp., 1 pl. — **1908d.** Ants found in Great Britain. *Trans. Leicester Lit. Phil. Soc.* 12, 2: 221–233.

Dorthes, J. A., 1790-'92. Notice sur un Phénomène occasionné par une espèce de fourmi. *Journ. Phys.* 37: 356–358. *Opusculi scelti* 15: 317–319.

Doubleday, E., 1836. Some Scraps by the Author of the Delta Letters (Plague of Ants in St. Domingo). *Ent. Mag.* 4: 106–113. — **1843.** *Note on the Capture of Claviger foveolatus. *Zoologist* 1: 200.

Douglas, Jacob, 1728. Descriptio Musculorum Corporis Humani et Quadrupedis, accedente historia musculorum Formicæ. *Lugduni Batavorum.*

Douglas, J. W., 1859. *Ants-nest Beetles. *Ent. Weekl. Intell.* 4: 15. — **1865-'66.** *On the Occurrence of Systellonotus triguttatus in Company with Formica fusca. *Ent. M. Mag.* (1) 2: 30–31. — **1874-'75.** *On the resemblance to Ants among the Hemiptera. *Ibid.* (1) 11: 138. — **1878-'79.** *Note on Pilophorus perplexus Dougl. and Scott. *Ibid.* (1) 15: 253. — **1886.** Ants and Coccidæ. *Ibid.* (1) 23: 6. — **1891.** *Note on some British and Exotic Coccidæ (no. 21). *Ibid.* (2) 2: 244–247. — **1900.** *Dinarda dentata: a reminiscence. *Ibid.* (2) 11: 11.

Dours, A., 1874. Catalogue synonymique des Hyménoptères de France. *Amiens* 1 vol.

Drewson, Chr., 1858. Briefliche Mittheilung des Herrn J. Nietner in Rambodde (Ceylon) über eine springende Ameise. *Stett. Ent. Zeit.* 19: 445, 446.

Drury, D., 1770-'73. Illustrations of Natural History. *London.* Vols. 1 and 2.

Dublin, L. I., 1907. *Natural and Artificial Mixed Colonies of Ants. *Sci. Amer.* 97: 310–311, 1 fig.

Ducke, A., 1906. Biologische Notizen über einige südamerikanische Hymenopteren. *Zeitschr. Wiss. Insect.-biol.* 2: 17–21.

Dudgeon, G. C., 1896. *Note on Virachola perse Hewitson, a Lycænid Butterfly. *Journ. Bombay Nat. Hist. Soc.* 10: 333–334.

Dufour, H., et Aug. Forel, 1902. La sensibilité des Fourmis à l'action de la lumière ultraviolette et à celle des rayons Röntgen. *Arch. Sc. Phys. Nat.* (4) 14: 558–559.

Dufour, L., 1856. Note sur la Formica barbara. *Ann. Soc. Ent. France* (3) 4: 341–343. — **1857.** Mélanges Entomologiques. III sur la Micromyrmica pygmæa, nouveau genre de Formicides. *Ibid.* (3) 5: 60–64. — **1862.** Note sur la Formica savignyi. *Ibid.* (4) 2: 141.

Dupuis, J., 1824. Journal of a Residence in Ashantee. *London.* (*Froriep's Notiz* 8: 245–246.)

EBNERUS, E., 1541. Encomium formicarum. *Amphitheatrum Dornavii* 1.

Ebrard, E., 1861. Nouvelles Observations sur les Fourmis. *Biblioth. Univ. Rev. Suisse. Genève,* Juillet p. 466.

Eckstein, K., 1905. Giftige Tiere. *Aus der Natur* 1: 33–36, 73–81, 1 pl., 14 figg.

Edwards, C. L., 1896. *Notes on the Biology of Phrynosoma cornutum Harlan. *Zool. Anz.* 498: 4.

Edwards, H., 1873a. Notes on the Honey-making Ant of Texas and New Mexico. *Am. Nat.* 7: 722–726, 1 fig. — **1873b.** Notes on the Honey-making Ant of Texas and New Mexico, Myrmecocystus Mexicanus of Westwood. *Proc. Calif. Acad. Sc.* 5: 72–75, 1 fig.

Edwards, W. H., 1878a. *Notes on Lycæna pseudargiolus and its larval history. *Canad. Ent.* 10: 1–14. — **1878b.** *On the Larvæ of Lycæna pseudargiolus and attendant Ants. *Ibid.* 10: 131–136, 1 fig. — **1884.** *The Butterflies of North America. 2. 12 *Boston.*

Elditt, H. L., 1845. *Beiträge zur Verwandlungsgeschichte von Microdon mutabilis L. *Stett. Ent. Zeitg.* 6: 384–390. — **1847.** *Die Ameisenkolonien und deren Mitbewohner. *Physik. Œkon. Gesell. Königsberg* 1: 353. — **1862-'63.** *Myrmecophila acervorum Panz; ein für die preussische Insektenfauna neues Thier. *Schrift. Physik. Œkon. Gesell. Königsberg* 3 (1862): 193–194. *Stett. Ent. Zeitg.* 24 (1863): 366–368.

Emery, C., 1869a. *Enumerazione dei Formicidi che rinvengonsi nei contorni di Napoli, con descrizioni di Specie nuove o meno conosciute. *Ann. Acad. Aspir. Nat.* — **1869b.** Formicidarum Italicorum Species Duæ Novæ. *Bull. Soc. Ent. Ital.* 1. — **1869c.** Genus Bothriomyrmex. *Ann. Mus. Zool. R. Univ. Napoli* 5: 117. — **1870.** Studi Myrmecologici. *Bull. Soc. Ent. Ital.*

2. — **1875a.** *Le Formiche Ipogee con descrizioni di Sp. nuove o poco note. Ann. Mus. Civ. Stor. Nat. Genova* 7: 465. — **1875b.** *Aggiunta alla Nota sulle Formiche Ipogee. Ibid.* 7: 895. — **1877a.** Saggio di un ordinamento naturale dei Myrmicidei e Considerazioni sulla filogenesi delle Formiche. *Boll. Soc. Ent. Ital.* 9: 17 pp., 1 pl. — **1877b.** Catalogo delle Formiche del Museo Civico di Genova. I Mar Rosso e Bogos. *Ann. Mus. Civ. Stor. Nat. Genova* 9: 363. — **1878a.** Catalogo delle Formiche del Museo Civico di Genova. II. Europa e regioni limitrofe in Africa e in Asia. *Ibid.* 12: 43. — **1878b.** Liste des Fourmis de la Collection de feu Camille Van Volxem, avec la description d'une espèce nouvelle. *C. R. Soc. Ent. Belg.* Séance du 5 janv. — **1880.** Crociera del Violante, comandato dal capitano armatore Enrico d'Albertis durante l'anno 1877. Formiche. *Ann. Mus. Civ. Stor. Nat. Genova* 15: 389–398. — **1881a.** Spedizione Italiana nell' Africa equatoriale. Risultati Zoologici; Formiche. *Ibid.* 16: 270. — **1881b.** Viaggio ad Assab nel Mar Rosso, dei Signori G. Doria ed O. Beccari con il R. Aviso "Esploratore" dal 16 novembre 1879 al 26 febbraio 1880. Formiche. *Ibid.* 16: 525. — **1883a.** Alcune Formiche della Nuova Caledonia. *Bull. Soc. Ent. Ital.* 15: 145–151. — **1883b.** Formiche del Crociero dell'Jacht "Corsaro" del Cap. arm. E. d'Albertis. II *Ann. Mus. Civ. Stor. Nat. Genova* 18. — **1884a.** Rassegna delle Formiche della Tunisia. *Ibid.* (2) 1. — **1884b.** Materiali per lo studio della Fauna Tunisina raccolti da G. e L. Doria. III Rassegna dell Formiche della Tunisia. *Ibid.* (2) 1: 373–386. — **1886a.** *Mimetismo e costumi parassitari del Camponotus lateralis Ol. Bull. Ent. Ital.* pp. 412–413. — **1886b.** Alcune formiche africane descritte da C. Emery. *Ibid.* 18: 355–356, pl. 17. — **1886c.** Ueber dimorphe und flügellose Männchen bei Hymenopteren. *Biol. Centralb.* 5: 686–689. — **1887a.** Formiche della provincia di Rio Grande do Sul nel Brasile, raccolti dal dott. Hermann von Ihering. *Bull. Ent. Ital.* 19: 352–366. — **1887b.** Catalogo delle Formiche esistenti nelle collezioni del Museo Civico di Genova. Parte III. Formiche della regione Indo-Malese e dell'Australia. *Ann. Mus. Civ. Stor. Nat. Genova* (2) 4: 209–258, pls. 3, 4; 5: 427–473 and 528–534, pls. 1, 2 and 9. — **1887c.** Le tre forme sessuali del Dorylus helvolus L. e degli altri Dorilidi. *Bull. Soc. Ent. Ital.* 19: 344–351, pl. 40. — **1888a.** Alcune Formiche della Republica Argentina raccolte dal Dott. C. Spegazzini, *Ann. Mus. Civ. Stor. Nat. Genova* (2) 6. — **1888b.** Catalogo delle Formiche esistenti nelle Collezioni del Museo Civico di Genova. Parte III (Supplemento). *Ibid.* (2) 5, 2: 7, pl. 9. — **1888c.** Ueber den sogenannten Kaumagen einiger Ameisen. *Zeitsch. Wiss. Zool.* 46: 378–412, pls. 27–29. — **1889a.** Intorno ad alcune Formiche della fauna palearctica. *Ann. Mus. Civ. Stor. Nat. Genova* (2) 7 (27): 485–520. — **1889b.** *Ueber myrmekophile Insekten. Biol. Centralb.* 9: 23–28 — **1890a.** Alcune considerazioni sulla Fauna mirmecologica dell' Africa. *Bull. Soc. Ent. Ital.* 21: 3/4: 69–75. — **1890b.** Formiche di Birmania e del Tennasserim raccolte da Leonardo Fea (1885–'87). *Ann. Mus. Civ. Stor. Nat. Genova* (2) 7: 485–520, pls. 10, 11. — **1890c.** Studi sulle Formiche della Fauna Neotropica. *Bull. Ent. Soc. Ital.* 22: 38–40, pls. 5–9. — **1890d.** Voyage de M. E. Simon au Venezuela. Formicides. *Ann. Soc. Ent. France* (6) 10. 55–76. — **1891a.** Note sinonomiche sulle Formiche. *Bull. Soc. Ent. Ital.* 23: 159–167. — **1891b.** Révision critique des Fourmis de la Tunisie. *Paris.* — **1891c.** Voyage de M. Ch. Alluaud dans le territoire d'Assinie. Formicides. *Ann. Soc. Ent. France* 60: 553–574, pl. 15. — **1891d.** Zur Biologie der Ameisen. *Biol. Centralb.* 11: 165–180. — **1891e.** Le Formiche dell'ambra siciliana nel museo mineralogico dell'Università di Bologna. *Mem. R. Acc. Sc. Ist. Bologna* (5) 1: 141–165, pls. 1–3. — **1892a.** *Aelteres über Ameisen in Dornen afrikanischer Akazien. Zool. Anz.* 15, 394: 237. — **1892b.** Cremasto-

gaster striatulus n. sp. *Bull. Soc. Ent. France* 41 : liii. — **1892c.** Diagnoses de cinq nouveaux genres de Formicides. *Ibid.* 41 (1893) : cclxxv–cclxxvii. **1892d.** Origine de la faune actuelle des fourmis d'Europe. *Bull. Soc. Vaud. Sc. Nat.* (3) *27,* 105 : 258–260. — **1892e.** Révision critique des Fourmis de la Tunisie. Exploration scientifique de la Tunisie. Hyménoptères. I, II : 1–21. — **1892f.** Sopra alcune Formiche raccolte dall'Ingegnere L. Bricchetti Robecchi nel paese dei Somali. *Ann. Mus. Civ. Stor. Nat. Genova* (2) 12 : 110–122. — **1893a.** Formicides de l'archipel malais. *Rev. Suisse Zool.* 1 : 187–229, pl. 8. — **1893b.** Intorno ad alcune Formiche della Collezione Spinola. *Boll. Mus. Zool. Anat. Comp. R. Univ. Torino* 8, 163 : 3 pp. — **1893c.** Notice sur quelques Fourmis des îles Galapagos. *Ann. Soc. Ent. France* pp. 89–92. — **1893d.** Voyage de M. Ch. Alluaud aux îles Canaries. Formicides. *Ibid.* pp. 81–88. — **1893e.** Voyage de M. E. Simon à l'île de Ceylon. Formicides. *Ibid.* pp. 239–258. — **1893f.** Voyage de M. E. Simon aux îles Philippines. *Ibid.* pp. 259–270, pl. 6. — **1893g.** Intelligenz und Instinkt der Tiere. *Biol. Centralb.* 13 : 151–153. — **1893h.** Zirpende und springende Ameisen. *Ibid.* 13 : 189, 190. — **1893–'94.** Beiträge zur Kenntniss der nordamerikanischen Ameisenfauna. *Zool. Jahrb. Abth. Syst.* 7 : 633–682, pl. 22; 8 : 257–360, pl. 8. — **1894a.** Die Entstehung und Ausbildung des Arbeiterstandes bei den Ameisen. *Biol. Centralb.* 14 : 53–59. — **1894b.** Camponotus sexguttatus Fab. e C. sexguttatus Sm. et Auct. *Boll. Mus. Zool. Anat. Comp. R. Univ. Torino* 9, 187 : 1–4. — **1894c.** Descriptions de deux fourmis nouvelles. *Ann. Soc. Ent. France* 63 : 72–74. — **1894d.** Die Entstehung und Ausbildung des Arbeiterstandes bei den Ameisen. *Biol. Centralb.* 14 : 53–59. — **1894e.** Descrizione di una nuova Formica di Sicilia. *Natural Sicil.* 14 : 28. — **1894f.** Estudios sobre las Hormigas de Costa Rica. *Ann. Mus. Costa Rica* pp. 45–64, pls. 1 and 2. — **1894g.** *Sur un Crabronide chasseur de Fourmis. *Ann. Soc. Ent. France* p. lxiii. — **1894h.** Gedanken zur Descendenz- u. Vererbungstheorie. *Biol. Centralb.* 14 : 721–727. — **1894i.** Mission scientifique de M. Ch. Alluaud aux îles Séchelles. 2e mémoire. Formicides. *Ann. Soc. Ent. France* 63 : 67–72. — **1894j.** *República de Costa Rica. Estudio contributivo à la Biologia de las Hormigas. *Ann. Mus. Costa Rica* (1888–'89) : 65–67. — **1894k.** Studio monografico sul genere Azteca Forel. *Mem. Acc. Bologna* (5) 3 : 119–152, 2 pls. — **1894l.** Studi sulle Formiche della Fauna neotropica. vii–xvi. *Bull. Soc. Ent. Ital.* 26 : 137–241, pls. 1–4. — **1894m.** Ueber Entstehung des Sociallebens bei Hymenopteren. *Biol. Centralb.* 14 : 60–62. — **1894n.** Viaggio del Dottor Alfredo Borelli nella Republica Argentina e nel Paraguay. Formiche. *Boll. Mus. Zool. Anat. Comp. R. Univ. Torino* 9, 186 : 4 pp. — **1895a.** Deuxième note sur les fourmis du Chili. *Act. Soc. Chili* 5 : 10–18. — **1895b.** Die Gattung Dorylus Fab. und die systematische Eintheilung der Formiciden. *Zool. Jahrb. Abth. Syst.* 8 : 685–788, pls. 14–17, 41 text figg. — **1895c.** Esplorazione del Giuba. 10. Formiche. *Ann. Mus. Civ. Genova* 35 : 175–184. — **1895d.** Le problème des Doryles (Hyménoptères). *Bull. Soc. Ent. France* 44 : lxxi–lxxiv, fig. — **1895e.** Mission scientifique de M. Ch. Alluaud dans le territoire de Diego Suarez (Madagascar-Nord). Formicides. *Ann. Soc. Ent. Belg.* 39 : 336–345. — **1895f.** Description de quelques fourmis nouvelles d'Australie. *Ibid.* 39 : 345–358. — **1895g.** Note sur les fourmis du Chili avec descriptions de deux espèces nouvelles. *Act. Soc. Chile* 4 : 213–216. — **1895h.** On a new species of ant from New Zealand. *Trans. N. Zeal. Inst.* 27 : 635, 636. — **1895i.** On the origin of European and North American Ants. *Nature* 52 : 399–400. — **1895j.** Sopra Alcune Formiche delle Fauna Mediterranea. *Mem. R. Accad. Sc. Ist. Bologna* Sess. Apr. 21 : 291–307, 1 pl. — **1895k.** Review of Wasmann's Kritisches Verzeichnis d. myrmekophilen Arthropoden. *Biol. Centralb.* 15 : 191–192. — **1895l.** Viaggio del Dr. E. Festa in Palestina, etc. Descrizione di un nuovo Camponotus. *Boll. Mus. Zool. Anat. Comp. R. Univ. Torino*

9: 185. — 1895m. Viaggio di Leonardo Fea in Birmania e regioni vicine 63. Formiche di Birmania, del Tenasserim e dei monti Carin raccolte da L. Fea. Part II. *Ann. Mus. Civ. Stor. Nat. Genova* 34: 450–483. — 1895n. Voyage de M. E. Simon dans l'Afrique australe. *Ann. Soc. Ent. France* 64: 15–56. — 1896a. Studi sulle Formiche della Fauna neotropica. *Bull. Soc. Ent. Ital.* 28: 33–107, 1 pl. — 1896b. Formiche raccolte dal Dott. E. Festa nei pressi del golfo di Darien. *Boll. Mus. Zool. Anat. Comp. R. Univ. Torino* 11, 229: 4 pp. — 1896c. *Alcune forme del genere Azteca For. e note biologiche. *Ibid.* 11, 230: 7 pp. — 1896d. Description d'une Fourmi nouvelle [Holcomyrmex Chobauti] d'Algérie. *Bull. Soc. Ent. France* pp. 418–419, 1 fig. — 1896e. Formiciden, gesammelt im Paraguay von Dr. J. Bohls. *Zool. Jahrb. Abth. Syst.* 9: 625–638, 6 figg. — 1896f. Formiche raccolte dal Cap. V. Bottego nella regione dei Somali. *Ann. Mus. Civ. Stor. Nat. Genova* 37: 153–160, 1 fig. — 1896g. Saggio di un catalogo sistematico dei generi Camponotus, Polyrhachis e affini. *Mem. Accad. Sc. Bologna* (5) 5: 761–780. — 1896h. Sur les Fourmis du genre Macromischa Rog. *Bull. Soc. Ent. France* 4 bis: 102–103. — 1896i. Sur les Fourmis des genres Sysphincta et Proceratium. *Ibid.* 4: 101–102, 2 figg. — 1896j. Clef analytique des genres de la famille des Formicides pour la détermination des neutres. *Ann. Soc. Ent. Belg.* 40, 5: 172–189. — 1896k. Le Polymorphisme des Fourmis et la Castration alimentaire. *C. R. 3 Congr. Internat. Zool. Leyde* pp. 395–410. — 1896l. Formicides récoltés à Buitenzorg (Java) par M. Massart, déterminés. *Ann. Soc. Ent. Belg.* 40, 6: 245–249, 7 figg. — 1897a. Descriptions de deux Fourmis. *Bull. Soc. Ent. France* 1: 12–14, 2 figg. — 1897b. Revisione del genere Diacamma Mayr. *Rend. Accad. Sc. Bologna* N. S. 1: 147–167, 1 pl. — 1897c. Viaggio di Lamberto Lorio nella Papuasia orientale 18. Formiche raccolte nella Nuova Guinea dal Dott. Lamberto Doria. *Ann. Mus. Civ. Stor. Nat. Genova* 38: 546–594, 1 pl., 1 fig. — 1897d. Formiche raccolte da Don Eugenio dei Principe Ruspoli, durante l'ultimo viaggio nelle regioni dei Somali e dei Galla. *Ibid.* 38: 595–605, 7 figg. — 1897–1900. Formicidarum species Novæ vel minus cognitæ in collectione Musæi Nationalis Hungarici, quas in Nova Guinea, colonia Germanica, collegit L. Biró. I *Terméz. Füzetek* 20 (1897): 571–599, pls. 14–15; II *Ibid.* 23 (1900): 310–338, pl. 8. — 1898a. Beiträge zur Kenntniss der palæarktischen Ameisen. *Öfvers. Finsk. Vet. Soc. Förh.* 40: 124–151, 5 figg. — 1898b. Aggiunte e correzioni al Saggio di un catalogo sistematico dei generi Componotus, Polyrachis [recte Polyrhachis] e affini. *Rend. Accad. Sc. Bologna* N. S. 2: 225–231. — 1898c. Instinkt, Intelligenz und Sprache. *Biol. Centralb.* 18, 1: 17–21. — 1898d. Formiche dell'ultima spedizione Bottego. *Ann. Mus. Civ. Stor. Nat. Genova* 39: 499–501, 1 fig. — 1898e. Descrizioni di Formiche nuove malesi e australiane; note sinonimiche. *Rend. Accad. Sc. Bologna* N. S. 2: 231–245, 1 pl. — 1899a. Végétarianisme chez les fourmis. *Arch. Sc. Phys. Nat. Genève* (4) 8: 488–490. — 1899b. Glanures myrmécologiques. *Bull. Soc. Ent. France* pp. 17–20, 4 figg. — 1899c. Fourmis d'Afrique. *Ann. Soc. Ent. Belg.* 43: 459–504, 13 figg. — 1899d. Ergebnisse einer Reise nach dem Pacific (Schauinsland 1896-'97). Formiciden. *Zool. Jahrb. Abt. Syst.* 12: 438–440. — 1899e. Intorno alle larve di alcune Formiche. *Mem. Accad. Sc. Bologna* N. S. 3: 93. — 1900a. Ueber Ameisenlarven. *Verh. Gesell. Deutsch. Nat. Aerzte* 71. München 2, 1: 233–234. — 1900b. Formiche Raccolte da Elio Modigliani in Sumatra, Engano e Mentawei. *Ann. Mus. Civ. Stor. Nat. Genova* (2) 20: 661–722, 16 figg. — 1900c. Formicidarum species novæ vel minus cognitæ in collectione Musæi nationalis hungarici, quas in Nova-Guinea, colonia germanica, collegit L. Biró. *Termesz. Füzetek.* 23: 310–338, 1 pl. — 1900d. Intorno al Torace delle Formiche. *Bull. Soc. Ent. Ital.* 32: 1–17, 14 figg. — 1901a. Ameisen gesammelt in Ceylon von Dr. W. Horn 1899.

Deutsch. Ent. Zeitschr. pp. 113–122, 4 figg. — **1901b.** Notes sur les sous-familles des Dorylines et Ponérines. (Famille des Formicides.) *Ann. Soc. Ent. Belg.* 45: 32–54. — **1901c.** Le formiche in rapporto alla fauna di Selebes. (Unione zool. ital.) *Monit. Zool. Ital.* 12: 178. — **1901d.** Der Geschlechts-polymorphismus der Treiberameisen und die flügellose Urform der Ameisen-weibchen. *Nat. Wochenschr.* 17: 54–55. — **1901e.** Formiciden von Celebes. *Zool. Jahrb. Abt. Syst.* 14: 565–580, 5 figg. — **1901f.** Remarques sur un petit groupe de Pheidole de la région sonorienne. *Bull. Soc. Ent. France* pp. 119–121. — **1901g.** Studi sul polimorfismo e la metamorfosi nel genere Dorylus. *Rend. Sess. R. Accad. Sc. Ist. Bologna* N. S. 5: 109–110. — **1901h.** Note sulle Doriline. *Bull. Soc. Ent. Ital.* 33, 1: 43–56, 8 figg. — **1901i.** Spicilegio Mirmecologico. *Ibid.* 33, 1: 57–63, 1 fig. — **1902a.** Formicidarum Species Novæ vel minus cognitæ in collectione Musæi Nationalis Hungarici, quas in Nova Guinea, colonia Germanica, collegit L. Biró. *Temész. Füzctek* 25: 152–160, 5 figg. — **1902b.** Description d'une nouvelle espèce de fourmi du Brésil. *Bull. Soc. Ent. France* p. 181. — **1902c.** Note mirmecologische. I. Revisione del gruppo dei generi affini a Cerapachys F. Sm. *Rend. Accad. Sc. Ist. Bologna* N. S. 6: 22–34. — **1902d.** An Analytical Key to the Genera of the Family Formicidæ for the Identification of the Workers. Transl. by W. M. Wheeler in *Amer. Nat.* 36, 429 (Sept.): 707–725. — **1903.** Intorno al alcune specie di Camponotus dell'America meridionale. *Rend. Sess. Accad. Sc. Ist. Bologna* N. S. 7: 62–81, 15 figg. — **1904a.** Zur Kenntniss des Polymorphismus der Ameisen. *Zool. Jahrb.* Suppl. 7 Festschr. Weismann pp. 587–610, 6 figg. — **1904b.** Le affinità del genere Leptanilla e i limiti delle Dorylinæ. *Arch. Zool. Napoli* 2: 107–116, 9 figg. — **1905a.** Ethologie, Phylogenie et Classification. *C. R. 6me Congr. Intern. Zool. Berne* 1904. 25 Mai: 160–174. — **1905b.** Studi sulle Formiche della Fauna Neotropica 26. *Bull. Soc. Ent. Ital.* 37: 107–194, 47 figg. — **1905c.** Le Forme Paleartiche di Camponotus maculatus F. *Rend. Sess. R. Accad. Sc. Ist. Bologna* N. S. 9: 27–44, 2 figg. — **1905d.** Sur l'origine des fourmil-ières. *C. R. 6me Congr. Intern. Zool. Berne* pp. 459–462. — **1905e.** Deux Fourmis de l'ambre de la Baltique. *Bull. Soc. Ent. France* pp. 187–189, 2 figg. — **1906a.** Ueber W. H. Ashmeads neues System der Ameisen. *Zool. Anz.* 29: 717–718. — **1906b.** Rassegna critica della specie paleartiche del genere Myrmecocystus. *Mem. Accad. Sc. Bologna* Sess. 28 Genn. 17 pp., 35 text-figg. — **1906c.** Note sur Prenolepis vividula Nyl. et sur la classifica-tion des espèces du genre Prenolepis. *Ann. Soc. Ent. Belg.* 50: 130–134, 5 figg. — **1906d.** Zur Kenntniss des Polymorphismus der Ameisen. *Biol. Centralb.* 26: 624–630, 4 figg. — **1907.** *Una formica nuova italiana spettante ad un nuova genere. *Rend. Sess. R. Accad. Sci. Ist. Bologna*, pp. 49–51, 1 fig. — **1908a.** Beiträge zur Monographie der Formiciden des paläarktischen Faunengebietes. *Deutsch. Ent. Zeitschr.* pp. 165–205; 305–338, 23 figg.; 437–465, 13 figg.; 549–558, 5 figg. — **1908b.** *Osservazioni ed Esperimenti sulla Formica Amazzone. *Ren. R. Accad. Sci. Ist. Bologna* (Feb. 9): 49–62. — **1908c.** *Remarques sur les Observations de M. de Lannoy touchant l'existence de Lasius mixtus dans les fourmilières de Lasius fuliginosus. *Ann. Soc. Ent. Belg.* 52: 182, 183. — **1908d.** Description d'un Genre Nouveau et de Plusieurs Formes Nouvelles de Fourmis du Congo. *Ibid.* 52: 184–189. — **1908e.** *Le Formiche e Gli Alberi in Italia. *Alpe, Org. Uffic. della Pro Montibus.* No. 19–20, 9 pp. — **1908f.** Myrmecocystus viaticus et Formes Voisines. *Bull. Soc. Vaud. Sc. Nat.* (5) 44: 213–218, 4 figg.

Emery, Carlo, and Auguste Forel, 1879. Catalogue des Formicides d'Europe. *Mittheil. Schweiz. Ent. Gesell.* 5, 8: 441–481.

Emery, C., and G. Cavanna, 1880. Escursione in Calabria 1877-'78. Formicidei. *Bull. Soc. Ent. Ital.* 12: 123–126.

Erichson, F. W., 1839. *Die Käfer der Mark Brandenburg. 1 vol. Berlin.—
1840. *Genera et Species Staphylinorum. Berlin.— 1842. Beitrag zur
Insectenfauna von Van Diemensland. Arch. Naturg. Wiegmann* 8: 83–287.
— **1847.** *Zur systematischen Kenntniss der Insecten-larven. Ibid.* 13, 1.
— **1848.** *Naturgeschichte der Insekten Deutschlands. Coleoptera.* 3.

Ernst, C., 1905-'06. Einige Beobachtungen an künstlichen Ameisennestern.
Biol. Centralb. 25 (1905): 47–51; 26 (1906): 210–220.

Escherich, K., 1897a. *Zur Kenntniss der Myrmekophilen Kleinasiens. I Coleopteren.* Mit einem Verzeichnis der in Kleinasien gesammelten Ameisen und
einer Neubeschreibung von Professor C. Emery. *Wien. Ent. Zeit.* 16, 9:
229–238,-Anhang p. 239.— **1897b.** *Ueber einige Ameisengäste. Ent. Nachr.*
23: 21–25.— **1898a.** *Zur Biologie von Thorictus foreli Wasm. Zool. Anz.*
21: 483–492, 3 figg.— **1898b.** *Zur Anatomie und Biologie von Paussus
turcicus Friv.* Zugleich ein Beitrag zur Kenntniss der Myrmecophilie. *Zool.
Jahrb. Abt. Syst.* 12: 27–70, 1 pl., 11 figg.— **1898c.** [*Künstliches Nest mit
Myrmecocystis megalocola und dem Ameisengast Thorictus foreli.] Verh.
Deutsch. Zool. Gesell.* 8: 172.— **1899a.** *Ueber myrmekophile Arthropoden
mit besonderer Berücksichtigung der Biologie. Zool. Centralb.* 6, 1.— **1899b.**
Ameisen-Psychologie. Beil. Allgem. Zeitg. München no. 100.— **1899c.** *Zur
Naturgeschichte von Paussus favieri Fairm. Verh. Zool. Bot. Gesell. Wien*
49: 278–283, 2 figg.— **1900a.** *Ueber Ameisengäste und Ameisenstaat. Verh.
Naturw. Ver. Karlsruhe* 13: 137–139.— **1900b.** *Ueber Myrmekophilen.
Ibid.* 13: 103–104.— **1902a.** *Ueber die Gäste der Ameisen. Mitteil. Philom.
Gesell. Elsass-Lothr.* 461–474, 2 pl.— **1902b.** *Biologische Studien über
algerische Myrmekophilen, zugleich mit allgemeinen Bemerkungen über die
Entwicklung und Bedeutung der Symphilie. Biol. Centralb.* 22: 638–663, 4
figg.— **1902c.** Zur Biologie der nordafrikanischen Myrmecocystus-Arten.
Allgem. Zeitschr. Ent. 7: 353–360, 390–395, 2 figg.— **1903a.** *Beiträge zur
Kenntniss der Thysanuren. I Reihe. Zool. Anz.* 26, 697: 345–366, 12 figg.
— **1903b.** *Ueber die Biologie der Ameisen.* Uebersicht über die neueren
Arbeiten. *Zool. Centralb.* pp. 209–250.— **1905.** *Das System der Lepis-
matiden. Zoologica* 18, 43: 164 pp., 4 pls., 67 text-figg.— **1906.** *Die Ameise.*
Schilderung ihrer Lebensweise. *Braunschweig, Fr. Vieweg und Sohn* 232
pp., 68 figg.— **1907a.** *Neue Beobachtungen über Paussus in Erythrea.
Zeitschr. Wiss. Insekten-Biol.* (2) 3, 1: 1–8, 2 figg.— **1907b.** *Muttermord
im Tierreich. Frankfurter Zeitg.* Apr. 6.

Escherich, K. and A. Ludwig., 1906. Beiträge zur Kenntnis der elsässischen
Ameisenfauna. *Mitth. Philomath. Gesell. Els.-Lothr.* 3: 381–389.

Eusebius, P. J., 1635. Historiæ Naturæ, Maxime Peregrinæ. *Nüremburg.*

Evans, W., 1906. Some Invertebrata, including Ixodes borealis from St. Kilda.
Ann. Scott. Nat. Hist. pp. 83–88, 1 fig.

Everts, Edm., 1887. *Nieuwe Naamlijst van Nederlandsche schildvleugelige
Insecten. Haarlem.* Addend. pp. 224–227. *Natuurk. Verh. Holl. Maatsch.
Wetensch.* 3, 4, 4.—**1889.** *Supplement op de Nieuwe Naamlijst, etc.
Tijdschr. Ent.* 32.— **1891.** *Tweede Supplement op de Nieuwe Naamlijst,
etc. Ibid.* 34.— **1893.** *Derde Supplement op de Nieuwe Naamlijst, etc.
Ibid.* 36.

Ewaldt, B., 1702. Dissertatio de formicarum usu in medicina. *Resp. Garmann.
Regiomonti.*

FABRE, J. H., 1882. Les Fourmis Rousses. *Nouveaux Souvenirs Entomologiques,* II, pp. 134–156. *Paris. Delagrave.*

Fabricius, J. Chr., 1775. Systema Entomologiæ. pp. 391–396.— **1776.** Genera
Insectorum p. 130.— **1781.** Species Insectorum 1: 488–494.— **1787.** Mantissa
Insectorum 1: 307–311.— **1793.** Entomologia Systematica Emendata et
Aucta 2: 349–365.— **1798.** Entomologiæ Systematicæ Supplementum pp.

279–281. — 1804. Systema Piezatorum secundum Ordines, Genera et Species,
pp. 395–428.

Faes, H., 1902. Sur quelques insectes nuisibles au printemps. *Chron. Agri. Vaud.*
15: 189–195; 297–305; 449–459; 521–523, 17 figg.

Fairmaire, L., 1879. *Description de Coléoptères nouveaux du nord de l'Afrique.
Ann. Soc. Ent. France pp. 156–172. — 1886. *Notes sur les Coléoptères
recueillis par M. Raffray à Madagascar. *Ibid.* (6) 6: 31–95. — 1898a.
*Description de trois Histérides myrmécophiles de Madagascar. *Bull. Soc.
Ent. France* pp. 323–325. — 1898b. *Descriptions de Psélaphiens myrméco-
philes de Madagascar. *Ibid.* pp. 336–338; 342–346.

Fairmaire, L., et A. Laboulbène, 1854. *Faune Entomologique Française. Coléoptères. *Paris.*

Fallou, J., 1891. Note sur un nid de fourmi. *Ann. Soc. Ent. France* 60: 4. —
1892. Notes sur les Hyménoptères de la Tribu des Fourmiciens. *Paris* 19
pp. (Ext. *Rev. Sc. Nat. Appl.* nos 1, (5 Jan.) : 1–17.)

Fauvel, A., 1861-'63, 1865. *Énumération des Insectes recueillis en Savoie et
en Dauphinée (1861–'63). *Not. Ent.* 3, 4, Ext. *Bull Soc. Linn. Norm.* 9
(1865) : 253 seq. — 1868-'70. *Faune Gallo-Rhenane. 3 Staphylinides. —
1878. *Les Staphylinides de l'Afrique boréale. *Not. Ent.* 4, 1, Ext. *Bull.
Soc. Linn. Norm.* (3) 2: 83 seq. — 1883. *Vingt ans après. Histoire du
Machærites Normand. *Rev. d'Ent.* 2: 153 seq. — 1886a. *Les Staphylinides
du Nord de l'Afrique. *Ibid.* 5: 9–100. — 1886b. *Faune Gallo-Rhenane.
Histérides. *Ibid.* 5: 152–213.

Felt, E. P., 1903. Insects Affecting Forest Trees. *7th Rep. Forest, Fish and
Game Commission N. Y. Albany* pp. 479–534, pls. 1–16.

Fenger, W. H., 1862. Allgemeine Orismologie der Ameisen, mit besonderer
Berücksichtigung des Werthes der Classificationsmerkmale. *Arch. Naturg.*
28, 1: 282–352, pl. 10–12. — 1863. Anatomie und Physiologie des Giftapparates
bei den Hymenopteren. *Ibid.* 29: 139–178, pl. 9.

Fenner, Dr. H. W., 1895. Arizona Ants. *Ent. News* 6, 7: 214–216.

Ferton, C., 1890. *Un Hyménoptère ravisseur de Fourmis. *Act. Soc. Linn.
Bord.* 44.

Fiebrig, Karl, 1907a. Eine Wespen Zerstörende Ameise aus Paraguay, Eciton
vagans Oliver. *Zeitschr. Wiss. Insekt.-Biol.* 3: 83–87. Nachtrag. *Ibid.*
3, 5: 154–156. — 1907b. *Eine ameisenähnliche Gryllide aus Paraguay,
Myrmegryllus dipterus nov. gen. et sp. *Ibid.* 3, 4: 101–106, 10 text-figg. —
1908. *Nachtrag zu Phylloscirtus macilentus Sauss. *Ibid.* 3, 10–11: 350–
352, 2 figg.

Fielde, A. M., 1894. Chinese Nights' Entertainments. — 1900. Portable Ant-
Nests. *Biol. Bull. Boston* 2: 81–85, 3 figg. — 1901a. A Study of an Ant.
Proc. Acad. Nat. Sc. Phila. 53: 425–449. — 1901b. Further Study of an Ant.
Ibid. 53: 521–544, 2 figg. — 1902. Notes on an Ant. *Ibid.* 54: 599–625, 2
figg. — 1903a. Supplementary Notes on an Ant. *Ibid.* 55: 491–495. — 1903b.
Experiments with Ants Induced to Swim. *Ibid.* 55: 617–624. — 1903c.
*Artificial Mixed Nests of Ants. *Biol. Bull.* 6: 320–325. — 1903d. A Cause
of Feud between Ants of the Same Species living in Different Communities.
Ibid. 5: 326–329. — 1904a. *On the Artificial Creation of Mixed Nests of
Ants. *Ibid.* 6: 326. — 1904b. Portable Ant-Nests. *Ibid.* 7: 215–220, 1 pl.,
2 figg. — 1904c. Effects of Light-rays on an Ant. *Ibid.* 6:309. — 1904d.
Observations on Ants in their Relation to Temperature and to Submergence.
Ibid. 7: 170–174. — 1904e. Power of Recognition among Ants. *Ibid.* 7:
227–250. — 1904f. Tenacity of Life in Ants. *Ibid.* 7: 300–309, 2 figg. —
1905a. Three Odd Incidents in Ant-Life. *Proc. Acad. Nat. Sc. Phila.* 56:
639–641, 1 fig. — 1905b (with G. H. Parker). The Reactions of Ants to
Material Vibrations. *Ibid.* 56: 642–650, 1 fig. — 1902c. The Progressive Odor
of Ants. *Biol. Bull.* 10: 1–16. — 1905d. The Sense of Smell in Ants. *The*

Independent Aug. 17: 375–378, 5 figg. — **1905e.** The Sense of Smell in Ants. *Ann. N. Y. Acad. Sc.* 16: 394. — **1905f.** Observations on the Progeny of Virgin Ants. *Biol. Bull.* 9: 355–360. — **1905g.** Temperature as a Factor in the Development of Ants. *Ibid.* 10: 361–367. — **1905h.** The Communal Life of Ants. *Nature-Study Review* 1, 6 (Nov.): 239–251, 4 figg. — **1905i.** Tenacity of Life in Ants. *Scient. Amer.* 93: 363–364, 5 figg. — **1907.** Suggested Explanations of Certain Phenomena in the Lives of Ants; with a Method of Tracing Ants to their Respective Communities. *Biol. Bull.* 13, 3: 134–137.

Fitch, A., 1855. First Report on the Noxious, Beneficial and Other Insects of the State of New York. 1 Vol.

Flach, C., 1887. *Biologische Kleinigkeiten. Stett. Ent. Zeitg.* p. 258.

Fleischer, A., 1892. *Coleopteren entnommen und gesiebt aus einem alten Eichenstamm. Wien Ent. Zeitg.* p. 206.

Fletcher, J. E., 1889. Fertile Eggs Laid by Workers of Leptothorax tuberum F. *Ent. M. Mag.* 25: 313, 314.

Flögel, J. H. L., 1878. Ueber den einheitlichen Bau des Gehirns in den verschiedenen Insektenordnungen. *Zeitschr. Wiss. Zool.* 30, Suppl.: 556.

Flügel, O. Zur Psychologie und Entwickelungsgeschichte der Ameisen. *Zeitschr. Exakt. Philos.* 20, 1: 66.

Focke, W. O., H. Schütte und K. Sartorius, 1906. Zur Kenntnis des Mellum-Eilandes. *Abh. Nat. Ver. Bremen* 18: 365–375.

Fonscolombe, Boyer de, 1846. Notes sur huit espèces nouvelles d'Hyménoptères et de Neuroptères trouvées aux environs d'Aix. *Ann. Soc. Ent. France* (2) 4: 39–51 *et Bull.* p. 69.

Fontana, F., 1778. Mémoire sur la nature de l'acide des animaux, des végétaux et des substances gommeuses et résineuses et sur la nature d'acide de fourmis et de quelques autres substances animales. *Journ. Phys.* 12: 64–75.

Forbes, E. L., 1888. *Relations of Ants and Aphids. Amer. Natur.* 21: 579.

Forbes, S. A., 1891. *A summary history of the Corn-root Aphis (Aphis maidiradicis). Insect Life* 3, 5 (Jan.): 233–238, and *17th Rep. State Ent. Ill.* pp. 64–70. — **1894.** *A Monograph of Insects Injurious to Indian Corn. 18th Rep. State Ent. Ill.* pp. 1–171, 15 pls. — **1905.** *The More Important Insect Injuries to Indian Corn. 23d Rep. Nox. Benef. Insects Ill.* pp. 1–273, 8 pls., 238 figg. — **1906.** *The Corn-root Aphis and its Attendant Ant. U. S. Dept. Agric. Div. Ent. Bull.* 60: 29–39. — **1908a.** *Experiments with Repellents against the Corn Root-Aphis, 1905 and 1906. Univ. Ill. Agric. Exper. Stat. Bull.* 130: 28 pp. — **1908b.** *Habits and Behavior of the Corn-field Ant, Lasius niger americanus. Ibid.* 131: 45 pp., 1 pl.

Forbes and Peal, 1881. (Sound Produced by Ants in Sumatra and Assam.) *Nature* 24: 101, 102, 484.

Forel, A., 1869. *Observations sur les mœurs du Solenopsis fugax. Mitth. Schweiz. Ent. Gesell.* 3: 105. — **1870.** *Notices Myrmécologiques sur le Polyergus rufescens — Descript. du Cremastogaster sordidula ♂. Ibid.* 3: 306–312. — **1874.** *Les Fourmis de la Suisse. Nouv. Mém. Soc. Helv. Sc. Nat. Zurich* 26: 447 pp., 2 pls. — **1875.** *Études Myrmécologiques en 1875, avec remarques sur un point de l'anatomie des Coccides. Bull. Soc. Vaud. Sc. Nat.* 14: 33–62. — **1878a.** Der Giftapparat und die Analdrüsen der Ameisen. *Zeitschr. Wiss. Zool.* 30, Suppl.: 28–66, 2 pls. — **1878b.** Ueber den Kaumagen der Ameisen. *Mitth. Morph. Phys. Gesell. München.* — **1878c.** Études Myrmécologiques en 1878 (1 part). Avec l'anatomie des gésier des fourmis et classification des S.-Genres et des Genres. *Bull. Soc. Vaud. Sc. Nat.* 15, 80: 337–392, pl. 23. — **1878d.** Beitrag zur Kenntniss der Sinnesempfindungen der Insekten. Part I. *Mitth. Münch. Ent. Ver.,* 21 pp. — **1878e.** Entomologie und Entomotomie. *Bibliogr. Notiz. Mitth. Schweiz. Ent. Gesell.* 5, 5: 285–291. — **1879a.** Études Myrmécologiques en 1879. *Bull. Soc. Vaud. Sc. Nat.*

15. — **1879b.** Description de l'Aphænogaster Schaufussi. *Nunquam Otiosus* pp. 465–466. — **1880.** An Weingeist-exemplaren der Honigameise (Myrmecocystus melliger Llave = M. mexicanus Wesmael) gemachte Beobachtungen. *Mitth. Morph. Phys. Gesell, München.* Jan. pp. 1, 2. — **1881.** Die Ameisen der Antille Saint-Thomas. *Mitth. Münch. Ent. Ver.* pp. 1–16. — **1884a.** Ueber das Nest von Cremastogaster. *Mitth. Schweiz. Ent. Gesell.* 7, 1 : 3. — **1884b.** Études Myrmécologiques en 1884. *Bull. Soc. Vaud. Sc. Nat.* 20 (Sept.) — **1884c.** (Notes on North American Ants.) *Mitth. Schweiz. Ent. Gesell.* 6, 1 : 20. — **1885.** Études Myrmécologiques en 1884 avec une description des organes sensoriels des Antennes. *Bull. Soc. Vaud.* 20: 316–380, pl. 11. — **1885-'86.** Indian Ants of the Indian Museum, Calcutta. *Journ. As. Soc. Bomb.* 54, 2 : 176–182; 55 : 239–249. — **1886a.** Einige Ameisen aus Itajahy (Brasilien). *Mitth. Schweiz. Ent. Gesell.* 7 : 210–217. — **1886b.** Les Fourmis percoivent-elles l'ultra-violet avec leur yeux ou avec leur peau? *Phys. et Nat. Genève* 16 (Oct.). — **1886c.** Diagnoses provisoires de quelques espèces nouvelles de Fourmis de Madagascar, réc. par M. Grandidier. *C. R. Soc. Ent. Belg.* (Mai) 72, 7 pp. — **1886d.** *Études Myrmécologiques en 1886. I Polymorphisme. — Observations sur les mœurs du Formicoxenus nitidulus Nyl. et de quelques autres hôtes de la Formica pratensis. Diverse observations de mœurs. *Ann. Soc. Ent. Belg.* 30: 131–215. — **1886e.** Nouvelles Fourmis de Grèce. *C. R. Soc. Ent. Belg.* 2, 77 : clix–clxviii. — **1886f.** Diagnoses provisoires de quelques espèces de Fourmis de Madagascar. *Ibid.* 72: ci–cvii. — **1886g.** Espèces nouvelles de Fourmis américaines. *Ibid.* 3, 69 : xxxviii–xlix. — **1886-'88.** Expériences et remarques critiques sur les sensations des insectes. 2 parties avec appendices. *Rec. Zool. Suisse* 2 and 4: 1–50; 145–240; 515–523, pl. 1. — **1887.** Fourmis récoltées à Madagascar par le Dr. Conrad Keller. *Mitth. Schweiz. Ent. Gesell.* 7 : 381–389. — **1888a.** Ameisen aus den Sporaden, den Cykladen, und Griechenland, gesammelt 1887 von Herrn v. Oertzen. *Berl. Ent. Zeitschr.* 32: 255–265. — **1888b.** Appendices à mon mémoire sur les sensations des Insectes. *Rec. Zool. Suisse* 4: 516–522. — **1889.** Ameise und Mensch oder Automatismus und Vernunft. *Die Sonntagspost (Wochenbeigabe des " Landboten ")* 45 : 353–357. — **1890a.** *Un Parasite de la Myrmecia forficata F. *C. R. Soc. Ent. Belg.* Févr. 1. 3 pp. — **1890b.** *Ueber neue Beobachtungen, die Lebensweise der Ameisengäste und gewisser Ameisen betreffend. *Humboldt* 9, 6 (June) : 190–194. — **1890c.** *Eine myrmekologische Ferienreise nach Tunisien und Ostalgerien, nebst einer Beobachtung des Herrn Gleadow in Indien über Ænictus. *Ibid.* 9, 9 : 296–306. — **1890d.** Une nouvelle Fourmi. *Le Nat.* 12: 217. — **1890e.** Ænictus-Typhlatta découverte de M. Wroughton. Nouveaux genres de Formicides. *C. R. Soc. Ent. Belg.* pp. cii–cxii. — **1890f.** Fourmis de Tunisie et de l'Algérie orientale récoltées et décrites par Aug. Forel. *Ibid.* pp. lxi–lxxvi. — **1890g.** Norwegische Ameisen und Drüsenkitt als Material zum Nestbau der Ameisen. *Mitth. Schweiz. Ent. Gesell.* 8: 229–233. — **1890h.** *Ænictus, and Some New Genera of Formicidæ (transl. by R. C. Wroughton). *Journ. Bomb. Nat. Hist. Soc.* 5 : 388. — **1891a.** Ueber die Ameisensubfamilie der Doryliden. *Verh. Deutsch. Naturforsch.* 63, 2 : 162–164. — **1891b.** *Histoire physique, naturelle et politique de Madagascar. 20 (Hyménoptères), 2 (Formicides). *Alf. Grandidier, Paris.* — **1891c.** Un nouveau genre de Myrmicides. *C. R. Soc. Ent. Belg.* 35: cccvii. — **1892a.** *Die Ameisenfauna Bulgariens. *Verh. Zool. Bot. Gesell. Wien* pp. 305–314. — **1892b.** Le mâle des Cardiocondyla et la reproduction consanguine perpétuée. *Ann. Soc. Ent. Belg.* 36: 458–461. — **1892c.** Die Ameisen Neu-Seelands. *Mitth. Schweiz. Ent. Gesell.* 8: 331–343. — **1892d.** Attini und Cryptocerini. Zwei neue Apterostigma-Arten. *Ibid.* 8: 344–349. — **1892e.** Liste der aus Somaliland von Hrn. Prof. Dr. Conr. Keller aus der Expedition des Prinzen Ruspoli im August und September 1891 zurück-

gebrachten Ameisen. *Ibid.* 8: 349–354. — **1892f.** Notes myrmécologiques. *Ann. Soc. Ent. Belg.* 36: 38–43. — **1892g.** Quelques Fourmis de la faune méditerranienne. *Ibid.* 36: 452–457. — **1892h.** Die Ameisenfauna Bulgariens (nebst biologischen Beobachtungen). *Verh. Zool. Bot. Gesell. Wien* 42: 305–318, pl. 5. — **1892i.** Die Nester der Ameisen. *Neujahrsbl. Gesell. Zürich* pp. 1–36, 2 pls. Transl. in *Ann. Rep. Smith. Inst.* for 1894 (publ. 1896) pp. 479–505, 2 pls; and in *Intern. Journ. Micr. Nat. Sc.* 16 (1897): 347–381, 2 pls. — **1892j.** *Die Akazien-Cremastogaster von Prof. Keller aus dem Somaliland. *Zool. Anz.* 15, 388: 140–143. — **1892k.** Hérmaphrodite de l'Azteca instabilis. *Bull. Soc. Vaud. Sc. Nat.* 28: 268–270, pl. 16. — **1892-'94.** Les Formicides de l'Empire des Indes et de Ceylan. Pt. 1 *Journ. Bomb. Soc.* 7: 219–245, pl. A; pt. 2 *Ibid.* 7: 430–439; pt. 3 *Ibid.* 8: 17–36; pt. 4 (1894) *Ibid.* 8: 396–420, pl. — **1893a.** *Observations nouvelles sur la biologie de quelques Fourmis. *Bull. Soc. Vaud. Sc. Nat.* (3) 29: 51–57. — **1893b.** Formicides de l'Antille St. Vincent Récoltées par Mons. H. H. Smith. *Trans. Ent. Soc. London* pp. 333–418. — **1893c.** Sur la classification de la famille des Formicides, avec remarques synonymiques. *Ann. Soc. Ent. Belg.* 37: 161–167. — **1893d.** Quelques Fourmis de la Faune méditerranienne. *Act. Soc. Espan.* 22: 90–94. — **1893e.** Nouvelles Fourmis d'Australie et des Canaries. *Ann. Soc. Ent. Belg.* 37: 454–466. — **1893f.** Nouvelles Espèces de Formicides de Madagascar (récoltées par M. Sikora). *Ibid.* (1) 37: 516–535. — **1893g.** Note sur les Attini. *Ibid.* 37: 586–607. — **1893h.** Note préventive sur un nouveau genre et une nouvelle espèce de Formicide. *Ibid.* 37: 607, 608. — **1894a.** Les Formicides de la province d'Oran (Algérie). *Bull. Soc. Vaud. Sc. Nat.* 30: 1–45, pl. 1, 2. — **1894b.** Ueber den Polymorphismus und Ergatomorphismus der Ameisen. *Verh. Gesell. Deutsch. Naturf.* 66, 2: 142–147. Transl. *Arch. Sc. Phys. Nat.* 32 (Oct.): 1–8 (sep. pag.). — **1894c.** Quelques fourmis de Madagascar (récolt. par M. le Dr. Voeltzkow); de Nouvelle Zélande (récolt. par M. W. W. Smith); de Nouvelle Calédonie (récolt. par M. Sommer); de Queensland (Australie) (récolt. par M. Wiederkehr); et de Perth (Australie occidentale) (récolt. par M. Chase). *Ann. Soc. Ent. Belg.* 38: 226–237. — **1894d.** *Les Formicides de la Province d'Oran (Algérie). *Lausanne* 45: 2, pl. Extr. *Bull. Soc. Vaud. Sc. Nat.* 30, 114. — **1894e.** Algunas formigas de Canareas recogidas pel Sr. Cabrera y Diaz. *Ann. Soc. Espan. Hist. Nat.* (2) 2: 22. — **1894f.** Abessinische und andere afrikanische Ameisen. *Mitth. Schweiz. Ent. Gesell.* 9, 2: 1–37. — **1895a.** Nouvelles fourmis d'Australie, récoltées à the Ridge, Mackay, Queensland, par M. Gilbert Turner. *Ann. Soc. Ent. Belg.* 39: 417–428. — **1895b.** Les Formicides de l'Empire des Indes et de Ceylan. Pt. 5 *Journ. Bomb. Soc.* 9: 417–428. — **1895c.** Une nouvelle fourmi melligère. *Ann. Soc. Ent. Belg.* 39: 429, 430. — **1895d.** Quelques fourmis du centre de Madagascar. *Ibid.* 39: 485–488. — **1895e.** A fauna das Formicas do Brazil. *Boll. Mus. Paraense* 1, 2: 89–143. — **1895f.** Südpalæarktische Ameisen. *Mitt. Schweiz. Ent. Gesell.* 9: 227–234. — **1895g.** Nouvelles fourmis de l'Imerina oriental (Moramanga). *Ann. Soc. Ent. Belg.* 39: 243–251. — **1895h.** Nouvelles fourmis de diverses provenances, surtout d'Australie. *Ibid.* 39: 41–49. **1895i.** Recension Wasmann. *Ibid.* 39: ——. — **1896a.** Die Fauna und die Lebenweise der Ameisen im kolumbischen Urwald und in den Antillen. *Verh. Schweiz. Nat. Gesell.* pp. 148–150. — **1896b.** Quelques particularités de l'habitat des fourmis de l'Amérique tropicale. *Ann. Soc. Ent. Belg.* 40, 5: 167–171. — **1896c.** Zur Fauna und Lebensweise der Ameisen im columbischen Urwald. *Mitth. Schweiz. Ent. Gesell.* 9: 372, 401–411. — **1896d.** Die Fauna und die Lebensweise der Ameisen im Kolumbischen Urwald und in den Antillen. *Verh. Schweiz. Nat. Gesell.* pp. 148–150. — **1896e.** Ants' Nests. *Ann. Rep. Smiths. Instit.* pp. 479–505, 2 pls. — **1897a.** Communication verbale sur les mœurs des Fourmis de l'Amérique tropicale. *Ann. Soc. Ent. Belg.* 41 : 329–332. — **1897b.** *Deux Fourmis d'Espagne. *Ibid.* 41 : 132–133. — **1897c.** Quelques Formicides de l'Antille de Grenada récoltées par Mr. H. H. Smith. *Trans. Ent. Soc. London* pp. 297–300. — **1897d.** Ameisen aus Nossi-Bé, Majunga, Juan de Nova (Madagaskar), den Aldabra Inseln und Sansibar, gesammelt von Herrn Dr. A. Voeltzkow aus Berlin. Mit einem Anhang über die von Herrn Privatdocenten Dr. A. Brauer in Marburg auf den Seychellen und von Herrn Perrot auf Ste. Marie (Madagaskar) gesammelten Ameisen. (*Wiss. Ergebn. Madagaskar Ostafr.*) *Abh. Senckenb. Nat. Gesell.* 21 : 185–208, 3 figg. — **1898a.** Die Ameise. *Die Zukunft.* 2 April. — **1898b.** *La parabiose chez le Fourmis. *Bull. Soc. Vaud. Sc. Nat.* (4) 34 : 380–384. — **1899a.** Hymenoptera. III Formicidæ *Biologia Centrali-Americana, London, R. H. Porter, Dulau & Co.* 160 pp., 4 pls. — **1899b.** Trois notices myrmécologiques. *Ann. Soc. Ent. Belg.* 43 : 303–310. — **1899c.** [Excursion myrmécologique dans l'Amérique du Nord.] *Ibid.* 43 : 438–447. — **1899d.** Von Ihrer Königl. Hoheit der Prinzessin Therese von Bayern auf einer Reise in Südamerika gesammelte Insekten. I Hymenopteren a. Fourmis. *Berlin Ent. Zeitschr.* 44 : 273–277, 2 figg. — **1900a.** Hymenoptera. III *Biologia Centrali-Americana London R. H. Porter, Dulau & Co.* pp. 161–169, Title-page. [Index.] — **1900b.** Un nouveau genre et une nouvelle espèce de Myrmicide. *Ann. Soc. Ent. Belg.* 44 : 24–26. — **1900c.** Ponerinæ et Dorylinæ d'Australie. *Ibid.* 44 : 54–77. — **1900d.** *Fourmis de Japon. Nids en toile. Strongylognathus huberi et voisins. Fourmilière triple. Cyphomyrmex wheeleri. Fourmis importées. *Mitth. Schweiz. Ent. Gesell.* 10 : 267–287. — **1900e.** Ebauche sur les mœurs des fourmis de l'Amérique du Nord. *Rivista Sc. Biol.* 2, 3 : 1–13; Transl. in *Psyche* 9 (1901) : 231–239; 243–245. — **1900f.** Ueber nordamerikanische Ameisen. *Verh. Gesell. Deutsch. Nat. Ærzte München* 2, 1 : 239–241. — **1900-'01.** Expériences et Remarques Critiques sur les Sensations des Insectes. *Rivista di Sc. Biol.* I. — 2, 8 (1900) : 1–41, pl. 3; II. — 9–10 (1900) : 1–76; III. — 3, 1–2 (1901) : 1–56. IV. — 3, 3 (1901) : 1–42. V (1901) : 1–60 — **1900-'03.** Les Formicides de l'Empire des Indes et de Ceylan. Pt. 6. *Journ. Bomb. Nat. Hist. Soc.* 12 : 52–65, 303–332, 462–477 ; 14 : 520–546, 679–715. — **1901a.** Variétés myrmécologiques. *Ann. Soc. Ent. Belg.* 45 : 334–382, 2 figg. — **1901b.** *Fourmis termitophages, Lestobiose, Atta tardigrada, sous-genres d'Euponera. *Ibid.* 45 : 389–398, 3 figg. — **1901c.** Formiciden des Naturhistorischen Museums zu Hamburg. Neue Calyptomyrmex-, Dacryon-, Podomyrma- und Echinopla-Arten. *Mitth. Nat. Mus. Hamburg* 18 : 43–82. — **1901d.** Formiciden aus dem Bismarck-Archipel. *Mitth. Zool. Mus. Nat. Berlin* 2, 1 : 37 pp. — **1901e.** Critique des expériences faites dès 1887 avec quelques nouvelles expériences. *Rivista Biol. Gen.* 3, 1–2. — **1901f.** I. Fourmis mexicaines récoltées par M. le professeur W. M. Wheeler. II. A propos de la classification des fourmis. *Ann. Soc. Ent. Belg.* 45 : 123–141. A propos de la classification des formicides par C. Emery, pp. 197–198, 3 figg. — **1901g.** Sketch of the Habits of North American Ants. I. *Psyche* 9 : 231–239. II. 9 : 243–245. — **1901h.** Die psychischen Fähigkeiten der Ameisen und einiger anderer Insekten; mit einem Anhang über die Eigenthümlichkeiten des Geruchsinnes bei jenen Thieren. Vorträge gehalten den 13 August am V. internationalen Zoologen-Kongress zu Berlin. *München, Ernest Reinhardt,* 57 pp. — **1901i.** Nouvelles espèces de Ponerinæ. (Avec un nouveau sous-genre et une espèce nouvelle d'Eciton). *Rev. Suisse Zool.* 9 : 325–353. — **1901j.** Einige neue Ameisen aus Südbrasilien, Java, Natal und Mossamedes. *Mitth. Schweiz. Ent. Gesell.* 10 : 297–311. — **1901k.** *Nuove Specie di Ænictus. *In* Note sulle Dorilini di C. Emery. *Bull. Soc. Ent. Ital.* Trim. I. — **1901l.** Die Eigentümlichkeiten des Geruchssinnes bei den Insekten. *Verh. V. Intern. Zool. Congr. Berl.,* pp. 806–815. — **1901m.** (Ants of Hawaii) In "Fauna Hawaiiensis, pp. 116–122. — **1902a.** Ueber die Empfindlichkeit der Ameisen für Ultraviolett und Röntgen'sche Strahlen. *Zool. Jahrb. Abt. Syst.* 17: 335–338. — **1902b.** Myrmicinæ nouveaux de l'Inde et de Ceylan. *Rev. Suisse Zool.* 10: 165–249. — **1902c.** Fourmis nouvelles d'Australie. *Ibid.* 10: 405–548. — **1902d.** Quatre notices myrmécologiques. *Ann. Soc. Ent. Belg.* 46: 170–182. — **1902e.** Descriptions of some Ants from the Rocky Mountains of Canada (Alberta and British Columbia), collected by Edward Whymper. *Trans. Ent. Soc. London* pp. 699–700.— **1902f.** Les fourmis du Sahara algérien récoltées par le Professor A. Lameere et le Dr. A. Diehl. *Ann. Soc. Ent. Belg.* 46: 147–158. — **1902g.** Fourmis d'Algérie récoltées par M. le Dr. K. Escherich. *Ibid.* 46: 462–463. — **1902h.** Beispiele phylogenetischer Wirkungen und Rückwirkungen bei den Instinkten und dem Körperbau der Ameisen als Belege für die Evolutionslehre und die psychophysiologische Identitätslehre. *Journ. Psych. Neurol.* 1: 99–110. — **1902i.** Variétés myrmécologiques. *Ann. Soc. Ent. Belg.* 46: 284–296. — **1902j.** The Social life of Ants. Transl. by Prof. F. C. de Sumichrast. *Internat. Monthly* 5 and 6: 563–579; 710–724. — **1903a.** Les Fourmis des iles Andamans et Nicobares. Rapports de cette faune avec ses voisines. *Rev. Suisse Zool.* 11: 399–418. — **1903b.** Mélanges entomologiques, biologiques et autres. *Ann. Soc. Ent. Belg.* 47: 249–268. — **1903c.** Recherches biologiques récentes de Miss Adèle Fielde sur les fourmis. *Bull. Soc. Vaud. Sc. Nat.* (4) 39: 95–99. — **1903d.** Die Sitten und Nester einiger Ameisen der Sahara bei Tugurt und Biskra. *Mitth. Schweiz. Ent. Gesell.* 10, 10: 453–459. — **1903e.** Nochmals Herr Dr. Bethe und die Insekten-Psychologie. *Biol. Centralb.* 23: 1–3. — **1903f.** Fauna myrmécologiques des noyers dans le Canton de Vaud. *Bull. Soc. Vaud. Sc. Nat.* (4) 39: 83–94. — **1903g.** Note sur les Fourmis du Musée Zoologique de l'Académie Impériale des Sciences à St. Pétersbourg. *Ann. Mus. Zool. Acad. Sc. St. Pétersb.* 8: 368–388. — **1903-'04.** Ants and Some Other Insects. An Inquiry into the Psychic Powers of These Animals with an Appendix on the Peculiarities of their Olfactory Sense. Transl. by W. M. Wheeler. *Monist* 14, 1 and 2 (Oct. and Jan.). Reprinted as No. 56 *Religion of Science Library*, Chicago, pp. 1–49. — **1904a.** Miscellanea myrmécologiques. *Rev. Suisse Zool.* 12: 1–52, 1 fig. — **1904b.** Fourmis de British Columbia. *Ann. Soc. Ent. Belg.* 48: 152–155. — **1904c.** Fourmis du Musée de Bruxelles. *Ibid.* 48: 168–177. — **1904d.** Ueber Polymorphismus und Variation bei den Ameisen. *Zool. Jahrb. Suppl. 7, Festschr. Weismann* pp. 571–586. — **1904e.** Note sur les Fourmis du Musée Zoologique de l'Académie Impériale des Sciences à St. Pétersbourg. *Annuaire Mus. Zool. Acad. Impér. Sc. St. Pétersb.* 8 (1903): 368–388. — **1904f.** The Psychical Faculties of Ants and some other Insects. *Ann. Rep. Smiths. Inst.* 1903 pp. 587–599. — **1904g.** Formiciden. *Ergebn. Hamburg. Magalhæns. Sammelr.* 7, 8: 7 pp. — **1904h.** Dimorphisme du mâle chez les fourmis et quelques autres notices myrmécologiques. *Ann. Soc. Ent. Belg.* 48: 421–425. — **1904i.** *In und mit Pflanzen lebende Ameisen aus dem Amazonas Gebiet und aus Peru, gesammelt von Herrn E. Ule. *Zool. Jahrb. Abt. Syst.* 20: 677–707. — **1905a.** Einige neue biologische Beobachtungen über Ameisen. *C. R. 6me Congr. Internat. Zool. Berne* pp. 449–456. — **1905b.** Miscellanea myrmécologiques (II). I. Fourmis récoltées au Venezuela par le Dr. Meinert, de Copenhague. *Ann. Soc. Ent. Belg.* 49: 155–160. II. Types de Fabricius du Musée de Copenhague, *Ibid.* pp. 160–162. III. Fourmis de Madagascar, *Ibid.* pp. 162–165. IV. Fourmis des Nicobares, pp. 165–167. V. Fourmis des bambous à São Paolo, *Ibid.* pp. 167–171. VI. Fourmis de Tunisie récoltées par le Dr. Santschi, *Ibid.* pp. 171–177. VII. Fourmis de Trieste et environs récoltées par M. Graeffe, *Ibid.* pp. 177–179. Diversa, *Ibid.* pp. 179–185, 2 figg. — **1905c.** *Sklaverei, Symbiose und Schmarotzertum bei Ameisen. *Mitth. Schweiz. Ent. Gesell.* 2: 85–90. — **1905d.** *Einige biologische Beobachtungen des Herrn Prof. Dr. E. Göldi an brasilianischen Ameisen. *Biol. Centralb.* 25 : 170–181, 7 figg. — **1905e.** Ameisen aus Java. Gesammelt von Prof. Karl Kraepelin 1904. *Mitth. Nat. Mus. Hamburg* 22 : 1–26. — **1905f.** Die sexuelle Frage. *München, Reinhardt.* — **1905g.** A Revision of the Species of Formicidæ (Ants) of New Zealand. *Trans. Proc. New Zealand Inst.* 37 : 353–355. — **1906a.** Fourmis d'Asia mineure et de la Dobrudscha récoltées par M. le Dr. Oscar Vogt et Mme. Cécile Vogt, Dr. méd. *Ann. Soc. Ent. Belg.* 50 : 187–190. — **1906b.** Les fourmis de l'Himalaya. *Bull. Soc. Vaud. Sc. Nat.* (5) 42 : 79–94. — **1906c.** Fourmis néotropiques nouvelles ou peu connues. *Ann. Soc. Ent. Belg.* 50 : 225–249. — **1906d.** *Mœurs des Fourmis parasites des genres Wheeleria et Bothriomyrmex. *Rev. Suisse Zool.* 14 : 51–69, 6 text-figg. — **1906e.** Les Fourmis. L'Énergie et l'Acide Formique. *Lyons Médical.* 107 : 372, 373. — **1907a.** Formicides du Musée National Hongrois. *Ann. Mus. Nat. Hungar.* 5 : 1–42. — **1907b.** Formicides du Musée National Hongrois déterminés et décrits par Prof. A. Forel. *Termez. Füzetek.* — **1907c.** Nova Speco Kaj nova Gentonomo de Formikoj. *Ap. Repr. Intern. Scienca Revuo.* 4. — **1907d.** Formiciden aus dem Naturhistorischen Museum in Hamburg. II. *Mitth. Naturhist. Mus.* 24 : 20 pp. — **1907e.** Formicidæ. Die Fauna Südwest-Australiens I, 7 : 263–310. — **1907f.** Fourmis nouvelles de Kairouan et d'Orient. *Ann. Soc. Ent. Belg.* 51 : 201–208. — **1908a.** *Konflikt zwischen zwei Raubameisenarten. *Biol. Centralbl.* 28 : 445–447. — ***1908b.** Fourmis de Ceylan et d'Égypte récoltées par le Prof. E. Bugnion. Lasius carniolicus. Fourmis de Kerguelen. Pseudandrie? Strongylognathus testaceus. *Bull. Soc. Vaud. Sci. Nat.* (5) 44 : 1–22, 1 pl. — **1908c.** Fourmis de Costa Rica récoltées par M. Paul Biolley. *Ibid.* pp. 35–72. — **1908d.** Remarque sur la réponse de M. le Prof. Emery. (Myrmecocystus viaticus.) *Ibid.* p. 218. — **1908e.** Descriptions d'un Genre Nouveau et de plusieurs Formes Nouvelles de Fourmis du Congo. *Ann. Soc. Ent. Belg.* 52 : 184–189, 2 figg. — **1908f.** Fourmis d'Ethiope récoltées par M. le baron Maurice de Rothschild en 1905. *Rev. d'Ent.* pp. 129–144. — **1908g.** Ameisen aus São Paulo (Brasilien), Paraguay, etc. Gesammelt von Prof. Herm. von Ihering, Dr. Lutz, Dr. Fiebrig, etc. *Verh. K. K. zool. bot. Gesell. Wien,* pp. 340–418, 2 figg. — **1908h.** Lettre à la Société Entomologique de Belgique. *Ann. Soc. Ent. Belg.* 52 : 180, 181. — **1908i.** Catalogo Systematico da Collecçao de formigas do Ceará. *Bol. Mus. Rocha* 1 : 62–69. — **1908k.** (Description of Pheidole anastasii var. cellarum.) *Report of " Der Bot. Gart. u. das Bot. Mus. Univ. Zürich"* for 1907, p. 6.

Forskål, P., 1775. Descr. Animal, p. 85.

Förster, A., 1850. Eine neue Centurie neuer Hymenopteren. *Verh. Naturhist. Ver. Preuss. Rheinlande* 7. — **1850-'56.** Hymenopterologische Studien. 1. Formicariæ; 2. Chalcidiæ, Proctotrupii. *Aachen, ter Meer.* 1 (1850) : 74 pp.; 2 (1856) : 152 pp.

Foster, E., 1908. The Introduction of Iridomyrmex humilis (Mayr) into New Orleans. *Jour. Econ. Ent.* 1, 5 : 289–293.

de Fourcroy, A. F., 1785. Entomologia Parisiensis, 2 : 451–453. — **1802.** Sur la nature chimique des Fourmis, et sur l'existence simultanée de deux acides chimiques dans ces Insectes. *Ann. Mus. Hist. Nat.* 1 : 333.

Fowler, M. A., 1887-'91. *The Coleoptera of the British Islands. *London.* — **1891.** *(Note on a Bug imitating Polyrhachis spiniger.) *Proc. Ent. Soc. London* p. 17.

Fowler, W. W., 1882. *Solenopsis fugax at Sandown, Isle of Wight. *Ent. M. Mag.* (1) 19 (Nov.) : 139. — **1884-'85.** *Atemeles paradoxus, etc., on the Isle of Wight. *Ibid.* (1) 21 : 18. — **1893.** *Coccids in Ants'-nests. *Ibid.* (2) 4 : 17.

Fox, W. H., 1887. *Note on a new Parasite of Camponotus pennsylvanicus.

Proc. Ent. Soc. Wash. I, 2 (Oct. 6) : 100. — **1892.** Notes on a small collection of Formicidæ from Jamaica. *Ent. News* 3 : 9.

Francé, R. H., 1906. Das Liebesleben der Pflanzen. *Stuttgart.*

de Fréitas, M. T. G., 1905. As formigas. *Revista Agricola Rio Grande do Sul.* 8, 4 : 57.

Freyer, C. F., 1836. *Beiträge zur Schmetterlingskunde, 2 : 121. *Augsburg.*

Friederichs, K., 1905. *Zur Kenntnis einiger Insekten und Spinnentiere von Villafranca (Riviera di Ponente). *Zeitschr. Wiss. Insektenbiol.* I : 455–461 ; 493–499, 3 figg.

Friese, H., 1902. Die arktischen Hymenopteren, mit Ausschluss der Tenthrediniden. *Fauna Arctica* 2 : 439–498, I pl., I map.

Frisby, G. E., 1906. Some Habits of the Hymenoptera. *Proc. Holmesdale Nat. Hist. Club* 1902–'05 : 6–20.

Frogatt, W. W., 1896. Honey Ants. *Horn Scient. Exped. Centr. Austral.* 2 : 385–392, I pl. — **1900.** *Australian Psyllidæ. *Proc. Linn. Soc. N. S. Wales* 2 (May 30) : 250–302, pls. II–14. — **1901.** Typical Insects of Central Australia. *Agri. Gaz. N. S. Wales* 511 (Oct.) : 1–10, I pl. — **1905.** Domestic Insects. Ants. With Catalogue of Australasian Species. *Ibid.* 16 : 861–866, I pl. — **1906.** *Rabbits and Ants. *Ibid.* 17 : 1113–1119.

Frohawk, F. W., 1904. *Life History of Lycæna argiades. *Entomol.* 37 : 245–249 ; *Ibid.* 36 : 58–59. — **1906.** *Completion of the Life History of Lycæna arion. *Ibid.* 39 : 145–147, I fig.

Fromholz, C., 1886. Die ägyptische Hausameise, Monomorium pharaonis L. *Berl. Ent. Nachr.* 12, 8.

Fruhstorfer, H., 1896. *[Bericht ueber die Lebensweise der Lycænidenraupen nach Herrn Aitken.] *Berl. Ent. Zeitschr.* 41 (Sitzb.) : 2.

Fukai, T., 1908. The Habits of Polyrhachis lamellidens (in Japanese). *Insect World,* 12, 7.

von Fürth, O., 1903. Vergleichende chemische Physiologie der niederen Tiere. *Jena* pp. 346–348.

Fuss, K., 1853. Notizen und Beiträge zur Insektenfauna Siebenbürgens. *Verh. Mitth. Siebenbürg. Vereins Naturw. Hermannstadt* 4. — **1855.** Beitrag zur Insectenfauna Siebenbürgens. *Ibid.* 4. — **1862.** *(Sammelbericht aus der Rheinprovinz). *Berl. Ent. Zeitschr.* pp. 427–430. — **1865.** *(Sammelbericht aus der Ahr- u. Rheingegend). *Ibid.* pp. 411–413.

GADEAU DE KERVILLE, H., 1884. *Mélanges entomologiques. II. Les métamorphoses du Microdon mutabilis L. *Bull. Soc. Amis. Sc. Nat. Rouen.* pp. 7–12.

Gadeceau, Émile, 1907a. *Les plantes Myrmécophiles. *La Nat. Ann.* 35 Sem., 2 : 295–298, 5 figg. — **1907b.** *Les Fourmis mycophages. *Ibid.* 36 Sem., I : 49–51, 5 figg.

Gallardo, Angel, 1907. De como se fundan los nuevos hormigueros de hormiga negra. *Rev. Jardin. Zool. Buenos Ayres* (2) 3 : 212–216.

Ganin, M., 1869. Ueber die Embryonalhülle der Hymenopteren und Lepidopteren-Embryonen. *Mem. Acad. Imp. Sci. St. Pétersb.*, (7) 14, 5 : 1–18, I pl. — **1876.** Matériaux pour l'histoire du développement postembryonnaire des Insectes (en russe). *Trav. 5 Congr. Soc. Nat. et Méd. Russes. Varsovie.* (Resumé par Hoyer. *Jahr. Anat. Phys. Zeitschr. W. Zool.* 28, 1877.)

Gardiner, J. Stanley, 1906. Notes on the Distribution of the Land and Marine Animals, with a List of the Land Plants and Some Remarks on the Coral Reefs. *Fauna and Geogr. Maldive Laccadive Archip.* 2 (Suppl. 2) : 1046–1079.

Gasperini, R., 1887. Notizie sulla Fauna Imenotterologica Dalmata. II. Formicidæ, Mutillidæ, Scoliadæ, Sapygidæ, Pompilidæ, Chrysididæ. *Zara* (20).

Gauckler, H., 1898. Bombardirende Ameisen. *Insektenbörse* 15 : 46.

Gebien, H., 1905. Das künstliche Ameisennest (Formicarium). *Natur und Schule* 4: 500–508, 2 figg.

Gehlerus, M., 1619. *Formica. Epistola seconda (ad Winceslaum Stephanum Archidecan. Cuttenb.). De gemma formicina. *Dornavius, Amphitheatr. Sap. Socraticæ Joco-Seriæ. Hanov.* pp. 93–95.

Géné, C. G., 1842. Memoria per servire alla Storia Naturale di alcuni Imenotteri. *Mem. Soc. Ital. Resid. Modena.* 23: 30–62.

Gentry, T. G., 1873. *The Milch-cows of the Ants. *Canad. Ent.* 5: 207–208. — **1874.** Observations on Formica flava, and Inferences Deducted Therefrom. *Ibid.* 6: 63–67.

Geoffroy, E. L., 1762. Histoire abrégée des Insectes des environs de Paris. 2: 420–429.

Gerdes, F., 1768. Rön och anmärkningar ofver Swart-Myrorna. *Vetensk. Acad. Handl.* p. 373, Germ. Transl. p. 374.

Germar, E. F., 1818. *Beyträge zur Naturgeschichte der Gattung Claviger. *Mag. der Ent.* 3: 60 — **1834.** *Description du genre Thorictus Silbermann. *Revue Ent.* 2: 15.

Gerstäcker, A., 1858. Diagnosen der von Peters in Mosambique gesammelten Käfer und Hymenoptera. *Ber. Verh. Akad. Berlin* pp. 251–254. — **1863.** Ueber ein merkwürdiges neues Hymenopteron aus der Abtheilung der Aculeata. *Stett. Ent. Zeitschr.* 24: 79–93. — **1872a.** Die Gliederthier-Fauna des Sansibar-Gebietes. Nach dem von Dr. O. Karsten während der v. d. Decken'schen Ost-Africanischen Expedition im Jahre 1862, und v. C. Cooke auf d. Insel Sansibar im Jahre 1864 gesammelten Material. Hymenoptera. — **1872b.** Ueber die verwandtschaftlichen Beziehungen zwischen Dorylus Fab. und Dichthadia Gerst. nebst Beschreibung einer zweiten Dichthadia-Art. Hymenopterologische Beiträge. *Stett. Ent. Zeit.* 33: 254–269. — **1892.** *Bestimmung der von Herrn Dr. Fr. Stuhlmann in Ostafrika gesammelten Hemiptera. *Jahrb. Hamb. Wiss. Anst.* 9, 2.

Gestro, R., 1888. *Nuove specie di Coleotteri (Viaggio di L. Fea in Birmania IV). *Ann. Mus. Civ. Gen.* 26: 87–132. — **1893.** *Cenno sui Paussidi (Viaggio di L. Fea in Birmania XLVI). *Ibid.* 32: 705–709.

Giard, A., 1895a. *Cinquième lettre sur le Margarodes: les fourmis et Thysanoures qui lui sont associés. *Act. Soc. Chile* 4, 5: ccix–ccx. — **1895b.** *Sixième lettre sur le Margarodes: Cyphoderus affinis A. Giard, et Lipura pusilla A. Giard, deux espèces nouvelles de Thysanoures myrmécophiles du Chili. *Ibid.* pp. ccxvii–ccxviii.

Gibson, R. J. H., 1894. *The Mushroom beds of the South American Ants. *Proc. Liverp. Lit. Soc.* 48: 99–105.

Girard, M., 1873-'85. *Les Insectes. Traité Élémentaire d'Entomologie (3 Vol.) 1 Coleoptera.

Giraud, J., 1870. *(Note on Paxylloma cremieri, a parasite of Lasius fuliginosus.) *Ann. Soc. Ent. France* p. lxiv. — **1871.** *Note sur l'Elasmosoma berolinense et description d'une espèce nouvelle (viennense) du même genre. *Ibid.* pp. 299–302.

Gleditsch, J. G., 1749. Descriptio multitudinis insignis Formicarum congregatarum, quæ auroram borealem referebant. *Act. Reg. Soc. Berol.* pp. 46–55; *Berl. Abhandl.* 3: 418; *Gleditsch. Phys. Bot. Œkon. Abhand.* 2: 1–18; *Hamb. Mag.* 8 (1751): 393–408.

Goeldi, Emil A. *Zur Orientirung in der Spinnenfauna Brasiliens. Sonderabdr. aus *Mitth. Osterlande.* N. F. 5: 200–248. — **1905a.** *Beobachtungen über die erste Anlage einer neuen Kolonie von Atta cephalotes *C. R. 6me Congr. Internat. Zool. Berne* pp. 457–458. — **1905b.** *Myrmecologische Mitteilung das Wachsen des Pilzgartens bei Atta cephalotes betreffend. *Ibid.* 508–509.

Goldsmith, E., 1879. On Amber Containing Fossil Insects. *Proc. Acad Nat. Sc. Phila.* pp. 207, 208.

Goodchild, J. G., 1903a. Ants. *Trans. Scott. Nat. Hist. Soc.* 2, 1: 49–72. — 1903b. *Ants in Relation to Flowers. *Trans. Edinb. Field. Soc.* 5: 10–23.

Goudie, J. C., 1898. *Ants and Aphids. *Victorian Natur.* 14: 148. — 1905. Fighting Ants. *Ibid.* 22: 75–76.

Gould, W. (Rev.), 1747. An Account of English Ants. *London, Millar* 109 pp. Ext. *Phil Trans.* 482: 351–365. Extr. *Danz. Wöchtl. Anz.* 1767, 13. Recens. *Hamb. Mag.* 1: 91–101. (Nodier *Bibl. Ent.* p. 24, cites an edition *Oxford* 1746, 8vo.)

Gounelle, E., 1896. Transport de terres affectué par des Fourmis au Brésil. *Bull. Soc. Ent. France* pp. 332–333. — 1900. Sur des bruits produits par deux espèces américaines de Fourmis et de Termites. *Ibid.* pp. 168–169.

de Graaf, H. W., 1854. *Een Kijkje in een Mierennest. *Jarg. K. Zool. Genootsch. Amsterdam* pp. 142–157.

Graber, V., 1882. Die Chordotonalen Sinnesorgane und das Gehör der Insecten. I Morph. Theil. *Arch. Mikr. Anat.* 20: 506–640, pls. 30–35, 6 text-figg.

Gradl, H., 1879. *Biologische Notizen (Über Metœcus und Hetærius). *Ent. Nachr.* pp. 224–225.

Graeffe, Ed., 1906. Beiträge zur Insektenfauna von Tunis. *Verh. Zool.-Bot. Gesell. Wien* 56: 446–471.

Grassi, B., and G. Rovelli, 1889-'90. *Il Sistema dei Tisanuri, fondato sopratutto sullo studio dei Tisanuri Italiani. *Nat. Sicil.*

Gray, G. R., 1832. The Class Insecta arranged by Baron Cuvier, with supplementary additions to each order by Edw. Griffith, and notices of new genera and species. *Animal Kingdom* 15.

Gredler, M. V., 1858. Die Ameisen Tirols. *8. Programm des Gymnasiums in Botzen. — 1859.* Zur geographischen Verbreitung der Ameisen in Oesterreich. *Verh. Zool.-Bot. Gesell. Wien* 9: 127–128. — 1866. *Die Käfer von Tirol. *Bozen.*

Green, E. E., 1896a. On the Habits of the Indian Ant (Œcophylla smaragdina F.). *Trans. Ent. Soc. London Proc.* pp. ix–x. — 1896b. (On the Habits of the Indian Ant, Œcophylla smaragdina Fabr.). (Abstr.) *The Zoologist* (3) 20 (March): 110. — 1896c. Id. *Ent. M. Mag.* (2) 7, 32 (Apr.): 95. — 1900a. Note on the Web-spinning Habits of the "Red Ant" Œcophylla smaragdina. *Journ. Bombay Nat. Hist. Soc.* 13: 181. — 1900b. Note on Dorylus orientalis West. *Indian Mus. Notes* 5: 39. — 1900c. *Note on the Attractive Properties of Certain Larval Hemiptera. *Ent. M. Mag.* 11: 185, 1 fig. — 1902. *On Carnivorous Lycænid Larvæ. *Entomol.* 35: 202. — 1903. Pupæ of the "Red Ant" (Œcophylla smaragdina). *Spolia Zeylanica* 1: 73–74, 1 fig.

Grenier, A., 1863. *Matériaux pour servir à la faune des Coléoptères de France. 1 (July).

Grim, B., 1845. *Die Myrmekophilen in Berlins Umgebung. *Stett. Ent. Zeit.* pp. 123–128; 131–136. — 1852. *Hister ruficornis n. sp. *Ibid.* pp. 221 seq.

Groshans, W. P. F., 1839. Prodromus Faunæ Homeri et Hesiodi (Œstrus, Tettix, Cicada, Gryllus, Formica, etc.). *Lugduni, Batavorum, Luchtmans* p. 32; 1843 p. 43 fascic. post.

Gueinzius, 1851. *Etwas über die Lebensweise einiger Paussiden. Mitgetheilt von C. A. Dohrn. *Stett. Ent. Zeit.* pp. 227–229. Transl. *Proc. Ent. Soc. London* (2) 1: 105–107. — 1858-'59. *On the Habits of Paussidæ, Communicated by Stevens. *Proc. Ent. Soc. London* (2) 5: 2–3.

Guenée, A., 1867. *D'un organe particulier que présente une chenille de Lycæna. *Ann. Soc. Ent. France* 5, 7: 605.

Guérin-Meneville, F. E., 1852. Notice sur une nouvelle espèce de fourmi découverte à Sainte-Domingue par M. A. Sallé et qui fait son nid dans les plaines marécageuses sur les buissons (Myrmica Sallei). *Rev. Mag. Zool.* 4: 73–79.

Guilding, B. A., L., 1829-'33. *An Account of Margarodes, a new genus of Insects found in the neighborhood of Ants'-nests. *Trans. Linn. Soc. London* 16: 115-119, pl. 12.

Gulde, 1897. *Ergates faber. *Ent. Zeitschr. Guben* 10: 150-151.

HAACKE, W., 1886. Ueber die geologische Thätigkeit der Ameisen. *Zool. Gart.* 27: 373-375.

Hacker, L., 1888. *Atome zur Biologie der Käfer. *Wien Ent. Zeitg.* p. 49.

von Hagens, J., 1863a. *Die Gastfreundschaft der Ameisen. *Jahresb. Naturw. Ver. Elberf. Barmen* pp. 111-128. — **1863b.** *[Gäste von Tapinoma (Sammelberichte).] *Berl. Ent. Zeitschr.* p. 233. — **1865a.** *Ueber Ameisengäste. *Ibid.* pp. 105-112. — **1865b.** *Ueber Myrmedonia plicata und erratica. *Ibid.* 112-113. — **1867.** *Ueber Ameisen mit gemischten Colonien. *Ibid.* 101-108. — **1868.** *Einzelne Bemerkungen über Ameisen. *Ibid.* pp. 265-268. — **1879.** *Ueber Hetærius in Ameisennestern. *Ent. Nachr.* pp. 259-260.

von Hagens and Cornelius, 1878. Ameisenfauna von Elberfeld und Umgegend. *Jahresb. Naturw. Ver. Elberf. Barmen* p. 103.

Hagmann, Gottfried, 1907. *Beobachtungen über einen myrmekophilen Schmetterling am Amazonenstrom. *Biol. Centralb.* 27: 337-341, pl. 2.

Haldeman, S. S., 1848. *Cremastocheilus in Ant-nests. *Am. Journ. Sc. Arts* (2) 6: 148; *Ann. Mag. Nat. Hist.* (2) 2: 221-222. — **1849a.** On the Identity of Anomma with Dorylus, suggested by specimens which Dr. Savage found together, and transmitted to illustrate his paper on the Driver Ants. *Proc. Acad. Nat. Sc. Phila.* 4: 200-202. — **1849b.** On several new Hymenoptera of the genera Ampulex, Sigalphus, Chelonus and Dorylus. *Ibid.* 4: 203-204. — **1852.** Insects. *Stansbury's Exploration and Survey of the Valley of the Great Salt Lake of Utah. Philadelphia, Lippincott, Grambo & Co.* pp. 366-379, pls. 9, 10 (pp. 367-368. 3 sp. of Labidus, Figs. 1-9).

Haliday, A. H., 1851. Summary of the Natural History of Ants. *Isis Sundayschool Mag.* 2, 13: 6-10; 2, 14: 30-32.

Haller, G., 1877. *Antennophorus Uhlmanni, ein neuer Gamaside. *Arch. Naturg.* 43: 57. — **1880.** *Die Milben als Parasiten der Wirbellosen, insbesondere der Arthropoden. *Halle a. S.*

Hallier, E., 1887. *Die Symbiose zwischen Ameisen und Pflanzen. *Humboldt* 6: 453-456.

Hamann, O., 1898. Mittheilungen zur Kenntnis der Höhlenfauna. *Zool. Anz.* 21: 529-531; 533-536.

Hamilton, J., 1888-'89. *Catalogue of the Myrmecophilous Coleoptera, with Bibliography and Notes. *Canad. Ent.* 20, 5: 161-166. *Suppl.* 21 (1889), 5: 105-108. — **1889.** *Corrections and Additions to previous Papers. *Ibid.* 21, 6 (June): 101-108. — **1890.** The inhabitants of a hickory nut hull. *Ent. News* 1: 49-50.

Handlirsch, Anton, 1906-'08. Die Fossilen Insekten und die Phylogenie der Rezenten Formen, ix + 1430 pp., 51 pls., 14 text-figg. *Leipzig. Verl. v. Wilh. Engelmann.*

Hanhart, 1825. Von den Kämpfen und Schlachten der Ameisen, nach Huber Recherches sur les mœurs des fourmis indigènes. *Wissenschaftl. Zeitschr. Baseler Hochschule* 2: 62-73.

Hardwicke, T., 1828. *Observations on the Loves of the Ants and the Aphids. *Zool. Journ.* 4: 113-115.

Harrach, 1890. *Ueber das Sammeln von Ameisengästen. *Humboldt* Apr. and May: 143-144; 183-184.

Harrington, W. H., 1891. Note on Amblyopone pallipes, Hald. *Canad. Ent.* 23: 138-139.

Harris, T. W., 1827. *Description of three Species of the genus Cremastocheilus. *Journ. Acad. Nat. Sc. Phila.* (1) 5, 2: 381-389, pl. 13.

Hart, C. A., and H. A. Gleason, 1907. On the Biology of the Sand Areas of Illinois. *Bull. Ill. Lab. Nat. Hist.* 7: 137–272, 16 pls., 1 map.

Hart, J. H., 1893. Natural History Notes. *Council Paper no. 43,* pp. 11–13. *Trinidad.*

Hartmann, A., 1879. *Die Kleinschmetterlinge des europäischen Faunengebietes. Mitth. Münch. Ent. Ver.*

Hartog, M., 1895. On certain habits and instincts of social insects. *Science* 1: 98–100.

von Hasselt, A. F. M., 1890a. *Catalogus Aranearum hucusque in Hollandia inventarum. Supplementum II. Hagæ. Comitum. — 1890b. *(Remarks on myrmecophilous and myrmecophagous Spiders.) *Versl. 45 Zommervergad. Ned. Ent. Ver.* p. xxxiv. — **1891.** *(On the myrmecophagy of Cœlotes atropos.) *Versl. 46 Zommervergad. Ned. Ent. Ver.* p. xxii.

Hatcher, J. B., 1896. Some Localities for Laramie Mammals and Horned Dinosaurs. *Amer. Natur.* 30: 112–120.

Headlee, T. J., and Geo. A. Dean, 1908. The Mound-building Prairie Ant (Pogonomyrmex occidentalis Cresson). *Kans. State Agric. Coll. Bull.* 154: 165–180, 13 figg.

Hecht, E., 1899. *Notes biologiques et histologiques sur la larve d'un Diptère (Microdon mutabilis L.). *Arch. Zool. Expér.* (3) 7: 363–382, 1 pl.

Heer, O., 1848. Ueber die vorweltlichen Käfer von Oeningen, die Florfliegen, fossile Ameisen. *Mitth. Naturf. Gesell. Zürich* 1, 1 and 2.—**1849.** Die Insektenfauna der Tertiärgebilde von Oeningen und von Radoboj in Croatien, II. *Neue Denkschr. Allgem. Schweiz. Gesell. Naturw.* 11: 1–264, 17 pls. — **1852.** Ueber die Hausameise Madeiras. *Züricherischer Jugend 1852 v. der Naturforsch. Gesell.* 54. — **1856.** Ueber die fossilen Insekten von Aix in der Provence. *Viertl. Nat. Gesell. Zürich.* 1: 1–40, 2 pls. — **1867.** Fossile Hymenopteren aus Oeningen und Radoboj. *Neue Denkschr. Allgem. Schweiz. Gesell. Naturw.* 22, 4: 1–42, 3 pls.

Heim, 1896. *Plantes et Fourmis. Relations biologiques. *Rev. Sc.* (4) 5, 4: 103–109, 3 figg.; no. 9 pp. 259–271, 6 figg.; no. 10 pp. 299–303, 1 fig. — **1898.** *The Biologic Relations between Plants and Ants. *Ann. Rep. Smithson. Inst.* 411–455, 6 pls.

von Heister, C., 1860. Einleitung in die Geschichte der Ameisen, Bienen und Termiten. *Naumberg, Trauerschmidt,* 64 pp.

Helfer, J. W., 1859. Schriften über die Tenasserim-Provinzen, den Mergui Archipel und die Andamanen. *Mitth. K. K. Geogr. Gesell. Wien* 3, 1: 167–390; (p. 356, Ants).

Hemsley, W. B., 1883. *Social Life of Ants and Plants. *Gard. Chron.* (2) 20: 71, 72.

Henking, H., 1886. *Nahrungserwerb und Nestbau von Theridium riparium. *Kosmos* 18: 1–11, 4 text-figg. — **1907.** Untersuchungen über die ersten Entwicklungsvorgänge in Eiern der Insekten. III. Specielles und Allgemeines. *Zeitschr. wiss. Zool.* 54.

Hennings, C., 1905. Insekten als Nahrungs- und Heilmittel. *Aus der Natur* 1: 530–536, 8 figg.

Herbst, C., 1901. Formative Reize in der Tierischen Ontogenese. *Leipzig. Arthur Georgi.*

Hermbstaedt. Anmerkungen über die Bereitung der Ameisensäure. *Crells. Chym. Annal.* 2: 209.

Hetschko, Alfred, 1907. *Der Ameisenbesuch bei Centaurea montana L. *Wien Ent. Zeitg.* 26, 10: 329–332.

von Heyden, C. H. G., 1837–'38. *Entomologische Beiträge. *Mus. Senckenberg.* II (1837): 287–299; Separ. 1838. — **1849.** *Beschreibung einer neuen Käfergattung aus der Familie der Pselaphen. *Stett. Ent. Zeitg.* 10: 182–184. —

1855. *Nachricht über eine in Gesellschaft der Ameisen lebende Lepismine. *Ibid.* 16: 368–370.

von Heyden, L., 1870. *Entomologische Reise nach dem südlichen Spanien. *Berlin.* — 1876–'77. *Die Käfer von Nassau und Frankfurt. *Jahrb. Nass. Ver. Naturk.* 29 and 30: 55–412. — 1905. Beiträge zur Kenntnis der Hymenopteren-Fauna der weiteren Umgegend von Frankfurt a. M. x–xii. *Ber. Senckenberg Nat. Gesell. Frankfurt a. M.* pp. 75–87.

Hicks, J. B., 1859. Further Remarks on the Organs of the Antennæ of Insects, described in a paper published in the "Transactions of the Linnean Society," vol. XXII, p. 155. *Trans. Linn. Soc.* 22: 383–399, pl. 67.

Hierne, U., 1753. Tentamen de Duplici formicarum sale tum acido tum volatili. *Tentamen Chemicis* 2: 4. *Stockholm.*

Hilbert, R., 1908. Zur Biologie von Tetramorium cæspitum L. *Zeitschr. Wiss. Insekt.-biol.* 4: 308.

Hildegard (Abbess of St. Rupert), 1533. Physica S. Hildegardis elementorum, fluminium aliquot Germaniæ, metallorum, leguminum, fructuum, et herbarum: arborum et arbustorum: piscium denique, volatilium, et animantium terræ naturas et operationes III libris mirabili experientia posteritati tradens, etc. *Hildegard* pp. 1–121 (pp. 118–119 on Ants and Fleas). *Argentorati apud Joh. Schottam.*

Hilgard, E. W., 1905. The Prairie Mounds of Louisiana. *Science* N. S. 21, 536 (Apr. 7): 551–552.

Hill, J. A., 1905. Fights between Two Species of Ants. *Victorian Natur.* 22: 35–36.

Hilzheimer, Max, 1904. Studien über den Hypopharynx der Hymenopteren. *Jena. Zeitschr. Nat.* 39: 119–150, 1 pl.

Hinds, W. E., 1907a. *Papers on the Cotton Boll Weevil and Related and Associated Insects. An Ant Enemy of the Cotton Boll Weevil. *U. S. Dept. Agri. Div. Ent. Bull.* No. 63: 45–48, 1 fig. — 1907b. *Some Factors in the Natural Control of the Mexican Boll Weevil. *Ibid.* Bull. No. 74, 79 pp., 4 pls., 2 text-figg.

Hochhuth, J. H., 1871. *Enumeration der in den russischen Gouvernements Kiew und Wolhynien bisher aufgefundenen Käfer. *Bull. Soc. Imp. Nat. Moscou* 3: 85 seq.

Hoffer, E., 1890. *Skizzen aus dem Leben unserer heimischen Ameisen. *Mitth. Nat. Ver. Steiermark* 26: 149–171.

Holliday, M., 1904. A Study of Some Ergatogynic Ants. *Zool. Jahrb. Abt. Syst.* 19: 293–328, 16 figg.

Hollman, M., 1883–'84. *Nachtrag zu Brüggemanns Verzeichniss der bisher in der Gegend von Bremen aufgefundenen Käferarten, mit besonderer Berücksichtigung der bei Ameisen gefundenen Käfer. *Abh. Nat. Ver. Bremen* 7: 477–479.

Holmgren, N., 1904. *Ameisen (Formica exsecta Nyl.) als Hügelbildner in Sümpfen. *Zool. Jahrb. Abt. Syst.* 20: 353–370, 14 figg.

Hooke, R., 1667. Micrographia or some physiological descriptions of minute bodies made by magnifying glasses, with observations and inquiries thereupon (p. 203 Formicæ). *London* 38 pls.

Hope, F. W., 1837. Inquiries into the ground for the opinion that Ants lay up stores of food for the Winter. *Trans. Ent. Soc. London* 2 Proc.: 37. — 1840. On some doubts respecting the Œconomy of Ants. *Ibid.* 2: 211–213. — 1845. *Description of some new species of Coleoptera from Adelaide in New Holland. *Ibid.* 4: 106 seq.

Hoppe, T. C., 1755. Verschiedene Nachrichten von Ameisen. *Mylius Physik. Belust.* 3, 25: 1075–1087.

Hopkins, A. D., 1905. Insect Injuries to Forest Products. *Yearbook U. S. Dept. Agric.* 1904: 381–398, 14 figg.

Horn, G. H., 1879. *Monographic Revision of the Species of Cremastocheilus and Synopsis of the Euphoridæ of the United States. *Proc. Am. Phil. Soc.* 18: 382–408, pl. 4. — **1886.** *Concerning Cremastocheilus. *Ent. Amer.* 1: 187, 188.

Horváth, G., 1886. Sur l'intelligence des Fourmis. Suppl. contenant la revue des articles publiés dans la Rovartani Lapok, 3: XII. — **1889.** Papirosból épitö hangyak. *Term.-tud. Közl.* 21: 151, 2 pls.

Hubbard, H. G., 1876-'78. *Notes on the Tree-nests of Termites in Jamaica. *Proc. Bost. Soc. Nat. Hist.* 19: 267–271.

Huber, F., 1804. *Extr. Sulle Formiche, uso delle loro antenne, e loro rapporti coi pidocchi delle piante e coi gallinsetti. *Nuov. Scelt. d'Opusc. Inter.* 1: 206–212.

Huber, P., 1810. *Recherches sur les mœurs des Fourmis indigènes. *Paris et Genèvc,* 1 Vol. — **1861.** Réimpression. *Genève.*

Huber, J., 1905. *Ueber die Koloniengründung bei Atta sexdens. *Biol. Centralb.* 25: 606–619; 625–635, 26 figg. — **1907.** *Idem.* (Transl.) *Smiths. Report for 1906:* 355–367, pls. 1–5. — **1908.** *A origem das colonias de Saúba (Atta sexdens). *Bol. Mus. Goeldi* 5, 1: 223–241.

Huepsch, 1777. Beschreibung einer Maschine die Ameisen und anderen Insekten zu vertilgen. (In Germ. and French.) *Cöln,* 1 pl.

Hutton, F. W., 1904. Index Faunæ Novæ Zealandiæ. *London, Dulau & Co.* (pp. 96, 97, list of Formicidæ).

Hudson, G. V., 1890. (Swarming of Atta antarctica.) *Ent. M. Mag.* (2) 1: 23.

Huth, E., 1886a. *Ameisen als Pflanzenschutz. *Mitth. Ver. Frankfurt a. O.* 4: 101, 138, 171. — **1886b.** *Myrmecophile und myrmekophobe Pflanzen. *Ibid.* 4: 317–337.

VON IHERING, H., 1882. Ueber Schichtenbildung durch Ameisen (Atta cephalotes). *Briefl. Mitth. aus Mundonovo, Rio Grande do Sul, Brasilien.* Oct., 1881. *Neues Jahr. Mineral.* 1: 156, 157. — **1891.** *Die Wechselbeziehungen zwischen Pflanzen und Ameisen in den Tropen. *Das Ausland* 24: 474–477. — **1894.** Die Ameisen von Rio Grande do Sul. *Berl. Ent. Zeitschr.* 39: 321–446, 1 pl. — **1898.** *Die Anlage neuer Colonien und Pilzgärten bei Atta sexdens. *Zool. Anz.* 21: 238–245, 1 fig. — **1903.** Zur Frage nach dem Ursprung der Staatenbildung bei den sozialen Hymenopteren. *Ibid.* 27, 4. — **1905.** A Formiga Cuyabana. *Revista Agricola* 124 (15 Nov.): 511–522, S. Paulo. — **1907.** *Die Cecropien und ihre Schutzameisen. *Engler's Botan. Jahrb.* 39: 666–714, pls. 6–10, 1 text-fig.

Illiger, J. C. W., 1802. Magasin für Insektenkunde, 1: 188.

Imhoff, L., 1838. Insecten der Schweiz. *Basel.* 2. — **1843.** Grosse Schwärme von Formica nigra am 17 Juli 1841. *Ber. üb. Verh. Naturf. Gesell. Basel* 5: 164–180. — **1852.** Ueber eine Art afrikanischer Ameisen. *Ibid.* 19: 175–177.

Istvanffi, G., 1894. *Gombatenyésztö hangyák. *Termes Kozl. Magyar. Tars.* pp. 378–387.

JACOBSON, EDWARD, 1907. Notes on Web-spinning Ants. *Victorian Nat.* 24: 36–38. — **1908.** Verfertigung der Gespinnstnester von Polyrhachis bicolor Sm. auf Java. (Communicated by E. Wasmann.) *Notes Leyden Mus.* 30: 63–67, pl. 6.

Jacobson, Edw., & E. Wasmann, 1905. Beobachtung über Polyrhachis dives auf Java die ihre Larven zum Spinnen der Nester benutzt. *Notes Leyden Mus.* 25: 133–140.

Jacquelin-Duval and Lespis, 1849. *(Observations on the Claviger testaceus found in an Ant's nest.) *Ann. Soc. Ent. France* p. lxxii.

Janet, C., 1872. *(Note on the insects living with Tetramorium cespitum.) *Ibid.* p. li. — **1892.** [Marques extérieurs correspondants aux organes Chordotonaux des Fourmis.] *Ibid.* 61 (Bull.): 247–248. — **1893a.** Nids artificiels en plâtre. Fondation d'une colonie par une femelle isolée. *Bull. Soc. Zool. France* 18: 168. *Paris* 183 4 p. (Note 3). — **1893b.** Sur la production des Sons chez les Fourmis et sur les Organes qui les produisent. *Ann. Soc. Ent. France* 62: 159. (10 p.) (Note 1.). — **1893c.** Appareil pour l'Élevage et l'Observation des Fourmis. *Ibid.* 62: 467 (16 p.), 3 figg. (Note 2). — **1893d.** *Études sur les Fourmis. 3me note Extr. *Bull. Soc. Zool. France* 18: 168–171. — **1893e.** *Sur les Nématodes des glandes pharyngiennes des Fourmis (Pelodera Janeti L. D.). *C. R. Hebd. Ac. Sc. Paris,* Séance du 20 Nov., 1 fig. — **1894a.** Sur l'Anatomie du pétiole de Myrmica rubra. *Mém. Soc. Zool. France* 7: 185, 18 pp., 6 figg. — **1894b.** Sur l'Appareil de stridulation de Myrmica rubra. *Ann. Soc. Ent. France* 63: 109, 9 pp., 2 figg. (Note 6). — **1894c.** Sur la Morphologie du squelette des segments post-thoraciques chez les Myrmicides (Myrmica rubra femelle). *Mém. Soc. Acad. l'Oise* 15: 591. *Beauvais* 9 pp., 11 figg. (Note 5). — **1894d.** *Pelodera des glandes pharyngiennes de Formica rufa. *Mém. Soc. Zool. France* 7: 45 *Paris* 18 pp., 11 figg. (Note 4). — **1894e.** Sur les Nerfs de l'antenne et les organes chordotonaux chez les Fourmis. *C. R. Sé. Acad. Sc. Inst. France* 118: 814, 2 figg. — **1894f.** Sur le Système glandulaire des Fourmis. *Ibid.* 118: 989 (Note 3). — **1895a.** Structures des Membranes articulaires des Tendons et des Muscles (Myrmica, Camponotus, Vespa, Apis). *Limoges,* 26 pp., 5 figg. (Note 12). — **1895b.** Sur les Muscles des Fourmis, des Guêpes et des Abeilles. *C. R. Sé. Acad. Sc. Inst. France* 121: 610, 1 fig. (Note 7). — **1895c.** Sur l'Organe de nettoyage tibio-tarsien de Myrmica rubra. *Ann. Soc. Ent. France* 63: 691 *Paris* 14 pp., 7 figg. (Note 8). — **1896a.** *Sur le Lepismina polypoda et sur ses rapports avec les Fourmis. *Bull. Soc. Ent. France* 65: 131. — **1896b.** *Sur les Rapports des Lépismides myrmécophiles avec les Fourmis. *C. R. Sé. Acad. Sc. Inst. France* 122: 799, 1 fig. (Note 8). — **1896c.** *Les fourmis. *Bull. Soc. Zool. France* 21: 60–93. — **1897a.** *Sur les rapports du Discopoma comata Berlese avec le Lasius mixtus Nylander. *C. R. Acad. Paris* 124, 2: 102–105, 4 figg. (Extr. *Rev. Sc.* (4), 7, 4: 117.) (Note 9.) — **1897b.** *Sur les rapports de l'Antennophorus Uhlmanni Haller avec le Lasius mixtus Nyl. *Ibid.* 124, 11: 583–585, 1 fig. (Transl. *Ann. Mag. Nat. Hist.* (6) 19: 620–623, 1 fig. Ausz. von *R. v. Hanstein, Nat. Rundschau* 12, 33: 422–423; von *S. Sch., Nat. Wochenschr.* 12, 30: 357–358; von *E. K[rause], Prometheus* 8, 403: 620–622, 1 fig. Abstr. *Journ. R. Micr. Soc. London* 3: 203; *Amer. Nat.* 31, 366: 544, 1 fig. 31, 368: 726–728.) (Note 10.) — **1897c.** Études sur les Fourmis, les Guêpes et les Abeilles. Limites morphologiques des anneaux post-céphaliques et musculature des anneaux post-thoraciques chez la Myrmica rubra. *Lille, le Bigot frères,* 36 pp., 10 figg. (Note 16). — **1897d.** *Appareils pour l'Observation des Fourmis et des Animaux myrmécophiles. *Mém. Soc. Zool. France* 10: 302, *Paris* 22 pp., 3 figg. 1 pl. (Note 15). — **1897e.** *Rapports des animaux myrmécophiles avec les fourmis. *Limoges, Ducourtieux,* 100 pp. (Abstr. *Nat. Sc.* 12: 323–327.) (Note 14.) — **1897f.** *Sur le Lasius mixtus, l'Antennophorus uhlmanni, etc. *Limoges,* 62 pp., 16 figg. (Note 13). — **1897g.** Les Fourmis. *Expos. Intern. Bruxelles, Section des Sciences. Bruxelles, Hayez,* 56 pp., figg. — **1898a.** Sur un organe non décrit, servant à la fermeture du réservoir du venin et sur le mode de fonctionnement de l'aiguillon chez les fourmis. *C. R. Acad. Sc. Paris* 127: 638–641, 13 figg. — **1898b.** Études sur les fourmis, les guêpes et les abeilles. Anatomie du corselet de la Myrmica rubra reine. *Mém. Soc. Zool. France* 11: 393–449, 1 pl., 25 figg. (Note 19). — **1898c.** Études sur les Fourmis, les Guêpes et les Abeilles. Aiguillon de la Myrmica rubra. Appareil de fermeture de la glande à venin. *Paris, G. Carré et C. Naud,* 27 pp., 3 pls., 5 figg. (Note 18). — **1898d.** Études sur les Fourmis, les Guêpes et les Abeilles. Système glandulaire tégumentaire de la Myrmica rubra. Observations diverses sur les Fourmis. *Paris, Geo. Carré et C. Naud,* 28 pp., 9 figg. (Note 17). — **1898e.** Sur une cavité du tégument servant, chez les Myrmicinæ, à étaler, au contact de l'air, un produit de sécrétion. *C. R. Acad. Sc. Paris* 126: 1168–1171 (Note 12). — **1898f.** Sur les Limites morphologiques des Anneaux du tégument et sur la situation des membranes articulaires chez les Hyménoptères arrivés à l'état d'imago. *C. R. Sé. Acad. Sc. Inst. France* 126: 435, 3 figg. (Note 11'). — **1898g.** Réaction alcaline des chambres et galeries des nids de Fourmis. Durée de la vie des Fourmis décapitées. *C. R. Acad. Sc. Paris* 127: 130–133. — **1898h.** *Observations de M. Piepers sur des chenilles myrmécoïdes. *Bull. Soc. Zool. France* 23: 130–131. — **1899a.** Sur le présence de nymphes nues dans les nids de Lasius flavus. *Ibid.* 24: 192–193. — **1899b.** Sur les nerfs céphaliques, les corpora allata et le tentorium de la fourmi (Myrmica rubra L.). *Mém. Soc. Zool. France* 12: 295–335, 4 pls., 3 figg. (Note 20). — **1899c.** Sur les corpuscles de nettoyage des fourmis. *Bull. Soc. Zool. France* 24: 177–178. — **1902.** Anatomie du gaster de la Myrmica rubra. *Paris, Geo. Carré et C. Naud,* 68 pp., 9 pls., 18 figg. — **1904.** *Observations sur les fourmis. *Limoges, Ducourtieux et Gout,* 68 pp., 7 pls., 11 figg. — **1905.** Anatomie de la tête du Lasius niger. *Limoges, Impr. Ducourtieux et Gout,* 40 pp., 5 pls., 2 figg. — **1906a.** Remplacement des Muscles Vibrateurs du Vol par des colonnes d'Adipocytes, chez les Fourmis après le Vol Nuptial. *C. R. Acad. Sc.* 142: 1095–1098, 2 figg. (Note 16). — **1906b.** Sur un Organe non décrit du thorax des Fourmis ailées. *Ibid.* 143: 522–524, 1 fig. (Note 17). — **1907a.** Histolyse, sans phagocytose, des muscles vibrateurs du vol, chez les reines des Fourmis. *Ibid.* 144: 393–396, 4 figg. — **1907b.** Histogénèse du Tissu adipeux remplaçant les muscles vibrateurs histolysés après le Vol nuptial, chez les reines des Fourmis. *Ibid.* 144: 1070–1073, 22 figg. — **1907c.** Histolyse des Muscles de mise en place des ailes, après le vol nuptial, chez les reines de Fourmis. *C. R. S. Acad. Sci. Paris* 145: 1205–1208, 1 fig. — **1907d.** Anatomie du Corselet et Histolyse des Muscles Vibrateurs, après le vol Nuptial, chez la Reine de la Fourmi (Lasius niger). *Limoges, Ducourtieux et Gout,* 149 + 20 pp., 13 pls.

Jankowsky, R., 1894. Ein neuer Forstschädling. *Centralb. d. Ges. Forstwesen.* 20: 431–434.

Janson, E. W., 1856. *New British Species noticed. *Ent. Ann.* p. 69. — **1857.** *Observations on the myrmecophilous Coleoptera or Ants'-nest Beetles of Britain. Accompanied by plain instructions for obtaining them, and a list of the species hitherto ascertained as indigenous. *Ibid.* pp. 85–96. — **1858.** *Notes on Ants'-nest Beetles. *Ibid.* pp. 78–84. — **1866-'67.** *Myrmedonia plicata at Bournemouth. *Entom.* 3: 44.

Jaworowski, A., 1884. O mrówkach (On ants). *Przyrodnik Tarnow.* 5: 129–136; 145–153; 161–172; 177–189; 193–197.

Jerdon, T. C., 1854. A Catalogue of the Species of Ants found in Southern India. *Ann. Mag. Nat. Hist.* (2) 13: 45–56. 100–110.

Jervis-Smith, Fredk. J., 1899. A Note on Catching Insects and the Behavior of the Bulldog Ant of South Australia. *Nature* 59: 295.

Johansen, J. P., 1904. *Om Undersögelse af Myretuer samt Fortegnelse over de i Danmark fundne saakaldte myrmecophile Biller. *Ent. Meddels Kjöbenhavn.* (2) 2: 217–265.

Johnson, W. F., 1907. Notes on Irish Hymenoptera. *Irish Nat.* 16: 244–247.

Joseph, G., 1882. Erfahrungen in wissenschaftlichem Sammeln und Beobachten der den Krainer Tropfsteingrotten eigenen Arthropoden (Typhlopone Clausii). *Berl. Ent. Zeitschr.* 1.

Jordain, Francis C. R., 1903. Staffordshire Aculeate Hymenoptera. *Ann. Rep. Trans. N. Stafford. Nat. Field Club* 37: 81–87.

Julin, J., 1803. Et stråcktåg flygande myror, anmärkt i Uleåborg 20 Jun. 1798. *Vet. Acad. Nya. Handl.* 24: 101–107.

Junker, 1881. (An Excellent edible oil procured from Ants by the negroes of Central Africa.) *Geogr. M. T.* 27: 153.

Jurine, L., 1807. Nouvelle Méthode de classer les Hyménoptères et les Diptères 1: 269–282.

KALM, 1748. Travels, 1: 238.

Kaltenbach, J. H., 1843. *Monographie der Familien der Pflanzenläuse (Phytophthires). 1. Die Blatt- und Erdläuse. *Aachen.*

Karawaiew, W., 1897. Vorläufige Mittheilung über die innere Metamorphose bei Ameisen. *Zool. Anz.* 20, 543: 415–422. (Abstr., *Journ. R. Micr. Soc. London* 1898. 1: 72.) — 1898. Die nachembryonale Entwicklung von Lasius flavus. *Zeitschr. Wiss. Zool.* 64: 385–478, 4 pls., 15 figg. — 1900. La métamorphose intérieure chez les larves de fourmies. *Mém. Soc. Nat. Kiew* 16: xli–xlii. (In Russian.) — 1903. On the observation of ants in artificial plaster nests. *Rev. Russe Ent.* 3: 94–98; 174–176. (In Russian.) — 1905a. Deux observations sur la vie des fourmis. *Mém. Soc. Nat. Kiew* 19 (1902): xlvii–l. (In Russian.) — 1905b. Versuche an Ameisen in Bezug auf das Uebertragen der Larven in die Dunkelheit. *Zeitschr. Wiss. Insekt.-biol.* 1: 215–244; 257–267. — 1905c. *Antennophorus uhlmanni Hall. und seine biologischen Beziehungen zu Lasius fuliginosus und zu anderen Ameisen. *Mém. Soc. Nat. Kiew* 19 (1903): 193–241, 1 pl., 2 figg. (In Russian.) — 1905d. Versuche an Ameisen in Bezug des Uebertragens der Larven in die Dunkelheit. *Ibid.* 20: 61–95. (In Russian.) — 1905e. Observations sur les fourmis dans les fourmilières artificielles de gypse. *Ibid.* 19 (1902): xxxv–xlv. (In Russian.) — 1905f. *Versuche über die internationalen Beziehungen einiger Antennophorus-Arten, nebst einigen systematischen Bemerkungen. *Zeitschr. Wiss. Insekt.-biol.* 1: 485–493. — 1906a. *Weitere Beobachtungen über Arten der Gattung Antennophorus. *Mém. Soc. Nat. Kiew* 20: 209–229. (In Russian with German resumé.) — 1906b. Systematisch-Biologisches über drei Ameisen aus Buitenzorg. *Zeitschr. Wiss. Insekt.-biol.* 2, 12: 369–376, 16 figg.

Karpelles, L., 1893. *Bausteine zu einer Acarofauna Ungarns. *Math. Nat. Ber. Ung.* 11.

Katuric, M., 1892a. Osservazioni biologiche sulle Formiche. *Glasnik Naravosl. Druzt.* 2: 105–110. — 1892b. Ulteriori osservazioni biologiche sulle Formiche. *Ibid.* 6: 14–28.

Keller, C., 1892. *Neue Beobachtungen über Symbiose zwischen Ameisen und Akazien. *Zool. Anz.* 388: 137–143. — 1906-'07. *Une collection de galles. *C. R. Soc. Helvét. Sc. Nat.* 89 Sess., p. 86. Eine Sammlung von Gallen aus dem Mittelmeergebiet. *Verh. Schweiz. Nat. Ges.* 89. Vers. p. 76–77.

Kellogg, V. L., 1905. American Insects. *New York, Henry Holt & Co.*, 674 pp., 13 pls., 812 figg.

Kellogg, V. L., and Ruby G. Bell, 1904. Studies of Variation in Insects. *Proc. Wash. Acad. Sc.* 6 (Dec. 14): 203–332, 81 figg.

Kerner, A., 1878. *Flowers and their unbidden Guests. Transl. by W. Ogle.

Kienitz-Gerloff, F., 1899. Besitzen die Ameisen Intelligenz? *Naturw. Wochenschr.* 14: 225–231; 240–243, 3 figg. Bemerkungen von G. Vorbringer, pp. 280–281.

Kieffer, J. J., 1904. *Nouveaux Proctotrypides myrmécophiles. *Bull. Soc. Hist. Nat. Metz.* (2) 11.

von Kiesenwetter, H., 1843. *Ueber einige Myrmekophilen. *Stett. Ent. Zeitg.* pp. 306–310. — 1861. *Beitrag zur Käferfauna Griechenlands. VII. *Berl. Ent. Zeitschr.* pp. 221–252. — 1865. *Eine entomologische Excursion nach

Spanien im Sommer. *Ibid.* pp. 359–396. — **1872.** *Uebersicht über die Arten der Gattung Merophysia. *Ibid.* pp. 163–166.

King, E., 1667. Observations concerning Emmets or Ants, their eggs, production, progress, coming to maturity, use. *Philos. Trans.* 2, 23: 425–428.

King, Geo. B., 1895. The Study of the Formicidæ of Lawrence, Mass. *Ent. News* 6, 7: 220–223. — **1897a.** *A New Ant-nest Coccid. *Psyche* 8: 150–151, 2 figg. — **1897b.** *Some Ants and Myrmecophilous Insects from Toronto. *Canad. Ent.* 29: 100–103. — **1897c.** Naked and Cocoon Pupæ of Ants. *Ibid.* 29: 147. — **1898-'99.** *China Asters infested by a Coccid. *Psyche* 8: 312. — **1901a.** A Check-List of the Massachusetts Formicidæ, with some Notes on the Species. *Ibid.* 9: 260–262. — **1901b.** Some New Records of the New England Formicidæ. *Ibid.* 9: 270–271. — **1902a.** Further Notes on New England Formicidæ. *Ibid.* 9: 367–368. — **1902b.** *Two New Ants'-nest Coccids from Texas. *Canad. Ent.* 34: 285–286.

King, Geo. B., and T. D. A. Cockerell, 1897. *New Coccidæ found Associated with Ants. *Ibid.* 29: 90–93.

King, Geo. B., and J. D. Tinsley, 1898. *A New Ant-nest Coccid [D. Cockerelli n. sp. in the nest of Lasius flavus]. *Psyche* 8: 297–298.

King, R. L., 1866a. *On the Pselaphidæ of Australia. *Trans. Ent. Soc. N. S. Wales* 1, 5. — **1866b.** *Description of Anapestus Kreusteri, a species of Coleopterous Insect inhabiting Ants'-nests in South Australia. *Ibid.* 1, 5: 316 seq. — **1869a.** *Description of New Species of Articerus. *Ibid.* 2, 1: 54–57. — **1869b.** *Description of Hiketes, a New Genus of Formicicolous Coleoptera. *Ibid.* 2, 1: 76–78.

Kirby, W., 1837a. Fauna Boreali-Americana, or the Zoology of the Northern Parts of British America. Part 4. Insects. — **1837b.** On the History, Habits and Instincts of Animals. 7th Bridgewater Treatise, *2d Am. Ed. Phila. Carey, Lea & Blanchard.*

Kirby, W. F., 1883. Mental Status of Ants. Evolution and Natural Theology, pp. 149–150. — **1884.** On the Hymenoptera Collected during the Recent Expedition of H. M. S. "Challenger." Formicidæ. *Ann. Mag. Nat. Hist.* (5) 13: 404–406. — **1888.** On the Insects (exclusive of Coleoptera and Lepidoptera) of Christmas Island. *Proc. Zool. Soc.* pp. 546–555. — **1898.** Marvels of Ant Life. *London, S. W. Partridge & Co.* 174 pp., figg.

Kirchner, L. A., 1855. *Beobachtungen über einige bei der Formica rufa wohnende Käfer. *Lotos* 5: 233. — **1867.** Catalogus Hymenopterorum Europæ, pp. 226–230.

Kirsch, Th., 1875. *(Notice on the occurrence of Centrotoma lucifuga with Tetramorium cespitum.) *Deutsch. Ent. Zeitschr.* p. 400.

Kittel, G., 1873-'84. *Systematische Uebersicht der Käfer, welche in Baiern und der nächsten Umgebung vorkommen. *Correspondenzbl. Zool. Min. Ver. Regensburg.*

Klapálek, Fr., 1896. Obojetník Camponotus ligniperdus Ltr. *Sitz.-Ber. Böhm. Ges. Wiss. Math.-Nat. Cl.; Věstn. Česke Spolecn. Náuk. Tř. Math.-Přírod.* 28, 2 figg.

Klug, J. Ch. F., 1853-'54. Note zu den auf Taf, 3 1853, abgebildeten Hermaphroditen. *Stett. Ent. Zeitg.* 15: 102–103. (Pl. 3, 1853.) — **1855.** Ueber die Ameisen in Ceylon. *Ber. Verh. Akad. Berl.* p. 683.

Knauer, Fr. 1883. Aus dem Leben der Ameisen. *Der Naturhistoriker.* 5: 340–351. — **1904.** Neues über Ameisen und Termiten. *Die Umschau.* 8. — **1906.** Die Ameisen. Aus *Natur u. Geisteswelt, Leipzig (Teubner)* 94: 156 pp., 61 figg.

Knaus, W., 1908. *Notes on Coleoptera. *Canad. Ent.* 40 (March): 91, 92.

Kneissl, L., 1908. *Nachtrag zur Beschreibung von Uropoda Wasmanni. Aufstellung einer neuen Varietät U. philoctena var. schmitzi m. *Zeitschr. Wiss. Ins.-biol.* 4: 226–229, 2 figg.

Koch, C.. L., 1857. *Die Pflanzenläuse (Aphiden). *Nürnberg.*

Kohl, Franz Friedrich, 1907. Zoologische Ergebnisse der Expedition der kaiserlichen Akademie der Wissenschaften nach Südarabien und Sokótra im Jahre 1898–1899. Hymenopteren. *Denkschr. Akad. Wiss. Wien* 71: 168–301, 11 pls.

Kolbe, J. H., 1884. *Beitrag zur Biologie der Aphiden. *Berl. Ent. Zeitschr.* p. 343.—**1890.** *Die getreidesammelnden und die ackerbautreibenden Ameisen. *Naturw. Wochenschr.* 5, 20: 193–195.—**1903.** *Ueber myrmekophile Insekten, speciell über Thorictus foreli Wasm. *SB. Ges. Naturf. Berlin,* pp. 237–253.

Kolenati, F. A., 1858. *Epizoon der Waldameise. *Wien Ent. Monatschr.* 2: 86–87.

Korlević, A., 1886. Forró földöri hangya Magyarországban. *Rovart. Lapok.* 3, 1: 18.

Koster, H., 1818. Ueber Ameisen Brasiliens. *Isis* 22: 2067–2073.

Kraatz, G., 1849. *Bemerkungen über myrmekophilen. I. *Stett. Ent. Zeitg.* pp. 184–187.—**1851.** *Id. II. *Ibid.* pp. 166–170.—**1857.** *Genera Aleocharinorum illustrata. *Linn. Ent.* 11: 1–43.—**1858a.** *Naturgeschichte der Insekten Deutschlands. Coleoptera. 2 Staphylinidæ. *Berlin.*—**1858b.** *Beitrag zur Käferfauna Griechenlands. *Berl. Ent. Zeitschr.* p. 140 seq.—**1892a.** *Paussus cervinus n. sp. *Deutsch. Ent. Zeitschr.* p. 8.—**1892b.** *Paussus opacus n. sp. *Ibid.* p. 377.—**1894.** *Zwei neue Paussus aus Madagascar. *Ibid.* pp. 317–318.

Kraepelin, K., 1873. Untersuchungen über den Bau, Mechanismus und die Entwickelungsgeschichte des Stachels der bienenartigen Thiere. *Zeitschr. Wiss. Zool.* 23: 303–305.—**1883.** Ueber die Geruchsorgane der Gliedertiere. *Program. Realschule des Johanneums zu Hamburg. Ostern* 48 pp., 3 pls.—**1903.** Einiges über Ameisennester. *Verh. Nat. Ver. Hamburg* (3) 10: xlvii.

Krausse, A. H., 1902. Einiges Terminologische über die Begriffe "Reflex," "Instinkt," "Intelligenz," "Modificationsvermögen," "Automatismus," "Plasticität," "Kleronomie," und "eubiontische Qualität," speciell in der Ameisenpsychologie. *Insektenbörse* 19: 259–260.—**1903a.** Erkennen Ameisen einer Kolonie andere, derselben Art angehörenden, aber aus einer andern Kolonie stammenden Ameisen? *Nerthus* 5: 7–8.—**1903b.** Die moderne Ameisen-Biologie und Psychologie. *Ibid.* 5: 493–496; 688–690.—**1904.** Lasius flavus Ltr., Tetramorium cæspitum L., and Formica nigra L. Biologische Beobachtungen. *Ent. Jahrb.* 14: 214–216.—**1907.** Die antennalen Sinnesorgane der Ameisen in ihrer Zahl u. Verteilung bei den Geschlechtern und Individuen einiger Arten. *Inaug. Dissert. Jena. Gust. Fischer.* 40 pp., 8 figg.

Kronfeld, 1890. *Ueber die künstliche Besiedelung einer Pflanze mit Ameisen. *Tag. Deutsch. Nat. Vers.* 62: 262.

Kubes, A., 1904. Ze života mravenčího. *Časop. Česke Společn. Ent. Acta Soc. Ent. Bohem. Ročn.* 1: 46–49.—**1905.** Fauna Bohemica. 1. Seznam českého hmyzu blanokřídleho. *Ibid.* 2: 81–86.

Kuhlgatz, Th., 1902. *Vorstudien über die Fauna des Betula-nana-hochmoores im Culmer Kreis in Westpreussen. *Nord. Wochenschr.* N. F. 1: 613.

LABOULBÈNE, A., 1882. *[On the metamorphoses of Microdon mutabilis.] *Ann. Soc. Ent. France* pp. xcvi–cvi.

Lacaze-Duthiers, H., 1850. Recherches sur l'armure génitale femelle des insectes. *Ann. Sc. Nat. Zool.* (3) 14: 17–52.

Lagerheim, G., 1900. *Ueber Lasius fuliginosus (Latr.) und seine Pilzzucht. *Ent. Tidskr.* 21: 17–29, 4 figg.

de Lamarche, C., 1900. La Cigale et la Fourmi. *Le Cosmos* N. S. 42: 423–425.

Lameere, A., 1892. Note sur les Fourmis de la Belgique. *Ann. Soc. Ent. Belg.* 36: 61–69. — **1902.** *Note sur les mœurs des fourmis du Sahara. *Ibid.* 46: 160–169.

Lampert, K., 1901. Aus dem Leben der Ameisen. *Jahresb. Ver. Vaterl. Naturk. Württemberg* 57: cxviii–cxxi.

Landois, H., 1874. Stridulationsapparat bei Ameisen. *31 General Versamml. Nat. Ver. Preuss. Rheinl.* p. 820.

Leney, A., 1893. Le chêne-liège, sa culture et son exploitation. *Paris et Nancy.*

Langkavel, B., 1884. Ameisen. *Zool. Garten.* 25, 11: 348–349.

Langstroth, 1852. [Honey-ants from Matamoras, Mexico.] *Proc. Acad. Nat. Sc. Phila.* 6: 71.

de Lannoy, F., 1906. Notes sur les mœurs du Lasius niger. *Ann. Soc. Ent. Belg.* 50: 43–46. — **1908.** Notes sur le Lasius niger et le Lasius fuliginosus. *Ibid.* 52: 47–53.

Lataste, F., 1896. *Quelques observations sur l'étiologie du Brachymyrmex Giardi Emery. *Act. Soc. Sc. Chili* 6, 2–3, Mém.: 84–88.

Latreille, P. A., 1798a. *Journ. Santé Bordeaux* 3: 141 (n. n.). — **1798b.** Essai sur l'histoire des Fourmis de la France. *Brives* An 6. — **1799.** Observations sur la Fourmi fongueuse de Fabricius. *Bull. Soc. Philom.* 2, 1, 25, fig. (Germ. Transl. *Wiedemann's Arch.* 2, 1: 181–182.) — **1802a.** Description d'une nouvelle espèce de Fourmi (F. coarctata). *Bull. Soc. Philom.* 3: 65. — **1802b.** Histoire Naturelle des Fourmis. *Paris* An. 10, 1 Vol. — **1802-'05.** Histoire Naturelle Générale et Particulière des Crustacés et des Insectes. *Paris.* — **1806-'09.** Genera Crustaceorum et Insectorum. 4 vols. *Paris, Amand Kœnig.* — **1817.** *Considerations nouvelles et générales sur les Insectes vivant en Société. *Mém. Mus. Hist. Nat.* 3: 407. — **1818.** Nouveau dictionnaire d'histoire naturelle de Déterville. *Les Insectes par Latreille.*

Lea, A. M., 1893. *Note on Insects Inhabiting Ants'- and Termites'-nests in New South Wales. *Proc. Linn. Soc.* N. S. Oct. 25. — **1905.** *On Nepharis and other Ants'-nest Beetles taken by Mr. J. C. Goudie at Birchip. *Proc. R. Soc. Vict.* 17: 371–385, 1 pl.

Leach, W. E., 1825. Descriptions of thirteen species of Formica and three species of Culex from Nice. *Zool. Journ.* 2: 289–293. — **1825-'26.** *On the stirpes and genera composing the family Pselaphidæ, with descriptions of some new species. *Ibid.* 2, 8: 445.

Ledebur, A., 1901. *Ueber Pilze züchtende Ameisen. *Nerthus* 3: 411–414; 422–425.

Leder, H., 1872. *Beschreibungen neuer Käfer aus Oran. *Berl. Ent. Zeitschr.* pp. 137–139.

Leesberg, A. F. A., 1906. Mieren als levende deuren. *Ent. Ber.* 2: 62–63.

von Leeuwenhoeck, Ant., 1719. Arcana Naturæ 2: 79.

Leidy, J., 1852. [Anatomy of Honey-Ants.] *Proc. Acad. Nat. Sc. Phila.* 6: 72. — **1877a.** *Remarks on the Yellow Ant. *Ibid.* p. 145. — **1877b.** *Remarks on Ants. *Ibid.* 3 (Sept.–Dec.): 304–305. — **1877c.** Circumspection of Ants. *Ibid.* 3 (Sept.–Dec.): 320; *Am. Journ.* (Sillim.) (3) 15, 88 (Apr.): 320–321. — **1882.** *The Yellow Ant and its flock of Aphis and Coccus. *Ibid.* 148. — **1884.** *(Camponotus pennsylvanicus De Geer, permeated by a fungus.) p. 9, *Phila.*

Lemoine, F., 1896. Observations biologiques et anatomiques à propos de trois fourmilières artificielles. *Bull. Soc. Ent. France* 4 bis: 129–131.

Lentz, F. L., 1857. *Neues Verzeichniss der preussischen Käfer. *Königsberg.*

Lepeletier de Saint-Fargeau, 1836. *Histoire Naturelle des Insectes Hyménoptères. 1. *Paris, Roret.*

Lesne, P., 1905. *Les rélations des fourmis avec les hémiptères homoptères de la famille des fulgorides. Domestication des Tettigometra. *C. R. Soc. Biol. Paris* 58: 1005.

Lespès, C., 1885. *(Note on the habits of Lomechusa paradoxa.) *Ann. Soc. Ent. France* p. li. — **1863.** Observations sur les Fourmis Neutres. *Ann. Sc. Nat. Zool.* (4) 19: 241. — **1866.** Conférence sur les Fourmis fait aux Soirées Scientifiques de la Sorbonne et publiée dans la Revue des Cours Scientifiques, 3 (Mar. 17): 257–265. — **1868a.** *(Note on the habits of various Clavigers.) *Ann. Soc. Ent. France* p. xxxviii. — **1868b.** *Sur la domestication des Clavigers par les Fourmis. *Bull. Soc. Anthr. Paris* (2) 3: 314–316.

Letzner, K., 1885-'88. *Verzeichniss der Käfer Schlesiens. *Schles. Zeitschr. Ent. Breslau.*

Lewis, G., 1884. *On some Histeridæ, new to the Japanese Fauna, and notes on others. *Ann. Mag. Nat. Hist.* (5) 13: 131–140. — **1885.** *On new species of Histeridæ. *Ibid.* (5) 15: 456 seq. — **1888a.** *On the Capture of Formicarious Histeridæ. *Entomol.* 21: 289–294. (Transl. *Rév. d'Entom.* pp. 61–66.) — **1888b.** *On new species of Formicarious Histeridæ, and notes on others. *Ann. Mag. Nat. Hist.* (6) 2: 144–155. — **1891.** *On the structure of Claws in Sternocœlis and Hetærius and notes on the geographical distribution of the species. *Ent. M. Mag.* (2) 2: 161–162. — **1892a.** On Eretmotus and Epiechinus. *Ann. Mag. Nat. Hist.* (6) 10: 231–236. — **1892b.** *Note on Sternocœlis, and on one new species. *Ent. M. Mag.* (2) 3: 236. — **1893.** *On new species of Histeridæ, and notes on others. *Ann. Mag. Nat. Hist.* (6) 11: 417–430.

Lewis, R. T., 1896. Note on a Stridulating Organ in a South African Ant, Streblognathus æthiopicus. *Journ. Quekett Micr. Club* (2) 6: 271–274, 1 pl.

Leydig, Fr., 1859. Zur Anatomie der Insekten. *Müller's Archiv. Anat. Physiol.* pp. 56–59, pls. 2–4. — **1864.** Vom Bau des thierischen Körpers, 1: 233, 236. — **1867.** Der Eierstock und die Samentasche der Insekten. *Verh. K. Leop. Carol. Deutsch. Acad. Naturf.* p. 21.

Lichtenstein, A. A. H., 1796. Catalogus Rerum Naturalium Rarissimarum. *Hamburg,* 3: 211.

Lichtenstein, J., 1870. *(Note on the relations of Tettigometra to the ants.) *Pet. Nouv. Ent.* 19: 74. — **1877-'80.** *(Note on the habits of Aphids and Tettigometra.) *Mitth. Schweiz. Ent. Gesell.* 5: 301–302. — **1880.** *(Note on the relations of ants to plant-lice.) *Ann. Soc. Ent. France* pp. ciii–cv. — **1884.** (Dichthadia and Labidus noticed.) *Bull. Soc. Ent. France* (6) 4: l. — **1885.** *Les Pucerons. Monographie des Aphidiens. 1. *Montpellier.*

Liebald, B., 1886. Hangyák a gyümölcsfan. *Gyümölcsészeti es konyhakertészeti Füzetek* 7: 122.

Liebeck, C., 1890. *Habits of Hatærius brunneipennis. *Ent. News* 2, 6: 120.

Liebrecht, F., 1874. Review of F. Schiern's article "Ueber den Ursprung der Sage von den goldgrabenden Ameisen." *Zeitschr. Ethnol.* 6: 98–101.

Lincecum, G., 1862. *Notice on the Habits of the "Agricultural Ants" of Texas ("Stinging Ant" or "Mound-making Ant,") Myrmica (Atta) molefaciens Buckley. Communicated by Charles Darwin. *Journ. Proc. Linn. Soc. Zool.* 6: 29–31. — **1866.** *On the Agricultural Ant of Texas. *Proc. Acad. Nat. Sc. Phila.* 18: 323–331. — **1867.** *The Cutting Ant of Texas (Œcodoma texana). *Ibid.* p. 24. — **1874a.** *The Agricultural Ant. *Am. Nat.* 8, 9: 513–517. — **1874b.** Robber Ants. *Ibid.* 8, 9: 564. — **1874c.** Sweet-scented Ants. *Ibid.* 8, 9: 564.

Linder, C., 1908. Observations sur les Fourmilières-Boussoles. *Bull. Soc. Vaud. Sci. Nat.* (5) 44: 303–310, 6 figg.

von Linné, Carl, 1735. Systema Naturæ T., 1. — **1741.** Anmaerkningar öfver Wisen hos Myrorne. *Vetenk. Akad. Handl.* pp. 37–49; 2nd. ed. pp. 36–48.

— 1761. Fauna Suecica sistens Animalia Sueciæ Regni, etc. *2 Ed., Stockholm.* — 1763. Centuria Insectorum Rariorum. Amœnitates Academiæ, seu dissertationes physicæ, etc. *Holmiæ* 6: 384. — 1764. Museum Ludovicæ Ulricæ Reginæ, etc. *Holmiæ.*

Lintner, J. A., 1898. "Camponotus Pennsylvanicus" and "Formica rufa." *15 Ann. Rep. N. Y. State Mus.* 1896: 181–182.

de Llave, Pablo, 1832. Registro Trimestre o Collection de Memorias de Historia Literatura Ciencias y Artes. *Mexico.*

Lloyd, R. W., 1892. *Note on Cetonia floricola Hbst. *Ent. M. Mag.* (2) 3: 310.

Lochner von Hummelstein, M. F., 1686. Lapis myrmecius falsus cantharidibus gravidus. *Ephem. Acad. Nat. Curios.* 6, 215: 436–441. — 1688. Sciagraphia myrmecologicæ medicæ. *Ibid.* 8 app.: 124.

Loeb, J., 1890. Der Heliotropismus der Thiere und seine Uebereinstimmung mit dem Heliotropismus der Pflanzen. *Würzburg, Georg Hertz.*

Loew, O., 1874. The Honey Ants. *Amer. Nat.* 8: 365–366.

Löfgren, A., 1905. As formigas Cuyabanas. *Bol. Agric.* (6) 5 (S. Paulo): 218.

Lokaj, Edm., 1860. *Beschreibung der in Böhmen vorkommenden Ameisenarten mit Rücksicht auf die bisher aus Böhmen bekannten Gäste der Ameisenhaufen. *Ziva* 8: 238 seq. — 1869. *Verzeichniss der Käfer Böhmens. *Arb. Zool. Sect. Landesdurchforsch. Böhm. Prag.*

Loman, J. C. C., 1887. *Freies Jod als Drüsensekret. *Tijdschr. Ned. Dierk. Vereen.* (2) 1, 3–4: 106–108.

de Longrée, A., 1901. Pluie de fourmis. *La Nature* 29, 2: 230–231.

Losana, Mattes, 1809. Mémoire pour servir à l'histoire des Insectes. Du siège de l'odorat dans les fourmis, etc. *Mém. Acad. Turin* 16: 80. — 1834. Saggio sopra le Formiche indigene del Piemonte. *Mem. Real. Acad. Sc. Torino* 37: 307–333.

Lubbock, Sir John, 1876–'84. *Observations on Ants, Bees and Wasps. Parts I, II, III. *Journ. Linn. Soc.* 12 (1876): 110–139; 227–251; 445–514. Part IV, 13 (1878): 216–258. Parts V and VI, 14 (1879): 265–290; 607–626. Parts VII and VIII, 15 (1881): 167–187; 362–387. Part IX, 16 (1883): 110–121. Part X, 17 (1884): 41–52, figg and pls. — 1877a. The Habits of Ants. *Royal. Instit. Great Brit.* Jan. 26. — 1877b. On Some Points in the Anatomy of Ants. *Month. Micr. Journ.* (Sept. 1): 121–142, pls. 189–192. — 1879a. On the Anatomy of Ants (Abstract). *Journ. Linn. Soc.* 14: 738–739. — 1879b. On the Anatomy of Ants. *Trans. Linn. Soc.* (2) Zool. 2: 141–154. — 1879c. On the Habits of Ants, etc. *Sc. Lect. London*, 1 vol. with pls. — 1880. Les Mœurs des Fourmis. Transl. by J. A. Battandier. *Alger.* 1 Vol. — 1881. Observations on Ants, Bees and Wasps. *Nature* 23: 255–258. — 1882. Observations on the Habits of Ants. *Ent.* 15: 33–36. — 1885. Longevity of Ants. *Am. Nat.* 20, 2: 170–171. — 1888a. Observations on Ants, Bees and Wasps. Part II. *Journ. Linn. Soc.* (Zool.) 20: 118–136, 2 figg. — 1888b. On the Senses, Instincts and Intelligence of Animals, with special reference to Insects. *London* 292 pp. — 1894. Ants, Bees and Wasps. *Revised Ed. Internat. Sc. Ser. N. Y. Appleton & Co.*

Lucas, Hipp., 1847. *(Note on Lepisma myrmecophila.) *Ann. Soc. Ent. France* p. xliv. — 1849. Histoire Naturelle des Animaux Articulés de l'Algérie. Exploration Scientifique de l'Algérie pendant les années 1840–1842, publiée par ordre du gouvernement et avec le concours d'une commission académique. Sciences physiques, Zoologie, 3. — 1851. *Observations sur les métamorphoses de la Tituboca octosignata F. *Ann. Soc. Ent. France* pp. 29 seq. — 1852. *Nouvelles observations sur les fourreaux de la Tituboca octosignata et de la Lachnæa vicina. *Ibid.* pp. 463 seq. — 1853. Observations sur la manière de vivre de la Typhlopone oraniensis. *Ann. Soc. Ent. France* (3) 1 Bull.: 37. — 1855a. *(Note on Hetærius cavisternus.) *Ibid.* pp. iii–iv. — 1855b. Note sur le Myrmecocystus mexicanus. *Ibid.* (3) 3: 54–55. —

1855c. *Observations sur deux nouveaux genres de Coléoptères (Oöchrotus et Merophysia). *Rev. Mag. Zool.* pp. 335-342; 358-365, pl. 9. — **1856a.** Note Synonymique sur la Formica scutellaris Ol. et la Myrmica testaceo-pilosa Luc. *Ann. Soc. Ent. France* (3) 4 Bull.: 20, 34. — **1856b.** Note sur quelques Fourmicides d'Europe rencontrés en Algerie. *Ibid.* (3) 4 Bull.: 29. — **1858a.** *(Note on Platyarthrus hoffmanseggi with F. rufa.) *Ibid.* p. ccxii. — **1858b.** Note sur un point de géographie Entomologique, etc. Sur la Formica fugax causant des dégats dans un magasin de chocolat. *Ibid.* (3) 6, Bull.: 80. — **1860a.** *(Note on Platyarthrus with different species of Ants.) *Ibid.* p. cx. — **1860b.** Observations sur les Busileras ou fourmis à miel du Mexique (Myrmecocystus melligerus). *Rev. Mag. Zool.* (2) 12: 269-280. — **1861.** *(Note on Hetærius sesquicornis with Myrmica scabrinodis, Leptothorax acervorum and Formica fuliginosa.) *Ann. Soc. Ent. France* p. xxxi. — **1873.** Note sur la Fourmi des Serres, Prenolepis longicornis. *Ibid.* (5) 3 Bull.: 66. — **1874a.** *(Note on Platyarthrus hoffmanseggi Brdt.) *Ibid.* p. xcix. — **1874b.** *(Note on Coluocera attæ Kr.) *Ibid.* p. ccxxxix. — **1875.** *Un mot sur les Animaux articulés myrmécophiles. *Ibid.* pp. 217-221. — **1884.** *(Note on Lucasius (Porcellio) myrmecophilus with Aphænogaster testaceopilosa and barbara.) *Ibid.* p. cxxxvii.

Ludolf, J., (alias Leutholf), 1681. Historia Æthiopica. *Francofurti ad Mœnum.* Pls. — **1691.** Ad suam historiam Æthiopicam ante hac editam Commentarius Francofurti ad Mœnum. Pls.

Ludwig, F., 1888a. *Schimper, A. F. W. Die Wechselbeziehungen zwischen Pflanzen und Ameisen im tropischen Amerika. *Biol. Centralb.* 8: 321-330. — **1888b.** *Weitere Untersuchungen über Ameisenpflanzen. *Ibid.* 8: 577-580. — **1899.** *Die Ameisen im Dienst der Pflanzenverbreitung. *Illustr. Zeitschr. Ent.* 4: 38-40. — **1907.** *Weiteres zur Biologie von Helleborus fœtidus. *Zeitschr. Wiss. Insekt.-Biol.* 3: 45-50. (Nachtrage p. 130-131.)

Luja, E., 1897. *La Cétoine dorée (Cetonia aurata) dans les Fourmilières. *Fauna, Luxembourg* 7: 52-53.

Lund, A. W., 1831. Lettre sur les habitudes de quelques fourmis du Brésil, addressée à M. Audouin. *Ann. Sc. Nat.* 23: 113-138.

McCOOK, H., 1876. Notes on the Architecture and Habits of Formica pennsylvanica. *Trans. Am. Ent. Soc.* 5: 277. — **1877a.** *The Agricultural Ant of Texas. *Proc. Acad. Nat. Sc. Phila.* Nov. 13, p. 299. — **1877b.** *The Mound-making Ants of the Alleghanies. *Trans. Am. Ent. Soc.* 6: 253 seq. — **1879a.** Note on the Marriage-flights of Lasius flavus and Myrmica lobicornis. *Proc. Acad. Nat. Sc. Phila.* p. 33; *Ann. Mag. Nat. Hist.* (5) 3: 326-328. — **1879b.** Combats and Nidification of the Pavement Ant, Tetramorium cæspitum. *Proc. Acad. Nat. Sc. Phila.* p. 156. — **1879c.** *The Natural History of the Agricultural Ant of Texas. A Monograph of the habits, architecture, and structure of Pogonomyrmex barbatus, p. 310, 24 pls., *Phila.* — **1879d.** On Certain Ants Associated with the Cotton worm (Aletia argillacea Hübn.). Extracted from Report on Cotton Insects by J. Henry Comstock, pp. 182-189. — **1879e.** Note on the Adoption of an Ant-Queen. *Proc. Acad. Nat. Sc. Phila.* p. 139. — **1879f.** On Myrmecocystus mexicanus Wesm. *Ibid.* pp. 197, 198; *Ann. Mag. Nat. Hist.* (5) 4: 474. — **1880a.** Note on a new Northern Cutting Ant, Atta septentrionalis. *Proc. Acad. Nat. Sc. Phila.* pp. 359-360, 1 figg. — **1880b.** *The Shining Slave-maker. Notes on the Architecture and Habits of the American Slave-making Ant, Polyergus lucidus. *Ibid.* pp. 376-384, pl. 19. — **1882a.** Ants as Beneficial Insecticides. *Ibid.* pp. 263-271. — **1882b.** The Honey Ants of the Garden of the Gods and the Occident. Ants of the American Plains. 13 pls. *Phila. Lippincott & Co.* — **1883a.** How a Carpenter Ant founds a Colony. *Proc. Acad. Nat. Sc. Phila.* pp. 303-307; *Ann. Mag. Nat. Hist.* (5) 13: 419-423. — **1883b.** The Occident

Ant of Dakota. *Proc. Acad. Nat. Sc. Phila.* pp. 294–296. — **1884a.** (Ants employed on the prairies to clear clothes from lice.) *Ibid.* p. 63. — **1884b.** Ants. *Encycl. Am.* 1 : 247–258, figg. — **1884c.** The Rufous or Thatching Ant of Dakota and Colorado. *Proc. Acad. Nat. Sc. Phila.* pp. 57–65, figg. — **1887a.** Modifications of Habit in Ants through fear of enemies. *Ibid.* pp. 27–30. — **1887b.** Note on the Sense of Direction in a European Ant, Formica rufa. *Ibid.* pp. 335–338; *Ann. Mag. Hist.* (6) 2 : 189–192. — **1906.** Honey Ants of the Garden of the Gods. *Harper's Monthly* (June) : 126–133, 6 figg. — **1907.** Nature's Craftsmen; Popular Studies of Ants and Other Insects. *Harper & Bro., New York and London,* 311 pp., 104 illustr.

MacLaren, J. D., 1887. The Occidental Ant in Kansas. *Bull. Washb. College* 2 : 7–10.

MacLeay, W. L., 1873. *Miscellanea Entomologica. *Trans. Ent. Soc. N. S. Wales* 2, 5 : 319 seq.

Maeklin, F. W., 1846. *Coleoptera Myrmecophila Fennica. *Bull. Soc. Imp. Nat. Moscow* 1 : 157–187.

Maerkel, J. C. F., 1841. *Beiträge zur Kenntniss der unter Ameisen lebenden Insekten I. *Germar's Zeitschr. Ent.* 3 : 203–225. — **1844.** *Id. II. *Ibid.* 5 : 193–271.

Maggi, Leop., 1874. Sopra un nido singolare della Formica fuliginosa Latr. *Atti. Soc. Ital. Sc. Nat.* 17 : 64. — **1875.** Intorno ai nidi della Formica fuliginosa. *Ibid.* 18 : 83.

Mangels, H., 1904. Wirtschaftliche, naturgeschichtliche und klimatologische Abhandlungen aus Paraguay. *München, J. P. Datterer & Co.* 8 : 364 pp., 10 pls.

von Mannerheim, C. G., 1843. *Mémoire sur la récolte d'Insectes Coléoptères faite en 1842. *Bull. Soc. Imp. Nat. Moscow* 1 : 70 seq. — **1844.** *Mémoire sur la récolte d'Insectes Coléoptères faite en 1843. *Ibid.* 1 : 160 seq.

Mantero, G., 1898. Res ligusticæ. XXX. Materiali per un catalogo degli imenotteri liguri. I. Formicidi. *Ann. Mus. Civ. Stor. Genova* 39 : 146–160, 1 fig.

Marcgraf, G., 1749. De oleo ex formicis expresso, ac de acido horum insectorum. *Acad. Reg. Beron.* p. 38; in his chemical works 1, 21; *Mineralog. Belustig.* 4 : 161; Transl. *Abhandl. Berl. Akad.* 3 : 444.

Marlatt, C. L., 1898. House Ants. *U. S. Dept. Agric. Div. Ent.* (2) 34, July 6.

de Marseul, S. A., 1853–'62. *Monographie des Histérides. *Ann. Soc. Ent. France.*

Marshall, W., 1889. *Leben und Treiben der Ameisen. *Zool. Vort.* 3 and 4 : 1–144.

Martins, M. N., 1907. Une Fourmi terrible envahissant l'Europe (Iridomyrmex humilis Mayr.). *Broteria, Revista Sc. Nat.* 6 : 101–102.

Marx, G., 1889. *(Note on the myrmecophilous genera of Spiders, Synemosyna and Synageles.) *Proc. Ent. Soc. Wash.* 1, 4 (Sept. 5) : 248. — **1891.** *A List of the Araneæ of the District of Columbia. *Ibid.* 2, 2 (Jan. 4) : 148–162.

Maskell, W. W., 1891. *Further Coccid notes; with descriptions of new species and remarks on Coccids from New Zealand, Australia, and elsewhere. *Trans. N. Zeal. Inst.* 24 : 1–64.

Matthews, A., 1872. *Trichopterygia illustrata et descripta. *London.* — **1884.** A Memoir of Ant-life. *Ent. M. Mag.* 20 (Feb.) : 269–310.

Mauduit, B. J. E. D., 1774. Lettre sur quelques objets du règne animal apportés de la Louisiane. *Journ. Phys.* 4 : 384–397, 1 pl.

Mayet, V., 1882. *(Note on the larvæ and pupæ of Microdon mutabilis in the formicaries of Lasius niger.) *Ann. Soc. Ent. France* p. CVI.

Mayr, G., 1852. Beschreibung einiger neuen Ameisen. *Verh. Zool. bot. Gesell. Wien* 2 : 143–150; 3 : 277–286. — **1853a.** Beiträge zur Kenntniss der

Ameisen. *Ibid.* 3: 100–114. — **1853b.** Ueber die Abtheilung der Myrmiciden und eine neue Gattung derselben. *Ibid.* 3: 387–394. — **1853c.** Beschreibung einiger neuen Ameisen. *Ibid.* 3: 277–286. — **1854.** Ueber die Synonymie der Myrmica rubriceps Nyl. oder Acroccœlia ruficeps Mayr. *Ibid.* 4: 30–32. — **1855.** Formicina Austriaca. Beschreibung der bisher im öster. Kaiserstaate aufgefundenen Ameisen, etc. *Ibid.* 5: 273–478, 1 pl.; Separate: Wien, Braumueller, 8°, 306 pp., 1 pl. — **1856.** Beiträge zur ungarischen Formiciden-Fauna. Ausflug nach Szegedin. *Ibid.* 6: 175–178. — **1857.** Ungarn's Ameisen. III Program der Städt. Oberrealschule in Pesth. — **1859.** Beiträge zur Ameisenfauna Russlands. *Stett. Ent. Zeitg.* 20: 87–90. — **1861.** Die Europäischen Formiciden. *Wien,* 1 Vol. — **1862.** Myrmecologische Studien. *Verh. Zool.-bot. Gesell. Wien* 12: 649–776, pl. 20. — **1863a.** Formicidarum Index Synonymicus. *Ibid.* 13: 385–460. — **1863b.** Beitrag zur Orismologie der Formiciden. *Wiegmann's Arch. Naturg.* 29: 103–118. — **1864.** Das Leben und Wirken der einheimischen Ameisen. *Österreich. Revue* 1: 201–209. — **1865.** Reise der österreichischen Fregatte Novara um die Erde. *Zool. Theil.* 2, 1 (Formicidæ) pp. 1–119, 4 pls. — **1866a.** Myrmecologische Beiträge. *Sitzb. K. Akad. Wiss. Wien. Math. Naturw. Cl.* 53: 484–517. — **1866b.** Diagnosen neuer und wenig gekannter Formiciden. *Verh. Zool.-bot. Gesell. Wien* 16: 885–908, pl. 20. — **1867a.** Adnotationes in monographiam Formicidarum indoneerlandicarum. *Tijdsch. Ent.* 10: 33–117, 2 pls. — **1867b.** Vorläufige Studien über die Radoboj-Formiciden. *Jahrb. K. K. Geolog. Reichsan.* 17: 47–62, 1 pl. — **1868a.** Die Ameisen des baltischen Bernsteins. *Beitr. zur Naturkunde Preussens I. K. Phys. Oekon. Gesell. Königs.* 102 pp., 5 pls. — **1868b.** Formicidæ Novæ Americanæ Collectæ a Prof. P. de Strobel. *Ann. Soc. Nat. Modena* 3: 161–181. — **1868c.** Cremastogaster Ransonneti n. sp. *Verh. Zool.-bot. Gesell. Wien* 18: 287, 288. — **1870a.** Neue Formiciden. *Verh. Zool.-bot. Gesell. Wien* 20: 939–996. — **1870b.** Formicidæ Novogranadensis. *Sitzb. k. Akad. Wiss. Wien.* 41: 370–417. — **1872.** Formicidæ Borneenses. *Ann. Mus. Civ. Stor. Nat. Genova* 2: 133–155. — **1876.** Die australischen Formiciden. *Journ. Mus. Godeff. Hamburg* 12: 56–115. — **1877a.** Voyage au Turkestan Formicides récoltées par A. P. Fedtschenko. *Soc. Amis. Saint-Pétersbourg.* (In Russian.) Zool. Formicidæ, 4°, pp. 40. — **1877b.** Ueber Dr. Emery's Gruppierung der Myrmiciden. *Sitzb. Zool.-bot. Gesell. Wien* 27: 23–26. — **1877c.** Formiciden gesammelt in Brasilien von Prof. Trail. *Verh. Zool.-bot. Gesell. Wien* 27: 867–878. — **1878.** Beiträge zur Ameisen-Fauna Asiens. *Verh. Zool.-bot. Gesell. Wien* 28: 645–686. — **1880.** Die Ameisen Turkestan's gesammelt von A. Fedtschenko. *Tijdsch. Ent.* 23: 17–40 (Transl. of 1877a). — **1883a.** Drei neue ostindische Formiciden-Arten. *Notes Leyden Mus.* 5, 4, 24: 245–247. — **1883b.** Az Epitritus argiolus Em. nevü hangya elöfordulása Magyarorszúgban. *Terméz. Füzet.* 6: 141. — **1883c.** Fourmis de Cayenne (par O. Radoszkowsky). *Hor. Soc. Ent. Ross.* 18: 30–39. — **1884.** Ueber das Vorkommen der Epitritus argiolus Em. genannten Ameise in Ungarn. *Ibid.* 6: 196–197. — **1886a.** Notizen über die Formiciden-Sammlung des British Museum in London. *Verh. Zool.-bot. Gesell. Wien* 36: 353–368. — **1886b.** Ueber Eciton-Labidus. *Wien Ent. Zeitschr.* 5: 33–36; 115–122. — **1886c.** Die Formiciden der Vereinigten Staaten von Nord-Amerika. *Verh. Zool.-bot. Gesell. Wien* 36: 419–464. — **1887.** Südamerikanische Formiciden. *Ibid.* 37: 511–632. — **1890.** Insecta in itinere Cl. Przewalskii in Asia Centrali novissime lecta. XVII Formiciden aus Tibet. *Hor. Ent. Ross.* 24: 278–280. — **1892a.** Drepanognathus rugosus Mayr. *Terméz. Füzet.* 15: 127. — **1892b.** Liometopum microcephalum Pz. *Verh. Zool.-bot. Gesell. Wien* 42: 317. — **1893a.** Ergänzende Bemerkungen zu E. Wasmann's Artikel über Springende Ameisen. *Wien Ent. Zeitschr.* 12: 23. — **1893b.** Formiciden von Herrn Dr. Stuhlmann in Ost-Afrika gesammelt. *Jahrb. Hamburg Wiss. Anst.* 10: 195–201. — **1895.** Afrikanische Formiciden. *Ann. K. K. naturh. Hofmus. Wien* 10: 124–154. — **1896.** Beiträge zur Kenntnis der Insektenfauna von Kamerun. 5. Formiciden, gesammelt von Herrn Yngve Sjöstedt. *Ent. Tidskr.* 17, 2/3: 225–252, 2 pls. — **1897.** Formiciden aus Ceylon und Singapur. *Terméz. Füzet.* 20: 420–436. — **1901a.** Südafrikanische Formiciden, gesammelt von Dr. Hans Brauns. *Ann. Nat. Hofmus. Wien* 16: 1–30, 2 pls. — **1901b.** Drei neue Formiciden aus Kamerun gesammelt von Herrn Prof. Dr. Reinhold Buchholz. *Ent. Tidskr.* 21: 273–279. — **1904a.** Formiciden aus Ægypten und dem Sudan. *Results Swed. Zool. Exped. Egypt* 1, 6: 11 pp. — **1904b.** Hymenopterologische Miscellen. III. *Verh. Zool.-bot. Gesell. Wien* 54: 559–598. — **1907.** Wissenschaftliche Ergebnisse der schwed. Exped. nach dem Kilimandjaro, dem Meru u. den umgebenden Massaisteppen Deutsch-Ostafrikas, 1905–1906 unter Leitung des Prof. Dr. Yngve Sjöstedt. 8. Hymenoptera. 2. Formicidæ. *Kgl. Schwed. Akad. Upsala.* 4°, pp. 7–23, 1 pl.

Mayr, G., and Chr. Aurivillius, 1896. Beschreibung der von Dr. Y. Sjöstedt heimgebrachten Ameisennester. *Ent. Tidskr.* 17, 2/3: 253–256, 2 pls.

Meckel, H., 1846. Mikrographie einiger Drüsenapparate. Der Giftapparat der Hymenopterenweibchen. *Müller's Arch. Anat. Phys.* pp. 47–50, pls. 1–3.

Medina y Ramos M., 1892. Catalogo provisionale de las hormigas de Andalucia. *Anal. Soc. Españ. Hist. Nat.* 20, 1: 95–104.

Meinert, Fr., 1860. Bidrag til de danske Myrers Naturhistorie. *Dansk. Vetensk. Selskab.* 5: 275–340. — **1890.** *Ænigmatias blattoides, Dipteron novum apterum. *Ent. Meddel.* 2: 212–226. — **1891.** *Bioeinene hos Tomognathus sublævis. *Ibid.* 3: 205–206.

Meisenheimer, J., 1902. Lebensgewohnheiten der Ponerinen. *Nat. Wochenschr.* 17: 487–489, 3 figg.

Meissen, K., 1889. Berittene Ameisen. *Humboldt* 8, 4: 157–158.

Meissner, O., 1907a. Hymenopterologische Notizen. *Intern. Ent. Zeitschr. Guben* 1: 239–240; 257–258. — **1907b.** Ueber die Lebenzähigkeit der Insekten. *Ent. Wochenbl.* 24: 191–192. — **1908.** Das Orientierungsvermögen der Ameisen. *Zeitschr. Wiss. Insekt.-biol.* 4: 344.

Melander, A. L., 1902. *A New Silphid Beetle from a Simple Insect-Trap. *Psyche* 9: 328–329.

Melander, A. L., and C. T. Brues, 1906. The Chemical Nature of Some Insects' Secretions. *Bull. Wis. Nat. Hist. Soc.* N. S., 4: 22–36.

Menzel, J., 1905. *Ueber einige Ameisengäste. *Inseketenbörse* 22: 100.

Mesmin, L., 1875–'78. *Mœurs de la Myrmedonia collaris. *Feuill. Jeun. Nat.* 6 (1875–'76): 118–119; transl. *Ent. M. Mag.* 13 (1876–'78): 64–65.

Metcalf, M. M., 1900. Hearing in Ants. *Science* N. S.: 194.

Meyer, 1854. Ueber coconlose Ameisen-puppen. *Stett. Ent. Zeitg.* 15: 131–141.

Meyer-Dür, L. R., 1859–'61. Die Ameisen um Burgdorf. *Bemer. Mittheil.* pp. 34–46; *Zeitschr. G. Naturw.* 18: 382. — **1870.** *(Note on the Homoptera living in ants'-nests.) *Pet. Nouv. Ent.* 14: 53.

Michelet, J., 1884. L'Insecte. *10th Ed. Paris, Hachette et Cie.*

Michael, A. D., 1884. *On the Hypopi question. *Journ. Linn. Soc. Zool.* 17: 371–394. — **1891.** *On the Association of Gamasids with Ants. *Proc. Zool. Soc. London* 4: 638–653, pls. 49 and 50.

Middleton, R. M., Jr., 1896. On a remarkable Use of Ants in Asia Minor. *Journ. Linn. Soc. London Zool.* 25, 164: 405–406. (Abstr. *Journ. R. Micr. Soc. London* p. 30.)

Miller, A. R., 1902. The Strength of Ants. *Science* N. S. 16: 514–515.

Mirande, M., 1905. Sur la présence d'un "corps réducteur" dans le tégument chitineux des Arthropodes. *Arch. Anat. Micr.* 7: 207–231, 6 figg.

Miskin, G. H., 1883. *On Ogyris Genoveva Hewitson and its life-history. *Trans. Ent. Soc. London* pp. 343–345.

Mjöberg, E., 1905. Biologiska och morfologiska studier öfver Fåröns insektfauna. *Arkiv. Zool.* 2, 17: 86 pp., 1 pl., 7 figg., 1 map. — **1906.** *Ueber Systellonotus triguttatus L. und sein Verhältnis zu Lasius niger. *Zeitschr. Wiss. Insektenbiol.* 2: 107–109.

Mocsáry, S., 1897. Az újguineai hangyákról. — Die Ameisen von Neu-Guinea. *Rovartani Lapok* 4: 107–108, 1 fig.

Moewes, 1889. *Symbiose zwischen Pflanzen und Ameisen im tropischen Amerika. *Humboldt* 7, 12: 456–459.

Moffat, C. B., 1896. Formica rufa L. in Co. Wexford. *Irish Nat.* 5, 5: 143–144.

Möller, A., 1893. *Die Pilzgärten einiger südamerikanischer Ameisen. *Jena* 6: 127 pp., 7 pls. (Heft 6 of *Schimper's Botanische Mittheilungen aus den Tropen;* Summary *Biol. Centralb.* 13: 280–285.)

Moggridge, J. T., 1873. *Harvesting Ants and Trapdoor Spiders, with Observations on their Habits and Dwellings. *London*, 2 Vols., 20 pls. — **1874.** *(On Coluocera attæ in the nests of Aphænogaster structor.) *Proc. Ent. Soc. London* p. V.

Moniez, R., 1890-'91. *Note sur les Thysanoures. IV. Sur deux Podurides qui vivent dans les fourmilières. Extr. de *Rev. Biol. Nord. France* 3, 2: 64–67. — **1892.** *Mémoire sur quelques Acariens et Thysanoures, parasites ou commensaux des Fourmis. *Ibid.* 4, 10; 377–391. — **1894.** *Sur quelques Arthropodes trouvés dans les fourmilières. *Ibid.* 6, 6: 201–215.

Moore, F., 1880-'81. *Lepidoptera of Ceylon. 1, *London*.

Mordwilko, A., 1896. *Contribution to the Biology of the plant-lice of the subfamilies Aphididæ and Pemphigidæ. *Warsaw.* (In Russian.) — **1901.** *Contribution to the Biology and Morphology of the Aphididæ. *Horæ Soc. Ent. Ross.* 33: 341–398; 438–452. (In Russian.) — **1907.** *Die Ameisen und Blattläuse in ihren gegenseitigen Bezeihungen und das Zusammenleben von Lebewesen überhaupt. *Biol. Centralb.* 27: 212–224; 233–252, 4 figg.

Moreno, A., 1900. *Observaciones acerca de las costumbres de las Hormigas. *Mem. Rev. Soc. Cient. Ant. Alzate* 14 Rev.: 60–62.

Morice, R. F. D., 1900. *(Queens and Males of Formica fusca in a nest of F. sanguinea.) *Nature* Nov. 22, p. 98.

Morris, C., 1880a. Living Honey Comb; a Novel Phase of Ant Life. *Journ. Sc.* Feb. — **1880b.** Habits and Anatomy of the Honey-bearing Ant. *Ibid.* July.

Morris, G. K., 1880. *A New Harvesting Ant. *Am. Nat.* Sept. pp. 669–670. — **1881.** *A New Leaf-cutting Ant. *Ibid.* Feb. pp. 100–102.

Moseley, H. N., 1892. *Notes by a Naturalist. An Account of Observations made during the Voyage of H. M. S. "Challenger." *Revised Ed. London, John Murray.*

von Motschulsky, V., 1838. *Coléoptères du Caucase et des Provinces Transcaucasiennes. *Bull. Soc. Imp. Nat. Moscou* 3: 175–188. — **1844.** *Bemerkungen zu den im 5. Bande der Zeitschrift für die Entomologie S. 192 von Hr. Maerkel gegebenen "Beiträge zur Kenntniss der unter den Ameisen lebenden Insekten." *Ibid.* 4: 812–823. — **1845.** *Ueber die Ptilien Russlands. *Ibid.* 4: 504–539. — **1851-'69.** *Enumération des nouvelles espèces de Coléoptères rapportés de ses voyages. *Ibid.* — **1855-'59.** Études Entomologiques. *Helsingfors* 4 and 8. — **1859.** Briefliche Notiz über springende Ameisen. *Stett. Ent. Zeitg.* 20: 201. — **1863.** Essai d'un Catalogue des insectes de l'île de Ceylan (Suite). *Bull. Soc. Imp. Nat. Moscou,* 36, 3: 1–153.

Mrázek, A., 1906. Gründung neuer Kolonien bei Lasius niger. *Zeitschr. Wiss. Insektenbiol.* 2: 109–111.

Muckermann, H., 1902. The Structure of the Nests of some North American Species of Formica. *Psyche* 9: 355–360. — **1904.** *Formica sanguinea subsp. rubicunda Em. and Xenodusa cava Lec.; or the Discovery of Pseudogynes in a District of Xenodusa cava Lec. *Ent. News* 15: 339–341, 1 pl.

Müller, F., 1874. *The Habits of Various insects (letter to Chas. Darwin). *Nature* (June 11): 102, 103. — **1876a.** *Ueber die Haarkissen der Imbauba. *Jen. Zeitschr. Nat.* 10. — **1876b.** On Brazil Kitchen-middens, Habits of Ants, etc. *Nature* 13: 304–305. — **1880-'81.** *Die Imbauba und ihre Beschützer. *Kosmos* 8: 109–116.

Müller, P. W. J., 1818. *Beiträge zur Naturgeschichte der Gattung Claviger. *Germar's Mag. Ent.* 3: 69–112, pl. 2.

Müller, Wilhelm, 1886. *Beobachtungen an Wanderameisen (Eciton hamatum Fabr.). *Kosmos* 18: 81–93.

Müller, 1907. *Ueber Myrmecophilen. *Mitt. Nat. Ver. Neu-Vorpommern Rügen* 38: xxiii–xxiv.

NAGEL, C., 1846. Der wunderbare Haushalt der Ameisen, aus eigenen Beobachtungen mitgetheilt. *Allgem. Deutsch. Naturhist. Zeitg.* 1: 549–554.

Nasonov, N. V., 1889. Contributions to the Natural History of the Ants (Formicariæ). *Publ. Lab. Zool. Mus. Univ. Moscow* 4, 1: 1–42; 1–6, pls. 1–9. (In Russian.)

Needham, J. T., 1780. Observations sur l'histoire naturelle de la fourmi, à l'occasion desquelles on relève quelques méprises de certain auteurs célèbres. *Mém. Acad. Bruxelles* 2: 295–312.

Neuhaus-Storkow, G. H., 1886. Die Ameisen der Mark Brandenburg. *Monatl. Mitth. Gesammtgeb. Naturwiss. Frankf. a.O.* 4, 9: 268–272; 4, 10: 296–300.

Neumann, C. De oleo destillato Formicarum æthereo. *Act. Phys. Med.* 2: 304, obs. 136. — **1737.** Lectiones quatuor subjectis pharmaceuticochymicis, sal commune, Formica, etc. *Lipsiæ.*

Newell, W., 1908a. *Notes on the Habits of the Argentine or "New Orleans" Ant, Iridomyrmex humilis Mayr. *Journ. Econ. Ent.* 1, 1 (Feb.): 21–34. — **1908b.** *Two Interesting Inquilines Occurring in the Nests of the Argentine Ant. *Ibid.* 1: 262–265.

Newstead, R., 1892. *On new or little known Coccidæ, chiefly English (No. 2). *Ent. M. Mag.* (2) 3: 141–148. — **1893a.** *New or little known Coccidæ, chiefly English (No. 3). *Ibid.* 4: 77–79. — **1893b.** *Paracletus cimiciformis in Ants'-nests in North Wales. *Ibid.* 4: 115. — **1893c.** *A New Coccid in an Ants' nest. *Ibid.* (2) 4: 138. — **1893d.** *Observations on Coccidæ. *Ibid.* (2) 4: 205–210. — **1900.** *Observations on Coccidæ (No. 18). *Ibid.* (2) 11: 247–251.

de Nicéville, L., 1888. *Butterflies and Ants. *Journ. Bomb. Nat. Hist. Soc.* 3: 164–168, pls. 26, 27. — **1889.** *Notes on Indian Insect Pests. *Indian Mus. Notes* 1, 1: 12. *Calcutta.* — **1890.** *The Butterflies of India, Burmah and Ceylon. 3, *Calcutta.* — **1900.** *The Food-plants of the Butterflies of the Kanara District of the Bombay Presidency, with a Revision of the Species of Butterflies there occurring. *Journ. Asiat. Soc. Bengal* 79, 2, 2: 187–278.

Nietner, J., 1858. Ueber eine springende Ameise in Ceylon. Brief an Drewson. *Stett. Ent. Zeitg.* 19: 445–446. — **1859.** On the apterous worker of Dorylus. *Trans. Ent. Soc. London* (2) 5 (Proc.): 27–28.

Nördlinger, H., 1860. Notiz über eine Myrmica. *Würtemberg. Jahreshefte* 16: 289–291.

Norton, E., 1868a. Remarks on Mexican Formicidæ (Eciton). *Trans. Am. Ent. Soc.* 2: 44–46. — **1868b.** Notes on Mexican Ants. *Am. Nat.* 2: 57–72, 1 pl. — **1868c.** Description of Mexican Ants noticed in the American Naturalist, April 1868. *Proc. Essex Inst.* 6: 10 pp., 11 figg.

Nyder, J., 1602. Formicarius, etc., notis Colveneri. *Dreaci Beller.* p. 431 et Præf. et Ind. *Ueber v: Vinc. Willart:* Le bien universel ou les fourmis mystiques de Jean Nyder. *Bruxelles* 1656, 4.

Nylander, W., 1846a. Strödda Anteckningar. (Försök att bestämma Linnés Svenska arter af slägtet Formica, etc.) Notiser ur *Sällsk pro Fauna et Fl. Fennica Förhandl.* 1: 289–299. — **1846b.** Adnotationes in Monographiam Formicarum borealium Europæ. *Act. Soc. Sc. Fenn.* 2: 875–944. — **1846c.** Additamentum adnotationum in Monographiam Formicarum borealium Europæ. *Ibid.* 2: 1041–1062. — **1848.** Additamentum alterum adnotationum in monographiam Formicarum borealium Europæ. *Ibid.* 3: 25–48. — **1851.** Remarks on Hymenopterologische Studien by Arn. Förster. *Ann. Mag. Nat. Hist.* 8. — **1856a.** Description de la Formica gracilescens, espèce nouvelle. *Ann. Soc. Ent. France* (3) 4 (Bull.): 28. — **1856b.** Note sur les Formicides du Mont Dore. *Ibid.* (3) 5 (Bull.): 78. — **1856c.** Synopsis des Formicides de France et d'Algérie. *Ann. Sc. Nat.* (4) 5: 50–109.

VON OERTZEN, E., 1886. *Verzeichniss der Coleopteren Griechenlands und Cretas. *Berl. Ent. Zeitschr.* pp. 189–293.

Oestlund, O. W., 1906. Personal Observations on Ants. *Bull. Minnesota Acad. Nat. Sci.* 4: 227–228.

Olivier, A. G., 1791. Encyclopédie Méthodique. *Histoire Naturelle Paris* 6: 487.

Olivier, E., 1893. *[Note on Elasmosoma berolinense Ruthe.] *Ann. Soc. Ent. France* p. LXXI.

Olliff, A. S., 1886. *A Revision of the Staphylinidæ of Australia. *Proc. Linn. Soc. N. S Wales* 1: 403–473; 887–907.

von Osten-Sacken, R., 1882. *Ants and Aphides. *Psyche* 3: 343. Transl. from *Stett. Ent. Zeitg.* 1862: pp. 127–128. — **1902.** A Remarkable Instance of Deliberation observed in an American Ant. *Ent. M. Mag.* (2) 13: 172–173.

Oudemans, J. Th., 1901. Zwei merkwürdige Hymenopteren-Nester von Lasius fuliginosus Latr. und von Osmia rufa L. *Allgem. Zeitschr. Ent.* 6: 179–181, 2 figg.

PACKARD, A. S., 1884. The Bees, Wasps, etc., of Labrador. *Amer. Nat.* 18: 1267.

Pagenstecher, H. A., 1861a. Ueber Honig-producirende Ameisen. *Froriep's Notiz.* 2, 13: 194–197. — **1861b.** Ueber Myrmecocystus mexicanus. *Heidel. Jahrb. Litt.* 3. (Cf. *Wien Ent. Monatschr.* 5: 317.)

Panzer, G. W. F., 1798. Faunæ Insectorum Germanicæ Initia, oder Deutschlands Insecten.

Parfitt, Edw., 1881-'82. *Hypopus parasitic on Ants. *Ent. M. Mag.* 18: 43.

Parona, C., 1884. *Sopra alcune Collembola e Thysanura di Tunisi. *Ann. Mus. Civ. Stor. Nat. Genova* (2) 1: 425– 438.

Parrot, F. H., 1882. *[Two ants'-nests of different species in close contiguity.] *Sc. Goss.* 18: 237.

de Parville, H., 1897. Fourmis et rhumatismes. *Fauna, Luxembourg* 7: 23–24.

Pascoe, F., 1866a. *Note on Articerus. *Proc. Ent. Soc. London* pp. xv, xvi. — **1866b.** *Description of Ectrephes formicarum. *Ibid.* p. xvi.

Paszlavszky, J., 1887. Meddig élnek a hangyák? *Természettud Közl.* 19: 182.

Patton, W. H., 1879. A Gall-inhabiting Ant. *Am. Nat.* (Feb.): 126–127.

Pavesi, P., 1904. Esquisse d'une faune valdôtaine. *Atti. Soc. Ital. Sc. Nat. Mus. Civ. Stor. Milano* 43: 191–260.

Pax, F., 1895. *Euphorbiaceæ africanæ. *Bot. Jahrb.* (*Engler*) 19: 76–126. — **1908.** Einige fossile Insekten aus den Karpathen. *Zeitschr. Wiss. Insekt.-biol.* 4, 3: 99–100.

Peckham, Geo. W., and Elizabeth G. Peckham, 1907. *The Attidæ of Borneo. *Trans. Wis. Acad. Sci.* 15: 603–653.

Pérez, Ch., 1899. Sur la Métamorphose des Insectes. *Bull. Soc. Ent. France* 20: 398–401. — **1900.** Une coopérative animale. *Rev. Encycl. Larousse* 10: 767–771, 6 figg. — **1901a.** Sur quelques phénomènes de la nymphose chez la Fourmis rousse. *C. R. Soc. Biol. Paris* 53: 1046–1049. — **1901b.** Sur quelques points de la métamorphose des Fourmis. *Bull. Soc. Ent. France* pp. 22–24. — **1901c.** Histolyse des tubes de Malpighi et des glandes séricigènes chez la Fourmi rousse. *Ibid.* pp. 307–310. — **1901d.** Sur les œnocytes de la Fourmi rousse. *Ibid.* pp. 352–353. — **1903.** Contribution à l'étude des métamorphoses. *Bull. Sc. France Belg.* 37: 195–427, 3 pls., 32 figg.

Pérez Arcas, L., 1872. *Especias neuvas ó criticas de la Fauna Española. 1. 2. Madrid* 43 pp., 3 pls.

Pergande, T., 1893. On a Collection of Formicidæ from Lower California and Sonora, Mexico. *Proc. Cal. Acad. Sc.* (2) 4: 26–36. — **1894a.** On a Collection of Formicidæ from Lower California and Sonora, Mexico. *Ibid.* 14: 26–36. — **1894b.** Formicidæ of Lower California, Mexico. *Ibid.* 14: 161–165. — **1900.** Papers from the Harriman Alaska Expedition XVII. Entomological Results (11), Formicidæ. *Proc. Wash. Acad. Sc.* 2: 519–521.

Péringuey, L., 1883. *Notes on three Paussi. *Trans. Ent. Soc. London* pp. 133–138. — **1883-'85.** *First Contribution to the South-African Coleopterous Fauna. *Trans. South-Afr. Phil. Soc.* 3 (2): 74–149, 4 pls. — **1886.** *Notes on Some Coleopterous Insects of the family Paussidæ. *Proc. Ent. Soc. London* pp. xxxiv–xxxvii. — **1886-'88.** *Second Contribution to the South-African Coleopterous Fauna. *Trans. South-Afr. Phil. Soc.* 4, 1: 67–190, 4 pls. — **1900.** *Notes sur certaines Cétonies (Cremastochilds) rencontrées dans les fourmilières ou termitières. Avec description d'espèces nouvelles. *Ann. Soc. Ent. France* 69: 66–72.

Perkins, G. A., 1870. The Drivers. *Amer. Nat.* 3: 360–364, 1 fig.

Perkins, R. C. H., 1891. Male and Worker characters combined in the same individual of Stenamma Westwoodi. *Ent. M. Mag.* (2) 2: 123.

Perrin, 1661. Divers Insects, la pouce, le moucheron, le papillon, la fourmi, le grillet, le ver à soie, l'abeille, pièces en poésie. *Paris, Duval.*

Perris, Edouard, 1873. *Notes sur quelques Hémiptères myrmécophiles. *Pet. Nouv. Ent.* 1, 84: 336–337. — **1876.** Sur la Micromyrma pygmæa Duf. *Ann. Soc. Ent. France* (5) 6: 219. — **1878a.** (Rectification à l'article précédent.) *Ibid.* (5) 8: 379. — **1878b.** *Larves des Coléoptères. *Paris* (Histoire Naturelle des Coléoptères de la France par E. Mulsant.) Sep. from *Ann. Soc. Linn. Lyon* 22.

Petivér, J., 1708. De variis Animalibus Philippensibus ex MSS. Cameli. (Formicæ.) *Phil. Trans.* 24: 241–248.

de Peyerimhoff, P., 1899. *Note sur la larve myrmécophile d'Astenus filiformis Latr. *Bull. Soc. Ent. France* pp. 287–289, 2 figg.

Pic, M., 1897. *Note sur les Coléoptères myrmécophiles. *Bull. Soc. Zool. France* 22, 9: 230–233. — **1900.** *Captures des Coléoptères myrmécophiles, en Orient. *Bull. Soc. Ent. France* pp. 170–171.

Piéron, H., 1904. Du rôle du sens musculaire dans l'orientation des fourmis. *Bull. Inst. Gén. Psychol. Paris* 4: 168–185; Discuss. pp. 185–186. (*Anal. Rev. Sc.* (5) 2: 603–604.) — **1905.** Contribution à l'étude du problème de la reconnaissance chez les Fourmis. *C. R. 6me Congr. Internat. Zool. Berne* pp. 482–491. — **1906a.** Géneralité du Processus Olfactif de Reconnaissance chez les Fourmis. *C. R. Séances Soc. Biol. Paris* 61: 385–387. — **1906b.** Exceptions et variations dans les processes olfactif de reconnaissance chez les fourmis. *Ibid.* 61: 433–435. — **1906c.** Le mécanisme de la reconnaissance chez les fourmis. Rôle des données olfactives. *Ibid.* 61: 471–473. — **1906d.** Le rôle de l'olfaction dans la reconnaissance des fourmis. *C. R. Acad. Sc. Paris* 143: 845–848. — **1907a.** L'Adaptation à la Recherche du

Nid chez les Fourmis. *C. R. Séances Soc. Biol. Paris* 62: 216–218. — 1907b. Sur la fondation de nouvelles colonies d'Aphænogaster (Messor) barbara nigra. *Bull. Soc. Ent. France* pp. 280–282.

Pierre, Abbé, 1893. *Un parasite des Fourmis (Elasmosoma Berolinense Ruthe). *Rev. Sc. Bourbonuf.* (June 6), p. 112.

Pintner, T., 1906. Aus dem Leben der Ameisen. *Schrift. Ver. Nat. Kenntn. Wien* 46: 101–146. — 1907. *Ameisen unter sich und ihre Gäste. *Ibid.* 47: 1–48.

Pinto, S., 1905. Méfaits de la Fourmi Quissondé. *Arch. Parasit.* 10: 121.

Piso, G., 1648. Historia Naturalis Brasiliæ. *Antwerp.*

Plant, J., 1844. On Formica rufa. *Zoologist* 2: 473.

Plant, R. W., 1854-'56. *Note on Paussidæ, communicated by Stevens. *Proc. Ent. Soc. London* (2) 3: 121.

Ploetz, C., 1865. *Eine neue Cavallerie. *Stett. Ent. Zeitg.* 26: 115–116.

Pluche, Natalis, 1735. Spectacle de la nature, ou Entretiens sur les Particularités de l'Histoire Naturelle. *Utrecht, Hage* 1737–1748; *Madrid* 1752, etc.

Popenoe, E. A., 1904. Pogonomyrmex occidentalis. *Canad. Ent.* 36: 360.

Poujade, G. A., 1883a. *Métamorphose d'un Diptère de la famille des Syrphides, genre Microdon. *Ann. Soc. Ent. France* pp. 23–30. — 1883b. *[Note on the Microdons.] *Ibid.* p. xcix.

Povelseus, B., 1722. Dissertatio de Millepedis, formica, etc. Qualem usum hæc insecta habeant in medicina. *Resp. J. A. Reuberus. Erfordiæ.*

Power, J. A., 1858. *Notes on Myrmecophilous Coleoptera. *Rep. Brit. Assoc. Adv. Sc.* Notices and Abstracts pp. 129–130.

de Pre, J. F., 1722. Disputatio tractans Millepedes, Formicas et Lumbricos terrestres, qualem usum hæc Insecta habeant in medicina; *resp. Joh. Andr. Reubers.*

Preston, 1884. Ants in Trinidad. *Rep. Bot. Gard. Trin.* quoted in *Gard. Chron* (2) 21: 280.

Preyssler, J. D. E., 1790. *Verzeichniss böhmischer Insekten. *Prag.*

Pricer, J. L., 1908. The Life History of the Carpenter Ant. *Biol. Bull.* 14, 3 (Feb.) : 177–218, 7 text-figg.

Provancher, L., 1882. [Edible Ants.] *Nat. Canad.* 13: 30, 31. — 1888. Additions à la fauna hyménoptérologique pp. 273–440.

Prowazek, S., 1901a. Aus dem Ameisenleben. *Die Natur* 50: 223–224. — 1901b. Ameisenbeobachtungen. *Zool. Garten* 42: 49–52.

Prudon, X., 1902. L'Instinct de la conservation chez les Myrmices. Myrmica cæspitum (Latreille). *Bull. Soc. Nat. Ain.* 11: 62–64.

Puls, 1868-'69. Note sur la fourmi de Pharaon. *Ann. Soc. Ent. Belg.* 12: lv–lvi.

Puton, A., 1869. *[Note on the Hemiptera living in ants'-nests.] *Pet. Nouv. Ent.* 12. — 1877. *[Note on the Pilophorus cinnamomæus Kb. with Formica congerens.] *Ann. Soc. Ent. France* p. cxxx.

QUEDENFELDT, M., 1883. *Beiträge zur Staphylinenfauna von Südspanien, Portugal und Marocco. *Berl. Ent. Zeitschr.* pp. 146–163.

RABL-RUCKHARD, 1875. Studien über Insektengehirne. Das Gehirn der Ameise. *Reichert's Arch. Anat. Phys.* pp. 480–499, pl. 14.

von Raciboski, M., 1900. *Ueber myrmekophile Pflanzen. *Flora* 87: 38 pp., seq. — 1902. *Rośliny i mrówki. *Kosmos Lwów Roczn.* 27: 11–18.

Radoszkowsky, G., 1875. Compte-rendu des Hyménoptères recueillis en Egypte et en Abyssinie en 1873. *Horæ Soc. Ent. Ross.* 12.

Radoszkowsky. O., 1884. Fourmis de Cayenne Française. *Ibid.* 18: 30–39.

Raffray, A., 1874. *[Observations on the Habits of Paussids and Cossyphodes, communicated by Deyrolle.] *Pet. Nouv. Ent.* 94: 376. — **1877.** *Descriptions d'espèces nouvelles de la famille des Psélaphides. *Rev. Mag. Zool.* pp. 279–296. — **1882–'87.** *Psélaphides nouveaux ou peu connus. *Rev. d'Ent.* (*Fauvel*). 1882 pp. 1 and 50; 1883 p. 229; 1887 p. 18 seq. — **1885–'87.** *Matériaux pour servir à l'étude des Coléoptères de la famille des Paussides. Extr. *Nouv. Arch. Mus. Hist. Nat. Paris* (2) 8, 5 pls. — **1890.** *Étude sur les Psélaphides. *Rev. d'Ent.* (*Fauvel*) pp. 1, 81, 193, 264, 3 pls. — **1892.** *Recherches anatomiques sur le Pentaplatarthrus paussoides. *Nouv. Arch. Mus. Hist. Nat. Paris* (3) 4: 91–102, 1 pl. — **1893.** *Révision des Psélaphides de Sumatra. *Ann. Soc. Ent. France* pp. 463–503. — **1898.** *Diagnoses de Staphylinides myrmécophiles nouveaux. *Bull. Soc. Ent. France* pp. 351–352.

Rafin, G., 1884. (Ignivorous Ant.) *Compt. Rendu.* 99: 212. See also *Journ. Roy. Micr. Soc.* 4 (1884) and *Am. Nat.* 1885: 403.

Rafinesque, C. S., 1814. Caratteri di alcuni nuovi generi e nuove specie di animali e piante della Sicilia. *Palermo.*

Ragusa, E., 1871. *Altre due nuove specie di Coleotteri trovate in Sicilia. *Bull. Soc. Ent. Ital.* 3: 194–196.

Ratzeburg, F. T. C., 1832. Ueber die Entwickelung der fusslosen Hymenopteren larven. *Nova Acta Acad. Nat. Curios. Bonn* 16, 1: 143–176, pl. — **1844.** Die Forstinsecten, oder Abbildung und Beschreibung der in den Wäldern Preussens und der Nachbarstaaten als schädlich oder nützlich bekannt gewordenen Insecten. 3: 36–45.

Ray, J., 1671. Extract of letter concerning spontaneous generation; as also of some insects smelling of musk (Formica, Ceramb. Moschatus, Apis). *Philos. Trans.* 6, 74: 2219–2220.

Rayger, C., 1694a. De formicis volantibus. *Ephem. Acad. Nat. Curios.* (Dec. 3) 2, 21: 27–29. — **1694b.** De Formicis et Locustis volantibus. Extr. in *Misc. Cur.* (Dec. 3) 2, 21–22: 27–29.

Rayward, A. L., 1906a. *Larvæ of Lycæna corydon and their Association with Ants. *Entom.* 39: 197–198. — **1906b.** *Larvæ of Lycæna bellargus and their Association with Ants. *Ibid.* 39: 219–220. — **1907.** *Larvæ of Polyommatus icarus and their Connection with Ants. *Ent. Rec. Journ. Var.* 19: 108–110.

von Razumovskij, G., 1789–? 1793. Histoire Naturelle du Jorat et de ses environs. 1: 225.

Redi, F., 1671. *Experimenta circa generationem Insectorum. *Amstelodami.*

Redtenbacher, L., 1858. *Fauna Austriaca. Die Käfer. 2 Ed. Wien.*

Reh. L., 1897. Biologische Beobachtungen an brasilianischen Ameisen. *Illustr. Wochenschr. Ent.* 2: 600–603; 612–616.

Reiber, Ferd. and A. Puton, 1876. *Catalogue des Hémiptères Hétéroptères de l'Alsace de la Lorraine 1876. Also Extr. *Bull. Soc. Hist. Nat. Colmar* 16 and 17 (1875–1876).

Reich, 1793. Kurze Beschreibung neuer oder wenig bekannter Thiere welche Herr Le Blond der naturforschenden Gesellschaft zu Paris aus Cayenne als Geschenk überschickt hat. *Mag. Thierr.* 1: 128–134, *Erlangen.*

Reiche, L., 1884. Note sur les propriétés lumineuses de Pyrophorus, Nyctophanes, et sur le bruit fait par les Passalus; Œcodoma cephalotes. *Ann. Soc. Ent. France* (2) 2 (Bull.): 63–67, pp. lxxxiv–lxxxv.

Reichenbach, H. T. L., 1816. *Monographia Pselaphorum. *Lipsiæ.* — **1894a.** *Ameisenstudien aus dem Frankfurter Walde. *Ber. Senkenb. Naturf. Gesell. Frankfurt a. M.* — **1894b.** *Eine Sklavenjagd am Grafenbruch. *Ibid.* pp. 99–104. — **1896.** *Bilder aus dem Leben der Ameisen. *Ibid.* pp. xcii–xcv. (*Ausz. von K. W. v. Dalla Torre, Zool. Centralb.* 4 (1897): 701–702.) — **1899a.** Ueber Ameisen. (Naturw. Feriencursus für Lehrer.) *Naturw. Wochenschr.* 14: 177–179, 1 fig. — **1899b.** Ueber lebende Ameisenkolonien in künstlichen Nestern. *Ber. Senck. Nat. Gesell. Frankfurt a. M.* pp. xcv–xcvi. — **1902.** Ueber Parthenogenese bei Ameisen und andere Beobachtungen an Ameisenkolonien in künstlichen Nestern. *Biol. Centralb.* 22: 461–465. — **1908.** Der Ameisenstaat und die Abstammungslehre. *Ber. Senckenb. Naturf. Gesell. Frankf. a. M.* pp. 126–147.

Reichert, Alex., **1897.** *Ueber Cetoniden, ihre Lebensweise und ihr Vorkommen in der Umgegend von Leipzig. *Illustr. Wochenschr. Ent.* 2: 167–173.

Reinhardt, L., **1906.** *Einige interessante Symbiosen bei Ameisen. *Beil. Allgem. Zeitg. München* 81 and 82.

Reinhart, H., **1906.** Weben der Ameisen. *Natur u. Haus.* 14: 248–249.

Reitter, E., **1879a.** *Coleopterologische Ergebnisse einer Reise nach Croatien und Slavonien. *Verh. Zool.-bot. Gesell. Wien* pp. 35–56. — **1879b.** *Neue Coleopteren aus dem südöstlichen Russland. *Ibid.* pp. 543–546. — **1881–'85.** *Bestimmungstabellen der europäischen Käfer. IV. *Ibid.* (1881): 86–95; V. *Ibid.* (1881): 443–592; X. *Ibid.* (1884): 59–94; XII. (1885) Necrophaga. *Verh. Naturf. Ver. Brünn.* 23. — **1882.** *Naturgeschichte der Insekten Deutschlands. Coleoptera. 3, 1. Berl.* (Clavigeridæ, Pselaphidæ, Scydmænidæ). — **1884.** *Resultate einer coleopterologischen Sammelcampagne auf den jonischen Inseln. *Deutsch. Ent. Zeitschr.* pp. 101–122. — **1885.** *Naturgeschichte der Insekten Deutschlands. Coleoptera. 3, 2. Berl.* (Leptinidæ, Silphidæ). — **1889.** *Zwei neue Coleopterengattungen aus Transkaukasien. *Wien Ent. Zeitg.* pp. 289–292. — **1895.** *Einiges über bekannte und neue Thorictus. *Deutsch. Ent. Zeitschr.* pp. 295–296. — **1899.** *Zur weiteren Kenntniss der Coleopteren-Gattung Myctochara Berthold. *Ent. Nachr.* 25: 155–159.

Rennie, J., **1834.** *The Amazon Ant. *Field Nat. Mag.* 2: 203–208.

Rettig, E., **1904.** *Ameisenpflanzen — Pflanzenameisen. Ein Beitrag zur Kenntnis der von Ameisen bewohnten Pflanzen und der Beziehungen zwischen beiden. *Bot. Centralb.* 17, Beih.: 89–122.

Retzius, A. J., **1783.** Gen. Sp. Ins. Geer. p. 75. — **1874.** *Ameisenähnlichkeit unter den Hemipteren. *Mitth. Schweiz. Ent. Gesell.* 4, 4: 156–159.

Reuter, O. M., **1878-'79.** *Till kännedomen om mimiska Hemiptera och deras lefnadshistoria. *Öfvers. Finsk. Vet. Soc. Förh.* 21: 141–198. — **1878-'91.** *Hemiptera Gymnocerata Europæ. 4 vols cum Suppl. *Helsingforsiæ.* — **1881.** *Analecta Hemipterologica. *Berl. Ent. Zeitschr.* pp. 155–196. — **1882.** Om Myrornas v. R. Instinkt med särskild hänsyn till de nyaste undersökningarne rörande densamma. *Öfvers Finsk. Vet. Soc. Förh.* 24: 136–164. — **1885.** Monomorium pharaonis L. en ny fiende till vor husro. *Ibid.* 26: 1–21. — **1886.** *[Bidrag till Kännedomen om våra Podurider.] *Meddel. Soc. Faun. Flor. Fenn.* 13: 179. — **1888.** Nya rön om Myrornas omtvistade medlidande och hjälpsamhet. *Ent. Tidskr.* 9: 55–90. Résumé in French pp. 91–95. — **1904a.** Lasius alienus Först. funnen i Finland. *Meddel. Soc. Faun. Flor. Fenn.* 29: 120–121. — **1904b.** Massuppträdande af insekter. *Ibid.* 29: 197–198. — **1908.** Die Seele der Tiere im Lichte der Forschung unserer Tage. Transl. from the Swedish by M. Buch, *Leipzig, T. O. Weigel.*

Rey, C., **1871-'75.** *Histoire Naturelle des Coléoptères de France. Brévipennes, Aléochariens. — **1886.** *Description de deux genres nouveaux de Tachyporiens. *Rev. d'Ent.* (Fauvel) pp. 252–256.

Richardson, E. L., **1886.** *Ants and Sunflowers. *Am. Nat.* 21, 3: 296–297.

Ridley, **1890.** (On Œcophylla.) *Journ. Straits Branch Roy. Asiat. Soc. Singapore* p. 345.

Riley, C. V., **1881.** Ants Injurious in Arizona. *Amer. Nat.* 15: 573, 574. — **1882a.** *Habits of Coscinoptera dominicana. *Am. Nat.* 16: 589. — **1882b.** The Utilization of Ants in Horticulture. *Nature* 26, 658: 126. — **1882c.** *Myrmecophilous Coleoptera. *Amer. Nat.* 16: 747–748. — **1883a.** *Hymenorus rufipes as a myrmecophilous species. *Amer. Nat.* 17: 1176. — **1883b.** *Myrmecophila. *Ibid.* 17: 975, 976. — **1889.** Some Insect Pests of the Household. Bed-bugs and Red Ants. *Ins. Life* 2: 104–108. — **1894.** Social Insects from psychical and evolutional points of view. *Proc. Ent. Soc. Wash.* 9: 1–74.

Robergitius, L. (Roberg, Lorenz), 1719. De Formicarum Natura. Dissertatio. *Resp. Lindwall. Upsaliæ.* 16 pp.

Robert, E., 1842. Observations sur les mœurs des Fourmis. *Ann. Sc. Nat.* (2) 18: 151–158.

Robertson, Chas., 1897. *Seed-Crests and Myrmecophilous Dissemination in certain Plants. *Bot. Gaz. Chicago* 24: 288–289.

Roesel von Rosenhof, Aug. Joh., 1749. *Die monatlich herausgegebene Insektenbelustigung. 2. *Nürnberg.*

Roger, J., 1856–'57. *Verzeichniss der bisher in Oberschlesien aufgefundenen Käferarten. *Breslau* 1857. Sep. aus *Breslau Zeitschr. Ent.* (1856). — **1857a.** Einiges über Ameisen. *Berl. Ent. Zeitschr.* 1: 10–20. — **1857b.** Ein Zwitter von Tetrogmus caldarius. *Ibid.* 1: 15–17, pl. 1, fig. 2. Kraatz G. in *Stett. Ent. Zeitg.* 23 (1862): 125. — **1859.** Beiträge zur Kenntniss der Ameisenfauna der Mittelmeerländer. *Berl. Ent. Zeitschr.* 3: 225–259. — **1860–'61.** Die Poneraartigen Ameisen. *Ibid.* 4: 278–311; 5: 1–54. — **1861.** Myrmecologische Nachlese. *Ibid.* 5: 163–174. — **1862a.** Einige neue exotische Ameisengattungen und Arten dazu beschrieben. *Ibid.* 6: 233–254, fig. — **1862b.** Beiträge zur Kenntniss der Ameisenfauna der Mittelmeerländer. II. *Ibid.* 6: 255–262. — **1862c.** Ueber Formiciden. Synonymische Bemerkungen. *Ibid.* 6: 283–297. — **1863a.** Die neu aufgeführten Gattungen und Arten meines Formiciden Verzeichnisses. *Ibid.* 7: 131–214. — **1863b.** Verzeichniss der Formiciden Gattungen und Arten. *Berlin.*

Rohwer, S. A., 1908. *The Aphid Genus Forda. *Psyche,* (Aug.): 67–68.

de Romand, B. E., 1846a. *[Notice of a new insect (Formilla Chevrolatii Rom.)]. *Ann. Soc. Ent. France* p. xxxii. — **1846b.** Sur Formica chevrolatii et Clytus quadripunctatus. *Ibid.* (2) 4 (Bull.): 32–34, fig.

Romanes, Geo. J., 1883. Animal Intelligence. *New York, Appleton & Co.* (*Internat. Sc. Ser.*) — **1893.** *The use of Ants to Aphids and Coccidæ. *Nature* 48, 1229: 54.

Rosenhauer, Wilh. G., 1842. *Entomologische Mittheilungen VI. Ueber die Larve der Clythra quadripunctata. *Stett. Ent. Zeitg.* pp. 50–53. — **1852.** *Ueber die Entwicklung und Fortpflanzung der Clythren und Cryptocephalen. *Erlangen.* — **1856.** *Die Thiere Andalusiens. *Erlangen.*

Rossi, Peter, 1790. Fauna etrusca systematica; insecta in Provinciis Florentina et Pisana collecta. *Libourne.* 2 Vols. — **1794.** Mantissa Insectorum 2: 125.

Rossmässler, E. A., 1862. Von den Ameisen. *Aus der Heimath,* pp. 45–48.

Roth, H. L., 1885. Notes on the Habits of Some Australian Hymenoptera Aculeata. *Journ. Linn. Soc.* 18: 318–328.

Rothney, G. A. J., 1889. *Notes on Indian Ants. *Trans. Ent. Soc. London* pp. 347–374. — **1891.** *Note on Rhinopsis ruficornis mimicking Sima rufonigra. *Ibid.* p. XI. — **1892.** *[Note on Leptothorax acervorum, etc., in nests of Formica sanguinea.] *Ent. M. Mag.* (2) 3: 50, 51. — **1893.** *[Notes on Leptothorax acervorum in nests of Formica sanguinea.] *Ibid.* (2) 4: 67. — **1895.** Notes on Indian Ants. *Trans. Ent. Soc. London* pp. 195–211. — **1903.** *The Aculeate Hymenoptera of Barrackpore, Bengal. *Ibid.* pp. 93–116.

Roubal, Jan, 1905. *Prodromus myrmecophilů českých. (Studie zoogeografická s ethologickymi poznámkami.) *Sitzb. Böhm. Ges. Wiss. Math.-nat. Cl.;* *Véstn. Česke Spolecň. Náuk. Tř. Math-přírod.* 1905, 15: 44 pp.

Rouget, A., 1857. *Note sur l'habitat et les différences sexuelles de Catopsimorphus arenarius Hampe. *Ann. Soc. Ent. France* pp. 756–760. — 1866. *[Note on Tettigometra læta with Tapinoma erraticum.] *Ibid.* p. lxxxiii. — 1870. *[Note on Tettigometra obliqua with Formica pratensis.] *Ibid.* p. lxxvi.

Roux, A. Effectus singularis vaporis formicarum. *Vandermonde Journ. Méd.* 17: 237. Transl. *Neu. Samml. Ausserlesenen Wahrnehmungen* 8: 196.

Rovelle. De Oleo Formicarum destillato. *Journ. Méd. Roux.* 39: 250.

Rudow, F., 1881. Die Nester der europäischen Ameisen. *Die Natur.* 36: 435. — 1896. Einige Ameisenwohnungen. *Illustr. Wochenschr. Ent.* 1: 473–475, 3 figg. — 1897. Einige Ameisenbauten. *Insektenbörse* 14: 67–69. — 1898a. Beobachtungen bei Ameisen. *Ibid.* 15: 223–224. — 1898b. Entomologische Notizen. *Soc. Ent.* 13: 83. — 1905a. Die Wohnungen der Ameisen. *Ent. Jahrb.* 15: 148–171. — 1905b. *Ameisen als Gärtner. *Insektenbörse* 22: 199–200. — 1906. Einige merkwürdige Gallenbildungen. *Ent. Jahrb.* 16: 73–105.

Rupertsberger, M., 1878. *Unter Ameisen. *Ber. Verh. Naturk. Linz.* 9: 1–11. — 1893. *Coleopterologische Kleinigkeiten aus meinem Tagebuche. 1. *Wien Ent. Zeitg.* pp. 247–249.

Rusby, H. H., 1881. Mischief caused by ants in Arizona. *Am. Nat.* 15: 573–574.

Ruysch, H., 1718. Theatrum Universale Omnium Animalium. 2. *Amstelodami.*

Ruzsky, M., 1902a. Neue Ameisen aus Russland. *Zool. Jahrb. Abt. Syst.* 17: 469–484, 8 figg. — 1902b. Ants of the Turgai Region. (In Russian.) *Rev. Russe d'Ent.* No. 2, Aug., 4 pp. — 1902c. On the Ant-fauna of the Caucasus and the Crimea. (In Russian.) *Note Proc. Soc. Nat. Imper. Univ. Kazan No. 206,* 33 pp. — 1902d. The Ants of the Vicinity of the Aral Lake. (In Russian.) 24 pp. — 1903a. Une nouvelle fourmi de la Transcaspienne. *Rev. Russ. d'Ent.* 3: 36–37. (In Russian.) — 1903b. Ants of the Transbaikalian Province. (In Russian.) *Ibid.* 3, 3–4: 3 pp. — 1903c. Die Ameisenfauna der Astrachanischen Kirgisensteppe. (In Russian.) *St. Petersburg,* 23 pp. — 1903d. Ocherk' myrmecologicheskoi faunui Kirghizskoi stepi. *Horæ Soc. Ent. Ross.* 36: 294–316. — 1905. Ueber Tetramorium striativentre Mayr. und Tetr. schneideri Emery. *Zool. Anz.* 29: 517–518. — 1908. Quelques Observations Nouvelles et remarques sur la Variabilité de l'Instinct de Nidification chez les Fourmis. *Jour. Psych. Neur.* 13: 136–149.

SAHLBERG, C. R., 1834. *Insecta Fennica, dissertationibus academicis annis 1817–1834 editis, enumerata. Pars 1 *Helsingforsiæ.*

Sahlberg, J., 1870. *Anteckningar till Lapplands Coleopter Fauna. *Notis. Sällsk. Faun. Fenn. Förh.* 11: 387–440. — 1876a. *Enumeratio Coleopterorum Brachyelytrorum Fenniæ. 1 Staphylinidæ. *Act. Soc. Faun. Flor. Fenn.* 1. — 1876b. *Om förekomsten af Formica gagates hos en röd Stack-Myrart. *Meddel. Soc. Faun. Flor. Fenn.* 1: 134–136. — 1876c. Notiser ur Sællskaptes pro Fauna et Flora Fennica 21: 310–313. — 1880–'81. *Bidrag till Nordvestra Sibiriens Insektfauna. Coleoptera 1. *K. Svensk. Vet. Ak. Handl.* 17. — 1881. *Enumeratio Hemipterorum Gymnoceratorum Fenniæ. *Meddel. Soc. Faun. Flor. Fenn.* 7: 1–109. — 1883. *Om larverna af slägtet Lomechusa. *Ibid.* 9: 89–93. — 1889. *Enumeratio Coleopterorum Brachelytrorum et Clavicornium Fenniæ. II. Pselaphidæ et Clavigeridæ. *Act. Soc. Faun. Flor. Fenn.* 6.

Sampaio de Azevedo, A. G., 1894. *Saúva ou Manhúaára. Monographia. *Saõ Paulo.*

Sanderson, E. D., 1904. *The Kelep and the Cotton Plant. *Science* N. S. 20: 887–888.

Santschi, F., 1906. *À propos des mœurs parasitiques temporaires des Fourmis du genre Bothriomyrmex. *Ann. Soc. Ent. France* 75: 363–392. — 1907. *Fourmis de Tunisie capturées en 1906. *Rev. Suisse Zool.* 15, 2: 305–334,

7 text-figg. — **1908a.** Quelques Observations Nouvelles et remarques sur la Variabilité de l'Instinct de Nidification chez les Fourmis. *Jour. Psych. Neur.* 13: 136–149. — **1908b.** Nouvelles Fourmis de l'Afrique du Nord (Égypte, Canaries, Tunisie) *Ann. Soc. Ent. France* 77: 517–534, 12 figg.

de Saulcy, F., 1862. *Observations sur les genres Choleva, Catops et Catopsimorphus, etc. *Ann. Soc. Ent. France* pp. 281–291. — **1864a.** *Faune Française et Européenne. Descriptions et remarques. *Ibid.* pp. 253–260. — **1864b.** *Descriptions et espèces nouvelles de Coléoptères recueillies en Syrie, en Egypte et en Palestine. *Ibid.* pp. 421–440. — **1874.** Pheidole jordanica nov. sp. *Bull. Soc. d'Hist. Nat. Metz.* 13: 17. — **1874-'76.** *Species des Paussides, Clavigérides, Psélaphides et Scydménides de l'Europe et des pays circonvoisins. *Bull. Soc. Hist. Nat. Dép. Moselle* 13: 1–132; 14: 25–100.

Saunders, Edw., 1880. Synopsis of British Heterogyna and Fossorial Hymenoptera. *Trans. Ent. Soc. London* pp. 201 seq. — **1883-'84.** *Coleoptera from the vicinity of Ants'-nests, Chobham. *Ent. M. Mag.* 20: 18, 19. — **1886.** *The Male of Formicoxenus nitidulus Nyl. *Ibid.* 23: 42. — **1888.** On a Collection of Ants from Gibraltar and Tangier. *Ibid.* 25 (June): 17. — **1892.** *Rare Hemiptera at Chobham and Surbiton. *Ibid.* (2) 3: 290. — **1896.** Honey Bees destroyed by Wood Ants (Formica rufa). *Ibid.* 32: 161. — **1903.** *Myrmocoris gracilis Sahlb. An addition to the British Hemiptera. *Ibid.* 39: 269. — **1904.** Hymenoptera Aculeata from Majorca (1901) and Spain (1901-'02). With Introduction, Notes and Appendix by Prof. Edward B. Poulton. The Mimicry of Aculeata by the Asilidæ and Volucella and its Probable Significance. *Trans. Ent. Soc. London* pp. 591–665. — **1906a.** Hymenoptera aculeata taken by Col. Yerbury, R. A., in Scotland, 1905. *Ent. M. Mag.* (2) 17: 60–61. — **1906b.** Additions and Corrections to the list of British Hymenoptera since 1896. *Ibid.* (2) 17: 151–155; 172–177; 202–206.

Saunders, W., 1875. The Mexican Honey Ant (Myrmecocystus Mexicanus). *Canad. Ent.* 7: 12–13, 1 fig. — **1878.** *Notes on the larva of Lycæna Scudderi. *Ibid.* 10: 14, 15.

de Saussure, H., 1883. Les Fourmis Américaines. *Bibl. Univ.* (3) 10: 28–38; 158–172.

Savage, T. S., 1847. On the Habits of the Drivers, or Visiting Ants of West Africa. *Trans. Ent. Soc. London* 5: 1–15; *Proc. Acad. Nat. Sc. Phila.* 4: 195–200.

Savi, P., 1819. *Osservazioni sopra la Blatta acervorum di Panzer, Gryllus myrmecophilus nobis. *Bibl. Ital.* 15, 44: 217–229, 1 pl.

Saville-Kent, W., 1897. The Naturalist in Australia. *London, Chapman & Hall, Ltd.* 302 pp., 59 pls., 100 text-figg.

Say, T., 1836-'37. Descriptions of New Species of North American Hymenoptera and observations on some already described. *Bost. Journ. Nat. Hist.* 1.

Schäffer, C., 1902. Ueber die geistigen Fähigkeiten der Ameisen. *Verh. Nat. Ver. Hamburg* (3) 9: 14–42, 3 figg.

Schäffer, J. C., 1769. Icones insectorum circa Ratisbonam indigenorum coloribus naturam referentibus expressæ.

Schaufuss, L. W., 1882. *Pselaphidarum Monographiæ I et II. Adranini et Clavigerodini. *Ann. Mus. Civ. Stor. Nat. Genova* 18: 173–206.

Schenck, A., 1852. *Beschreibung nassauischer Ameisenarten. *Jahrb. Ver. Naturk. Nassau* 8, 1: 3–149. — **1863.** *Naturgeschichte der Ameisen und Anleitung zur Bestimmung der nassauischen Arten. I. *Prag. Gym. Weilburg. Ostern.*

Schenck, C. F., 1853-'54. *Die Nassauischen Ameisen Species. *Stett. Ent. Zeitg.* 14: 157–163; 185–198; 225–232; 296–301; 15: 63–64. — **1855.** Ueber die (im Heft VIII). Eciton testaceum genannte Ameise. *Jahrb. Ver. Naturk. Herzogth. Nassau* 10: 137–149. — **1856.** Systematische Eintheilung der Nassauischen Ameisen nach Mayr. *Ibid.* 11: 90–94. — 1861. Die deutschen Vesparien nebst Zusätzen und Berichtigungen zu der Bearbeitung der nassauischen Grabwespen, Goldwespen, Bienen und Ameisen. *Ibid.*

Schenck, C. T., 1877. Ueber Lasius incisus. *Ent. Nachr. Herausgeg. v. Dr. Kattcr* 3: 2.

Schenk, H., 1900. *Ueber die Wechselbeziehungen zwischen Pflanzen und Ameisen im tropischen Wald. *Bcr. Senck. Nat. Gesell. Frankfurt a. M.* pp. civ–cvi.

Schenckling, S., 1896. *Ueber echte Ameisengäste. *Illustr. Wochenschr. Ent.* 1: 364–367.

Schenkling-Prévôt, 1896a. *Ameisen als Pilz-Züchter und -Esser. *Ibid.* 6: 89–93. — 1896b. *Die Höckerameisen und ihre Pilzgärten. *Insektenbörse* 13: 264. — 1896c. *Die Pilzgärten der Haarameisen. *Ibid.* 13: 153–154. — 1897a. Etwas über Myrmeco-Architektur. *Ibid.* 14: 25–26; 32–33. — 1897b. *Rozites gongylophora, die Kulturpflanze der Blattschneide-Ameisen. *Illustr. Wochenschr. Ent.* 2: 56–60.

Scheuchzer, J. J., 1735. Physica sacra cum tabulis Johannis Andreæ Pfeffel. Aug. vindicorum et Ulmiæ in fol. Tom. 4, 750 tab. æn. textu latino *Amstelodami.* In fol. Tom. 15 cum Tab. 750 Textu belgico.

Schiern, F., 1863. Ueber den Ursprung der Sage von den goldgrabenden Ameisen. *Verh. Kgl. Dän. Gesell. Wiss.* Transl. *Leipzig. Alfr. Lorentz.* 53 pp.

Schiller-Tietz, 1902. *Ameisen, Blattläuse und Honigthau an Kulturpflanzen. *Schweiz. Bauer* 56: 70.

Schilling, P. S., 1838. Bemerkungen über die in Schlesien und der Grafschaft Glatz vorgefundenen Ameisen. *Schles. Gesell. Vaterländ Cultur. Breslau.*

Schimmer, F. 1908. Beitrag zur Ameisenfauna des Leipziger Gebietes. *Sitzb. Naturf. Gesell. Leipzig* 35: 11–20.

Schimper, A. F. W., 1888. *Die Wechselbeziehungen zwischen Pflanzen und Ameisen im tropischen Amerika. 1 (*Jena*): 95 pp., 3 pls. — 1898. Pflanzengeographie. *Ibid.* pp. 147–170.

Schiner, J. R., 1860–'64. *Fauna Austriaca. Die Fliegen, Diptera. *Wien.*

Schioedte, J. G., 1844. *[Remarks on Myrmecophiles.] *Germar's Zeitschr. Ent.* 5: 473, 474.

Schleip, W., 1908. Die Richtungskörperbildung im Ei von Formica sanguinea. *Zool. Jahrb. Abth. f. Anat. u. Ont.* 26: 651–677, 2 pls.

Schleyer, 1898. Ameisenschwärme auf Bergeshöhen. *Natur* 47: 477.

Schlüter, K., 1896. Die Intelligenz der Ameisen. I. *Illustr. Wochenschr. Ent.* 1, 9: 142–144.

Schmidt, J. A., 1684. Dissertatio de Republica formicarum. *Resp. Dilger. Jena.*

Schmidt, Johannes, 1888. *Drei neue Hetærius. *Ent. Nachr.* 14: 236–239. — 1889. *Neue Histeriden aus Paraguay. *Berl. Ent. Zeitschr.* pp. 317–324. — 1893. *Myrmekophile Histeriden aus Amerika. *Deutsch. Ent. Zeitschr.* pp. 171–190.

Schmidt, W. L. E., 1841. *Ueber Clythra quadripunctata L. und ihre nächsten Verwandten. *Stett. Ent. Zcitg.* pp. 146–155.

Schmidt-Goebel, H. M., 1836. *De Pselaphis Faunæ Pragensis, cum anatomia Clavigeri. *Prag.* — 1876. *Coleopterologische Kleinigkeiten. *Stett. Ent. Zeitg.* p. 389.

von Schmidtz, Carl, and R. Oppikofer, 1904. Die Feinde der Biene. *Ascona, Carl von Schmitz,* 24 pp.

Schmitz, Ern., 1896–'97. As Formigas da Madeira. *Ann. Sc. Nat. Porto.* 3: 55–58; 4: 77.

Schmitz, H. (S. J.), 1906. *Das Leben der Ameisen und ihrer Gäste. *G. J. Manz. Regensburg,* 190 pp., 46 figg. — 1907a. Wie besiedelt man künstliche Ameisennester? *Ent. Wochenbl.* 24: 23–24, 26–28. — 1907b. Künstliche

Ameisennester. (Mit Beschreibung neuer Formen.) *Ibid.* 24: 121–122; 125–126; 133; 137–138, 5 figg. — **1908.** *Claviger longicornis Müll. sein Verhältnis zu Lasius umbratus und seine internationalen Beziehungen zu anderen Ameisenarten. *Zeitschr. Wiss. Insekt.-biol.* 4, 3: 84–87 (not yet completed).

Schneider, O., 1893. *San Remo und seine Thierwelt im Winter. *Sitzungsber. Abh. Gesell. Isis. Dresden* Note 1.

Schnetzler, J. B., 1885. Sur les propriétés antiseptique de l'acide formique. *Arch. Sc. Nat.* 11: 5–14.

Schoenichen, W., 1898. *Antennophorus Uhlmanni. *Zeitschr. Naturw.* 71: 145–146. — **1900.** Ueber Tier- und Menschenseele. *Stuttgart.* — **1904.** *Ameisen als Schutztruppen. *Prometheus* 15: 548–551, 2 figg.

Scholz, R., 1899. *Microglossa (Haploglossa) nidicola Fairm. kommt auch in Ameisennestern vor. *Insektenbörse* 16: 272.

Schouteden, H., 1902. *Les Aphides radicicoles de Belgique et les fourmis. *Ann. Soc. Ent. Belg.* 46: 136–142.

Schrank, Frz. von Paula, 1781. Enumeratio Insectorum Austriæ indigenorum. *August. Vindelicor. Klett.* 548 pp.

Schroeder, Ew., 1867. *Von den Ameisen. *Zool. Gart.* 8: 225–229.

Schroeter, J. S., Von der Klugheit der Ameisen, wenn sie genöthiget sind ihre Wohnung zu verändern. *Schröters Abh. Naturgesch.* 1: 251–257.

Schulze, J. H. De Usu Formicarum in paralysi. *Ephem. Nat. Curios.* Dec. 1 ou 4, et 5 obs. 127 p. 129.

Schumann, K., 1889. *Die Ameisenpflanzen. *Hamburg.* — **1902.** *Ameisenpflanzen. *Gartenflora.*

Schütte, H., 1907. Die untergegangene Jadeinsel Arngast. *Abh. Nat. Ver. Bremen* 19: 88–120, 1 pl.

Schwarz, E. A., 1889. *Myrmecophilous Coleoptera found in Temperate North America. *Proc. Ent. Soc. Wash.* 1, 4 (June 27): 237–247. — **1890a.** *A list of the blind or nearly eyeless Coleoptera hitherto found in North America. *Ibid.* 2, 1 (Feb. 6): 23–26. — **1890b.** *[Note on the myrmecophilous habits of Tachys incurvus Say.] *Ibid.* 2, 1 (Oct. 2): 88. — **1891.** *[Note on Emphylus americanus living with Formica sanguinea.] *Ibid.* 2, 2 (Oct. 1): 227.

von Schwenkfeld, C., 1603. *Theriotropheum Silesiæ, in quo animalium, hoc est quadrupedum, reptilium, avium, piscium, insectorum natura, vis et usus sex libris perstringuntur. *Lignicii.*

Scopoli, J. A., 1763. Entomologia Carniolica. *Vindobonæ.*

Scott, J., 1860. *Ants'-nests and their inhabitants. *Zool.* 18: 7024–7026.

Scriba, W., 1863–'69. *Die Käfer im Grossherzogthum Hessen und seiner nächsten Umgebung. *Ber. Oberhess. Gesell. Nat. Heilk.* 10–13.

Scudder, S. H., 1869. *Entomological Correspondence of Thaddeus William Harris. *Occas. Pap. Bost. Soc. Nat. Hist.* 1: 375 pp., 4 pls. — **1877.** On the first discovered traces of fossil insects in the American tertiaries. *Bull. Geol. Geograph. Survey of the U. S.* 3, 4 (*Washington* Aug. 15): 742. — **1885.** *Systematische Uebersicht der fossilen Myriapoden, Arachnoiden und Insekten. Sep. aus *Zittel & Schimper, Handb. Paläont* 1 (*Paläozool.*), 2. *München.* — **1886.** *Systematic review of our present knowledge of fossil Insects. *Bull. U. S. Geol. Surv.* 31. — **1888–'89.** *The Butterflies of the Eastern United States and Canada. 3 Vols. *Cambridge, Mass.* 1: 15 Lycænid larvæ, and Excursus XXXV: 962–963. — **1890.** The Tertiary Insects of North America. *U. S. Geol. Survey, Washington.*

Seba, A., 1734–'35. Locupletissimi Rerum Naturalium Thesauri Accurata Descriptio. 4 Vols. fol. *Amstelædami.*

de Sébille, A., 1897. *La cétoine dorée (Cetonia aurata). *Bull. Soc. Centr. Forest. Belg.* 4: 811–812.

Semon, R., 1905. Die Mneme. *Leipzig.*

Semper, C., 1881. *Natural Conditions of Existence p. 391, fig. 104.

Sergi, G., 1892. Richerche su alcuni organi di senso nelle antenne delle Formiche. *Bull. Ent. Ital.* 24: 18–25.

Sernander, R., 1903. *Den Skandinaviska Vegetationens Spridningsbiologie, *Upsala.* — **1906.** *Entwurf einer Monographie der europäischen Myrme-kochoren. *Upsala,* 410 pp., 11 pls.

Seurich, P., 1891. *Ueber die Wechselbeziehungen zwischen Pflanzen und Ameisen. *Elft. Ber. Naturw. Gesell. Chemnitz.* pp. xxxviii–xliv.

Séverin, G., 1896. *Les Fourmis. Extr. *Mouvement Georgr. Bruxelles, P. Weissenbruch,* 16 pp., 7 figg. — **1898.** Règlement sur les insectes nuisibles. *Bull. Soc. Centr. Forest. Belg.* 5: 609–632; 699–724.

Sharp, D., 1872a. *The Staphylinidæ of Japan. *Trans. Ent. Soc. London* pp. 1–103. — **1874b.** *The Pselaphidæ and Scydmænidæ of Japan. *Ibid.* pp. 105–130. — **1874c.** *Descriptions of new genera and species of Pselaphidæ and Scydmænidæ from Australia and New Zealand. *Ibid.* pp. 483–517. — **1876.** *Contributions to the Staphylinidæ of the Amazon-valley. *Ibid.* pp. 27–425. — **1883.** *Revision of the Pselaphidæ of Japan. *Ibid.* pp. 291–331. — **1888-'89.** *On the Staphylinidæ of Japan. *Ann. Mag. Nat. Hist.* (6) 2 (1888): 277–295; 369–387; 3 (1889): 108–121. — **1892.** *Description of two new Pselaphidæ, found by Mr. J. J. Walker in Australia and China. *Ent. M. Mag.* (2) 3: 240–242. — **1893.** On stridulation in ants. *Trans. Ent. Soc. London* pp. 199–213, pl. 9. — **1901.** Insecta [II]. *Cambridge Nat. Hist.* 6: 626 pp., 293 figg. — **1883.** *Biologia Centrali-Americana. Coleoptera, 1, 2 Staphylinidæ, pp. 145–747. — **1887.** *Biologia Centrali-Americana. Coleoptera 2, 1 Pselaphidæ, pp. 1–46. Histeridæ (by Lewis) pp. 182–244.

Shipp, J. W., 1893. *Claviger testaceus in Wychwood Forest. *Ent. M. Mag.* (2) 4: 144.

Shuckard, W. E., 1838. Description of a new species of Myrmica which has been found in houses, both in the Metropolis and Provinces. Myrmica domestica. *Mag. Nat. Hist.* (2) 2: 626–627. — **1840.** Monograph of the Dorylidæ, a Family of the Hymenoptera Heterogyna. *Ann. Nat. Hist. or Mag. Zool. Bot. and Geol.* 5: 188–202; 258–272; 315–329; append. pp. 396–398. — **1841.** Differences of Neuters in Ants. *Ibid.* 7: 525.

Sichel, J., 1856. Note sur les Fourmis introduites dans les Serres Chaudes. *Ann. Soc. Ent. France* (3) 4 (Bull.) : 23.

Siewers, C. G., 1882. *[A slave-foray.] *Journ. Cincinn. Soc.* 5: 60–61.

Silverlock, Oscar C., 1907. The Senses of Ants as Regards Heat and Light. *Nat. Notes* 18: 165–169.

Silvestri, F., 1903. *Contribuzioni alla conoscenza dei Mirmecofili. I. Osservazioni su alcuni mirmecofili dei dintorni di Portici. *Ann. Mus. Zool. Univ. Napoli* 1, 13: 5 pp.

Simon, E., 1874-'79. *Les Arachnides de France. *Paris.* — **1899.** *Description d'une Araignée myrmécophile du cap de Bonne-Espérance (Andromma Raffrayi n. sp.). *Bull. Soc. Ent. France* pp. 179–180, 1 fig.

Sjöstedt, Y., 1908. *Akaziengallen und Ameisen auf den afrikanischen Steppen. *Wiss. Ergeb. Schwed. Zool. Exped. u. d. Kilimandjaro, Meru,* etc. *8. Hymenoptera. Upsala,* pp. 97–118, 3 pls.

Slosson, Annie T., 1906. Additional List of Insects Taken in Alpine Region of Mt. Washington. *Ent. News* 17: 323–326.

Smalian, C., 1894. Altes und Neues aus dem Leben der Ameisen. *Zeitschr. Naturw.* 67: 1–46.

Smith, F., 1842. Notes on the Habits of Various Species of British Ants. *Trans. Ent. Soc. London* 3: 151–154. — **1843a.** *Notes on Formica sanguinea and other Hymenoptera. *Zool.* 1: 262. — **1843b.** *Notes on Entomological captures in Hampshire. *Ibid.* 1: 262–265. — **1843c.** *Notes on the capture of Claviger foveolatus and other Coleopterous Insects inhabiting Ants'-nests.

Ibid. 1: 266–269. — **1851.** List of the British Animals in the Collection of the British Museum. Part IV. Hymenoptera Aculeata. — **1854.** *Essays on the genera and species of British Formicidæ. Trans. Ent. Soc. London* (2) 3: 95–135. — **1855a.** Descriptions of some species of Brazilian Ants belonging to the genera Pseudomyrma, Eciton and Myrmica, with observations on their Economy by Mr. Bates. *Ibid.* (2) 3: 156–169, fig. — **1855b.** Economy of Brazilian Ants. *Zool.* 13: 4604. — **1857.** Catalogue of the Hymenopterous Insects Collected at Sarawak, Borneo; Mount Ophir, Malacca; and at Singapore by A. R. Wallace. *Journ. Proc. Linn. Soc. Zool.* 2 (1858): 42–130, pls. 1, 2. — **1858a.** Revision of an Essay on the British Formicidæ published in the transactions of the Society. *Trans. Ent. Soc. London* (2) 4: 274–284. — **1858b.** Catalogue of British Fossorial Hymenoptera, Formicidæ and Vespidæ, in the Collection of the British Museum. 236 pp., 6 pls. — **1858c.** Catalogue of Hymenopterous Insects in the Collection of the British Museum. VI. Formicidæ, 216 pp., 14 pls. — **1859.** Catalogue of the Hymenopterous Insects in the Collection of the British Museum. VII. Dorylidæ and Thynnidæ. 76 pp., 3 pls. — **1860.** Description of new Genera and Species of Exotic Hymenoptera. *Journ. Ent. London* 1: 65–84; 146–155. — **1861.** Description of some new Species of Ants from the Holy Land, with a Synonymic List of others previously described. *Journ. Proc. Linn. Soc.* 6: 31. — **1862.** Description of New Species of Aculeate Hymenoptera collected at Panama by R. W. Stretch, with a List of Described Species, and the various localities where they have previously occurred. *Trans. Ent. Soc. London* (3) 1: 29–44. — **1864.** (The male of Asemorhoptrum lippulum.) *Ent. Ann.* fig. 2. — **1865a.** On Formica exsecta.) *Ibid.* p. 87, fig. 2. — **1865b.** Observations on the Genus Dorylus, and upon a new genus of Aphidæ. *Ent. M. Mag.* 2: 3–5. — **1865c.** Notes on British Formicidæ. *Ibid.* 2: 28–30. — **1874a.** On Hermaphroditism in Ants. *Ent. Ann.* pp. 147–148, pl., fig. 3. — **1874b.** On a Hermaphrodite Ant, Myrmica lævinodis, from Cheshire. *Trans. Ent. Soc. London* (Proc.) p. iv.

Smith, J. B., 1886. *Ants'-nests and their inhabitants. *Am. Nat.* 5, 20: 680.

Smith, Theodora, 1898. Ant Neighbors. *Halifax Nat.* 3: 1–5; 27–31, 2 figg. The Hibernation of Ants pp. 116–119.

Smith, W. W., 1892a. *On the Origin of Ants'-nests. *Ent. M. Mag.* (2) 3: 60–65. — **1892b.** *Coccids in Ants'-nests. *Ibid.* (2) 3: 307. — **1896.** *On the Habits of New Zealand Ants. *Trans. Proc. N. Zeal. Inst.* 28: 468–479. — **1900.** Large Colonies of Ants in New Zealand. *Ent. M. Mag.* (2) 11: 7–9.

Snellen, P. C. T., 1908. *Batrachedra myrmecophila Snell. nov. spec. *Tijdschr. Ent.* 51: 181–184, 1 pl.

Snow, F. H., 1906. List of Species of Hymenoptera Collected in Arizona by the University of Kansas Entomological Expeditions of 1902, 1903, 1904, 1905 and 1906. *Trans. Kansas Acad. Sc.* 20: 127–139.

Snow, L. M., 1902. The Microcosm of the Drift Line. *Amer. Nat.* 36: 855–864.

Solsky, S., 1872. *Coléoptères de la Sibérie orientale. *Hor. Soc. Ent. Ross.* 8: 232–277.

Soós, Lajos, 1903. Hangya-darazsharcz. *Rovart. Lapok.* 10: 171–172. — Kampf zwischen Ameisen und Wespen. *Auszüge* p. 15.

Southcombe, W. H., 1907. Formation of a New Nest by Lasius niger. *Trans. Ent. Soc. London* 1906: lxxv–lxxvii.

Spence, W., and W. Kirby. *An Introduction to Entomology or Elements of the Natural History of Insects 2 (by Spence) 5th Ed.

Spencer, H., 1893a. The Inadequacy of "Natural Selection." *Contemp. Review* pp. 153–166; 439–456. — **1893b.** Professor Weismann's Theories. *Ibid.* pp. 743–760. — **1893c.** A Rejoinder to Professor Weismann. *Ibid.* pp. 893–912. — **1894a.** Weismannism Once More. *Ibid.* pp. 592–608. — **1894b.** Origin of classes among the "Parasol" Ants. *Nature* 51: 125–126.

Sperling, P. G., 1689. Dissertatio de chemica formicarum analysi. *Resp. Samuel Gotthilf Manitius. Auctor. Wittebergæ* 64 pp., 1 pl.

Spinola, M., 1808. Insectorum Liguriæ species novæ aut rariores 1: 243. *Gènes.* — **1853.** Compte-rendu des Hyménoptères inédits provenant du voyage entomologique de M. Ghiliani dans le Para en 1846. *Mém. Real. Accad. Sc. Torino* (2) 13: 19–94.

Sprenger, B., 1767. Perdix a formicis exclusa. *Nova. Act. Acad. Nat. Curios.* 3, 30.

Stainton, H. T., 1859. *Note on a Lepidopterous Insect in Ants'-nests. *Proc. Ent. Soc. London* (2) 5: 68.

de Stefani, T., 1897. Note per servire allo studio delle Mutille di Sicilia. *Nat. Sicil.* (2) 11, 4: 77–86.

Stein, J. P. E. F., 1859. *Einige neue europäische Isopoden-Arten. *Berl. Ent. Zeitschr.* pp. 259–267.

Steinvorth, 1897. *Ameisenpflanzen. 44–47. *Jahrsb. Nat. Gesell. Hann.* p. 32.

Stephan, J., 1905. *Schmetterlinge und Ameisen. *Natur. u. Haus* 13: 150–152.

Stoll, O., 1898. Zur Kenntnis der geographischen Verbreitung der Ameisen. *Mitth. Schweiz. Ent. Gesell.* 10: 120–126.

Stolpe, H., 1882. Förteckning öfver Svenska Myror. Preliminärt Meddelande. *Ent. Tidskr.* 3: 127–151.

Stone, J. H., 1881. *(Lychnis viscaria a trap for ants.) *Nature* 25: 151, 152.

Strang, E., 1903. *Hymenopterologisk Bidrag til Norges Fauna. *Christiania Vid.-selsk. Förh.* 8: 8.

Strohmayer, J., 1906. Beobachtungen über Ameisen-Gefrässigkeit. *Ent. Jahrb.* 16: 180–181.

Sumichrast, Fr., 1868. Notes on the Habits of certain Mexican Hymenoptera presented to the American Entomological Society. *Trans. Amer. Ent. Soc.* 2: 39–44.

Swainson, W., 1859. On the Habits and Instincts of Animals. *London, Longman, Brown, Green & Longman.*

Swammerdam, J., 1737. Biblia Naturæ. *Leyden.*

Swingle, W. T., 1896. *Fungus Gardens in the Nest of an Ant (Atta tardigrada Buckl.) near Washington, D. C. *Proc. Amer. Assoc. Adv. Sc. 44th Meet.:* 185–186.

Swinton, A. H., 1878-'79. Note on the Stridulation of Myrmica ruginodis and other Hymenoptera. *Ent. M. Mag.* 14: 187.

Sykes, W. H., 1835. Descriptions of new species of Indian Ants. *Trans. Ent. Soc. London* 1: 99–107, fig. 1.

Szabó, J., 1908. Hangyászati jegyzetek. *Rovart. Lapok* 15: 175–178.

TANNER, J. E., 1892a. *Œcodoma cephalotes. The Parasol or Leaf-cutting Ant. *Trinidad Field. Nat. Club* 1, 3 (Aug.): 68, 69. — **1892b.** Œcodoma cephalotes. Second Paper. *Ibid.* 1, 5 (Dec.): 123–127.

Taylor, G. W., 1884. *The Entomology of Vancouver Island. *Canad. Ent.* 16, 5 (May): 90–92.

Tepper, J. G. O., 1882. *Observations about the Habits of some South Australian Ants. *Trans. and Proc. Roy. Soc. S. Austral.* 5: 24–26; 106, 107. — **1896.** *Note on a Genus of Gryllidæ, New for South Australia; and Description of a New Species of Myrmecophila. *Ibid.* 20, 1: 149–151.

Thesing, C., 1906. Ueber den Nestbau einiger Ameisen. *Aus der Natur.* 1: 664–668, 6 figg. — **1907.** Altes und Neues aus der Ameisenbiologie. *Himmel. u. Erde* 19: 23–33, 5 figg.

Thomann, H., 1901. *Schmetterling und Ameisen. Beobachtungen über eine Symbiose zwischen Lycæna argus L. und Formica cinerea Mayr. *Jahresber. Nat. Gesell. Graubünden* N. F. 44: 1–40, 1 pl. — **1908.** *Schmetterlinge und

Ameisen. Ueber das Zusammenleben der Raupen von Psecadia pusiella
Röm. and der P. decemguttella Hb. mit Formiciden. *Ibid.* 50: 21–31.

Thomas, T. H., 1890. Note upon an Ants'-nest in a Cardiff Garden. *Rep.
Trans. Cardiff. Nat. Soc.* 20: 106.

Thomson, Wm. M. The Land and the Book. 1: 520, 521; 2: 262, 263.
Harpers' ed.

Thunberg, C. P., 1781. *Beskrifning på tvänne nya insecten, Paussus. *Vetensk.
Acad. Nya. Handl.* 2: 168–171. Germ. Trans. 1781, p. 170.

Thwaites, D., 1881. *[Observations on Lycænid larvæ attended by Œcophylla
Smaragdina.] Moore, Lepid. of Ceylon 1: 70, *London.*

Thwaites, G. H. K., 1854. *On Ants destructive to Cocci. *Trans Ent. Soc.
London* (2) 3 (Proc.): 10.

Tinsley, J. D., 1898. *An Ants'-nest Coccid from New Mexico. *Canad. Ent.*
30: 47–48, 1 fig.

Tischbein, 1851-'53. Zwitter von Formica sanguinea. *Stett. Ent. Zeitg.* 12:
295–297; 14, pl. 3, fig. 2. Cf. 15 (1854): 102.

Titus, E. S. G., 1905. Report on the "New Orleans" Ant (Iridomyrmex humilis
Mayr). *U. S. Dept. Agri. Bur. Ent. Bull.* 52: 79–84, fig. 7.

Townsend, B. R., 1870. The Red Ant of Texas. *Am. Ent. and Bot. St. Louis,
Mo.* 2, 11: 324–325.

Townsend, C. H. T., 1893 or '94. "Tom Raffles" An Ant of Jamaica. *Notes
Museum Inst. Jamaica.* 45. — **1897a.** On the Biogeography of Mexico and
the South Western United States II. *Trans. Tex. Acad. Sc.* 2, 1: 33–86. —
1897b. *Contributions from the New Mexico Biological Station. No. 2.
On a collection of Diptera from Lowlands of the Rio Naubla, in the State
of Vera Cruz. *Ann. Mag. Nat. Hist.* (6) 19: 23.

Trelease, W., 1881. *The foliar nectar glands of Populus. *Bot. Gaz.* 6, 11: 384–
390. — **1882.** *Unusual Care of Ants for Aphides. *Psyche* 3, 94: 310–311.
— **1889.** *Myrmecophilism. *Ibid.* 5: 171–180.

Treat, Mary, 1877. *Chapters on Ants. *Harpers' Half Hour Series.* — **1878.**
*The Harvesting Ants of Florida. *Harpers' New Month. Mag. N. Y.* Nov. —
1879a. *Notes on the Slave-making Ant (F. sanguinea). *Amer. Nat.* 13:
707–708. — **1879b.** A Chapter in the History of Ants. *Harpers' New M.
Mag. N. Y.* Jan. — **1880.** *Notes on Harvesting Ants in New Jersey. *Am.
Ent.* Sept. pp. 225–226.

Treviranus, G. R. Sur les Individus privés de sexe, de l'ordre des Hyménoptères, particulièrement du genre des Abeilles. *Zeitschr. Physiol.* 3, 2: 220.

Trimen, R., 1870. *[Letter on the Habits of some species of Paussidæ.] *Proc.
Ent. Soc. London* pp. iii–iv. — **1880.** On a Supposed Female of Dorylus
helvolus. *Trans. Ent. Soc. London* pp. 24–33. — **1886.** *Notes on Insects
apparently of the genus Margarodes, Lansd.-Guild., stated to occur abundantly in the nests of White Ants and also of true Ants in certain western
districts of the Cape Colony. *Ibid.* pp. 461 seq. — **1895.** [Note on South
African honey-ant.] *Proc. Ent. Soc. London* p. xxiii.

Tryon, H., 1888. Notes on Queensland Ants. *Proc. R. Soc. Queensl.* 2: 146–162.

Türk, R., 1879. *Noticias acerca de la Myrmecophila acervorum y la Saga
serrata. *An. Soc. Españ. Hist. Nat.* 8, 1: 15–17.

Turner, C. H., 1906. A Preliminary Note on Ant Behavior. *Biol. Bull.* 12: 31–
36. — **1907a.** Do Ants Form Practical Judgments? *Ibid.* 13, 6: 333–343,
2 figg. — **1907b.** The Homing of Ants, an Experimental Study of Ant Behavior. *Journ. Comp. Neur. Psych.* 17: 367–434, 3 pls.

Turner, G., 1897. Notes upon the Formicidæ of Mackay, Queensland. *Proc.
Linn. Soc. N. S. Wales* 1: 129–144.

ULE, E., 1897. *Symbiose zwischen Asclepias curassavica und einem Schmetterling. *Berl. Deutsch. Bot. Gesell.* 15: 385–387. — **1900.** *Verschiedenes über

den Einfluss der Tiere auf das Pflanzenleben. *Ibid.* 18: 122–130. — **1904.** *Ameisengärten im Amazonas Gebeit. *Engler's Bot. Jahrb.* 30, 68: 45–52. — **1905a.** *Ueber Blumengärten der Ameisen am Amazonenstrom. *Verh. Gesell. Deutsch. Nat. Aerzte* 76, 2, 1: 245–249. — **1905b.** *Wechselbeziehungen zwischen Ameisen und Pflanzen. *Flora* 94. — **1905c.** *Blumengärten der Ameisen am Amazonenstrome. Vegetationsbilder herausg. von G. Karsten u. H. Schenck. Heft 1. *Jena,* 1905, 6 pls., with explanation. — **1906a.** *Eigentümliche mit Pflanzen durchwachsene Ameisennester am Amazonenstrom. *Nat. Wochensch.* 21: 145–150, 1 pl., 2 figg. — **1906b.** *Ameisenpflanzen. *Bot. Jahrb.* 37: 335–352, pls. 6 and 7.

Ulke, H., 1887-'88. *A new species of Amphotis. *Ent. Amer.* 3: 77. — **1890.** *[Account of the habits of Tachys incurvus.] *Proc. Ent. Soc. Wash.* 2, 1: 87.

Unzer, J. A. Unpartheyisches Gutachten über die Ameisen. *Anzer's Physikal. Schrift.* 1: 372–381. *Neu. Hamb. Mag.* 82: 373–383.

Umpark, J., 1706. Dissertatio de formicis. *Resp. L. Kyllenius. Upsaliæ* 44 pp.

Urich, F. W., 1893-'94. Notes on Some Insect Pests of Trinidad, British West Indies. *Insect Life* 6: 196–198. — **1895a.** *Notes on the fungus growing and eating habit of Sericomyrmex opacus Mayr. *Trans. Ent. Soc. London* pp. 77–78. — **1895b.** *Notes on some fungus-growing Ants in Trinidad. *Journ. Trinidad Club* 2, 7: 175–182.

VALERIANUS, P., 1678. Hieroglyphica. 8, 2: 89. *Ed. Kirchner.*

Veatch, A. C., 1905. Natural Mounds of Louisiana. *Science* N. S. 21 (March).

Vercoutre, A., 1892. Pline et les fourmis d'Amérique. *Rev. Sc.* 48, 6: 187.

Verhoeff, K., 1892. *Einige biologische Fragmente. *Ent. Nachr.* pp. 13–14. — **1908.** *Zwei neue Gattungen der Glomeroidea. *Zool. Anz.* 33, 12: 413–416.

Viehmeyer, H., 1900. Beobachtungen über das Zurückfinden von Ameisen (Leptothorax unifasciatus Ltr.) zu ihrem Neste. *Illustr. Zeitschr. Ent.* 5: 311–313. — **1902a.** Allerhand aus dem Leben der Ameisen. *Ent. Jahrb.* 12: 210–215. — **1902b.** *Lomechusa strumosa F. und die Pseudogynen. *Allgem. Zeitschr. Ent.* 7: 472–476. — **1904.** *Experimente zu Wasmanns Lumechusa-Pseudogynen-Theorie und andere biologische Beobachtungen an Ameisen. *Ibid.* 9: 334–344. — **1905a.** *Kleinere Beiträge zur Biologie einiger Ameisengäste. *Zeitschr. Wiss. Insekt.-biol.* 1: 292–294. — **1905b.** *Myrmekophile Käfer. *Natur und Schule* 4: 49–62, 16 figg. — **1905c.** Beobachtungsnester für Ameisen. *Aus der Heimat.* — **1905d.** *Kleinere Beiträge zur Biologie einiger Ameisengäste. II. *Zeitschr. Wiss. Insekt.-biol.* 1, 7: 292–294. — **1906.** Beiträge zur Ameisenfauna des Königreiches Sachsen. *Abh. Nat. Ges. Isis Dresden* pp. 55–69, 1 pl. — **1907a.** *Vorläufige Bemerkungen zur Myrmekophilie der Lycæniden-raupen. *Ent. Wochenbl.* 24: 4. — **1907b.** *Preliminary remarks on the Myrmecophily of the Caterpillars of the Family Lycænidæ. *Ent. News* 18, 328–332. — **1908a.** *Zur Koloniengründung der parasitischen Ameisen. *Biol. Centralb.* 28, 1: 18–32. — **1908b.** *Bilder aus dem Ameisenleben. *Leipzig, Quelle u. Meyer,* 159 pp., 48 figg.

Viereck, H. L., 1903. Hymenoptera of Beulah, New Mexico. *Trans. Am. Ent. Soc.* 29: 43–99.

de Villers, C. J., 1789. Linnæi Entomologia. 3 *Lyon.*

Viturat, 1876. *[Note on Amphotis marginata with Formica rufa.] *Pet. Nouv. Ent.* 2, 154: 62.

van Vollenhoven, S. C., 1855. *Mierengasten. *Jahrb. K. Zool. Genootsch. Nat. Artis. Mag.* pp. 140–148.

Vosseler, J., 1905. Die Ostafrikanische Treiberameise (Siafu). *Der Pflanzer* 19: 289–302. — **1906.** *Verhinderung des Fruchtansatzes bei Cobæa durch Ameisen. *Zeitschr. Wiss. Insekt.-biol.* 2: 204–206.

WAGA, 1882. [Lasius niger clearing clothes infested with vermin.] *Le Nat.* 2: 46.

von Wagner, F., 1894. Die Allmacht der Naturzüchtung. *Biol. Centralb.* 14: 1–11.

Wahnschaffe, M., 1883. *Verzeichniss der im Gebiete des Aller-Vereins aufgefundenen Käfer. *Neuhaldensleben.* — *Collectaneum über Myrmekophilen-Literatur. *Nachgelassenes Manuscript, im Besitze des Städt. Ent. Mus. zu Magdeburg.*

Wakefield, R., 1854. On Some of the Habits of Ants. *Proc. Linn. Soc. London* 2: 293–294.

Walker, A. O., 1893. *The Use of Ants to Aphids and Coccidæ. *Nature* 48, 1229: 54.

Walker, F., 1871. A List of Hymenoptera Collected by J. K. Lord, Esq., in Egypt, etc. *London.*

Walker, J. J., 1888–'89. *Notes on the Ants'-nest Beetles at Gibraltar and Tangier, with especial reference to the Histeridæ. *Ent. M. Mag.* 25: 374–378.

Wallace, A. R., 1878. Tropical Nature and other Essays. *London. Macmillan & Co.*

Walsh, B. D., 1862. *On the Genera of Aphidæ found in the United States. *Proc. Ent. Soc. Phila.* 1, 9: 294–311.

Walsh, B. D., and C. V. Riley, 1869. *Ants and Aphids. *Amer. Ent.* 1, 6: 110.

Walsh, J. H. T., 1891a. *On certain spiders which mimic ants. *Journ. Asiat. Soc. Beng.* 60, 2: 1–4. — **1891b.** *On the habits of certain "Harvesting" Ants. *Sc. Mem. Med. Off. Army of India* 6: 6 pp., 1 pl.

Wanach, B., 1905. Einige auffällige Beobachtungen aus dem Insektenleben. *Berl. Ent. Zeitschr.* 50: 235–236.

Warburg, O., 1892. *Ueber Ameisenpflanzen (Myrmekophyten). *Biol. Centralb.* 12, 5: 129–142. Abstr. in *Journ. R. Micr. Soc. London* 3: 358–359.

Wasmann, E. (S. J.), 1884. Die Honigameise des Göttergartens. *Stimmen aus Maria-Laach.* pp. 275–285. — **1886.** *Ueber die Lebensweise einiger Ameisengäste. 1. *Deutsch. Ent. Zeitschr.* pp. 49–66. — **1887a** *Ueber die europäischen Atemeles. *Ibid.* pp. 97–107. — **1887b.** *Ueber die Lebensweise einiger Ameisengäste. 2. *Ibid.* pp. 108–122. — **1887c.** *Neue brasilianische Staphyliniden, bei Eciton Foreli Mayr (hamatum autor.) gesammelt von Dr. W. Müller. *Ibid.* pp. 403–416, pl. 5. — **1888.** *Beiträge zur Lebensweise der Gattungen Atemeles und Lomechusa. *Haag. Sep. aus *Tijdschr. Ent.* 31: 245–328. — **1889a.** *Die Getreide sammelnden Ameisen in alter und neuer Zeit. Ausz. in *Tijdschr. Ent. Nederl. Vereen.* 31, 2: 104–108 [Aus "*Stim. Maria-Laach.*" 33 (1887)]. — **1889b** *Ueber sklavenhaltende Ameisen. Ausz. in *Ent. Nachr. Karsch.* 15, 4: 65–66. (Aus *Natur. Offenb.* 35: 1–11.) — **1889c.** *Neue Ecitongäste aus Südbrasilien. *Deutsch. Ent. Zeitschr.* pp. 185–190, pl. 1. — **1889d.** *Ueber einige myrmekophile Heteropteren. *Ibid.* pp. 191–192. — **1889e.** *Nachträgliche Bemerkungen zu Ecitochara und Ecitomorpha. *Ibid.* p. 414. — **1889f.** *Zur Lebens- und Entwicklungsgeschichte von Dinarda. *Wien. Ent. Zeit.* pp. 153–162. — **1889g.** *Zur Kenntniss der Dinarda-Formen. *Ibid.* pp. 181–182. — **1890a.** *Apteranillus Foreli n. sp. *Deutsch. Ent. Zeitschr.* pp. 318–320. — **1890b.** Einige neue Hermaphroditen von Myrmica scabrinodis und M. lævinodis. *Stett. Ent. Zeitg.* 51: 298–299. — **1890c.** *Oöchrotus unicolor Luc. *Deutsch. Ent. Zeitschr.* p. 296. — **1890d.** *Myrmecophila Salomonis n. sp. *Ibid.* pp. 303–304. — **1890e.** *Neue myrmekophile Staphyliniden aus Brasilien. *Ibid.* pp. 305–318, pl. 2. — **1890f.** *Ueber die verschiedenen Zwischenformen von Weibchen und Arbeiterinnen bei Ameisen. *Stett. Ent. Zeitg.* 51: 300–309. — **1890g.** *Vergleichende Studien über Ameisengäste u. Termitengäste. *Haag. Sep. aus *Tijdschr. Ent.* 33: 27–97, pl. 1. 2 Nachtr. pp. 262–266. — **1890h.** *Verzeichniss der von Dr. Aug. Forel in Tunesien und Ostalgerien gesammelten Ameisengäste. *Deutsch. Ent. Zeitschr.* pp. 297–302. — **1890i.** *Zur Lebensweise dei gelbrothen Säbelameise (Strongylognathus testaceus). *Natur u. Offenb.* 12. **1891a.** Ueber Lautäusserungen von Myrmica ruginodis und Gehörsvermögen von Formica rufa. *Stimm. Maria-Laach* 50: 214. — **1891b.** *Eine neue Clavigeride aus Madagaskar (Rhynchoclaviger cremastogastris), mit vergleichenden biologischen Bemerkungen. *Stett. Ent. Zeitg.* pp. 3–10, pl. 1. — **1891c.** Parthenogenesis bei Ameisen durch künstliche Temperaturverhältnisse. *Biol. Centralb.* 11: 21–23. — **1891d.** *Verzeichniss der Ameisen und Ameisengäste von Holländisch-Limburg. *Haag.* Sep. aus *Tijdschr. Ent.* 34: 39–64. — **1891e.** *Zur Bedeutung der Fühler bei Myrmedonia. *Biol. Centralb.* 11, 1: 23–25. — **1891f.** Zur Frage nach dem Gehörsvermögen der Ameisen. *Ibid.* 11, 1: 26. — **1891g.** *Vorbemerkungen zu den internationalen Beziehungen der Ameisengäste. *Ibid.* 11, 11: 331–343. — **1891h.** *Die zusammengesetzten Nester und gemischten Kolonien der Ameisen. 262 pp., 2 pls., 16 figg. *Münster i. W. Aschendorffsche Buchdruckerei.* — **1892a.** *Ein neuer Paussus vom Somaliland. *Mitth. Schweiz. Ent. Gesell.* 8, 9. — **1892b.** *Die internationalen Beziehungen von Lomechusa strumosa. *Biol. Centralb.* 12, 18–21; 584–559; 638–669. — **1892c.** Einiges über springende Ameisen. *Wien. Ent. Zeitschr.* 11: 316, 317. — **1892d.** *Zur Biologie einiger Ameisengäste. *Deutsch. Ent. Zeitschr.* pp. 347–351. — **1893a.** Lautäusserungen der Ameisen. *Biol. Centralb.* 13: 39, 40. — **1893b.** *Neue Myrmekophilen. *Deutsch. Ent. Zeitschr.* pp. 97–112, pl. 5. — **1893c.** *Zwei neue Staphylinidengattungen aus Sikkim. *Ibid.* pp. 206–208. — **1893d.** *Ueber Paussiger und Articeropsis Wasm. *Wien. Ent. Zeitg.* p. 257. — **1893e.** *Eine myrmekophile Ceratopogon-Larve (C. Braueri n. sp.). *Ibid.* pp. 277–279. — **1893f.** *Centrotoma rubra Saulc. in Böhmen. *Ibid.* p. 279. — **1894a.** *Zur Myrmekophilenfauna des Rheinlandes. *Deutsch. Ent. Zeitschr.* pp. 273 and 274. — **1894b.** *Die europäischen Dinarda, mit Beschreibung einer neuen deutschen Art. *Ibid.* pp. 275–280. — **1894c.** *Zur Lebens- und Entwicklungsgeschichte von Atemeles pubicollis, mit einem Nachtrag über Atemeles emarginatus. *Ibid.* pp. 281–283. — **1894d.** *Ueber Atemeles excisus Thoms. *Ibid.* pp. 283–284. — **1894e.** *Ueber Xantholinus atratus Heer (picipes Thoms.). *Ibid.* pp. 285–287. — **1894f.** *Formica exsecta Nyl. und ihre Nestgenossen. *Verh. Nat. Ver. Bonn.* 51, 1: 10–22. — **1894g.** *Kritisches Verzeichniss der myrmekophilen und termitophilen Arthropoden. Mit Angabe der Lebensweise und Beschreibung neuer Arten. xvi + 231 pp. *Berlin.* — **1895a.** *Zur Kenntniss einiger schwieriger Thorictus-Arten. *Deutsch. Ent. Zeitschr.* 1: 41–44. — **1895b.** *Verzeichniss der von Prof. Aug. Forel im Frühling 1893 in der algerischen Provinz Oran gesammelten Ameisengäste. *Ibid.* pp. 45–48. — **1895c.** *Zur Kenntniss der myrmekophilen und termitophilen Arthropoden. *Zool. Anz.* 471: 111–114. — **1895d.** *Die Ameisen- und Termitengäste von Brasilien. 1. *Verh. Zool. Bot. Gesell. Wien* 4: 137–179. (Sept. 1–45.) — **1895e.** *Zur Kenntniss einiger Thorictus-Arten. 2. *Deutsch. Ent. Zeitschr.* 2: 291–293. — **1895f.** *Zur Biologie von Lomechusa strumosa. *Ibid.* 2: 294. — **1895g.** *Die ergatogynen Formen bei den Ameisen und ihre Erklärung. *Biol. Centralb.* 15, 16 and 17: 606–646. — **1896a.** *Eine Ameisenkolonie durch Nematoden zerstört. *Tijdschr. Ent.* 41: 18–19. — **1896b.** *Os hospedes das formigas e dos termites (cupim) no Brazil. *Bolet. Mus. Paraense* 1, 3: 273–324, 2 pls. — **1896c.** *Kritische Bemerkungen über einige Myrmekophilen und Termitophilen. *Wien. Ent. Zeitg.* 1: 32–36. — **1896d.** *Notes sur la chasse des Coléoptères myrmécophiles et termitophiles. *Rennes,* 4 pp. — **1896e.** *Dinarda-Arten oder -Rassen? *Wien. Ent. Zeitg.* 4 and 5: 125–142. — **1896f.** *A revision of the genus Clidicus. *Notes Leyd. Mus.* 18: 14–18. — **1896g.** *Die Myrmekophilen u. Termitophilen. Vortrag gehalten am 16 Sept. 1895 zu Leyden. *C. R. 3 Congr. Internat. Zool. Leyde,* pp. 411–440, 1 text-fig. *Ausz. von K. W. v. Dalla Torre. Zool. Centralb.*

3, 18: 636–638. — **1896h.** *Einige neue Paussus aus Java, mit Bemerkungen über die myrmekophile Lebensweise der Paussiden. *Notes Leyden Mus.* 18: 63–80, 1 pl. — **1896i.** *Zur Kenntniss einiger Thorictus-Arten. 3. *Deutsch. Ent. Zeitschr.* 2: 242–243. — **1896j.** *Revision der Lomechusa-Gruppe. *Ibid.* 2: 244–256. — **1896k.** *Zoologische Ergebnisse einer von Dr. K. Escherich und Dr. L. Kathariner nach Centralkleinasien unternommenen Reise. Myrmekophilen. *Ibid.* 2: 237–241. — **1897a.** *Selbstbiographie einer Lomechusa. *Stimm. Maria-Laach.* 1. — **1897b.** *Instinkt und Intelligenz im Thierreich. 94 pp. *Freiburg i/B.* — **1897c.** *Vergleichende Studien über das Seelenleben der Ameisen und der höheren Thiere. 122 pp. *Freiburg i.B.* — **1897d.** *Zur Entwicklung der Instinkte (Entwicklung der Symphilie). *Verh. Zool.-bot. Gesell. Wien.* 3: 168–183. — **1897e.** *Ueber einige myrmekophile Acarinen. I. *Zool. Anz.* 20, 531: 170–173. — **1897f.** *Bemerkungen über einige Ameisen von Madagaskar. *Ibid.* 20, 536: 249–250. (Abstr. *Journ. R. Micr. Soc. London* 1897: 375.) — **1897g.** *Eine neue Xenodusa aus Colorado, mit einer Tabelle der Xenodusa-Arten. *Deutschr. Ent. Zeitschr.* 2: 273–274, pl. 1, fig. 9. — **1897h.** *Ueber ergatoide Weibchen und Pseudogynen bei Ameisen. *Zool. Anz.* 20, 536: 251–253. — **1897i.** *Ein neuer Fustigerodes aus der Kapkolonie. *Wien. Ent. Zeitg.* 7: 201. — **1897j.** *Ueber einige myrmekophile Acarinen. II. *Zool. Anz.* 541: 346–350. — **1897k.** *Neue Myrmekophilen aus Madagaskar. *Deutsch. Ent. Zeitschr.* 2: 257–272, pls. 1 and 2. — **1897l.** *Zur Biologie der Lomechusa-Gruppe. *Ibid.* 2: 275–277. — **1897m.** *Ein neuer Dorylidengast aus Südafrika. *Ibid.* 2: 278, pl. 2, fig. 6. — **1897n.** *Ein neuer Eciton-Gast aus Nord-Carolina. *Ibid.* 2: 280–282, pl. 2, fig. 4. — **1897o.** *Ein neues myrmekophiles Silphidengenus aus Costa-Rica. *Ibid.* 2: 283–285, pl. 2, fig. 5. — **1897p.** *Zur Morphologie und Biologie der Lomechusa-Gruppe. *Zool. Anz.* 546: 463–471. — **1897q.** *Die Familie der Paussiden. *Stimm. Maria-Laach.* 9 and 10. — **1898a.** *Ameisenfang von Theridium triste Hahn. *Zool. Anz.* 21, 555: 230–232. — **1898b.** *Ueber Novoclaviger und Fustigerodes. *Wien. Ent. Zeitg.* 3: 96–99. — **1898c.** *Eine neue dorylophile Tachyporinengattung aus Südafrika. *Ibid.* 3: 101–103, figg. 1–4. — **1898d.** *Eine neue Philusina vom Cap. *Ibid.* 3: 103–104. — **1898e.** *Ein neuer Claviger aus Bosnien. *Ibid.* 4 and. 5: 135. — **1898f.** Die Gäste der Ameisen und Termiten. *Illustr. Zeitschr. Ent.* 3, 10–16, 1 pl. — **1898g.** *Erster Nachtrag zu den Ameisengästen von Holländisch-Limburg, mit biologischen Notizen. *Haag. Tijdschr. Ent.* 41: 1–18. — **1898h.** *Ein kleiner Beitrag zur Myrmekophilenfauna von Vorarlberg. *Mitth. Schweiz. Ent. Gesell.* 10: 134–135. — **1898i.** *Zur Kenntniss der Myrmekophilen und Ameisen von Bosnien. *Wiss. Mitth. Bosn. Herz. Landesmus.* 6. — **1898j.** *Einige neue myrmecophile Anthiciden aus Indien. *Verh. Zool.-bot. Gesell. Wien* 7: 482–484. — **1898k.** *Ueber die Gäste von Tetramorium cæspitum, sowie über einige andere Myrmecophilen. *Versl. 53 Somerverg. Ned. Ent. Ver.* (11 Jun.) pp. 60–65. — **1898l.** *Zur Lebensweise von Thorictus Foreli. Mit einem anatomischen Anhang und einer Tafel. *Natur. Offenb.* 8: 466–478. — **1898m.** *Neueres über Paussiden. *Verh. Zool.-bot. Gesell. Wien* 7: 507–515. — **1898n.** *Die Höhlenthiere. *Stimm. Maria-Laach.* 6 and 7. — **1898o.** *Ueber Myrmecophilen. *Tijdschr. Ent.* 41 Versl. pp. 60–65. — **1898p.** *Thorictus Foreli als Ectoparasit der Ameisenfühler. *Zool. Anz.* 21, 564: 435–436, 7 figg. — **1898q.** *Nochmals Thorictus Foreli als Ectoparasit der Ameisenfühler. *Ibid.* 21, 570: 536–546. — **1898r.** Eine neue Reflextheorie des Ameisenlebens. *Biol. Centralb.* 18: 578–589. — **1898s.** *Eine Ameisenkolonie durch Nematoden zerstört. *Tijdschr. Ent.* 41: 18–19. — **1899a.** *Instinct und Intelligenz im Thierreich. *Freiburg i/B. Herder'sche Verlagshandlung.* — **1899b.** *Lasius fuliginosus als Raubameise. *Zool. Anz. 22:* 85–87, 153, 1 fig. — **1899c.** *Zur Kenntniss der bosnischen Myrmekophilen und Ameisen. *Wiss. Mitth. Bosn. Hercegov.* 6: 767–772, 3 figg. — **1899d.** *Neue Termitophilen und Myrmecophilen aus Indien. *Deutsch. Ent. Zeitschr.* pp. 145–169, 2 pls. — **1899e.** *Ein neues myrmecophiles Curculionidengenus aus der Kapkolonie. *Ibid.* pp. 170–171, 1 pl. — **1899f.** *Eine neue dorylophile Myrmedonia aus der Kapkolonie, mit einigen anderen Notizen über Dorylinengäste. *Ibid.* pp. 174–177. — **1899g.** *Die psychischen Fähigkeiten der Ameisen. (95. *Beitr. Kenntn. Myrmekoph. Termitoph.*) *Zoologica* 11, 26: 132 pp., 3 pls. — **1900a.** *Zur Kenntniss der termitophilen und myrmekophilen Cetoniden Südafrikas. *Illustr. Zeitschr. Ent.* 5: 65–68; 81–84, 1 pl. Nachtrag pp. 103–104. — **1900b.** *Neue Dorylinengäste aus dem neotropischen und dem äthiopischen Faunengebiet. (114. *Beitr. Kenntn. Myrmekoph. Termitoph.*) *Zool. Jahrb. Abt. Syst.* 14: 215–289, 2 pls. — **1900c.** *Zwei neue Lobopelta-Gäste aus Südafrika. *Deutsch. Ent. Zeitschr.* pp. 403–404, 1 fig. — **1900d.** *Ein neuer Gast von Eciton carolinense. *Ibid.* pp. 409–410. — **1900e.** *Zwei neue myrmekophile Philusina-Arten aus Südafrika. *Ibid.* pp. 405–406. — **1900f.** *Ueber Atemeles pubicollis und die Pseudogynen von Formica rufa L. *Ibid.* pp. 407–409. — **1901a.** Zum Orientierungsvermögen der Ameisen. *Allgem. Zeitschr. Ent.* 6: 19–21; 41–43, 1 fig. — **1901b.** *Zwei neue Liometopum-Gäste aus Colorado. (*116. Beitr. Kenntn. Myrmekoph. Termitoph.*) *Wien. Ent. Zeitg.* 20: 145–147. — **1901c.** *Zur Lebensweise der Ameisengrillen (Myrmecophila). *Natur. Offenb.* 5, 47, 3: 129–152. — **1901d.** *On Some Genera of Staphylinidæ, described by Thos. L. Casey. *Canad. Ent.* 5, 33: 249–252. — **1901e.** *Giebt es thatsächlich Arten, die heute noch in der Stammesentwicklung begriffen sind? Zugleich mit allgemeinen Bemerkungen über die Entwicklung der Myrmekophilie und Termitophilie und über das Wesen der Symphilie. *Biol. Centralb.* 5, 21, 22 and 23. — **1901-'02.** *Neues über die zusammengesetzten Nester und gemischten Kolonien der Ameisen. *Allgem. Zeitschr. Ent.* 6: 353–355; 369–371; 7: 1–5; 33–37; 72–77; 100–108; 136–139; 167–173; 206–208; 235–240; 260–265; 293–298; 340–345; 385–390; 422–427; 441–449, 1 pl. (Ref. R. von Hanstein. *Nat. Rundsch.* 18: 368–370.) — **1902a.** *Neue Bestätigungen der Lomechusa-Pseudogynentheorie. *Verh. Deutsch. Zool. Gesell.* 12: 98–108. — **1902b.** Noch ein Wort zu Bethe's Reflextheorie. *Biol. Centralb.* 22: 573–576. — **1902c.** *Zwei neue europäische Coleopteren. *Deutsch. Ent. Zeitschr.* p. 16. — **1902d.** *Verzeichniss der von Dr. W. Horn auf Ceylon 1899 gesammelten Termiten, Termitophilen und Myrmekophilen. *Ibid.* pp. 79–80. — **1902e.** *Coléoptères myrmécophiles recueillis par le prof. A. Lameere en Algérie. *Ann. Soc. Ent. Belg.* 46: 159. — **1902f.** *Biologische und phylogenetische Bemerkungen über die Dorylinengäste der alten und der neuen Welt, mit specieller Berücksichtigung ihrer Convergenzerscheinungen. *Verh. Deutsch. Zool. Gesell.* 12: 86–89. — **1902g.** *Riesige Kurzflügler als Hymenopteren-Gäste. (*132. Beitr. Kenntn. Myrmekoph. Termitoph.*) *Insektenbörse* 19: 267–268; 275–276; 282, 3 figg. — **1902h.** *Ein neuer myrmekophiler Ilyobates aus dem Rheinland (Ilyobates brevicornis n. sp.). *Deutsch. Ent. Zeitschr.* p. 62. — **1902i.** Zur Ameisenfauna von Helgoland. *Ibid.* pp. 63–64. — **1902j.** *Zur Kenntnis der myrmecophilen Antennophorus und anderer auf Ameisen und Termiten reitender Acarinen. (*121. Beitr. Kenntn. Myrmecoph. Termitoph.*) *Zool. Anz.* 25: 66–76. — **1902k.** *Termiten, Termitophilen und Myrmekophilen, gesammelt auf Ceylon von Dr. W. Horn 1899, mit anderm ostindischen Material bearbeitet. *Zool. Jahrb.* 5, 17, Syst.: 99–164, pls. 4, 5. — **1903a.** *Zur Brutpflege der blutroten Raubameise (Formica sanguinea Ltr.). *Insektenbörse* 20: 275–276. — **1903b.** *Zum Mimicrytypus der Dorylinengäste. (*135. Beitr. Kenntn. Myrmecoph. Termitoph.*) *Zool. Anz.* 26: 581–590. — **1903c.** *Zur näheren Kenntnis des echten Gastverhältnisses (Symphilie) bei den Ameisen- und Termitengästen. *Biol. Centralb.* 23: 63–72; 195–207; 232–248; 261–276; 298–310. — **1904a.** Ameisen-arbeiterinnen als Ersatzköniginnen. *Mitth. Schweiz. Ent. Gesell.* 11: 67–70. — **1904b.** *Zur Kenntniss der Gäste der Treiberameisen und ihrer Wirthe am obern Congo, nach den Sammlungen und Beobachtungen von P. Herm. Kohl C. SS. C. bearbeitet. (*138. Beitr. Kenntn. Myrmekoph. Termitoph.*) Zool. Jahrb. Suppl. 7 Festschr. Weismann* pp. 611–682, 3 pls. — **1904c.** *Neue Beiträge zur Kenntniss der Paussiden mit biologischen und phylogenetischen Bemerkungen. (*142. Beitr. Kenntn. Myrmekoph. Termitoph.*) Notes Leyden Mus.* 25: 1–82, 6 pls. — **1904d.** *Die moderne Biologie und die Entwicklungstheorie. 2 Ed.* 323 pp., 4 pls., 40 text-figg. *Herdersche Buchh. Freiburg. i/B.* — **1905a.** *Die phylogenetische Umbildung ostindischer Ameisengäste in Termitengäste. *Mitth. Schweiz. Ent. Gesell.* 11: 66–70. *C. R. 6me. Congr. Internat. Zool. Berne* pp. 436–449, 1 pl. — **1905b.** *Versuche mit einem brasilianischen Ameisennest in Holland. (*150. Beitr. Kenntn. Myrmekoph. Termitoph.*) Tijdschr. Ent.* 48: 209–213, 1 pl. — **1905c.** Berichtigungen zu Note I dieses Bandes. *Notes Leyden Mus.* 25: 110. — **1905d.** *Ursprung und Entwickelung der Sklaverei bei den Ameisen. (*146. Beitr. Kenntn. Myrmekoph. Termitoph.*) Biol. Centralb.* 25: 117–127; 129–144; 161–169; 256–270; 273–292, 2 figg. (Analyse *Rev. Sc.* (5) 5: 820–823.) — **1905e.** *Some Remarks on Temporary Social Parasitism and the Phylogeny of Slavery among Ants. *Biol. Centralb.* 25: 637–644. — **1905f.** *Nochmals zur Frage über die temporär gemischten Kolonien und den Ursprung der Sklaverei bei den Ameisen. *Ibid.* 25: 644–653. — **1905g.** *Zur Lebensweise einiger in- und ausländischen Ameisengäste. (*148. Beitr. Kenntn. Myrmekoph. Termitoph.*) Zeitschr. Wiss. Insekt.-biol.* 1: 329–336; 384–390; 418–428. — **1906a.** *Zur Geschichte der Sklaverei beim Volke der Ameisen. *Stimm. Maria-Laach* 70: 405–425; 517–531. — **1906b.** *Zur Myrmekophagie des Grünspechts. *Tidschr. Ent.* 48: 6–12. — **1906c.** *Zur Lebensweise von Atemeles pratensoides Wasm. *Zeitschr. Wiss. Insekt.-biol.* 2: 1–12; 37–42, 3 figg. Anhang. Ein merkwürdiges Heizmaterial bei Formica pratensis. pp. 42–43. — **1906d.** *Beispiele rezenter Artenbildung bei Ameisengästen und Termitengästen. *Biol. Centralb.* 26: 565–580. — **1906e.** *Zur Kenntniss der Ameisen und Ameisengäste von Luxemburg. (*153. Beitr. Kenntn. Myrmekoph. I and II Teil.) Arch. Trimestr. Inst. Grand-Ducal. Sect. Sc.* 1 and 2: 17 pp., 2 pls. — **1906f.** K. Escherich, Die Ameise, Schilderung ihrer Lebensweise. *Biol. Centralb.* 26: 801–806. — **1906g.** *Die Gäste der Ameisen und der Termiten. Vortrag 77 *Versamml. Deutsch. Naturf. Aerzte Meran. Verh.* 1906. 2. — **1906h.** *Die moderne Biologie und die Entwickelungstheorie. *3rd Ed. Freiburg i. Breisgau.* — **1907a.** Ameisennester "Boussole du Montagnard." *Naturwiss. Wochenschr.* N. F. 6: 391, 392, fig. — **1907b.** Sur les Nids des Fourmis migrantes (Eciton et Anomma). *Atti Pontif. Accad. Rom. Nuov. Linc.* 60: 6 pp. — **1907c.** *Ueber einige afrikanische Paussiden. *Deutsch. Ent. Zeitschr.* pp. 147–153, pl. 1. — **1907d.** *Ueber einige Paussiden des Deutschen Entomologischen National-Museums. *Ibid.* pp. 561–566, 3 figg. — **1908a.** Zur Kastenbildung und Systematik der Termiten. *Biol. Centralb.* 28: 68–73. — **1908b.** *Weitere Beiträge zum sozialen Parasitismus und der Sklaverei bei den Ameisen. *Ibid.* 28: 257–271; 289–306; 321–333; 353–382; 417–441, 3 figg. Nachtrag, *Ibid.* 28: 726–731. — **1908c.** *Ein neuer Paussus von Togo. *Deutsch. Ent. Zeitschr.* p. 576. — **1908d.** Die Sinne der Ameisen. Vortrag gehalten auf der Wander-Versammlung "Luxemburger Naturfreunde" in Ettelbrück, am 3. Mai 1908. *Luxemburg, P. Worré-Merkens.* — **1908e.** *Myrmechusa; eine neue Gattung zwischen Myrmedonia und Lomechusa. *Ann. Mus. Civ. Hor. Nat. Genova* (3) 4: 38–42, 5 figg. — **1908f.** L'Udito nelle Formiche. *Riv. Fis. Mat. Sci. Pavia* 9, 108: 1–7. — **1908g.** * On the Evolution of Dinarda, a genus of Coleoptera. Transl. by Horace Donisthorpe. *Zoologist*, pp. 68–71.

Wasmann, E., and Edw. Jacobson, 1905. Beobachtungen über Polyrhachis dives auf Java die ihre Larven zum Spinnen der Nester benutzt. *Notes Leyden Mus.* 25: 133–140.

Waterhouse, C. O., 1882. *[Note on Paramellon sociale Waterh.] *Proc. Ent. Soc. London* pp. iv–v. — **1907.** ♀ of Genus Dorylus. *Trans. Ent. Soc. London* p. vi, 2 figg.

Webster, F. M., 1887-'88. *The relation of Ants to the Corn-Aphis. *Rep. Comm. Agric. Wash.* pp. 148–149. Also *Insect Life* I, 5: 152. — **1899.** *On the Relations of a Species of Ant, Lasius americanus, to the Peach Root Louse, Aphis prunicola. *Canad. Ent.* 31: 15–16. — **1907.** *The Corn Leaf-Aphis and Corn Root-Aphis. *U. S. Dept. Agric. Bureau Ent. Circ. No. 86*, 13 p.

Weed, C. M., 1891. *Sixth Contribution to a Knowledge of the Life History of Certain Little Known Aphididæ. *Bull. Ill. State Lab. Nat. Hist.* 3: 207–214.

von Weidenbach, C., 1859. *Verzeichniss der in der Umgegend von Augsburg vorkommenden Myrmekophilen. *12 Ber. Nat. Ver. Augsb.* p. 83.

Weir, J., 1898. The Ears of Worms, Crustaceans and Ants. *Sci. Amer.* Apr. p. 214.

Weismann, Aug., 1892. Das Keimplasma. Eine Theorie der Vererbung. *Jena, Gustav Fischer.* pp. 494–498. — **1893a.** The All-Sufficiency of Natural Selection. *Contemp. Rev.* Sept. pp. 309–338. — **1893b.** Die Allmacht der Naturzüchtung. Eine Erwiderung an Herbert Spencer. *Jena, Gust. Fischer.* 96 pp. — **1894.** The Effect of External Influences upon Development. *Romanes Lecture, London, Henry Frowde* pp. 29–48. — **1902.** Vorträge über Descendenz-theorie. *Jena, Gustav Fischer* 2: 101–118.

Weld, LeRoy D., 1899. The Sense of Hearing in Ants. *Science* N. S. 10: 766–768. Remarks by M. M. Metcalf, *Ibid.* 11: 194.

Wellenius, O., 1904a. Ett meddelande om Tomognathus sublævis Nyl. *Meddel. Soc. Faun. Flor. Fenn.* 29: 70–72. — **1904b.** För Finland nya eller sällsynta myror. *Ibid.* 29: 124.

Wesmael, C., 1825. *[Observations on the habits of Claviger testaceus.] Lettre adressée à M. le comte Dejean par M. C. Wesmael. *Encyc. Méth. Hist. Nat. Ent.* 10: 223. — **1838.** Sur une nouvelle espèce de fourmi de Mexique. *Bull. Acad. Roy. Soc. Brux. Bell. Lettr.* 5: 766–771, pl. 19, figg. 1–4.

Westhoff, Friedrich, 1881-'82. *Die Käfer Westfalens. *Suppl. Verh. Nat. Ver. Rheinl. Westf.* 38.

Westwood, J. O., 1839-'40. *Introduction to the modern classification of insects. 2 Vols. *London.* — **1840.** Observations on the genus Typhlopone, with Descriptions of several exotic species of Ants. *Ann. Mag. Nat. Hist.* 6: 81–89, 1 pl. — **1843-'45.** *Monograph of the Coleopterous Family Paussidæ. *Arch. Ent.* 2, *London.* — **1847a.** Description of a New Dorylideous insect from South Africa, belonging to the genus Ænictus. *Trans. Ent. Soc. London* 4: 237–238, fig. — **1847b.** Description of the Driver Ants. (Anomma arcens.) *Ibid.* 5: 296–300, fig. — **1852.** *Description of some new species of the Coleopterous family Paussidæ, with a synopsis of the family. *Ibid.* (2) 2: 84–96. — **1854.** Contributions to Fossil Entomology. *Quart. Journ. Geol. Soc. London* pp. 378–396, pls. 14–18. — **1855.** *Description of a new genus of Coleopterous Insects inhabiting the interior of Ants'-nests in Brazil. *Trans. Ent. Soc. London* (2) 3: 90–94. — **1856.** *Descriptions of various species of the Coleopterous family Pselaphidæ, natives of New South Wales and South America. *Ibid.* (2) 3: 268–280. — **1861.** *Notice of the Occurrence of a Strepsipterous Insect parasite on Ants, discovered in Ceylon by J. Nietner. *Ibid.* (2) 5: 418–420. — **1869.** *Remarks on the genus Ectrephes and descriptions of New Exotic Coleoptera. *Ibid.* pp. 315–320. — **1874.** *Thesaurus Entomologicus Oxoniensis. *Oxford.*

Wetherill, C. M., 1852. Chemical Investigation of the Mexican Honey Ant. *Proc. Acad. Nat. Sc. Phila.* 6: 111, 112.

von Wettstein, R., 1888. *Ueber Kompositen der österreich-ungarische Flora mit zuckerabscheidenden Hüllschuppen. *Sitzber. Akad. Wien.* — **1890.** *Pflanzen und Ameisen. *Schrift. Ver. Verbreit. Naturw. Kenntn. Wien* 29: 307–327.

Wheeler, W. M., 1900a. *The Female of Eciton sumichrasti Norton, with some Notes on the Habits of Texan Ecitons. *Amer. Nat.* 34: 563–574, 4 figg. — **1900b.** A Study of Some Texan Ponerinæ. *Biol. Bull. Boston* 2: 1–31, 10 figg. — **1900c.** *The Habits of Myrmecophila nebrascensis Bruner. *Psyche* 9: 111–115, 1 fig. — **1900d.** *A New Myrmecophile from the Mushroom Gardens of the Texan Leaf-Cutting Ant. *Amer. Nat.* 34: 851–862, 6 figg. — **1900e.** The Habits of Ponera and Stigmatomma. *Biol. Bull. Boston* 2: 43–69, 8 figg. — **1901a.** Notices biologiques sur les fourmis mexicaines. *Ann. Soc. Ent. Belg.* 45: 199–205. [In English.] — **1901b.** *Microdon Larvæ in Pseudomyrma nests. *Psyche* 9: 222–224, 1 fig. — **1901c.** *The Compound and Mixed Nests of American Ants. *Amer. Nat.* 35: 431–448; 513–539; 701–724; 791–818, 20 figg. — **1901d.** *The Parasitic Origin of Macroërgates Among Ants. *Ibid.* 35: 877–886, 1 fig. — **1901e.** *An Extraordinary Ant-guest. *Ibid.* 35: 1007–1016, 2 figg. — **1902a.** New Agricultural ants from Texas. *Psyche* 9: 387–393. — **1902b.** A New Agricultural Ant from Texas, with Remarks on the known North-American Species. *Amer. Nat.* 36: 85–100, 8 figg. — **1902c.** A Neglected Factor in Evolution. *Science* N. S. 15: 766–774. — **1902d.** The Occurrence of Formica cinerea Mayr and Formica rufibarbis Fabricius in America. *Amer. Nat.* 36: 947–952. — **1902e.** An American Cerapachys, with Remarks on the Affinities of the Cerapachyinæ. *Biol. Bull.* 3: 181–191, 5 figg. — **1902b.** A Consideration of S. B. Buckley's "North American Formicidæ." *Trans. Texas Acad. Sc.* 4, 2, 2: 15 pp. — **1902c.** Formica fusca Linn. subsp. subpolita Mayr. var. perpilosa, n. var. *Mem. Soc. Cient. Ant. Alzate Mexico* 17: 141–142. — **1903a.** The Origin of Female and Worker Ants from the Eggs of Parthenogenetic Workers. *Science* N. S. 18: 830–833. — **1903b.** Some New Gynandromorphous Ants, with a Review of the Previously Recorded Cases. *Bull. Amer. Mus. Nat. Hist.* 19: 653–683, 11 figg. — **1903c.** *Erebomyrma, a New Genus of Hypogæic Ants from Texas. *Biol. Bull.* 4: 137–148, 5 figg. — **1903d.** *A Revision of the North American Ants of the Genus Leptothorax Mayr. *Proc. Acad. Nat. Sc. Phila.* 55: 215–260, 1 pl. — **1903e.** Extraordinary Females in Three Species of Formica, with Remarks on Mutation in the Formicidæ. *Bull. Amer. Mus. Nat. Hist.* 19: 639–651, 3 figg. — **1903f.** *Ethological Observations on an American Ant (Leptothorax Emersoni Wheeler). *Arch. Psycol. Neurol.* 2: 1–31, 1 fig. — **1903g.** A Decad of Texan Formicidæ. *Psyche* 10: 93–111, 10 figg. — **1903h.** The North American Ants of the Genus Stenamma (sensu stricto). *Ibid.* 10: 164–168. — **1903i.** Some notes on the Habits of Cerapachys augustæ. *Ibid.* 10: 205–209, 1 fig. — **1904a.** A Crustacean-Eating Ant (Leptogenys elongata Buckley). *Biol. Bull.* 6: 251–259, 1 fig. — **1904b.** *Three New Genera of Inquiline Ants from Utah and Colorado. *Bull. Amer. Mus. Nat. Hist.* 20: 1–17, 2 pls. — **1904c.** The American Ants of the Subgenus Colobopsis. *Ibid.* 20: 139–158, 7 figg. — **1904d.** Ants from Catalina Island, California. *Ibid.* 20: 269–271. — **1904e.** Dr. Castle and the Dzierzon Theory. *Science* N. S. 19: 587–591. — **1904f.** The Ants of North Carolina. *Bull. Amer. Mus. Nat. Hist.* 20: 299–306. — **1904g.** On the Pupation of Ants and the Feasibility of Establishing the Guatemalan Kelep or Cotton-weevil Ant in the United States. *Science* N. S. 20: 437–440. — **1904h.** *A New Type of Social Parasitism among Ants. *Bull. Amer. Mus. Nat. Hist.* 20: 347–375. — **1904i.** Some Further Comments on the Guatemalan Boll-weevil Ant. *Science* N. S.

20: 766–768. — **1904j.** Social Parasitism among Ants. *Amer. Mus. Nat. Hist. Journ.* 4, 4 (Oct.) : 74–75. — **1905a.** *An Interpretation of the Slave-making Instincts in Ants. *Bull. Amer. Mus. Nat. Hist.* 21 : 1–16. — **1905b.** The Ants of the Bahamas, with a List of the Known West Indian Species. *Ibid.* 21 : 79–135, 1 pl., 11 figg. — **1905c.** New Species of Formica. *Ibid.* 21 : 267–274. — **1905d.** The North American Ants of the Genus Dolichoderus. *Ibid.* 21 : 305–319, 2 pls., 3 figg. — **1905e.** The North American Ants of the Genus Liometopum. *Ibid.* 21 : 321–333, 3 figg. — **1905f.** An Annotated List of the Ants of New Jersey. *Ibid.* 21 : 371–403, 4 figg. — **1905g.** Worker Ants with Vestiges of Wings. *Ibid.* 21 : 405–408, 1 pl. — **1905h.** Ants from the Summit of Mount Washington. *Psyche* 12 : 111–114. — **1905i.** *How the Queens of the parasitic and slave-making Ants establish their Colonies. *Amer. Mus. Journ.* 5, 4: 144–148. — **1905j.** *Some Remarks on Temporary Social Parasitism and the Phylogeny of Slavery among Ants. *Biol. Centralb.* 25: 637–644. — **1905k.** Dr. O. F. Cook's "Social Organization and Breeding Habits of the Cotton-protecting Kelep of Guatemala." *Science* N. S. 22: 706–710. — **1906a.** The Queen Ant as a Psychological Study. *Pop. Sc. Month.* (April) : 291–299, 7 figg.; also *Suppl. Scientific American* (1906). — **1906b.** *The Habits of the Tent-building Ant (Cremastogaster lineolata Say). *Bull. Amer. Mus. Nat. Hist.* 22: 1–18, 4 pls., 3 text-figg. — **1906c.** *On the Founding of Colonies by Queen Ants, with Special Reference to the Parasitic and Slave-making Species. *Ibid.* 22: 33–105, 7 pls. — **1906d.** On Certain Tropical Ants Introduced into the United States. *Ent. News* 17: 23–26. — **1906e.** New Ants from New England. *Psyche* 13: 38–41, 1 pl. — **1906f.** The Ants of Japan. *Bull. Amer. Mus. Nat. Hist.* 22: 301–328, 1 pl., 2 figg. — **1906g.** The Ants of the Grand Cañon. *Ibid.* 22: 329–345. — **1906h.** The Ants of the Bermudas. *Ibid.* 22: 347–352, 1 fig. — **1906i.** Concerning Monomorium destructor Jerdon. *Ent. News* 17: 265. — **1906j.** Fauna of New England. 7. List of the Formicidæ. *Occas. Papers Bost. Soc. Nat. Hist.* 7: 1–24. — **1906k.** The Kelep Excused. *Science* N. S. 23: 348–350. — **1906l.** *An Ethological Study of Certain Maladjustments in the Relations of Ants to Plants. *Bull. Amer. Mus. Nat. Hist.* 22: 403–418, pls. 53–58. — **1907a.** *The Polymorphism of Ants, with an Account of some Singular Abnormalities due to Parasitism. *Ibid.* 23: 1–93, pls. 1–6. — **1907b.** A Collection of Ants from British Honduras. *Ibid.* 23: 271–277, 2 pls. — **1907c.** *The Fungus-growing Ants of North America. *Ibid.* 23: 669–807, 5 pls., 31 figg. — **1907d.** The Ants of Porto Rico and the Virgin Islands. *Ibid.* 24: 117–158, pls. 11, 12. — **1907e.** The Ants of Jamaica. *Ibid.* 24: 159–163. — **1907f.** Ants of Moorea, Society Islands. *Ibid.* 24: 165–167. — **1907g.** Ants from the Azores. *Ibid.* 24: 169–170. — **1907h.** *Notes on a New Guest Ant, Leptothorax glacialis, and the Varieties of Myrmica brevinodis Emery. *Bull. Wis. Nat. Hist. Soc.* 5, 2 (April) : 70–83. — **1907i.** On Certain Modified Hairs Peculiar to the Ants of Arid Regions. *Biol. Bull.* 13, 4 (Sept.) : 185–202, 14 text-figg. — **1907j.** *The Origin of Slavery among Ants. *Pop. Sc. Month.* 71, 6 (Dec.) : 550–559. — **1908a.** The Polymorphism of Ants. (Abstract) *Ann. Ent. Soc. Amer.* 1, 1: 39–69, pl. 1. (Abstr. of Art. in *Bull. Amer. Mus. Nat. Hist.* 23: 1–93, pls. 1–6. — **1908b.** *Studies on Myrmecophiles. I Cremastocheilus. *Jour. N. Y. Ent. Soc.* 16, 2: 68–79, 3 figg. — **1908c.** *Studies on Myrmecophiles. II Hetærius. *Ibid.* 16, 3: 135–143, 1 fig. — **1908d.** *Studies on Myrmecophiles. III Microdon. *Ibid.* 16, 14: 202–213, 1 fig. — **1908e.** Honey Ants, with a Revision of the North American Myrmecocysti. *Bull. Amer. Mus. Nat. Hist.* 24: 345–397, 28 figg. — **1908f.** *The Ants of Casco Bay, Maine, with Observations on Two Races of Formica sanguinea Latreille. *Ibid.* 24: 619–645. — **1908g.** A European Ant (Myrmica levinodis) Introduced into Massachusetts. *Journ. Econ. Ent.* 1, 6: 337–339.

Wheeler, W. M., and W. H. Long, 1901. The Males of Some Texas Ecitons. *Amer. Nat.* 35: 157–173, 3 figg.

Wheeler, W. M., and J. F. McClendon, 1903. Dimorphic Queens in an American Ant (Lasius latipes Walsh). *Biol. Bull.* 4: 149–163, 3 figg.

White, F. B., 1871-'72. *The Nest of Formica rufa and its inhabitants. *Scott. Nat.* 1: 216–222; 258–263.

White, W. F., 1883. Ants and their Ways; with illustrations, and an appendix giving a complete list of genera and species of the British Ants. *London.* xvi + 279 pp.

White, 1882. [Great swarms of Œcodoma in the Paraná.] In *"Cameos from the Silver Land."* 2: 437, 438.

Wickham, H. F., 1889. *Collecting Notes. *Ent. Amer.* 5, 4: 77–78. — 1890. *Remarks on some western Tenebrionidæ. *Ibid.* 6, 5: 83–88. — 1892. *Notes on some myrmecophilous Coleoptera. *Psyche* 6: 321–323. — 1893. *Field Notes from Texas and Louisiana. *Canad. Ent.* 25, 6: 139–143. — 1894. *Further notes on Coleoptera found with Ants. *Psyche* 7: 79–81. — 1898. *On Coleoptera found with Ants. (Fourth Paper.) *Ibid.* 8: 219–221, 1 pl. — 1900. *On Coleoptera found with Ants. (Fifth Paper.) *Ibid.* 9: 3–5. — 1901. *Two New Blind Beetles, of the Genus Adranes, from the Pacific Coast. *Canad. Ent.* 33: 25–28, 3 figg.

Wilde, J., 1615. De formica liberimus. *Ambergæ, Schonfeld,* 108 pp.

Wilkinson, T., 1865. *Ants'-nest Beetles at Scarborough. *Ent. M. Mag.* 2: 14.

Will, F., 1885. Die Geschmacksorgane der Insekten. *Zeitschr. Wiss. Zool.* 42: 674–707, pl. 27.

Wissmann, 1848. *Entomologische Notizen IX. *Stett. Ent. Zeitg.* p. 79.

Wollaston, T. V., 1854. *Insecta Maderensia. *London.* — 1864. *Catalogue of the Coleopterous Insects of the Canaries in the Collection of the British Museum. *London.*

Wood, W., 1821. Illustrations of the Linnæan Genera of Insects. *London* 2: 61.

Wray, J. De acido formicarum succo. *Phil. Trans.* 68: 2063; *Crell's Chym. Arch.* 1: 27.

Wroughton, R. C., 1892. *Our Ants. *Journ. Bomb. Nat. Hist. Soc.* Part 1: 48 pp., 2 pls.; Part II: 29 pp., 2 pls.

XAMBEU, V., 1889. *Description de deux larves de Coléoptères. *Rev. d'Ent.* pp. 332–335. — 1889-'90. *Paussides, Clavigérides et Scydmænides, recuellis dans le Bassin du Rhône et dans la vallée de la Têt. *Feuill. Jeun. Nat.* 20: 21–22. — 1891-'93. *Mœurs et métamorphóses d'Insectes. I. *Ann. Soc. Linn. Lyon.* 38, 39 (Sep. Lyon. 1893). — 1901-'02. Mœurs et métamorphóses d'insectes (suite). *Ibid.* 48: 1–40; 49: 1–53; 95–160.

YUNG, E., 1899. Dénombrement des nids de la Fourmi fauve. (F. rufa L.) *Arch. Zool. Expér.* (3) 7, Notes et Rev., 3: xxxiii–xxxv. — 1900. Combien y a-t-il des fourmis dans une fourmilière? (Formica rufa). *Arch. Sc. Phys. Nat. Genève* (4) 10: 46–56; *Rev. Sc.* (4) 14: 269–273.

ZAVATTARI, E., 1907a. Di alcuni Imenotteri della Somalia Italiana. *Boll. Mus. Zool. Anat. Comp. Torino* 22, 548: 4 pp. — 1907b. Imenotteri dell'Alto Zambesi, raccolti dal Rev. L. Jalla. *Ibid.* 22, 550: 4 pp.

Zeller, P. C., 1852. *Die Schaben mit langen Kiefertastern. *Linn. Ent.* 6: 81–198.

Zetterstedt, J. W., 1840. Insecta Lapponica Descripta. *Lipsiæ.*

von Zur Mühlen, 1888. Ueber hiesige Formiciden. *Sitzb. Nat. Gesell. Dorpat.* 8, 2: 327–333.

ANONYMOUS

(Blois), "H. B.", 1833. Has anyone observed the under-described Act in the Great Black Ant? *Mag. Nat. Hist.* 6: 287–288.

(D.), 1743. Das Lob des Flohes, der Ameisen und der Spinne.

(D.), 1771 or 1781 (?). Die Säure von den Ameisen abzuscheiden. *Almanach Scheidekünstler.* p. 54.

(E.) Erzählung von einem Ameisen Kriege. *Hamb. Mag.* 2: 317; *Allerneueste Mannigfaltigk.* 3: 139.

(v. Ferrari, J. A.), 1845. *Zur Beurtheilung der in Ameisennestern vorkommenden Insekten, insbesondere der Käfer, von einem süddeutschen Entomologen. *Stett. Ent. Zeitg.* p. 119 seq.

"A. H.", 1884. [Swarms of winged ants in New Zealand.] *New Zeal. Journ. Sc.* 2: 128.

(H.) Historia naturalis Formicarum. *Urban's Gentlem. Mag.* 23: 363.— 1728. Historia musculorum Formicæ. (publ. with *J. Donglin's Histoire des Muscles*).

(N.) Naturgeschichte der Ameisen. *Börner's Samml. Naturgesch.* 1: 179.

(N.), 1753. Nachricht von einer Ameisenschlacht. *Gentlem. Mag.* Aug.; *Mylii. Phys. Belustig.* 21: 839.

(O.), 1701. Observations sur les Fourmis nommées fourmis de visite, connues à Paramaribo; province de Surinam, dans l'Amérique Méridionale. *Mém. Acad. Sc. Paris. Histoire* p. 16. *Ed. in 8vo. Histoire* p. 19.

(S.) Sur les fourmis qui à la Martinique nuisent aux cannes à sucre. *Rosier Observ. Physique* 8: 384.

(V.) Von einem Heer fliegender Ameisen. *Schreber's Neue Cameralschriften* 1: 218.

(J. G. W.), 1874. Bemerkungen zu F. Liebrecht's Artikel "Ueber die goldgrabenden Ameisen." *Zeitschr. Ethnol.* 6: 316–318.

1786. Von den grossen braunen Ameisen in Surinam. *Lichtenberg Mag.* 4: 47–48.

1885. [Note on Mounds of Pogonomyrmex occidentalis.] *Amer. Nat.* 19: 305.

1891-'92. *Chrysomelid Larvæ in Ants'-nests. *Insect Life* 4: 148, 149.

1896. *L'esclavage chez les fourmis. *Nat. Canad.* 23: 21–26.

1897. [Ueberbrückung einer mit Wasser gefüllten Rinne durch Ameisen.] *Insektenbörse* 14: 51.

1897. Early Appearance of Formica rufa. *Ent. M. Mag.* (2) 8: 141; 158; 183.

1899. *Tropische Ameisen als Pilzzüchter. *Natur.* 48: 135–137.

1899. Ameisen und Bienen. Dürfen wir diesen Tieren seelische Eigenschaften zuschreiben? *Ibid.* 48: 198–199.

1907. *[On fungi formed in ants' nests.] *Gard. Chron.* (2) 18: 401, figg.

INDEX

A

Abdomen 26
Acacia 207, 224, 298, 299, 305, 307; *A. fistulosa* 298, 312, 313; *A. hindsii* 298; *A. spadicigera* 298; *A. sphærocephala* 298, 300, 309, 311
Acamatus 138, 255; *A. schmitti* 258
Acanthognathus 141, 180
Acantholepis 125, 143, 148, 403; *A. abdominalis* 365
Acanthomyops 80, 143, 150, 156, 159, 182, 203, 342, 347, 416, 515; *A. claviger* 80, 88, 94, 203; *A. interjectus* 203; *A. latipes* 94, 193
Acanthomyrmex 112, 139, 150
Acanthoponera 135
Acanthostichii 137
Acanthostichus 136, 137, 151, 227, 266
Acromyrmex 141, 180, 319, 327, 328, 338; *A. coronata* 324, 325; *A. discigera* 324, 328; *A. lundi* 397; *A. mælleri* 324, 325; *A. octospinosa* 17, 324
Acron 51
Acropyga 143
Acrostichum 299
Acrostigma 167, 171
Adelphogamy 439
Adipocytes 47, 48, 49
Adlerzia 139
Adranes 404; *A. cæcus* 405; *A. lecontei* 400, 405
Ænictogeton 137, 248
Ænictus 26, 28, 66, 137, 245, 248, 253, 255, 256, 266, 386; *Æ. aitkeni* 250; *Æ. eugenii* 254; *Æ. grandis* 252; *Æ. wroughtoni* 255
Aëromyrma 140, 158, 159, 163, 174, 429; *A. nossindambo* 428
Agricultural ants 187
Ailanthus 299, 300
Akermes colimæ 349
Alaopone 137, 248
Alchorea 299
Aleocharinæ 405
Alfaria 135
Alimentary Tract 31
Allodape 110
Allomerus 140, 303
Allotinus horsfieldi 360
Alpha-female 113
Alydus calcaratus 422
Amaranthus viridis 277, 278
Amazons 471
Amblyoponii 26, 134
Amblyopone 26, 134, 227

Amblyteles 91
Ambrosia beetles 338
Ammochætæ 16
Ammophila hirsuta 91
Amœbocytes 48, 49
Amorphocephalus 412
Amphisbænians 422
Amphotis 407
Ancleus 140
Aner 93
Anergates 36, 95, 107, 113, 114, 138, 139, 182, 183, 224, 449; *A. atratulus* 39, 40, 498, 499, 500, 501, 502, 503
Aneuretus 142, 148, 245; *A. simoni* 172, 244
Annular lamina 29
Anochetus 96, 136, 227, 230, 234; *A. sedilloti* 180
Anomma 137, 167, 174, 175, 248, 259; *A. arcens* 146, 249, 251, 252; *A. molestum* 253; *A. nigricans* 252; *A. rubella* 165
Anommatophilus 386
Anommatoxenus 386
Anoplognathus 229
Anoplotermes ater 429; *A. morio* 429
Antennæ 20
Antennophorus 412, 415, 416; *A. foreli* 413; *A. grandis* 413; *A. pubescens* 408, 413, 414; *A. uhlmanni* 413
Ants of North America, list of, 561
Ant-nests, architecture of, 192
Anus 36
Aorta 46
Aphænogaster 70, 74, 107, 140, 166, 167, 268, 282, 320, 391, 393, 403, 449, 513; *A. beccarii* 125; *A. fulva* 24, 81, 83, 150, 206, 389, 404, 447, 448, 453; *A. lamellidens* 151; *A. levis* 447; *A. longæva* 173; *A. mariæ* 151, 448; *A. occidentalis* 150; *A. picea* 82, 87, 98, 106, 195, 282, 447, 448; *A. rudis* 448; *A. subterranea* 40, 150; *A. tennesseensis* 113, 114, 393, 447, 448, 450; *A. testaceopilosa* 282, 387; *A. treatæ* 151, 200, 404
Aphidicolous ants 11
Aphids 11, 339
Aphis 347, 352; *A. maidi-radicis* 11, 354; *A. papaveris* 352
Aphnæus 359; *A. lohita* 258
Aphomomyrmex 143
Apis 72; *A. cypria* 115; *A. mellifica-fasciata* 115
Apocephalus pergandei 419